NEW YORK

Geometry

COMMON CORE

AMSCO SCHOOL PUBLICATIONS, INC.,

a division of Perfection Learning®

Mathematics Consultant

Joyce Bernstein, Ed.D.
Secondary Supervisor for Mathematics, (retired)
East Williston Union Free School District
Old Westbury, New York

Reviewers

Barbara Camp
Mathematics Department Coordinator,
(retired)
Terryville High School
Plymouth Public Schools
Plymouth, CT

Jaclyn Carey
Mathematics Teacher
Delran High School
Delran Public Schools
Delran, NJ

Celia Foster
Assistant Principal Mathematics
Grover Cleveland High School
New York City Department of Education
Queens, NY

Diane M. Mayer
Mathematics Teacher & Physics Teacher
Lopez Island High School
Lopez Island School District
Lopez Island, WA

Tara McCasland
Mathematics Teacher
Kankakee Jr High and High School
Kankakee School District #111
Kankakee, IL

Heather Ott
Mathematics Teacher
Executive Leadership and Entrepreneurial
Development at Olympic High School
Charlotte-Mecklenburg School District
Charlotte, NC

Tony Pickar
Mathematics Teacher
D.C. Everest Senior High
D.C. Everest School District
Schofield, WI

Stephanie Thompson
Mathematics Teacher
Torrey Pines High School
San Dieguito Union High School District
Del Mar, CA

© 2016 Perfection Learning®

Please visit our Web sites at:
www.amscopub.com and *www.perfectionlearning.com*

When ordering this book, please specify:
Hardcover: ISBN 978-0-7891-8931-8 or **9415206**
Softcover: ISBN 978-0-7891-8458-0 or **9415201**
eBook: ISBN 978-1-63419-625-3 or **94152D**

7 8 9 EBM 20 19 18 17 16

he United States of America

Contents

Key to the icons:

The computer icon indicates Digital Activities that can be found at **www.amscomath.com.**

The globe icon indicates where Real-World Model Problems are found in the text.

Chapter 6: Relationships Within Triangles

Chapter 7: Similarity and Trigonometry

Chapter 9: Polygons

Chapter 12: Probability

Getting Started

About This Book

New York Geometry is a full-year course, written to help students understand and explore the concepts of geometry as well as prepare them for the Geometry (Common Core) Regents Examination. All instruction, model problems, and practice items were developed to support the Common Core Learning Standards (CCLS) and modules and lessons of engage[ny]. Each chapter opens with lesson-by-lesson alignment with the standards. The eight Mathematical Practice Standards are embedded throughout in selected Model Problems, extensive practice problem sets, and the comprehensive Chapter and Cumulative Reviews. Correlations of the lessons in *New York Geometry* to engage[ny] lessons are available in the Teacher Manual.

In *New York Geometry*, students will use transformations to explore congruence and similarity and apply their knowledge to contextual problems. Students will also identify patterns and use inductive reasoning to make conjectures and learn the meaning and nature of mathematical proofs. By learning how to formally describe and analyze relationships among lines, parts of lines, planes, triangles, and circles, students will be able to apply geometric concepts in modeling situations. Students will use the rules of probability to compute probabilities and evaluate outcomes of decisions. Finally, throughout the text, algebraic skills learned in Algebra 1 are maintained, strengthened, and expanded as a bridge to Algebra 2 and Trigonometry.

Each chapter incorporates multiple performance tasks that measure the ability of students to think critically and apply their knowledge in real-world situations. In addition, students and teachers have access to a companion Web site (**www.amscomath.com**) with activities and simulations linked directly to lessons in *New York Geometry*. Teachers also have the option to include a full range of digital simulations, electronic whiteboard lessons, videos, and interactive problems to stimulate conceptual understanding through the Digital Teacher's Edition.

Careful and consistent use of this text and the supporting materials will give students a firm grasp of geometry, prepare them for the Geometry Regents Examination, and give them the tools they need to be college and career ready.

Eight Standards for Mathematical Practice

The mathematical practices are a common thread for students to think about and understand math as they progress from Kindergarten through high school. Students should use the mathematical practices as a method to break down concepts and solve problems, including representing problems logically, justifying conclusions, applying mathematics to practical situations, explaining the mathematics accurately to other students, or deviating from a known procedure to find a shortcut.

MP 1 Make sense of problems and persevere in solving them.

Attack new problems by analyzing what students already know. Students should understand that many different strategies can work. Ask leading questions to direct the discussion. Take time to think.

- explain the meaning of the problem
- analyze given information, constraints, and relationships
- plan a solution route
- try simpler forms of the initial problem
- use concrete objects to help conceptualize
- monitor progress and change course, if needed
- continually ask, "Does this make sense?"

MP 2 Reason abstractly and quantitatively.

Represent problems with symbols and/or pictures.

- make sense of quantities and their relationships
- decontextualize—represent a situation symbolically and contextualize—consider what given symbols represent
- create a clear representation of the problem
- consider the units involved
- attend to the meaning of numbers and variables, not just how to compute them
- use properties of operations and objects

MP 3 Construct viable arguments and critique the reasoning of others.

Ask questions, defend answers, and/or make speculations using correct math vocabulary.

- use assumptions, definitions, and previously established results
- make conjectures and build a valid progression of statements
- use counterexamples
- justify conclusions and communicate them to others
- determine whether the arguments of others seem right

MP 4 Model with mathematics.

Show the relevance of math by solving real-world problems. Look for opportunities to use math for current situations in and outside of school in all subject areas.

- apply mathematics to solve everyday problems
- analyze and chart relationships using diagrams, two-way tables, graphs, flowcharts, and formulas to draw conclusions
- apply knowledge to simplify a complicated situation
- interpret results and consider whether answers make sense

MP 5 Use appropriate tools strategically.

Provide an assortment of tools for students and let them decide which ones to use.

- choose appropriately from existing tools (pencil and paper, concrete models, ruler, protractor, calculator, spreadsheet, dynamic geometry software, etc.) when solving mathematical problems
- detect possible errors by using estimation or other mathematical knowledge
- use technology to explore and compare predictions and deepen understanding of concepts

MP 6 Attend to precision.

Use precise and detailed language in math. Instead of saying "I don't get it," students should be able to elaborate on where they lost the connection. Students should specify units in their answers and correctly label diagrams.

- speak and write precisely using correct mathematical language
- state the meaning of symbols and use them properly
- specify units of measure and label axes appropriately
- calculate precisely and efficiently
- express answers with the proper degree of accuracy

MP 7 Look for and make use of structure.

See patterns and the significance of given information and objects. Use these to solve more complex problems.

- see the big picture
- discern a pattern or structure

- recognize the significance of given aspects
- apply strategies to similar problems
- step back for an overview and shift perspective
- see complicated things as being composed of several objects

MP 8 **Look for and express regularity in repeated reasoning.**

Understand why a process works so students can apply it to new situations.

- notice repeated calculations and look for both general methods and shortcuts
- maintain oversight of the process while paying attention to the details
- evaluate the reasonableness of intermediate results
- create generalizations founded on observations

Test-Taking Strategies

General Strategies

- *Become familiar with the directions and format of the test ahead of time.* There will be both multiple-choice and extended response questions where you must show the steps you used to solve a problem, including formulas, diagrams, graphs, charts, and so on, where appropriate.
- *Pace yourself.* Do not race to answer every question immediately. On the other hand, do not linger over any question too long. Keep in mind that you will need more time to complete the extended response questions than to complete the multiple-choice questions.
- *Speed comes from practice.* The more you practice, the faster you will become and the more comfortable you will be with the material. Practice as often as you can.

Specific Strategies

- *Always scan the answer choices* before beginning to work on a multiple-choice question. This will help you to focus on the kind of answer that is required. Are you looking for fractions, decimals, percents, integers, squares, cubes, and so on? Eliminate choices that clearly do not answer the question asked.
- *Do not assume that your answer is correct just because it appears among the choices.* The wrong choices are usually there because they represent common student errors. After you find an answer, always reread the problem to make sure you have chosen the answer to the question that is asked, not the question you have in your mind.
- *Sub-in.* To sub-in means to substitute. You can sub-in friendly numbers for the variables to find a pattern and determine the solution to the problem.
- *Backfill.* If a problem is simple enough and you want to avoid doing the more complex algebra, or if a problem presents a phrase such as $x = ?$, then just fill in the answer choices that are given in the problem until you find the one that works.
- *Do the math.* This is the ultimate strategy. Don't go wild searching in your mind for tricks, gimmicks, or math magic to solve every problem. Most of the time the best way to get the right answer is to do the math and solve the problem.

Chapter R Algebra Review

Chapter Content

Vocabulary

area	hypotenuse	Pythagorean theorem
binomial	intercept	radius
circle	leg	ratio
circumference	monomial	right triangle
completing the square	parabola	slope
diameter	perfect square	solving by elimination
difference of squares	perimeter	solving by substitution
factoring	proportion	system of equations
FOIL		

LESSON R.1

R.1 Solving Equations

Solving One-Variable Equations

To solve an equation like $3z + 7 = 28$, you need to have z by itself. To achieve this, you need to apply both the addition and multiplication properties of equality.

Algebraic Properties of Equality	
Addition property	If $a = b$, then $a + c = b + c$ and $a - c = b - c$.
Multiplication property	If $a = b$, then $ac = bc$.
Division property	If $a = b$ and $c \neq 0$, then $a \div c = b \div c$.
Substitution property	If $a = b$, then a can be replaced by b in expressions or equations.

Properties of Addition and Multiplication	
Commutative properties	$a + b = b + a$ $ab = ba$
Associative properties	$(x + y) + z = x + (y + z)$ $(a \cdot b) \cdot c = a \cdot (b \cdot c)$

Distributive Property	
Multiplication	$a(b + c) = ab + ac$ $a(b - c) = ab - ac$
Division	If $c \neq 0$, then $(a + b) \div c = \dfrac{a}{c} + \dfrac{b}{c}$

MODEL PROBLEMS

1. Solve $3z + 7 = 28$ for z.

SOLUTION

Isolate the variable term
$$3z + 7 = 28$$
$$3z + 7 - 7 = 28 - 7$$
$$3z = 21$$
Subtract 7 from both sides.

Divide by the coefficient
$$\frac{3z}{3} = \frac{21}{3}$$
$$z = 7$$
Divide both sides by 3.

2. Solve $5x + 5 - 4x = 2$ for x.

SOLUTION

Put like terms together $\qquad 5x - 4x + 5 = 2$

Combine like terms $\qquad\qquad x + 5 = 2$

Subtract 5 from both sides $\quad x + 5 - 5 = 2 - 5$
$$x = -3$$

> This example requires us to combine constants as well as variable terms.

3. Solve $-\dfrac{x}{4} = 5$.

SOLUTION

Multiply by reciprocal of coefficient
$$-\frac{x}{4} = 5$$
$$(-4)\left(-\frac{x}{4}\right) = -4 \cdot 5$$

> In model problem 3, the variable is part of a fraction.

Do operations $\qquad\qquad\qquad x = -20$

Solving Literal Equations

MODEL PROBLEMS

1. A basic formula says that distance (d) equals the product of speed (s) and time (t).
   Solve $s \cdot t = d$ for s.

SOLUTION

Solve for s
$$s \cdot t = d$$
$$\frac{st}{t} = \frac{d}{t}$$

Do the operation
$$s = \frac{d}{t}$$

Model Problems continue . . .

2. Solve for *a* in $p = 2(3 + a + 5) + 4$.

SOLUTION

Combine like terms	$p = 2(a + 8) + 4$
Distributive property	$p = 2a + 16 + 4$
Combine like terms	$p = 2a + 20$
Additive inverse and identity	$p - 20 = 2a$
Multiplication property of equality	$\dfrac{p - 20}{2} = \dfrac{2a}{2}$
Multiplicative inverse and identity	$a = \dfrac{p - 20}{2}$

> We note which principles we use as we solve the equation $p = 2(3 + a + 5) + 4$ for *a*. This is practice for problems that ask you to explain your reasoning.

Ratios and Proportions

Ratios and proportions are heavily used in geometry. A **ratio** is a quotient that compares two quantities, with the first quantity divided by the second. This is typically written as a fraction, $\dfrac{5}{2}$, or with a colon, 5 : 2.

An equation stating that ratios are equal is a **proportion**. The fractions $\dfrac{3}{2}$ and $\dfrac{9}{6}$ are equivalent, which means they represent the same number. A proportion has equivalent ratios on each side of the equation.

MODEL PROBLEMS

1. Write a proportion of golf balls to tees to describe the diagram.

SOLUTION

Write an equation stating that two ratios are equal	$\dfrac{3 \text{ golf balls}}{2 \text{ tees}} = \dfrac{9 \text{ golf balls}}{6 \text{ tees}}$	The ratio of golf balls to golf tees on the left is 3 to 2, and on the right it is 9 to 6.
Show proportions are equivalent	$\dfrac{3}{2} \cdot \dfrac{3}{3} = \dfrac{9}{6}$	We multiply $\dfrac{3}{2}$ by $\dfrac{3}{3}$ (which is equal to 1) to show that $\dfrac{3}{2}$ equals $\dfrac{9}{6}$.

Model Problems continue . . .

2. There are 3 hamburgers served for every 2 tacos served at a restaurant. If 21 hamburgers are served, how many tacos are served?

SOLUTION

State as proportion

$$\frac{x \text{ tacos}}{21 \text{ hamburgers}} = \frac{2 \text{ tacos}}{3 \text{ hamburgers}}$$

Multiply both sides by 21

$$21 \cdot \frac{x}{21} = 21 \cdot \frac{2}{3}$$

$$x = \frac{42}{3}$$

$$x = 14 \text{ tacos}$$

> The *multiplication property of equality* lets you solve a proportion as you would solve similar equations.

PRACTICE

1. Carmen swam 8 fewer laps than three times the number of laps Marlo swam. They swam 72 laps altogether. How many laps did Marlo swim?

- A. 18
- B. 20
- C. 42
- D. 52

Exercises 2–20: Solve for the variable.

2. $5x + 3 = 23$

3. $2x + 6 = 20$

4. $2y + 3 = 13$

5. $4k - 5k + 4 = 1$

6. $4k - 3k + 4 = 7$

7. $5r + 3 = 4r + 8$

8. $5r + 2 = 2r + 14$

9. $4r + 3 = 3r + 5$

10. $9z = 64 + z$

11. $6x - 27 = 3x - 54$

12. $16x - 32 = 4x - 128$

13. $-2(4x - 2) = -12$

14. $-3(5x - 4) = -33$

15. $-4(5x - 6) = -16$

16. $-2(6x - 2) = -68$

17. $\frac{x}{48} = \frac{1}{16}$

18. $\frac{x}{45} = \frac{1}{15}$

19. $\frac{a}{42} = \frac{8}{21}$

20. $\frac{a}{42} = \frac{3}{21}$

21. Solve $12x + 3y = 24$ for y.

22. Solve $8y - 16x = 32$ for y.

23. Solve $8y - 16x = 64$ for x.

24. Solve $xy - z = 1$ for y.

25. Solve $V = \frac{kQ}{r}$ for Q.

26. Solve $a = \frac{v^2}{r}$ for r.

27. Arnold spends $14 more on groceries this week than last week. He spent $108 on groceries during the two weeks. How much did he spend each week?

28. MP 2 Based on the diagram, if the football coach wants you 12 yards from the line of scrimmage at the end of the pass, how many yards do you first run before turning back?

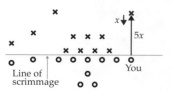

29. The sum of 3 consecutive integers is 24. Find the smallest integer.

Practice Problems continue . . .

30. Kendra is 6 years older than one-half Gitta's age. Their ages sum to 57 years. How old are Kendra and Gitta?

31. You drive for four hours, and you drive twice as fast for the first two hours as you do for the second two hours. You drive 150 miles during the four hours. What is your slower driving speed in miles per hour?

32. **MP 3** Adrian is trying to solve an equation. What is her mistake and when does she make it?

Equation: $3(x - 2) = x + 4$

Step 1: $3x - 6 = x + 4$

Step 2: $3x = x + 4 - 6$

Step 3: $3x = x - 2$

Step 4: $2x = -2$

Step 5: $x = -1$

33. Due to a reduction in earnings, Ryan is currently able to donate 6 fewer dollars per charity than he has in the past. He donates an equal amount of money to 12 charities and donates $2,148 in all. How much did he donate to each charity in the past?

34. A benefit concert sold 48 tickets to students and faculty and collected $930 from ticket sales. Each student ticket was $18, and each faculty ticket was $24. How many students bought tickets? How many faculty bought tickets?

35. At the hit film, *Revenge of the Algebra Teacher*, tickets for adults are $7.00 and for children they are $5.00. The theater sold 71 tickets for $475. How many children saw the film?

36. You want to increase the size of a 4-inch-wide and 6-inch-tall picture to a width of 36 inches without changing its aspect ratio. What is its new height?

37. **MP 1** The two triangles shown are similar. If $y = 28$, then what is the length x?

LESSON R.2

R.2 Solving Inequalities

Addition Property of Inequality

To solve an inequality, we write an equivalent inequality where the variable is alone on one side. You can add (or subtract) the same number on each side of an inequality and the result is an equivalent inequality, one that has exactly the same solutions.

MODEL PROBLEM

Solve $x + 2 < 7$ for x.

SOLUTION

Isolate the variable by subtracting 2 from both sides

$$x + 2 < 7$$
$$x + 2 - 2 < 7 - 2$$
$$x < 5$$

We apply the property, subtracting 2 from both sides of the inequality $x + 2 < 7$.

Multiplication Property of Inequality

Since adding the same number to each side of an inequality results in an equivalent inequality, you might think that multiplication has the same property. Unfortunately, it is not that simple.

- If c is positive, $a < b$ and $ac < bc$ are equivalent:

$$2x < 6$$

$$\frac{1}{2}(2x) < \frac{1}{2}(6)$$

$$x < 3$$

- If c is negative, $a < b$ and $ac > bc$ are equivalent then the direction of the inequality changes:

$$-\frac{1}{4}x < -2$$

$$-4\left(-\frac{1}{4}x\right) > -4(-2)$$

$$x > 8$$

MODEL PROBLEMS

1. $-2x \le 6$

SOLUTION

Divide both sides by -2 $\qquad$ $-2x \le 6$

$$\frac{-2x}{-2} \ge \frac{6}{-2}$$

Change direction of inequality $\qquad$ $x \ge -3$

2. Solve $6x + 3 \le 15$ for x.

SOLUTION

Subtract 3 from both sides $\qquad$ $6x + 3 - 3 \le 15 - 3$

$$6x \le 12$$

Divide both sides by 6 $\qquad$ $\dfrac{6x}{6} \le \dfrac{12}{6}$

$$x \le 2$$

3. Solve $2x < 12 + 5x$ for x.

SOLUTION

Subtract $5x$ from both sides $\qquad$ $2x - 5x < 12 + 5x - 5x$

$$-3x < 12$$

Divide both sides by -3 $\qquad$ $\dfrac{-3x}{-3} > \dfrac{12}{-3}$

Remember to change the direction of the inequality!

$$x > -4$$

Model Problems continue . . .

4. Solve $3(x + 2) - 2x > 10$ for x.

SOLUTION

Distribute	$3x + 6 - 2x > 10$	Start by distributing the 3.
Combine like terms	$x + 6 > 10$	Combine like terms, subtracting $2x$ from $3x$ on the left.
Isolate the variable by subtracting 6 from both sides	$x + 6 - 6 > 10 - 6$ $x > 4$	Subtract 6 from both sides so the variable is by itself on the left.

> Concepts such as the distributive property and combining like terms apply to solving inequalities.

PRACTICE

1. Which of the following represents the solution to the inequality, $-3x + 4 > -2$?

    A. $x > -2$ C. $x < -2$

    B. $x < 2$ D. $x > 2$

2. Which of the following represents the solution to the inequality, $16x - 12 \leq 36$?

    A. $x \leq -3$ C. $x \leq -4$

    B. $x \leq 4$ D. $x \leq 3$

Exercises 3–7: Solve.

3. $10x - 8 < 42$

4. $7x - 8 < 6$

5. $\dfrac{x}{2} + 6 < 3$

6. $\dfrac{x}{8} + 8 < 9$

7. $-8x + 3 \geq 27$

Exercises 8–11: Write and solve the inequality that models the statement.

8. The sum of y and 20 is less than 37.

9. The product of a number and 7 is less than 126.

10. 8 less than twice a number is more than 32.

11. Three times the sum of a number and 6 is greater than or equal to 72.

12.   **MP 4**   Amanda rents a car at the airport. She pays $1,028 to rent the car for 21 days. Each additional day beyond this period is $36, which includes taxes and fees. She has budgeted $1,244 for the car rental. Write an inequality describing the number of additional days she can request and solve for the number of additional days she can afford.

LESSON R.3

R.3 The Slope-Intercept Form of a Line

Slope of a Line

You may be familiar with **slope**, the measure of a line's steepness. Slope is calculated by dividing a line's vertical change by the line's horizontal change, as we demonstrate to the right. This may be review, and we will apply the concept of slope to geometry.

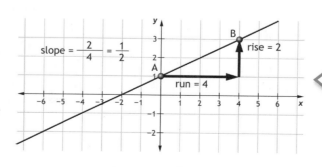

> Slope equals rise divided by run:
> $$\text{slope} = \frac{2}{4} = \frac{1}{2}$$

What is the slope of the line that passes through the points $(-1, -2)$ and $(3, 4)$? Check your answer using a graph.

SOLUTION

Formula $\qquad$ $\text{slope} = \dfrac{\text{rise}}{\text{run}} = \dfrac{\text{change in } y}{\text{change in } x} = \dfrac{y_2 - y_1}{x_2 - x_1}$

To state the formula, we use the subscripts 2 and 1. For example, we subtract y_1 from y_2 to calculate the change in y.

Substitute $\qquad$ $\text{slope} = \dfrac{y_2 - y_1}{x_2 - x_1} = \dfrac{4 - (-2)}{3 - (-1)}$

To calculate the slope, we substitute the y- and x-coordinates of the points into the formula.

Evaluate $\qquad$ $\text{slope} = \dfrac{4 - (-2)}{3 - (-1)} = \dfrac{6}{4} = \dfrac{3}{2}$

We subtract and simplify.

Graph

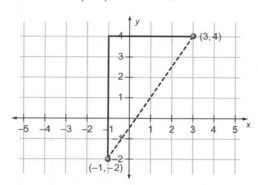

From the point $(-1, -2)$ go up 6 and over 4 to the point $(3, 4)$.

The slope is $\dfrac{6}{4} = \dfrac{3}{2}$.

Horizontal and Vertical Lines

Horizontal and vertical lines are two special cases when it comes to slope.

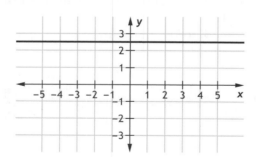

Horizontal line
Slope = 0
Rise = 0

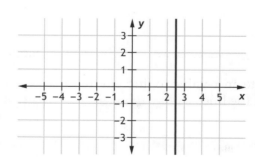

Vertical line
Slope = undefined
Run = 0

The equation for a horizontal line has the form $y = b$, such as $y = 2.5$. It passes through the vertical axis at $y = 2.5$.

The equation for a vertical line has the form $x = k$, such as $x = 2.5$. It passes through the horizontal axis at $x = 2.5$.

Graphing Equations Using Slope and Intercept

The slope-intercept form of a linear equation, $y = mx + b$, is convenient for quickly graphing the equation.

> The **intercept** is the point at which a line crosses either the x- or y-axis. The y-intercept is calculated by setting $x = 0$ in an equation, and is equal to b in the equation $y = mx + b$.

MODEL PROBLEMS

1. Graph a line using m and b: $y = 2x + 1$

SOLUTION

Identify the y-intercept. y-intercept $= 1$

Slope is coefficient of x.   Slope $= 2$

Substitute an x-value to find another point on the line.

$$y = 2x + 1$$
$$y = 2(1) + 1$$
$$y = 2 + 1$$
$$y = 3$$

Plot the y-intercept and $(1, 3)$. Connect the points with a line.

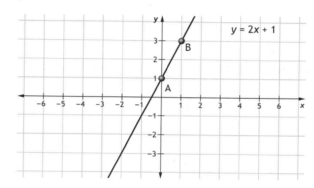

2. Graph a line with a fractional slope: $y = \dfrac{1}{4}x - 2$

SOLUTION

Identify the y-intercept. y-intercept $= -2$

Slope is coefficient of x.   Slope $= \dfrac{1}{4}$

Substitute an x-value to find another point on the line.

$$y = \frac{1}{4}x + (-2)$$
$$y = \frac{1}{4}(4) + (-2)$$
$$y = 1 + (-2)$$
$$y = (-1)$$

Plot the y-intercept $(0, -2)$ and $(4, -1)$. Connect the points with a line.

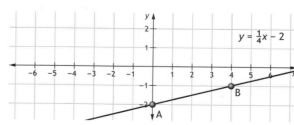

Model Problems continue . . .

3. Graph a line with a negative slope: $y = -2x + 3$

SOLUTION

Identify the y-intercept.

y-intercept $= 3$

Slope is coefficient of x.

Slope $= -2$

Substitute an x-value to find another point on the line.

$y = -2x + 3$

$y = -2(1) + 3$

$y = 1$

Plot the points and connect the points with a line.

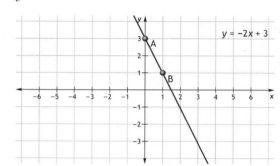

Determining an Equation from Two Points

The points (4, 11) and (2, 5) are on a line. To find the equation for a line using two points, we start by calculating the slope and then use the coordinates of a point to calculate b.

MODEL PROBLEM

Calculate a line equation from points (4, 11) and (2, 5).

SOLUTION

Use definition of slope

$$\text{slope} = \frac{\text{rise}}{\text{run}} = \frac{11 - 5}{4 - 2}$$

$$\text{slope} = \frac{6}{2} = 3$$

Substitute slope for m, and coordinates of either point for x and y in the equation

(4, 11)

$y = mx + b$

$y = 3(x) + b$

$11 = 3(4) + b$

Solve for b

$11 = 12 + b$

$b = -1$

Write equation

$y = 3x + (-1)$

$y = 3x - 1$

> We can check the equation by substituting the second point, (2, 5), into the equation. We get $5 = 3(2) - 1$, which simplifies as $5 = 5$. Our work was correct.

PRACTICE

1. Which of the following equations represents the line that passes through the points $(-2, 24)$ and $(3, -31)$?

    A. $y = -12x + 4$ C. $y = -11x + 2$

    B. $y = -9x - 3$ D. $y = -10x - 6$

2. Write the equation for a horizontal line that passes through $(-19, -14)$.

3. Write the equation for a vertical line that passes through $(13, 8)$.

Exercises 4–5: Write the equation of the graphed line.

4.
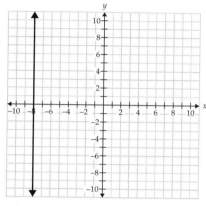

5.
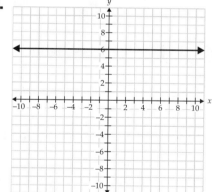

Exercises 6–7: What is the slope of the line shown?

6.
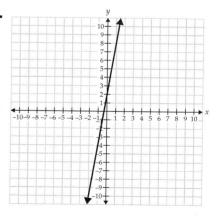

7.
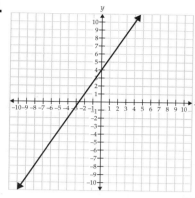

Exercises 8–13: Write the equation for the line shown in slope-intercept form, $y = mx + b$.

8.
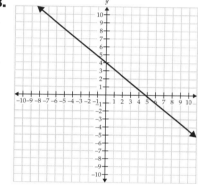

9.
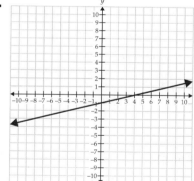

10.
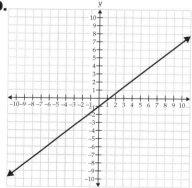

Practice Problems continue . . .

11.

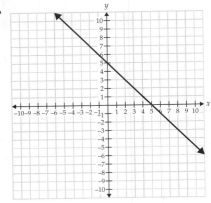

12.

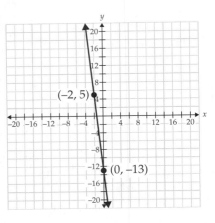

13.

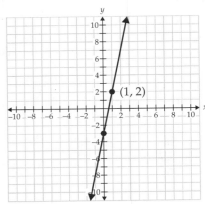

14. What is the *y*-intercept of $y = 7x + 2$?

15. What is the slope of the line given by the equation $y = -11x + 10$?

Exercises 16–17: Graph the line.

16. $y = 9x - 3$

17. $y = -7x + 1$

Exercises 18–20: Write the equation of the line that passes through the points listed.

18. $(-4, -42)$ and $(2, 18)$

19. $(-3, 23)$ and $(1, -1)$

20. $(-1, -16)$ and $(2, 20)$

21. **MP 1** This is a simplified elevation profile of Alpe d'Huez, a famous pass in the Alps which is often part of the Tour de France bike race. The profile shows the change in altitude, starting at 0 meters at the base of the climb. What is its average slope, in meters per kilometer, to the nearest integer?

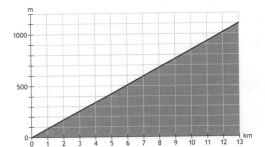

LESSON R.4

R.4 Solving a System of Equations

Solving by Substitution

A **system of equations** is two or more equations with the same set of variables. When solving a system of equations, you try to find values for the variables that make all equations true.

> When **solving by substitution**, you solve one of the equations for one variable.

1. Solve by substitution: $y = 2x + 5$ and $y = 3x + 4$

SOLUTION

Substitute expression into other equation	$y = 2x + 5$ $3x + 4 = 2x + 5$
Solve equation	$x + 4 = 5$ $x = 1$
Use value for variable to find the other	$y = 2x + 5$ $y = 2(1) + 5$ $y = 7$
State solution	$(x, y) = (1, 7)$

2. Solve by substitution: $y - 2x = -1$ and $-x + y = 2$

SOLUTION

Solve equation for one variable	$y - 2x = -1$ $y = 2x - 1$
Substitute expression into other equation	$-x + y = 2$ $-x + 2x - 1 = 2$
Solve equation	$x - 1 = 2$ $x = 3$
Use value for variable to find the other	$y - 2x = -1$ $y - 2(3) = -1$ $y - 6 = -1$ $y = 5$
State solution	$(x, y) = (3, 5)$

> In this problem we have to do some work to first solve one equation for a variable, and then substitute.

Solving by Elimination

When **solving by elimination**, you get rid of (eliminate, to put it more elegantly) one of the variables by adding the equations, or equivalent equations, together. The result is a single equation with one variable, which you then solve.

MODEL PROBLEMS

1. Solve for x and y using elimination by addition: $x + 3y = 1$ and $2x - 3y = 5$

SOLUTION

Add equations together to eliminate a variable

$$\begin{array}{r} x + 3y = 1 \\ + \; 2x - 3y = 5 \\ \hline 3x - 0y = 6 \\ 3x = 6 \end{array}$$

Solve for x

$$x = 2$$

Replace x with 2 to find y

$$\begin{array}{r} x + 3y = 1 \\ 2 + 3y = 1 \\ 3y = -1 \\ y = -\dfrac{1}{3} \end{array}$$

> When we have solved for one variable, we can then solve for the other by substituting the solution into either equation. We chose $x + 3y = 1$.

State solution

$$(x, y) = \left(2, -\dfrac{1}{3} \right)$$

2. Solve for x and y using elimination by subtraction: $4x = y + 5$ and $2x = y - 3$

SOLUTION

Subtract to eliminate a variable

$$\begin{array}{r} 4x = y + 5 \\ - \; 2x = y - 3 \\ \hline 2x = 0y + 8 \end{array}$$

Solve for x

$$\begin{array}{r} 2x = 8 \\ x = 4 \end{array}$$

Use value of x to find y

$$\begin{array}{r} 4x = y + 5 \\ 4(4) = y + 5 \\ 16 = y + 5 \\ y = 11 \end{array}$$

> You can add or subtract equations because of the addition property of equality. In this problem we show how to solve a system of equations by subtracting one equation from another.

State solution

$$(x, y) = (4, 11)$$

3. Solve for x and y using elimination by multiplying then adding: $3x + y = 5$ and $5x + 2y = 7$

SOLUTION

Multiply first equation by -2

$$\begin{array}{r} -2(3x + y) = -2(5) \\ -6x - 2y = -10 \end{array}$$

Add the equations

$$\begin{array}{r} -6x - 2y = -10 \\ + \; 5x + 2y = 7 \\ \hline -x + 0y = -3 \end{array}$$

Solve for one variable

$$\begin{array}{r} -x = -3 \\ x = 3 \end{array}$$

> With one variable known, we substitute it into one of the equations above to find the value of the other variable.

Replace x with 3 to find y

$$\begin{array}{r} 3x + y = 5 \\ 3(3) + y = 5 \\ y = -4 \end{array}$$

State solution

$$(x, y) = (3, -4)$$

PRACTICE

Exercises 1–8: Solve by elimination.

1. $2x - y = 6$
  $x + y = 3$

2. $5x - 3y = -3$
  $-5x + 9y = 39$

3. $3x + 2y = 7$
  $5x - 2y = 9$

4. $-x + 4y = 12$
  $x - 3y = -6$

5. $2x + y = -1$
  $-3x - 2y = 0$

6. $-3x + 3y = 3$
  $x - 2y = -6$

7. $y = 5x + 3$
  $y = 11x + 9$

8. $-0.4x + y = 2.6$
  $-1.2x + y = 1.8$

Exercises 9–12: Solve by substitution.

9. $y = x + 3$
  $y = 4x - 3$

10. $y = 2x - 4$
  $y = x$

11. $y = 5x - 19$
  $y = -2x + 9$

12. $y = 3x + 2$
  $2x + y = 7$

13. The sum of two numbers is 23. Their difference is 15. What is the larger number?

14. The sum of two numbers is 74. Their difference is 28. What is the smaller number?

15. MP 1 There are 20 coins in a jar. Each coin is either a penny or a nickel. The total value of the coins is 52 cents. Write two equations to describe this situation, and solve the system to find how many pennies and how many nickels are in the jar.

16. There are 28 coins in a sock drawer. Each coin is either a dime or a quarter. The total value of the coins is $4.00. Write two equations to model this situation, and solve the system to find how many quarters and how many dimes there are.

17. Ten llamas and 20 ostriches cost $14,000. Twenty llamas and 10 ostriches cost $13,000. What does one llama cost you?

18. Five road bikes and four mountain bikes will cost you $6,400. One of each will cost you $1,400. What does a road bike cost?

LESSON R.5

R.5 Multiplying Polynomials

Multiplying a Binomial by a Monomial

You multiply $2(x + 3)$ by distributing: $2(x + 3) = 2 \cdot x + 2 \cdot 3$. You can multiply polynomials of higher degree using the distributive property as well.

MODEL PROBLEMS

1. Multiply $3x(4x + 2)$.

SOLUTION

Distribute $3x$	$3x \cdot 4x + 3x \cdot 2$	To multiply $4x + 2$ by $3x$, we distribute the **monomial** $3x$. We multiply each term in the **binomial**, $4x$ and 2, by $3x$.
Simplify each term	$12x^2 + 6x$	We simplify the terms. The product of $3x$ and $4x$ is $12x^2$.

Model Problems continue . . .

2. Multiply $(2x + 3)(5x + 9)$.

SOLUTION

Distribute	$(2x)(5x + 9) + (3)(5x + 9)$
Multiply	$10x^2 + 18x + 15x + 27$
Combine like terms	$10x^2 + (18x + 15x) + 27$
	$10x^2 + 33x + 27$

> In this problem we multiply two binomials using the distributive property by distributing one binomial to each term of the other.

Multiplying Binomials Using FOIL

FOIL is a way to multiply binomials. FOIL stands for **F**irst, **O**uter, **I**nner, **L**ast. You multiply the first terms in each binomial, then the outer terms, then the inner, and, finally, the last terms. This is a way to organize multiplication using the distributive property.

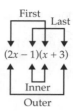

MODEL PROBLEMS

1. Multiply $(3x - 2)(2x - 7)$.

SOLUTION

Multiply using FOIL: First, Outer, Inner, Last	$3x \cdot 2x + 3x \cdot (-7) + (-2 \cdot 2x) + (-2 \cdot -7)$	We start by multiplying the first terms of each binomial, $3x$ and $2x$. The result is $6x^2$.
Combine like terms	$6x^2 - 21x - 4x + 14$ $6x^2 - 25x + 14$	We combine like terms. We subtract $4x$ from $-21x$ to get $-25x$.

2. Multiply $(x + 4)^2$.

SOLUTION

Square of a binomial sum	$(x + 4)^2$ $(a + b)^2 = a^2 + 2ab + b^2$ $a = x$ $b = 4$	We represent the terms of the sum with a and b. The square of the sum equals $a^2 + 2ab + b^2$. We will use this formula with $(x + 4)^2$. With $(x + 4)$, the first term, a, is x. The second term, b, is 4.
Substitute into the formula	$(x)^2 + 2(x)(4) + (4)^2$	We substitute x for a and 4 for b into the formula.
Do the operations	$x^2 + 8x + 16$	We do the operations. The first term is x^2. The second term is 2 times 4 times x, which equals $8x$. The last term is 4 squared, which equals 16.

> The expression $(x + 4)^2$ means $(x + 4)(x + 4)$. It is a *square of a binomial.* You could evaluate the square using FOIL, but the square of a binomial has two special formulas that you can use instead:
> $(a + b)^2 = a^2 + 2ab + b^2$ and
> $(a - b)^2 = a^2 - 2ab + b^2$.

PRACTICE

Exercises 1–17: Multiply. State the product as a polynomial in standard form.

1. $x(8x)$

2. $7x(4x)$

3. $5(x^3 + x)$

4. $4x(x^3 + 2)$

5. $(x + 2)(x + 4)$

6. $(x + 1)(x + 7)$

7. $(x - 1)(x + 4)$

8. $(y + 2)(y - 3)$

9. $(5 - 2x)(2x - 5)$

10. $(3x - 1)(x + 2)$

11. $(5x - 2)(2x - 5)$

12. $(3z + 1)(2z - 4)$

13. $(x + 3)^2$

14. $(1 + y)^2$

15. $(x - 5)^2$

16. $(2a + 1)^2$

17. $(2x - 1)^2$

LESSON R.6

R.6 Factoring Polynomials

Factoring $x^2 + bx + c$

A table is a good way to organize and check the possible binomial constants when **factoring** a trinomial, as we show below. We use the table to list the factors, and then to check their sums.

MODEL PROBLEMS

1. Factor $x^2 + 5x + 6$ using product and sum.

SOLUTION

Create a table of factors and the sums of the factors

$x^2 + 5x + 6 = (x + 2)(x + 3)$

Factors	Sum
1, 6	7
2, 3	5

Middle-term coefficient equals sum of these factors

middle term = $5x$; coefficient = 5
$(x + 2)(x + 3)$

2. Factor $x^2 + 4x - 5$ using product and sum.

SOLUTION

Create table of factors and the sums of the factors

$x^2 + 4x - 5 = (x - 1)(x + 5)$

Factors	Sum
1, −5	−4
−1, 5	+4

Middle-term coefficient equals sum of these factors

middle term = $4x$; coefficient = 4
$(x - 1)(x + 5)$

Model Problems continue . . .

3. Factor $x^2 - 11x + 10$ using product and sum.

SOLUTION

Create table of factors and the sums of the factors

$$x^2 - 11x + 10 = (x - 1)(x - 10)$$

Factors	Sum
$-1, -10$	-11
$-2, -5$	-7

Middle-term coefficient equals sum of these factors

middle term $= -11x$; coefficient $= -11$
$(x - 1)(x - 10)$

> The trinomial has the pattern of a negative coefficient for the middle term, -11 with this polynomial, and a positive constant, 10.

There is a pattern to factoring trinomials of the form $x^2 + bx + c$.

middle term $= b =$ sum of factors

final term $= c =$ product of factors

For example, if $x^2 + bx + c = (x + m)(x + n)$, then $b = m + n$ and $c = mn$.

Difference of Squares

The quadratic polynomial $x^2 - 9$ is called a **difference of squares**, since one squared term is subtracted from another. The factors of the difference of squares follow a specific form: $A^2 - B^2 = (A + B)(A - B)$.

MODEL PROBLEM

Factor $x^2 - 9$ using difference of squares.

SOLUTION

Take the square root of the first term, x^2 $(x \quad)(x \quad)$

Plus and minus square root of second term, 9 $(x + 3)(x - 3)$

PRACTICE

Exercises 1–24: Factor.

1. $x^2 + 5x + 4$

2. $x^2 + 6x + 8$

3. $x^2 + 2x - 15$

4. $x^2 + 8x + 15$

5. $x^2 - 6x - 27$

6. $x^2 + 4x + 4$

7. $x^2 + 9x + 14$

8. $x^2 + 11x + 24$

9. $x^2 - 4x - 12$

10. $x^2 + 3x - 28$

11. $x^2 + 11x - 12$

Practice Problems continue . . .

12. $x^2 - 6x - 16$

13. $x^2 - 9x + 18$

14. $x^2 - 4x + 4$

15. $x^2 - 10x + 24$

16. $x^2 - 25$

17. $z^2 - 7z + 10$

18. $x^2 - 11x + 30$

19. $x^2 - 144$

20. $x^2 - 2x + 1$

21. $x^2 - 1$

22. $x^2 - 64$

23. $x^2 - a^2$

24. $4x^2 - 49$

LESSON R.7

R.7 Simplifying Square Roots

The number 12 is not a perfect square, but we can simplify the square root of 12. To simplify a radical means to remove all perfect square factors from the radicand, the expression inside the radical.

> A **perfect square** is the product of an integer or polynomial multiplied by itself.

MODEL PROBLEMS

1. Simplify $\sqrt{12}$.

SOLUTION

Factor radicand	$\sqrt{12} = \sqrt{2 \cdot 2 \cdot 3}$
Pairs of identical factors are perfect squares	$\sqrt{2 \cdot 2 \cdot 3} = \sqrt{2 \cdot 2} \cdot \sqrt{3}$
Take square root of perfect square	$\sqrt{2 \cdot 2} \cdot \sqrt{3} = 2\sqrt{3}$

2. Simplify $\sqrt{72}$.

SOLUTION

Factor radicand	$\sqrt{72} = \sqrt{2 \cdot 2 \cdot 2 \cdot 3 \cdot 3}$
Pairs of identical factors are perfect squares	$\sqrt{2 \cdot 2 \cdot 3 \cdot 3} \cdot \sqrt{2}$ $\sqrt{2 \cdot 2} \cdot \sqrt{3 \cdot 3} \cdot \sqrt{2}$
Take square root of perfect square	$2 \cdot 3 \cdot \sqrt{2} = 6\sqrt{2}$

PRACTICE

Exercises 1–8: Simplify.

1. $\sqrt{320}$

2. $\sqrt{300}$

3. $\sqrt{108}$

4. $\sqrt{252}$

5. $\sqrt{272}$

6. $\sqrt{208}$

7. $\sqrt{540}$

8. $\sqrt{84}$

R.8 Completing the Square

To **complete the square** means to add a constant to a binomial like $x^2 + 6x$ to create a perfect square trinomial. To do this, take half the coefficient of the x term, square it, and add. A perfect square trinomial is a polynomial like $x^2 + 6x + 9$ that results from squaring another binomial, in this case, $(x + 3)^2$.

MODEL PROBLEMS

1. Add a constant to $x^2 + 10x$ to make it a perfect square.

SOLUTION

Take half of coefficient of x	$\dfrac{10}{2} = 5$	To determine what to add to create a perfect square trinomial, first take half of the coefficient of x. In this example, half of 10 is 5.
Square and add	$x^2 + 10x + 5^2$ $x^2 + 10x + 25$	Then square this number and add it to the other two terms. This completes the square.

> Note that the coefficient of the squared term must be **1**, such as x^2 as opposed to, say, $3x^2$, for you to apply this method. Shortly, we will discuss how to complete the square when the coefficient does not equal 1.

2. What constant added to $x^2 - 8x$ makes the resulting trinomial a perfect square?

SOLUTION

Find half the coefficient of x	half the coefficient of $x = -4$	Start by finding half the coefficient of x. The coefficient is negative.
Square it	$(-4)^2 = 16$	Square -4. A negative number squared is positive.
Add to binomial	$x^2 - 8x + 16$	Add the result of the previous step to the original binomial. The resulting trinomial is a perfect square.

Check your solution
$$(x - 4)^2 = (x - 4)(x - 4)$$
$$(x - 4)^2 = x^2 - 4x - 4x + (-4)^2$$
$$(x - 4)^2 = x^2 - 8x + 16$$

3. What constant added to $x^2 - 11x$ makes the resulting trinomial a perfect square? Hint: the constant is not an integer.

SOLUTION

Find half the coefficient of x	half the coefficient of $x = \dfrac{-11}{2}$	Start by finding half the coefficient of x. The coefficient is negative.
Square it	$\left(\dfrac{-11}{2}\right)^2 = \dfrac{121}{4}$	Square both the numerator and denominator of the fraction. A negative number squared is positive.
Add to binomial	$x^2 - 11x + \dfrac{121}{4}$	Add the result of the previous step to the original binomial. The resulting trinomial is a perfect square.

Model Problems continue . . .

4. Rewrite $3x^2 + x = 2$ by completing the square so that the left side is a binomial square.

SOLUTION

Divide by 3, coefficient of x^2

$$3x^2 + x = 2$$

$$x^2 + \frac{1}{3}x = \frac{2}{3}$$

To complete the square, the x^2 term should have a coefficient of 1. Divide this equation by 3 so that is the case.

> In the equation $3x^2 + x = 2$, the coefficient of the x^2 term is 3, not 1. The coefficient of x^2 must be 1 in order to complete the square.

Complete the square

$$x^2 + \frac{1}{3}x + \frac{1}{36} = \frac{2}{3} + \frac{1}{36}$$

$$x^2 + \frac{1}{3}x + \frac{1}{36} = \frac{24}{36} + \frac{1}{36}$$

$$x^2 + \frac{1}{3}x + \frac{1}{36} = \frac{25}{36}$$

The coefficient of the x term is $\frac{1}{3}$. Half of that is $\frac{1}{6}$, and the square of $\frac{1}{6}$ is $\frac{1}{36}$. We add $\frac{1}{36}$ to each side of the equation so the left side is a perfect square trinomial.

Factor

$$\left(x + \frac{1}{6}\right)^2 = \frac{25}{36}$$

Factor the left side of the equation to write it as a binomial squared.

PRACTICE

Exercises 1–17: What constant should be added to each expression to complete the square?

1. $x^2 - 10x$

2. $x^2 + 4x$

3. $x^2 + 16x$

4. $x^2 + x$

5. $x^2 + 5x$

6. $x^2 + 3x$

7. $x^2 + 8x$

8. $x^2 - 14x$

9. $x^2 + 2x$

10. $x^2 + 18x$

11. $x^2 + 20x$

12. $x^2 - 22x$

13. $x^2 - 16x$

14. $x^2 + 30x$

15. $x^2 - 9x$

16. $x^2 - x$

17. $x^2 - 11x$

Exercises 18–26: Rewrite the equation by completing the square so that the left side is a binomial squared.

18. $x^2 + 4x = 12$

19. $x^2 - 8x = -7$

20. $x^2 - 10x = 11$

21. $x^2 + 2x = 3$

22. $x^2 + 14x = -40$

23. $x^2 - 16x = -48$

24. $2x^2 - 5x - 7 = 0$

25. $2x^2 + 12x + 9 = 0$

26. $3x^2 + 4x - 12 = 0$

R.9 Graphing Parabolas

Graphing Parabolas of the Form $y = ax^2$

We graph a **parabola** starting with one that describes $f(x) = x^2$. All points on the graph are solutions to the equation $y = x^2$, just as all points on the graph of $y = mx + b$ are solutions to that equation.

To graph a parabola of the form $f(x) = x^2$:

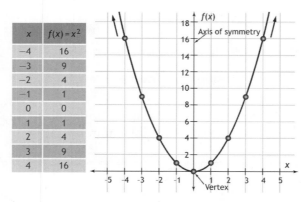

x	$f(x) = x^2$
−4	16
−3	9
−2	4
−1	1
0	0
1	1
2	4
3	9
4	16

In general, we can describe this form of a parabola as $f(x) = ax^2$, with $a = 1$ in this case.

1. **Graph points.** One way to graph any function is to simply graph points. Create an x-y table to keep your information organized. As the absolute values of x increase, so will the y values.

2. **Identify the vertex.** The minimum or maximum point of a function of this form is called the *vertex*. In this example, with the parabola opening up, the vertex is a minimum. The parabola has a vertex at (0, 0).

3. **Identify the axis of symmetry.** Parabolas are symmetrical about the axis of symmetry, a line that passes through the vertex. In this example, the parabola is symmetrical about the line $x = 0$, which is the axis of symmetry.

MODEL PROBLEMS

1. Determine if the graphs of $f(x) = 4x^2$ and $f(x) = \dfrac{1}{2}x^2$ are steeper than $f(x) = x^2$ using the absolute values of a.

SOLUTION

Graph $f(x) = 4x^2$

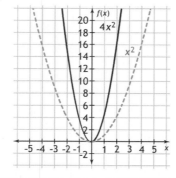

Model Problems continue . . .

Identify a

$$f(x) = ax^2$$
$$a = 4$$
$|a| > 1$: graph is steeper than $f(x) = x^2$

The coefficient of a function can be identified as a. So $a = 4$ for $f(x) = 4x^2$. When the absolute value of a is greater than 1, then the graph is steeper than the graph of $f(x) = x^2$.

Graph $f(x) = \dfrac{1}{2}x^2$

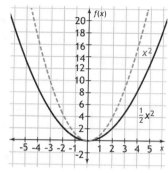

Identify a

$$a = \dfrac{1}{2}$$
$|a| < 1$: graph less steep than $f(x) = x^2$

With this function, the absolute value of a is less than one, and the graph is less steep than the graph of $f(x) = x^2$.

2. Graph $f(x) = -x^2$ and $f(x) = -2x^2$. Determine whether the vertex is a minimum or maximum.

SOLUTION

Graph $f(x) = -x^2$

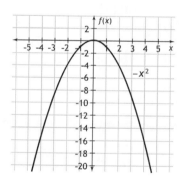

$a = -1$
when a is negative, graph curves down, vertex is maximum

The graph of $f(x) = -x^2$ curves down. When a is negative, the graph curves down, and the vertex is a maximum.

Graph $f(x) = -2x^2$

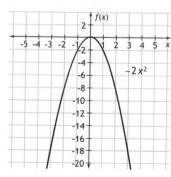

$a = -2$
$|a| > 1$ then graph is steeper, vertex is maximum

With this function, $a = -2$, and the graph opens down. Since $|a| > 1$, it is steeper than the first graph.

Graphing Parabolas in Vertex Form

The function $f(x) = x^2$ is the parent function of the graphs of parabolas. Any parabola can be described with the function $f(x) = a(x - h)^2 + k$ where a, h, and k are constants.

The constants h and k translate the function from the origin. As with other functions, k translates the graph vertically, and h translates it horizontally.

To describe how the parabola translates, we locate its vertex using h and k. The vertex of the parabola $f(x) = a(x - h)^2 + k$ is at (h, k).

The value of a does not change the location of the vertex, but it does determine the shape and direction of the parabola.

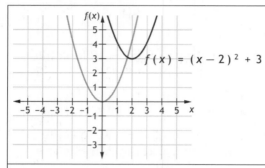	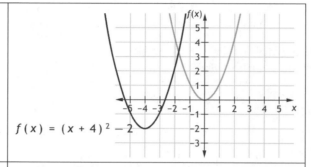
$f(x) = (x - 2)^2 + 3$ Vertex is $(2, 3)$	$f(x) = (x + 4)^2 - 2$ $f(x) = [x - (-4)]^2 + (-2)$ Vertex is $(-4, -2)$
The vertex is shifted to the right 2 and up 3 compared to the parent function, $f(x) = x^2$.	With this function, we need to restate the function so that h is subtracted and k is added. The vertex is translated left 4 and down 2 compared to the parent function.

MODEL PROBLEM

Determine the vertex and axis of symmetry for the function $f(x) = -2(x + 3)^2 + 4$. Graph the function.

SOLUTION

Locate vertex $h = -3$, $k = 4$	$f(x) = -2[x - (-3)]^2 + 4$ $(-3, 4)$	The vertex is at $(-3, 4)$, since -3 is subtracted from x, and 4 is added to the function expression.
Determine direction	Opens down ($a < 0$)	The sign of a determines which way the parabola opens. When a is positive, it opens up, and when a is negative, it opens down. This function opens down because $a = -2$.
State axis of symmetry	$x = h$ $x = -3$	The axis of symmetry is a vertical line that passes through the vertex, which has the x-coordinate h. For this parabola, $h = -3$.

Model Problem continues . . .

Plot points and graph
parabola

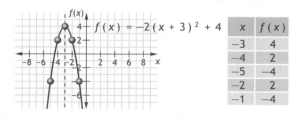

PRACTICE

1. What does the graph of $f(x - 5)$ look like compared to the graph of $f(x)$?

   A. $f(x - 5)$ is translated up 5
   B. $f(x - 5)$ is translated down 5
   C. $f(x - 5)$ is translated right 5
   D. $f(x - 5)$ is translated left 5

2. What does the graph of $f(x - 7)$ look like compared to the graph of $f(x)$?

   A. $f(x - 7)$ is translated up 7
   B. $f(x - 7)$ is translated down 7
   C. $f(x - 7)$ is translated right 7
   D. $f(x - 7)$ is translated left 7

3. What does the graph of $f(x) + 8$ look like compared to the graph of $f(x)$?

   A. $f(x) + 8$ is translated up 8
   B. $f(x) + 8$ is translated down 8
   C. $f(x) + 8$ is translated right 8
   D. $f(x) + 8$ is translated left 8

4. What does the graph of $f(x) + 6$ look like compared to the graph of $f(x)$?

   A. $f(x) + 6$ is translated up 6
   B. $f(x) + 6$ is translated down 6
   C. $f(x) + 6$ is translated right 6
   D. $f(x) + 6$ is translated left 6

5. What does the graph of $f(x - 3)$ look like compared to the graph of $f(x)$?

   A. $f(x - 3)$ is translated up 3
   B. $f(x - 3)$ is translated down 3
   C. $f(x - 3)$ is translated right 3
   D. $f(x - 3)$ is translated left 3

6. What does the graph of $f(x) - 10$ look like compared to the graph of $f(x)$?

   A. $f(x) - 10$ is translated up 10
   B. $f(x) - 10$ is translated down 10
   C. $f(x) - 10$ is translated right 10
   D. $f(x) - 10$ is translated left 10

7. What is the vertex of $f(x) = 3(x - 4)^2 + 2$?

8. What is the vertex of $f(x) = -5(x + 2)^2 + 6$?

9. What is the vertex of $f(x) = (x - 1)^2 - 8$?

Exercises 10–17: For each parabola, identify the coordinates of the vertex.

10. $y = \dfrac{1}{2}(x - 3)^2 - 2$

11. $y = -4(x + 1)^2 - 3$

12. $y = -\dfrac{1}{3}(x + 2)^2 + 2$

13. $y = -4(x + 1)^2 + \dfrac{1}{2}$

14. $y = 2\left(x - \dfrac{3}{5}\right)^2 - 3$

15. $y = 5x^2 - 3$

16. $y = -\dfrac{x^2}{2} + 1$

17. $y = \dfrac{x^2}{4} - 2$

Practice Problems continue . . .

Exercises 18–21: Graph each of the equations, and identify the coordinates of the vertex and the equation of the axis of symmetry.

18. $y = \frac{1}{4}(x + 3)^2$

19. $y = -(x + 1)^2 - 2$

20. $y = \frac{1}{2}(x + 3)^2 - 2$

21. $y = -\frac{1}{2}(x - 2)^2 + 10$

22. In a computer game, the equation $f(t) = -(t - 5)^2 + 25$ is used to describe the height, in feet, of a projectile over time, in seconds.

   a Graph this function for all values of t between 0 and 10.

   b State the maximum height of the projectile, and the time at which it reaches its maximum height.

23. **MP 3, 7** Jake says that since the vertex of a parabola is independent of the a value in the vertex form; the quadratic function $y = -2[(x + 1)^2 - 1.5]$ is a parabola opening downward with the vertex $(-1, -1.5)$. Is his description of the function correct? Explain.

LESSON R.10

R.10 Area and Perimeter Fundamentals

Squares, Rectangles, and Triangles

The **perimeter** is the distance around a two-dimensional shape.

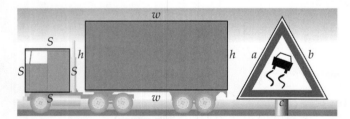

Square perimeter	Rectangle perimeter	Triangle perimeter
S = side length	h = height	$P = a + b + c$
	w = width	
$P = 4S$	$P = 2h + 2w$	

The **area** is the amount of surface inside the boundary of that shape. The formulas for the areas of some common figures are given below.

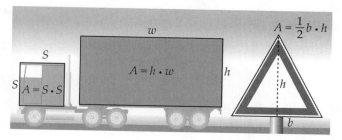

Area of square	Area of rectangle	Area of triangle
$A = S \cdot S = S^2$	$A = h \cdot w$	$b =$ base $h =$ height $A = \dfrac{1}{2}b \cdot h$

Circles

A **circle** is the set of all points in a plane that are the same distance from a point, called the *center of the circle*. The distance of the points from the center is the **radius** of the circle. The distance across the circle, through its center, is called the **diameter**. Each point on the circle is the same distance, r, from the center.

The number π (pi) equals 3.141592…. The dots mean the number continues forever. π is pronounced like "pie." The number π is used to calculate the **circumference** of a circle, which is its perimeter. Pi is also used to calculate a circle's area.

> $\pi \approx 3.14$. The symbol $\approx$ means *approximately equal*. We approximate π as 3.14 for calculations.

Radius of a circle	Diameter of a circle
$r =$ distance from center to circle	$d =$ distance through center $=$ twice radius $d = 2r$

Circumference of a circle
$C =$ circumference
$C = 2\pi r$ or $C = \pi d$

Area of a circle
$A =$ area
$A = \pi r^2$

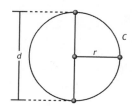

MODEL PROBLEMS

1. Calculate the circle's radius and circumference to the nearest inch.

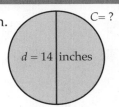

SOLUTION

Calculate radius	$d = 2r$	The diameter equals twice the radius.
	$14 = 2 \cdot r$	The problem states the diameter is 14.
	$r = 7$ inches	Substitute and calculate the radius.
Calculate circumference	$C = 2\pi r$	Write the formula for the circumference.
	$C \approx 2 \cdot 3.14 \cdot 7$	Substitute the values and multiply. Approximate π as 3.14.
	$C \approx 43.96$	
	$C \approx 44$ inches	The problem asks to calculate the circumference to the nearest inch, so round to 44 inches.

2. A circle's circumference is 9.42 feet. What is its radius to the nearest tenth of a foot?

> If you only know a circle's circumference, you can calculate its radius.

SOLUTION

Substitute into formula	$C = 2\pi r$	Start with the formula for the
	$9.42 \approx 2 \cdot 3.14 \cdot r$	circumference. Substitute the value given in the problem.
Solve for r	$9.42 \approx 6.28 \cdot r$	Divide both sides of the equation by 6.28
	$\dfrac{9.42}{6.28} \approx r$	to cancel the coefficient of r. The result is 1.5 feet.
	$r \approx 1.5$ feet	

3. A circle's radius is 2 inches. What is the area of this circle to the nearest tenth of a square inch?

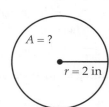

SOLUTION

Formula	$A = \pi r^2$	The area of a circle equals πr^2.
Calculate area based on diagram	$A = \pi \cdot (2)^2$	To calculate the area of the circle,
	$A = 4\pi$	substitute the value of the radius shown in the diagram and evaluate.
	$A \approx 4 \cdot 3.14$	Substitute an approximate value of π and multiply.
	$A \approx 12.6$ square inches	The problem asks for the area to the nearest tenth of an inch, so the answer is 12.6 square inches.

PRACTICE

1. A rectangle has a base of 4 and a height of 24. What is its area?

2. A rectangle has a perimeter of 8 and a width of 3. What is its height?

3. A rectangle has a perimeter of 12 and a height of 4. What is its width?

4. A triangle has a base of 7 and a height of 9. What is its area?

5. A rectangle has a width of 7 centimeters and a height of 13 centimeters. What is its perimeter in centimeters?

6. A triangle has a base of 15 and a height of 20. What is its area?

7. The length of one side of a square is 7 feet. What is the perimeter of the square, in feet?

8. The length of one side of a square is 9 inches. What is the area of the square, measured in square inches?

9. What is the area of a circle with a diameter of 4.5?

10. What is the circumference of a circle with a radius of 6.5 inches?

11. A circle has a circumference of 21.98 meters. What is its radius?

12. The area of a circle is 1.563π km^2. What is its radius?

LESSON R.11

R.11 Pythagorean Theorem

Triangles are composed of three angles that sum to 180 degrees. A **right triangle** is a triangle with one angle equal to 90 degrees, which is called a *right angle*. The two sides that meet at the right angle are called **legs**, and the side of the triangle opposite the right angle is called the **hypotenuse**. It is typical to call the legs a and b, and the hypotenuse c.

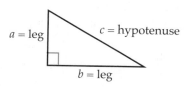

The **Pythagorean theorem** states that in a right triangle, the hypotenuse squared equals the sum of the squares of the legs, $c^2 = a^2 + b^2$.

> **Pythagorean theorem**
> $$a^2 + b^2 = c^2$$

You may find yourself calculating the length of a hypotenuse frequently. You may see the equation for the hypotenuse's length stated as $c = \sqrt{a^2 + b^2}$. We can also apply a similar idea to calculate the length of a leg, $a = \sqrt{c^2 - b^2}$.

> The converse of the Pythagorean theorem is also true. In any triangle, if the lengths of the 3 sides, a, b, c, satisfy the equation $a^2 + b^2 = c^2$, then the triangle is a right triangle and the side of length c is the hypotenuse.

1. What is the length of the hypotenuse of a right triangle with legs 9 and 12?

SOLUTION

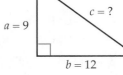

Right triangle $a, b =$ lengths of legs
$\qquad\qquad\qquad\; c =$ length of hypotenuse

The side across from the 90-degree angle is called the *hypotenuse*. The other sides are called *legs*.

$a^2 + b^2 = c^2$ $\qquad 9^2 + 12^2 = c^2$

The Pythagorean theorem states that the sum of the squares of the legs equals the square of the hypotenuse. The legs have lengths 9 and 12, so substitute those values in the equation.

$$81 + 144 = c^2$$
$$225 = c^2$$

Evaluate. Square 9 and 12, getting 81 and 144, and add. The result is 225.

$$c = \sqrt{225} = 15$$

Since c^2 is equal to 225, c is the square root of 225, which is 15.

2. Is a triangle with sides of lengths 3 meters, 4 meters, and 5 meters a right triangle?

SOLUTION

If the sides of a triangle have lengths, a, b, c that satisfy $a^2 + b^2 = c^2$

$3^2 + 4^2 \overset{?}{=} 5^2$

The longest side must be the hypotenuse, since its square is the sum of the squares of the legs. If this triangle is a right triangle, the side of length 5 meters must be the hypotenuse, c. Enter the values into the Pythagorean theorem.

> We will use the converse of the Pythagorean theorem to determine if this is a right triangle.

Then the triangle is a right triangle

$9 + 16 \overset{?}{=} 25$
$25 = 25$

Square 3, 4, and 5, and add the squares 9 and 16. Their sum, 25, equals the square of 5, confirming that this is a right triangle.

3. A leg of a right triangle is 12 and the hypotenuse is 13. How long is the other leg?

SOLUTION

Start with Pythagorean theorem

$a^2 + b^2 = c^2$

Start with the Pythagorean theorem.

Solve for a^2

$a^2 = c^2 - b^2$

Solve the equation for a^2. Subtract b^2 from both sides.

Substitute hypotenuse for c and leg for b

$a^2 = 13^2 - 12^2$

Substitute in the length of the hypotenuse, 13, and the length of the leg, 12.

$a^2 = 169 - 144$
$a^2 = 25$
$a = 5$

Square the numbers and subtract, then take the positive square root, since lengths are positive. The length of the leg is 5.

PRACTICE

1. Which of the following sets of side lengths cannot form a right triangle?

   A. 3, 4, 5
   B. 5, 12, 13
   C. 8, 15, 17
   D. 5, 6, 8

2. A right triangle has two legs, one with length 8 and the other with length 2. What is the length of the hypotenuse?

3. A right triangle has one leg of length 5 and a hypotenuse of length $\sqrt{125}$. What is the length of the other leg?

4. A right triangle has a hypotenuse of length 12 and one leg with length 6. What is the length of the other leg?

5. A 19-foot ladder leans against a wall. If the base of the ladder is 10 feet from the wall, how far up the wall is the top of the ladder?

6. **MP 2** To get from his house to the grocery store, Peter must drive 6 miles directly east and then 8 miles directly north. How far is Peter's house from the grocery store, as the crow flies?

Chapter 1 Geometry Fundamentals

Chapter Content

Lessons		Standards
1.1	**Geometry Essentials** Points, Lines, and Planes Angles Construction: Copying Segments and Angles	G-CO.1; G-CO.12
1.2	**Measuring Distances** Segment Addition The Distance and Midpoint Formulas Ratios and Line Segments	G-GPE.6
1.3	**Transformations and Congruent Figures** Rigid Motions Rigid Motion and Congruent Figures	G-CO.4; G-CO.5; G-CO.6; G-CO.7
1.4	**Translation in a Coordinate Plane**	G-CO.2; G-CO.5; G-CO.6
1.5	**Rotation** Rotation Fundamentals Mathematics of 180° and 90° Rotations ***Multi-Part Problem Practice***	G-CO.2; G-CO.4; G-CO.5; G-CO.6
1.6	**Reflection, Rotation, and Symmetry** Reflecting an Image About an Axis Lines of Symmetry Rotational Symmetry Three-Dimensional Symmetry	G-CO.2; G-CO.3; G-CO.4; G-CO.5; G-CO.6
1.7	**Composition of Transformations** Order of Composite Transformations Glide Reflections Parallel Reflections Composition of Transformations ***Multi-Part Problem Practice***	G-CO.2; G-CO.4; G-CO.5; G-CO.6

CHAPTER 1 REVIEW

Chapter Vocabulary

acute angle	isometry	ray
angle	line	reflection
angle of rotation	line of symmetry	right angle
composition of transformations	line segment	rigid motion
congruent	midpoint	rotation
construction	obtuse angle	rotational symmetry
coordinate plane	paragraph proof	straight angle
corresponding angles	plane	symmetrical
corresponding sides	point	theorem
endpoint	polygon	transformation
glide reflection	postulate	translation

LESSON 1.1

1.1 Geometry Essentials

Points, Lines, and Planes

A **point** occupies no volume or space. It is a location and is represented with a dot in a diagram and a capital letter such as A, B, C, D, or E.

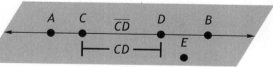

A **line** can be defined by two points it passes through. Using two points on a line, it is written as $\overleftrightarrow{AB}$ or with a single lowercase letter, such as l. It continues forever in both directions and has no thickness.

A **line segment** is part of a line. It has two **endpoints** such as C and D and is written $\overline{CD}$. The length of the segment is represented as CD (the letters with no line on top).

> Two or more points on a line are *collinear*.

A **ray** is a portion of a line that starts at a point and extends forever in a certain direction. It has an endpoint, such as C, and is defined by another point on the ray, such as A. It is written $\overrightarrow{CA}$.

A **plane** is a two-dimensional figure. A plane continues forever in two dimensions. A plane can be defined by listing any three points on it which are not on a line.

A **postulate** is a statement that is accepted to be true without proof. Postulates are used to help prove other statements.

Point, line, and plane postulates

Go to **www.amscomath.com** to review more postulates and theorems.

A line contains at least two points.
Exactly one line passes through any two points.
If two lines intersect, they intersect at exactly one point.
A plane contains at least three points that are not on a line.
Exactly one plane passes through any three points which are not on a single line.
If two planes intersect, their intersection is a line.
If two points are in a plane, then the line containing those points also is in that plane.

MODEL PROBLEM

MP 3, 6 Determine which statements are true about the diagrams. Explain your reasoning using the postulates for points, lines, and planes.

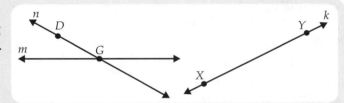

(1) Lines m and n intersect at points D and G.

(2) Only line k passes through X and Y.

SOLUTION

(1) False. As the diagram shows, the lines intersect at G. In general, two distinct lines can intersect at one point at most.

(2) True. Only one line passes through any two points.

PRACTICE

Exercises 1–4: Use the diagram to answer the questions.

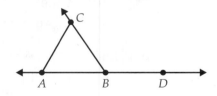

1. What is $\overline{AC}$?

   A. A point   D. A ray
   B. A line   E. An angle
   C. A line segment

2. What is $\overleftrightarrow{AD}$?

   A. A point   D. A ray
   B. A line   E. An angle
   C. A line segment

3. What is A?

   A. A point   D. A ray
   B. A line   E. An angle
   C. A line segment

4. What is $\overrightarrow{BC}$?

   A. A point   D. A ray
   B. A line   E. An angle
   C. A line segment

Practice Problems continue . . .

5. Which length is longest?

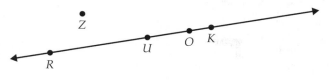

A. *RU*

B. *UO*

C. *RK*

D. *OK*

6. Provide three examples of surfaces in the real world that are parts of geometric planes.

7. Kevin states, "All lines are composed of infinitely many line segments." Is he correct? Why or why not?

8. Explain the difference between a line and a line segment. Provide an illustration of each.

9. What is the minimum number of points needed to define two distinct planes? Explain your reasoning.

10. Use the postulates in the section text to explain why every plane must contain at least one line.

Angles

An **angle** is formed by two rays with the same endpoint, which is called the *vertex*.

There are two ways to name an angle:

1. We can call the angle ∠*B*, for its vertex.

2. We can use three points, with the vertex in the middle— ∠*ABC* or ∠*CBA*—the order of the first and last points doesn't matter.

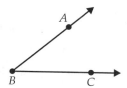

To indicate the measure of an angle, such as 44°, we use the letter *m*, so "the measure of ∠*B*" is written "*m*∠*B*".

There are different types of angles:

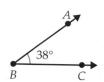

An **acute angle** is greater than 0° but less than 90°.

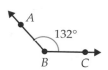

An **obtuse angle** is greater than 90° but less than 180°.

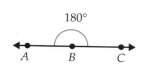

A **straight angle** is 180°.

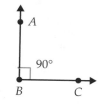

A **right angle** is 90°.

> The bracket you see by the 90° angle is the symbol for a right angle.

Angle addition postulate

If *S* lies within ∠*PQR*, then *m*∠*PQS* + *m*∠*SQR* = *m*∠*PQR*.

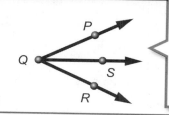

> The *angle addition postulate* allows us to sum the measures of angles. Two angles that share the same vertex and a common side are called *adjacent angles*.

MODEL PROBLEM

MP 3 $m\angle ABC = 105°$. If $m\angle ABD$ is twice $m\angle DBC$, what is $m\angle DBC$?

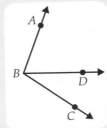

a Draw a diagram of the situation.

b Solve for $m\angle DBC$ and show your reasoning.

SOLUTION

a

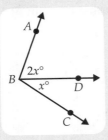

b Angle addition postulate	$m\angle ABD + m\angle DBC = m\angle ABC$	Start by using the angle addition postulate that lets us add the two angles.
Write equation	$x = m\angle DBC$ $x + 2x = 105°$	Let x represent $m\angle DBC$. The problem says $m\angle ABD$ is twice $m\angle DBC$, so $m\angle ABD$ is $2x$. They sum to $105°$.
Solve equation	$3x = 105°$ $x = 35°$ $m\angle DBC = 35°$	Solve the equation. Since x represents $m\angle DBC$, that is the answer to the question.

Construction: Copying Segments and Angles

An example of a simple geometric construction might be to use a piece of string to create another line segment with the same length. Stretch the string, mark the two endpoints of the segment, and transfer that length to draw a segment of the same length.

Segments of the same length are called **congruent** segments. The symbol for congruence is ≅, so $\overline{AB} \cong \overline{CD}$ means the two segments are congruent.

We show how a compass and a straightedge can be used to **construct** a copy of a single line segment:

1. Start with a given segment, such as $\overline{AB}$, and mark a point for the endpoint, such as C.

3. Pick and mark a point on arc D.

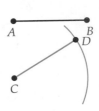

2. Draw arc from C with the compass set to the length of the original segment.

4. Connect points with a straightedge.

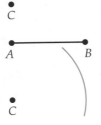

We show how a compass and a straightedge can be used to perform a slightly more difficult task: copying an angle. Two angles with the same measure are called *congruent angles*. So $\angle BAC \cong \angle DAE$ means that those two angles are congruent.

1. Start with a given angle, such as $\angle BAC$.

2. Draw a line segment with straightedge.

3. Set compass at vertex of original angle. Draw arc across $\angle BAC$.

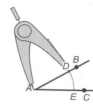

4. Keep compass width the same and draw a new arc. Draw an arc passing through $\overline{YZ}$.

5. Set compass width to DE and place at W. Draw arc.

6. Draw line through Y and U. $AD = YU$ and $\angle XYZ$ and $\angle BAC$ have the same measure (they are congruent).

PRACTICE

1. What type of angle is formed by the clock's hands?

A. Right angle
B. Acute angle
C. Obtuse angle
D. Straight angle

2. At exactly 3 o'clock, what type of angle is formed by a clock's hands?

A. Right angle   C. Obtuse angle
B. Acute angle   D. Straight angle

3. An angle is formed from the negative x-axis and the positive x-axis. What is the measure of the angle?

A. 90°
B. 180°
C. 270°
D. 360°

Practice Problems continue . . .

4. An angle is defined by the positive *x*-axis and a ray that has the point $(-2, 2)$ on it. What is a possible measure of the angle that this ray defines?

   A. 45°   C. 225°

   B. 135°   D. 315°

5. How could the angle below be written? Choose all that apply.

   A. ∠*EDF*

   B. ∠*FED*

   C. ∠*DEF*

   D. ∠*F*

   E. ∠*E*

6. How could the angle below be written? Choose all that apply.

   A. ∠*HQX*

   B. ∠*HXQ*

   C. ∠*QXH*

   D. ∠*X*

   E. ∠*Q*

7. Refer to the diagram below. Which of these are true statements about the construction of ∠*XYZ*, a copy of ∠*BAC*? Choose all of the true statements.

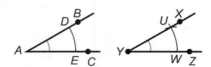

   A. $\overline{YZ}$ must be parallel to $\overline{AB}$.

   B. The two angles, ∠*XYZ* and ∠*BAC*, have the same measure.

   C. $\overline{AD}$ and $\overline{YU}$ are the same length.

8. What angle measure is formed by the minute and hour hands on a clock when they point to 12 and 3, respectively? Express the answer as a positive value between 0° and 360°.

9. What is the measure of the angle below?

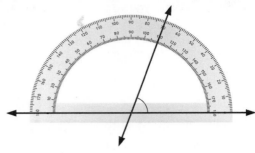

10. Provide one real-world example of each of the following: acute, obtuse, right, and straight angles. A real-world example describes a physical situation such as "the angle between a laptop's screen and keyboard when it is being used."

11. Two adjacent angles (two angles that share a common side and vertex) form a straight angle. One of the angles measures 140°. What is the measure of the other angle?

12. Two adjacent angles (two angles that share a common side and vertex) form a right angle. One measures 36°. What is the measure of the other angle?

13. Two adjacent angles (two angles that share a common side and vertex) form a 120° angle. One of the angles is a right angle. What is the measure of the other angle?

14. Four adjacent angles form a straight angle. The angles measure $b°$, $14b°$, $12b°$, and $18b°$. What is the measure of each of the four angles?

15. $m\angle YWZ$ is 67°, and $m\angle XWY$ is 54°. What is $m\angle XWZ$? The diagram is not to scale.

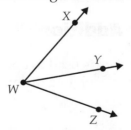

16. Given the diagram below, what is $m\angle GEF$? Show your work.

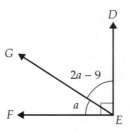

17. $m\angle ABC = 84°$. If $m\angle ABD$ is six times $m\angle DBC$, what is $m\angle DBC$? Show your work.

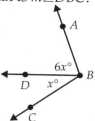

18. **MP 3** Given the diagram below, what is $m\angle DEG$ if $m\angle DEF = 150°$? What is $m\angle GEF$? Show all work, and explain your reasoning.

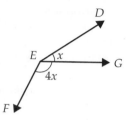

19. Given the diagram below, what is $m\angle DBC$ and $m\angle ABD$?

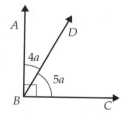

20. An architect designs $\angle ABC$, composed of two adjacent angles, $\angle ABD$ and $\angle DBC$.

   a If $m\angle ABD = 3a$ and $m\angle DBC = a$, what is the measure of $\angle DBC$ if $\angle ABC$ measures 160°?

   b What is the measure of $\angle ABD$?

21. Draw an angle. Construct a congruent angle using a compass and ruler. Label the measure of each angle.

22. Draw the following common angles using a protractor: 30°, 45°, 60°, and 90°.

23. Draw a straight angle composed of two adjacent 90° angles.

24. **MP 6** Identify 3 angles in the figure below. Which angle is the largest? Explain how you know.

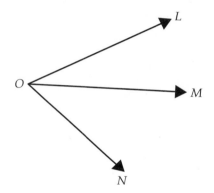

LESSON 1.2

1.2 Measuring Distances

Segment Addition

The ruler postulate is used to determine if two line segments are the same length. This method of calculating distances is valid for any line.

Ruler postulate	
Every point on a line can be paired with a real number.	
That number corresponds to its coordinate.	
The distance between any two points equals the absolute value of the difference of their coordinates.	The distance $AB = |x_2 - x_1|$.

> The ruler postulate enables us to calculate distances between points. A distance must always be positive or zero. Taking the absolute value of a number ensures that this will be the case.

Segment addition postulate

If B is between A and C on a line segment, then $AB + BC = AC$.

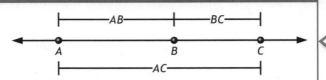

> The segment addition postulate confirms that we can add segment lengths.

MODEL PROBLEMS

1. **MP 1** Is $AB = CD$?

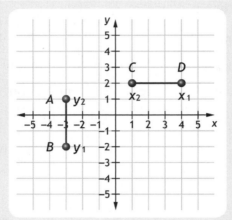

> This graph is an example of coordinate geometry. In this type of geometry, points, lines, and figures are graphed on a **coordinate plane** so the algebra of the real number system can be applied to them. The coordinate plane provides a bridge between algebra and geometry.

SOLUTION

Calculate AB
$$AB = |y_2 - y_1|$$
$$AB = |1 - (-2)|$$
$$AB = |3|$$
$$AB = 3$$

To determine if $AB = CD$, calculate the lengths. Start with $\overline{AB}$. Since the line segment is vertical, its length is the absolute value of the difference in its y-coordinates. Use y_2 to represent one y-coordinate and y_1 to represent the other, and then evaluate.

Calculate CD
$$CD = |x_2 - x_1|$$
$$CD = |1 - 4|$$
$$CD = |-3|$$
$$CD = 3$$

Substitute and subtract. The absolute value of -3 is 3.

Compare AB and CD
$$AB = CD$$

The line segments have equal length.

2. What is MB?

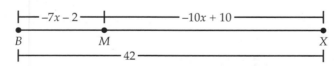

SOLUTION

Add segments
$$MB + MX = 42$$
$$(-7x - 2) + (-10x + 10) = 42$$

The segment addition postulate says we can add these segments to get the combined length.

Solve equation
$$-7x + (-10x) - 2 + 10 = 42$$
$$-17x + 8 = 42$$
$$-17x = 34$$
$$x = -2$$

First group and then combine like terms. Evaluate.

Substitute
$$MB = -7(-2) - 2$$
$$MB = 14 - 2 = 12$$

Substitute the value of x into the expression for the segment on the left. The length of the segment on the left is 12.

> Remember to check your answer! Substitute $x = -2$ into the expression for the segment on the right and you get 30, and the sum of the segments is 42.

Model Problems continue . . .

3. **MP 2** A slug is falling vertically alongside its spacecraft in deep space. It falls at 20 centimeters per second for 4 seconds, then at 40 centimeters per second for 1.5 seconds. If it started at a position of 90 centimeters above the base of the spacecraft, show its change in position and calculate how far it moved.

> Distance equals the product of speed and time. Distance will be measured in centimeters in this case, since the speed is in centimeters per second.

SOLUTION

Calculate first move	distance = speed · time 20 cm/s · 4 s = 80 cm	Calculate the distance it first falls as the product of its speed, 20 centimeters per second, and the time, 4 seconds. The slug moves 80 centimeters in the negative direction, down to a position of 10 centimeters.
Calculate second move	40 cm/s · 1.5 s = 60 cm	In its second period of motion, it travels at 40 centimeters per second for 1.5 seconds. It travels 60 centimeters, again in the negative direction.
Sum segments	80 + 60 = 140 cm	Use the segment addition postulate to add segments.

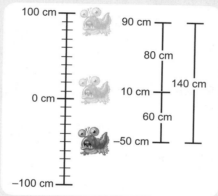

> Check the answer using a diagram! The slug moved from 90 to −50. The distance traveled is $|-50 - 90| = 140$.

PRACTICE

1. What is the length of $\overline{AB}$?

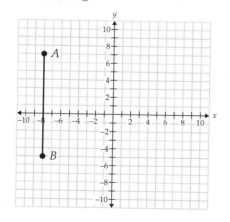

2. What is the length of the longest line segment graphed in the diagram below?

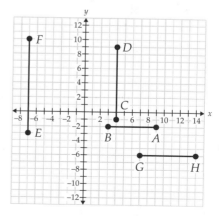

Practice Problems continue . . .

3. Given $AC = 133$, what is the length of $\overline{AB}$?

A   2x + 3   B   4x + 4   C

4. Given $DF = 37$, what is the length of $\overline{EF}$?

D   5a + 2   E   4a – 1   F

5. Point B is located on $\overline{AC}$. If $\overline{AC}$ is 139 cm long, and $\overline{BC}$ is 36 cm long, how long is $\overline{AB}$?

6. Point S is located on $\overline{RT}$. If $\overline{RS}$ is 89 inches long, and $\overline{ST}$ is 14 inches long, what is the length of $\overline{RT}$?

7. The segments $\overline{AB}$ and $\overline{CD}$ are graphed on a coordinate plane. The endpoints of $\overline{AB}$ are at $(9, 4)$ and $(9, 20)$. $\overline{CD}$ is parallel to the x-axis, and one of its endpoints is at $(5, 8)$. If $\overline{AB} \cong \overline{CD}$ and $\overline{CD}$ is entirely in the first quadrant, what is the other endpoint of $\overline{CD}$?

8. Point B lies on $\overline{AC}$. $AC = 127$, AB is represented by the expression $-12x + 11$, and BC is represented by the expression $-8x - 4$. What is the length of $\overline{AB}$?

9. Point E lies on $\overline{DF}$. DE is represented by the expression $2x - 8$. EF is represented by the expression $2x - 4$. If $DF = 36$ inches, what is the length of $\overline{DE}$? What is the length of $\overline{EF}$?

10. On a coordinate grid, draw a vertical line segment $\overline{AB}$ with a length of 8 units. Draw a horizontal line segment $\overline{CD}$ with a length of 12 units.

11. **MP 1** Draw a line segment containing a point that divides it into two segments. Make up a problem that provides algebraic expressions for each of the newly created line segments (such as "$AB = 2b - 4$") and a length for the original line segment. Then solve your problem to determine the length of each of the adjacent line segments.

12. The endpoints of $\overline{MN}$ are at $(7, 5)$ and $(7, -2)$, and the endpoints of $\overline{GH}$ are $(6, -11)$ and $(3, -11)$. Is $\overline{MN} \cong \overline{GH}$? Explain.

13. The endpoints of $\overline{AB}$ are at $(1, 432)$ and $(-1, 432)$, and the endpoints of $\overline{YZ}$ are $(0, -455)$ and $(2, -455)$. Is $\overline{AB} \cong \overline{YZ}$? Explain.

The Distance and Midpoint Formulas

When the endpoints of a line segment do not fall on a vertical or horizontal line, use the distance formula to find the length of the segment.

The distance formula: $d = \sqrt{(x_2 - x_1)^2 + (y_2 - y_1)^2}$

> The distance formula is based on the Pythagorean theorem.

The midpoint formula: **midpoint** $= \left(\dfrac{x_1 + x_2}{2}, \dfrac{y_1 + y_2}{2} \right)$

> The midpoint formula is used to calculate the coordinates of a point halfway between two points.

1. What is the distance between $(2, -1)$ and $(5, 3)$? Draw a diagram to confirm your answer.

SOLUTION

Use the distance formula $\quad d = \sqrt{(x_2 - x_1)^2 + (y_2 - y_1)^2}$ $\qquad$ State the formula.

Substitute into formula $\quad x_1 = 2,\ y_1 = -1$ $\qquad$ Substitute the coordinates of
$\qquad\qquad\qquad\qquad\quad x_2 = 5,\ y_2 = 3$ $\qquad\qquad$ the two points into the formula.
$\qquad\qquad\qquad\qquad\quad d = \sqrt{(5 - 2)^2 + [3 - (-1)]^2}$

Do the operations $\qquad d = \sqrt{3^2 + 4^2}$ $\qquad\qquad\qquad$ Evaluate.
$\qquad\qquad\qquad\qquad\quad d = \sqrt{9 + 16}$
$\qquad\qquad\qquad\qquad\quad d = \sqrt{25} = 5$

Draw diagram

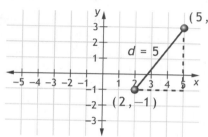

A diagram confirms that 5 is a reasonable answer to the problem.

2. What is the midpoint of the segment?

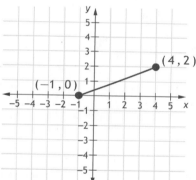

SOLUTION

Formula $\qquad$ midpoint $= \left(\dfrac{x_1 + x_2}{2},\ \dfrac{y_1 + y_2}{2} \right)$ $\qquad$ Use the midpoint formula.

Substitute $\qquad x_1 = -1,\ x_2 = 4$ $\qquad\qquad\qquad$ The endpoints have the coordinates $(-1, 0)$
and evaluate $\qquad y_1 = 0,\ y_2 = 2$ $\qquad\qquad\qquad\quad$ and $(4, 2)$. Substitute in the values and
evaluate.

$\qquad\qquad\qquad$ midpoint $= \left(\dfrac{-1 + 4}{2},\ \dfrac{0 + 2}{2} \right)$

$\qquad\qquad\qquad$ midpoint $= \left(\dfrac{3}{2},\ 1 \right)$

Model Problems continue . . .

MODEL PROBLEMS *continued*

3. *B* is the midpoint between *A* and *C*. Find the *x*- and *y*-coordinates of *C*.

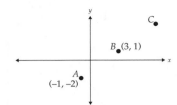

Note that we are still using the midpoint formula, but in this case we have the coordinates of the *midpoint* and are solving for the coordinates of one of the *endpoints*.

SOLUTION

Substitute midpoint and endpoint

$$midpoint = \left(\frac{x_1 + x_2}{2}, \frac{y_1 + y_2}{2} \right)$$

$$(3, 1) = \left(\frac{-1 + x_2}{2}, \frac{-2 + y_2}{2} \right)$$

Start with the midpoint formula. *B* is the midpoint, so substitute its coordinates, as well as the coordinates of *A*, an endpoint.

Locate *C*'s *x*-coordinate

$$3 = \frac{-1 + x_2}{2}$$

$$2 \cdot 3 = \left(\frac{-1 + x_2}{2} \right)$$

$$6 = -1 + x_2$$

$$x_2 = 7$$

Solve for x_2, the *x*-coordinate of *C*, the other endpoint. Solve the equation by multiplying both sides by the denominator, 2, and then adding 1 to both sides.

Locate *C*'s *y*-coordinate

$$1 = \frac{-2 + y_2}{2}$$

$$2 \cdot 1 = 2 \left(\frac{-2 + y_2}{2} \right)$$

$$2 = -2 + y_2$$

$$y_2 = 4$$

Solve for y_2, the *y*-coordinate of *C*. Evaluate.

Write solution

$$C = (7, 4)$$

PRACTICE

1. What is the length of the line segment shown below?

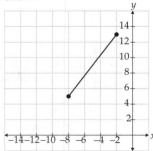

2. What is the length of a line segment with endpoints at $(-8, 7)$ and $(5, 1)$?

3. What is the length of a line segment with endpoints at $(-11, 17)$ and $(-6, 5)$?

4. A line segment has a total rise of 4 units and a total run of 3 units. What is the distance between the endpoints of the line segment?

5. A line segment has a total rise of 16 units and a total run of 12 units. What is the distance between the endpoints of the line segment?

6. Find the midpoint between $(-8, 5)$ and $(2, 7)$.

7. Find the midpoint between $(6, -1)$ and $(-3, -13)$.

8. What is the midpoint of the line segment shown below?

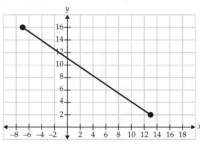

Practice Problems continue . . .

9. Line segment $\overline{AC}$ has a midpoint, B, at $(4, 6)$. The endpoint A is represented by the ordered pair $(2, 1)$. What is the ordered pair that represents the endpoint C?

10. Line segment $\overline{EG}$ has a midpoint, F, at $(-3, 2)$. The endpoint E is represented by the ordered pair $(4, -8)$. What is the ordered pair that represents the endpoint G?

11. On a coordinate grid, draw a diagonal line segment that is 10 units long. Label the endpoints.

12. On a coordinate grid, draw a diagonal line segment that is approximately 14 units long. Label the endpoints.

13. Draw a line segment that has a midpoint at $(3, -8)$. Label the endpoints.

14. On a coordinate grid, draw diagonal line segments $\overline{AB}$ and $\overline{CD}$ such that $\overline{AB}$ is longer than $\overline{CD}$. State the length of each line segment.

15. On a coordinate grid, create a unique diagonal line segment with a length equal to a positive integer. Note: By "unique," we mean one that has not been included in this chapter so far.

16. A line segment has one endpoint located at $(5a, 7b)$, and a midpoint located at $(-3a, 4b)$. What are the coordinates of the second endpoint?

17. $\overline{JK}$ is exactly 15 units long. Point J is located at $(10, -8)$. Point K is located in quadrant II and is one unit above the x-axis. What are the coordinates of point K?

18. **MP 3** Alan states, "The midpoint of any line segment can be found by multiplying the difference between the two x-values by $\frac{1}{2}$ and multiplying the difference between the two y-values by $\frac{1}{2}$." Is he correct? Why or why not?

Ratios and Line Segments

Suppose that we have a line segment, such as the one in the model problem below. Point B partitions, or divides, the line segment into two pieces with a given ratio of lengths. We call $\overline{AC}$ a *directed line segment* because it is a line segment from one point to another point in the coordinate plane with a specific order. For example, both $\overline{AC}$ and $\overline{CA}$ have the same length, 10, but $\overline{AC}$ is partitioned in the ratio $3 : 2$, while $\overline{CA}$ is partitioned in the ratio $2 : 5$.

> If a point partitions a directed line segment into a 1 : 1 ratio, that point is the midpoint of the line segment and its location can be calculated using the midpoint formula. In fact, the midpoint formula is a special case of partitioning a directed line segment.

MODEL PROBLEM

If B partitions directed line segment $\overline{AC}$ into the ratio $3 : 2$, what is the length of $\overline{AB}$? Draw a diagram of the situation to check your answer.

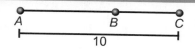

SOLUTION

Use ratio to state equation	$AB + BC = 10$ $3x + 2x = 10$	We use the segment addition postulate to sum AB and BC. The problem gives their ratio as $3 : 2$.
Solve the equation	$5x = 10$ $x = 2$	We solve the equation for x.
Substitute in the expression	$AB = 3x$ $AB = (3)(2) = 6$	Substituting 2 for x, we find that 3 times 2 is equal to 6.
Draw a diagram of the situation	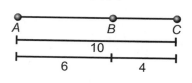	AC is $\frac{3}{2}$ larger than BC. Expressed equivalently, AC is $\frac{5}{2}$ of BC, AC is $\frac{5}{3}$ of AB, and AC is $\frac{2}{3}$ larger than AB.

PRACTICE

1. The point K partitions the directed line segment $\overline{AB}$ into a ratio of 1 : 1. What is true about point K?

   A. Point K is the midpoint of $\overline{AB}$.
   B. Point K is not the midpoint of $\overline{AB}$.
   C. Point K is not on the line $\overline{AB}$.
   D. Based on the information given, no determination can be made about point K.

2. The points R, S, and T are on the same directed line segment. The ratio of $RS : ST$ is 1 : 2. If point R is located at $(6, 3)$ and point S is located at $(0, -1)$, what are the coordinates of point T?

3. The directed line segment ABC has coordinates $A = (5, 8)$; $B = (2, 12)$; and $C = (-1, 16)$. What is the ratio $AB : BC$?

4. The points X, Y, and Z are on the same directed line segment. The ratio of $XY : YZ$ is 2 : 3. If point X is located at $(6, 10)$ and point Y is located at $(-1, 8)$, what are the coordinates of point Z?

5. The points A, B, and C are on the same directed line segment. The ratio of $AB : BC$ is 1 : 1. If point A is located at $(7, 8)$ and point C is located at $(-3, -4)$, what are the coordinates of point B?

6. Suppose the length of directed line segment $\overline{KLM}$ is 18 units. If the ratio of $KL : LM$ is 4 : 5, what is the length of KL?

7. If the length of a directed line segment is 12 units and the length of the first partition is 9 units, what is the ratio of the first partition's length to the second partition's length?

8. If three points, F, G, and H, are all on the same directed line segment and point G partitions $\overline{FH}$ into the ratio 3 : 8, what is the length of $\overline{GH}$? The length of $\overline{FH}$ is 22 units.

9. The point P partitions the directed line segment $\overline{WY}$ into a ratio of 5 : 3. If $WY = 36$ units, what is the length of $\overline{WP}$?

10. P is on $\overline{ST}$, and $ST = 63$.

    a If $\dfrac{SP}{PT} = \dfrac{2}{5}$, how far is P from T?
    b If $ST = 90$ and $\dfrac{SP}{PT} = \dfrac{9}{1}$, how far is P from T?

11. P is on $\overline{MN}$, and $MN = 24$. If $\dfrac{MP}{PN} = \dfrac{1}{7}$, how far is P from N?

LESSON 1.3

1.3 Transformations and Congruent Figures

Rigid Motions

A **transformation** is a change in the location or size of a figure. Types of transformations include:

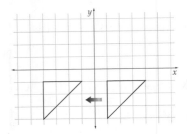

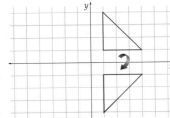

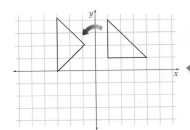

> Rigid motion transformations produce congruent figures.

Translation　　**Reflection**　　**Rotation**

All three types of transformations noted previously are examples of **rigid motion**. We will discuss each of the rigid motions in more detail in subsequent lessons, but here we describe the concept generally. With rigid motion, the lengths of the sides and the angles of a figure stay the same. You can think about this as a figure, such as a triangle, cut out from a piece of paper. You can move the paper triangle as you like—rotating it, flipping it onto the other side—but its lengths and angles will not change. Since the lengths of the sides and measures of the angles stay the same, rigid motion transformation creates congruent figures.

 In this activity, you translate a segment by adjusting its *x*- and *y*-coordinates and determine whether the resulting segment has the same length. Are the two segments congruent?

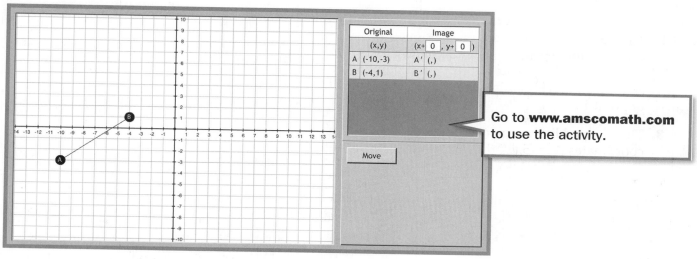

Go to **www.amscomath.com** to use the activity.

 In this activity, you translate an angle by adjusting its *x*- and *y*-coordinates and determine whether the resulting angle has the same measure. In other words, is it congruent?

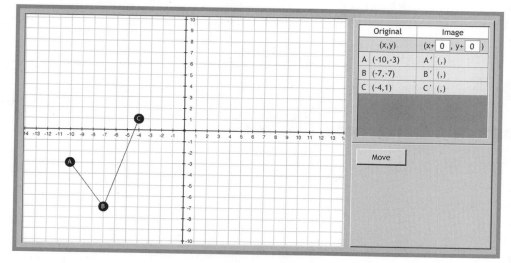

Rigid Motion and Congruent Figures

Two triangles are congruent if and only if their corresponding sides and angles are congruent. We can use rigid motion to show why this is true. One way to demonstrate this is to see what happens in both cases—when two triangles have corresponding sides and angles that are congruent, and when not all of the corresponding sides and angles are congruent.

If the relative position of angles or sides is the same in plane figures, those angles or sides are *corresponding*.

For example, cut out two triangles that have congruent sides and angles. You can see that they cover each other perfectly, even if you rotate, reflect, or translate them.

On the other hand, do as many transformations as you like with a pair of triangles where not all of the corresponding sides and angles are congruent, and you can never make them perfectly overlap.

You have used rigid motion to show that if and only if the corresponding sides and angles are congruent, then the triangles congruent. We often focus on triangles, but rigid motion transformations preserve congruence for other **polygons** as well.

> A **corresponding side** has the same place in two figures and a **corresponding angle** does as well. For instance, the two right angles in two right triangles would be corresponding angles.

Reflection Creates a congruent figure	**Translation** Creates a congruent figure	**Rotation** Creates a congruent figure

As we do with triangles, other polygons need to be named so their corresponding (congruent) sides are in the correct sequence. For example, $ABCD$ is congruent to $HGFE$ because $\overline{HG}$ is congruent with $\overline{AB}$, $\overline{GF}$ is congruent with $\overline{BC}$, and so on.

MODEL PROBLEM

MP 3, 6 Determine whether triangles $\triangle EFD$ and $\triangle XYZ$ are congruent to $\triangle ABC$ by rigid motion.

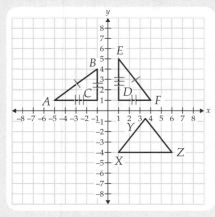

> Hash marks or arcs show congruence. The same number of hash marks or arcs means the sides are congruent.

SOLUTION

$\triangle ABC$ and $\triangle EFD$ — These are two congruent triangles with sides of length 3, 4, and 5. Their corresponding angles and sides are congruent, so the triangles are congruent. This is known from the diagram.

Model Problem continues . . .

Show
△*ABC* ≅ △*EFD*
by rigid motion

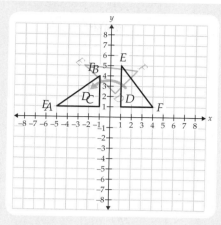

Rotate and translate △*EFD* to cause it to perfectly overlap △*ABC*. Rigid motions show that triangles are congruent.

△*ABC* and
△*XYZ*

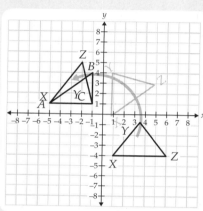

△*XYZ* and △*ABC* are not congruent. If you calculated the lengths of the sides of △*XYZ*, you would see it is not a 3, 4, 5 triangle. No matter how much you rotate, reflect, or translate it, △*XYZ* will never perfectly overlap △*ABC*.

PRACTICE

1. The triangles shown below are congruent. Which pair of angles are congruent?

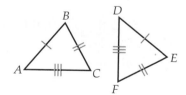

A. ∠*A* and ∠*E*
B. ∠*A* and ∠*F*
C. ∠*C* and ∠*F*
D. ∠*D* and ∠*C*

2. Select all the congruent pairs of sides.

A. $\overline{AB}$ and $\overline{BC}$
B. $\overline{AB}$ and $\overline{AC}$
C. $\overline{AB}$ and $\overline{EF}$
D. $\overline{AB}$ and $\overline{ED}$
E. $\overline{AC}$ and $\overline{ED}$
F. $\overline{ED}$ and $\overline{EF}$

Practice Problems continue . . .

3. The two polygons below are congruent. Which answer choice correctly names each polygon so the congruent sides are in the correct sequence?

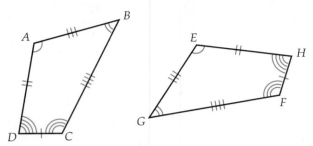

   A. $ABCD \cong EFGH$
   B. $ABCD \cong EFHG$
   C. $ABCD \cong EGFH$

4. The two polygons below are congruent. Which answer choice correctly names each polygon so the congruent sides are in the correct sequence?

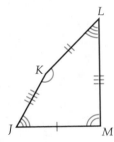

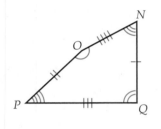

   A. $JKLM \cong NOPQ$
   B. $JKLM \cong OPQN$
   C. $JKLM \cong PQNO$

5. The two polygons below are congruent. Which answer choice correctly names each polygon so the congruent sides are in the correct sequence?

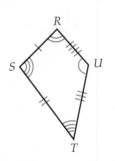

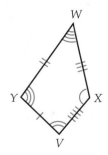

   A. $RSTU \cong VWXY$
   B. $RSTU \cong VWYX$
   C. $RSTU \cong VYWX$

6. The two polygons below are congruent. Which answer choice correctly names each polygon so the congruent sides are in the correct sequence?

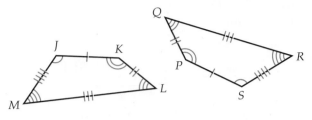

   A. $JKLM \cong PQRS$
   B. $JKLM \cong QRSP$
   C. $JKLM \cong SPQR$

7. Did the transformation produce a congruent figure? Explain.

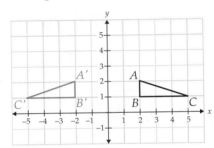

   A.   Yes
   B.   No
   C.   Not enough information to tell

8. A triangle was rotated and then flipped over. The resulting triangle is

   A.   The same shape and larger than the original triangle.
   B.   A different shape and smaller than the original triangle.
   C.   Congruent to the original triangle.
   D.   A different shape and the same size as the original triangle.

Practice Problems continue . . .

9. Which of the following transformations of the original image is an example of rigid motion? Choose all that apply.

Original Image

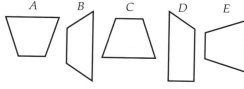

A. A
B. B
C. C
D. D
E. E

10. Which of the following figures (1, 2, or 3) can be obtained from the original orange figure through a single translation?

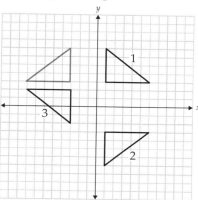

A. 1
B. 2
C. 3
D. None of them

11. Which of the triangles (1, 2, or 3) can be obtained from the original orange triangle through rigid motion?

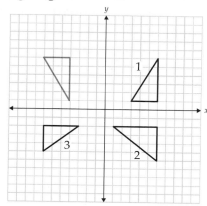

A. 1
B. 2
C. 3
D. None of the above

12. △ABC ≅ △ZYX. If m∠A = 10° and m∠B = 20°, what does ∠X equal? Hint: Consider what ∠X corresponds to in △ABC.

13. △ABC ≅ △ZYX. If m∠A = 20° and m∠B = 110°, what does X equal? Hint: Consider what ∠X corresponds to in △ABC.

14. Use the diagram to answer the questions.

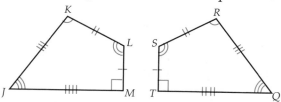

a Which angle is congruent to ∠J?
b Which angle is congruent to ∠R?
c Which line segment is congruent to $\overline{KL}$?
d Which line segment is congruent to $\overline{LM}$?
e If the measure of ∠L is 108°, what is the measure of ∠S?
f The length of $\overline{TQ}$ is 7 centimeters. What is the length of $\overline{MJ}$ in centimeters?

15. Triangle NMP is congruent to triangle FGH. $\overline{NM} \cong \overline{FG}$ and $\overline{MP} \cong \overline{GH}$. NP = 20 inches. How long is $\overline{FH}$?

16. What type of rigid motion will result in the N of the compass rose continuing to point up but exchanging the locations of E and W?

17. What type of rigid motion relates the two cats?

18. Draw horizontal line segment $\overline{GH}$. Then, draw two congruent polygons that are reflections of each other over $\overline{GH}$.

19. When an isosceles triangle (a triangle with two sides of the same length) is reflected over its base, what shape is formed by the four legs of the two triangles?

Practice Problems continue . . .

20. **MP 2** Find an object in real life that contains congruent shapes. Make a sketch of the object and indicate which parts are congruent.

21. **MP 3** Walter says the transformation that changed parallelogram *ABCD* to parallelogram *EFGH* is an example of rigid motion because all the sides stayed the same length. Is Walter correct? Why or why not?

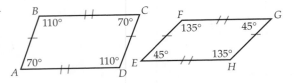

22. **MP 3, 6** A figure is flipped, moved up, and then rotated, producing a new figure. Is the new figure congruent to the original figure? Explain your reasoning.

23. **MP 2, 4** Elizabeth is working on a sewing project. She has a piece of fabric that is 6 inches wide by 5 inches high. From this, she needs to cut out two pieces that are equilateral triangles (a triangle with three sides of the same length) measuring 4 inches on each side and that are approximately 3.5 inches high. Elizabeth says she does not have enough fabric to cut out the triangles. Sketch a way to place the triangles so that they can be cut from the existing fabric.

24. **MP 1** Triangle *PDX* has vertices located at $P(-2, 1)$, $D(-2, -2)$, and $X(2, -2)$. Graph $\triangle PDX$. Then create and graph $\triangle SEA$, which is congruent to $\triangle PDX$, but has its vertices at locations different from those of $\triangle PDX$. State the coordinates of the vertices S, E, and A.

LESSON 1.4

1.4 Translation in a Coordinate Plane

Translation is a rigid motion that slides every point on a figure the same distance in the same direction. Translations are especially useful in the animation of figures.

When we want to refer to the points on the original figure, we use capital letters: *A*, *B*, *C*, and so on. The same points on the translated image are indicated with a prime symbol: *A′*, *B′*, *C′*, and so on. The point *A′* is read as "*A* prime."

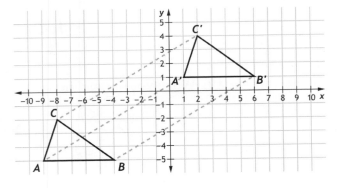

In a translation, each point in the figure moves the same distance and direction.

In this activity, you can draw and experiment with moving a figure left, right, up, or down on a graph. What is the result?

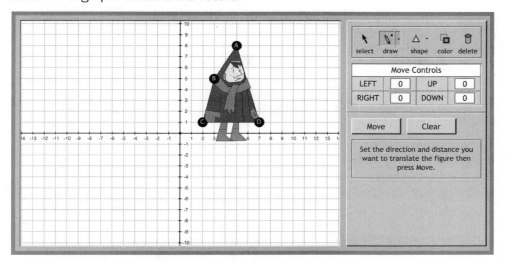

 In this activity, you can draw and experiment with translating a figure by adjusting its *x*- and *y*-coordinates. What is the result?

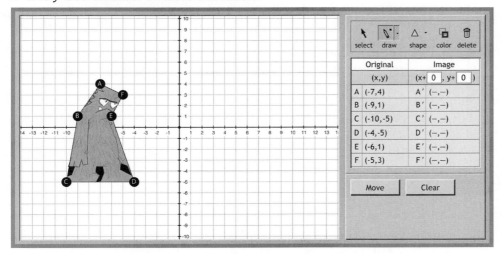

 In this activity, you determine the necessary change to a figure's *x*- and *y*-coordinates to produce the desired translation.

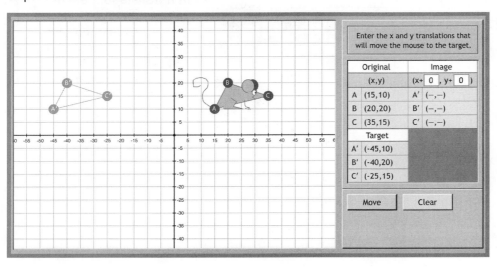

To translate an object in particular directions, you can add or subtract the same number to its coordinates.

Translate the figure on the left 15 right and 10 down using coordinates:

x-axis: right is positive, left is negative

- To move the triangle, add constants to each of its coordinates. Start by writing the *x*- and *y*-coordinates of the original figure. For example, *A* is located at $(-20, -10)$. We want to translate the triangle 15 to the right, so add 15 to its *x*-coordinates. Translate the triangle 15 to the right, to the *x*-coordinates calculated.

y-axis: up is positive, down is negative

- To move the triangle down, add -10 to the *y*-coordinates. Translate the triangle -10 vertically, to the *y*-coordinates calculated.

Add a constant to each coordinate.

- $(x + 15, y + (-10))$ or $(x + 15, y - 10)$

	Original (x, y)		Image $(x + 15, y + (-10))$
A	$(-20, -10)$	A'	$(-5, -20)$
B	$(-20, 20)$	B'	$(-5, 10)$
C	$(-10, 40)$	C'	$(5, 30)$

> A transformation that creates a congruent figure is called an **isometry**. Rigid motion transformations are isometric.

MODEL PROBLEMS

1. A point is located at the *x*- and *y*-coordinates (E, F). It is translated 3 units down and 5 units to the right. Its new location is described by the coordinate pair:

    A. $(E + 3, F + 5)$ C. $(E - 5, F + 3)$

    B. $(E - 3, F + 5)$ D. $(E + 5, F - 3)$

SOLUTION

The answer is D. Up and down are motion along the *y*-axis, so vertical change should be added or subtracted from the second, the *F*, coordinate. Down is negative, so 3 is subtracted. To the right is positive, so 5 is added to the *E*, the first coordinate.

2. The diagram shows two moves of a checkers piece. Describe its movement as a translation. Use the row and column numbers as coordinates.

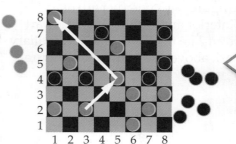

> The piece moves (translates) twice. This is called a *composition of translations.*

SOLUTION

First move: Two to right, two up $(x + 2, y + 2)$

Second move: Four to left, four up $(x - 4, y + 4)$

Add to calculate composite translation $(x + 2 - 4, y + 2 + 4)$ $(x - 2, y + 6)$

Model Problems continue . . .

3. Calculate the translation from the diagram.

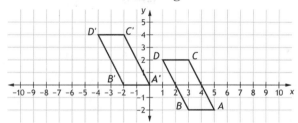

> To calculate a translation, you subtract the coordinates of a point on the *original* object from the coordinates of the corresponding point on the *resulting* image.

SOLUTION

State *x*-coordinates of corresponding points in object and image	D *x*-coordinate = 1 D' *x*-coordinate = -4	We want to calculate the change expression required to translate the parallelogram. To do so, pick a point on the figure and its corresponding point on the image. We choose D and D'. Write the *x*-coordinates.
Calculate change	$-4 - 1 = -5$	Make the change from 1 to -4. That is a change of -5. A key point: Subtract D from D'. In other words, subtract the location of the object from the location of the image.
State *y*-coordinates of corresponding points in object and image	D *y*-coordinate = 2 D' *y*-coordinate = 4	Write the *y*-coordinates of D and D'.
Calculate change	$4 - 2 = 2$	Calculate the change from 2 to 4. That is a change of 2. Again, a key point: Subtract D from D'.
Solution	$x + (-5)$ and $y + 2$ $(x - 5), (y + 2)$	Write the solution. Add -5 to the *x*-coordinate. This shifts it to the left 5. Add 2 to the *y*-coordinate. This shifts it up 2.

4. **MP 3** Translation creates a congruent triangle, and it is an isometry for triangles. Determine if translation is an isometry for all figures. Explain your reasoning.

SOLUTION

> We use a format called a **paragraph proof**, using a series of sentences, to explain our reasoning.

Paragraph Proof

Before we translate the figure, we construct auxiliary segments so that each interior angle of the figure is part of a triangle. Then we translate the figure and its auxiliary segments. From our work above, we know that a figure's sides and auxiliary segments will be congruent to its image's sides and auxiliary segments. Because a translation is an isometry for triangles, each triangle inside the figure is congruent to the corresponding triangle in the image. This means that each interior angle of the figure is congruent to the corresponding angle in the image.

All angles and sides of the figure are congruent to those in the image, so translation is an isometry for all figures. We have proved that translation preserves congruency for all figures.

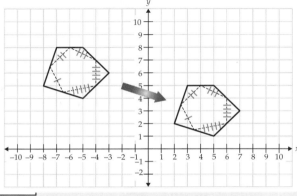

PRACTICE

1. Triangle PQR is the translated image of triangle ABC with vertices $A(-2, 5)$, $B(3, 3)$, and $C(0, -1)$. Which one of the following set of vertices could triangle PQR have?

   A. $P(0, 5)$, $Q(0, 3)$, and $R(0, -1)$
   B. $P(-2, 0)$, $Q(3, -2)$, and $R(0, 4)$
   C. $P(5, 7)$, $Q(-4, 5)$, and $R(7, 1)$
   D. $P(-4, 1)$, $Q(1, -1)$, and $R(-2, -5)$

2. A point is moved to $(-6, 4)$ by the translation $(x + 3, y - 8)$. What is the original point?

   A. $(-9, 4)$
   B. $(-9, 12)$
   C. $(-3, -4)$
   D. $(9, -12)$

3. A point P is translated 5 units right and y units down to point P'. If the length of the line segment from P to P' is 13 units, which of the following could be the value of y?

   A. 8
   B. 12
   C. 15
   D. 21

4. Which of the following is the composed translation of the following two individual translations: 4 units left and 2 units down, and 1 unit right and 9 units up?

   A. 3 units right and 7 units down
   B. 3 units left and 7 units up
   C. 5 units right and 11 units down
   D. 5 units left and 11 units up

5. Determine the constants required to translate the figure to the location of its image.

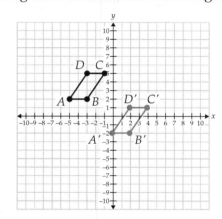

6. $\triangle ABC$ is translated as shown below. What was the translation?

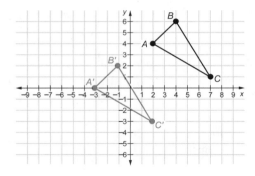

7. $\triangle ABC$ is translated as shown below. What was the translation?

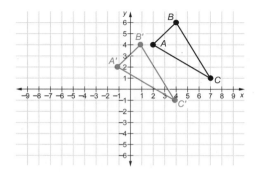

8. A point is translated up 3, 4 to the left, down 5, and 6 to the left. What was the translation from its original to its final position?

9. A point is translated down 7, down 4, 6 to the left, and 7 to the right. What was the translation from its original to its final position?

Exercises 10–15: The arrow notation represents movement of point P to point P' on a translated figure in the x-y coordinate plane. Describe the movement of the point in words.

10. $P(-4, -9) \rightarrow P'(-14, -16)$

11. $P(-5, 4) \rightarrow P'(-8, 13)$

12. $P(-3, 3) \rightarrow P'(1, 4)$

13. $P(-9, -9) \rightarrow P'(-5, -9)$

14. $P(3, 2) \rightarrow P'(1, -2)$

15. $P(-5, 1) \rightarrow P'(-9, 2)$

Practice Problems continue . . .

16. You want to move a figure 3 to the left and up 6. What constant do you add to the x-coordinate?

17. You want to move a figure 5 to the right and up 9. What constant do you add to the y-coordinate?

18. You want to move a figure 2 to the right and down 3. What constant do you add to the y-coordinate?

19. A figure moves up 9 and right 13. What constants do you add to the coordinates of each point to translate it?

20. A figure moves up 1 and right 17. What constants do you add to the coordinates of each point to translate it?

21. You want to translate a figure 3 units horizontally and -4 units vertically. What constants do you add to the x- and y- coordinates for this translation?

MP 7, 8 Exercises 22–25: Find the length of the translation from A to A'. (Hint: Use the distance formula.)

22. Point A is translated -5 units horizontally and -6 units vertically to the point A'.

23. Point A is translated 3 units horizontally and -3 units vertically to the point A'.

24. Point A is translated -5 units horizontally and -7 units vertically to the point A'.

25. Point A is translated 2 units horizontally and 9 units vertically to the point A'.

Exercises 26–29: Sketch the following composition of translations starting at the point P. Then determine the coordinates of the translated point.

26. $P(1, 4)$ translated first 5 units right and 2 units down, then 3 units left and 6 units up

27. $P(-5, 0)$ translated first 8 units right and 4 units up, then 4 units right and 9 units down

28. $P(-8, 8)$ translated first 2 units right and 6 units down, then 8 units right and 1 unit up

29. $P(0, 3)$ translated first 7 units left and 2 units up, then 10 units down

30. Explain in words why a figure and its translated image are congruent.

31. What does "a translation of a figure" mean? Give an example.

32. **MP 3, 6** Let A' be the point translated a units right and b units up from point A. The distance from A to A' is $\sqrt{a^2 + b^2}$. Can a translation of point A to A' be described using only the distance from A to A'? Why or why not?

33. If $\triangle ABC$ is translated a units horizontally and b units vertically to form its image $\triangle XYZ$, what is the translation that takes $\triangle XYZ$ back to $\triangle ABC$?

34. In the triangle formed by the points $A(-3, 4)$, $B(1, 5)$, and $C(0, 3)$, the distance from the origin is 5 units to point A and 3 units to point C. Kylie shifts the triangle down 2 units. Then she states that since translations are distance-preserving, the distance from the origin to C' is 1 unit and the distance from the origin to A' is 3 units. Is she correct? Explain.

1.5 Rotation

Rotation Fundamentals

A **rotation** is a rigid motion that moves a figure along a circular path about a fixed point called the *center of rotation*. The center of rotation can be any point on the coordinate plane.

The **angle of rotation** is defined by two rays. One ray goes from the center of rotation to a starting point on the figure, and the other ray goes from the center of rotation to the corresponding final point on the figure. The rotation can be clockwise, in the same direction as hands on a clock, or counterclockwise, which is opposite the direction a clock's hands move.

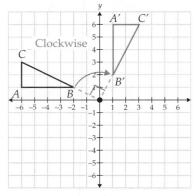 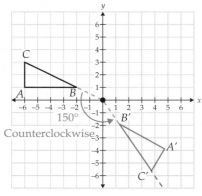

> In this text, we rotate figures about the origin.

A regular polygon can be formed by duplicating and rotating an isosceles triangle. Below, a triangle is rotated to form an octagon (an eight-sided figure). Notice how after a 360° rotation, the triangle is back in its original position. This will be true of any point, line, or polygon rotated 360°.

A complete rotation is 360°. We will rotate a triangle to have 8 total triangles, including our original. We divide 360° by 8 to determine how much we should rotate the triangle each time. Each rotation will be 45°. We rotate each new triangle by 45° each time.

$$\frac{360°}{8} = 45°$$

> The triangle angle with its vertex at the origin also must be 45°.

MODEL PROBLEM

MP 2 Using the wheel's center as the center of rotation, what is the angle of rotation from *A* to *B*?

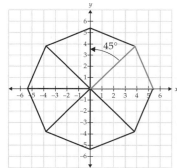

> We first calculate the angle between *adjacent* spokes of this aerodynamic bicycle wheel, and then calculate the angle formed by *A* and *B*.

SOLUTION

Calculate angle between spokes	$\frac{360°}{5} = 72°$	There are 360° in a circle. Divide that by 5, the number of spokes.
Two spoke angles	$2 \cdot 72° = 144°$	From *A* to *B* is two spoke angles, so multiply by 2.

Mathematics of 180° and 90° Rotations

Recall that the hands on an analog clock move in a specific direction that is referred to as *clockwise*. If we imagine the hands on the clock could move in the opposite direction, that movement is called *counterclockwise*. Rotating a point or figure 90° or 180° clockwise or counterclockwise around the origin produces a special pattern in the coordinates of the point(s). Use the following activities to investigate these patterns. What generalizations can you make?

 In this activity, you rotate a segment 90°. Notice the result. What happens when it is rotated 180°? 360°?

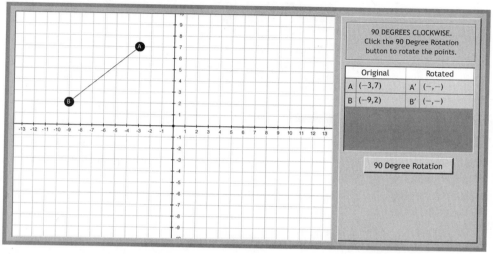

 In this activity, you rotate an angle. Does a rotation change the measure of the angle?

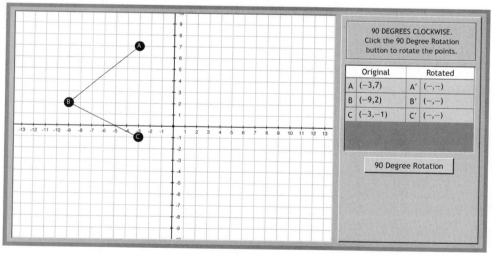

In this activity, calculate a rotation.

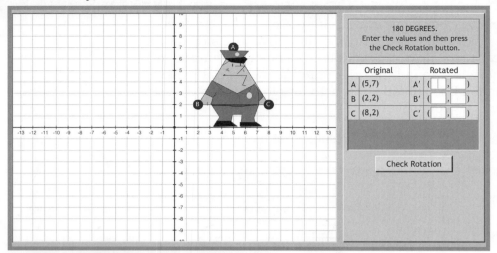

MODEL PROBLEMS

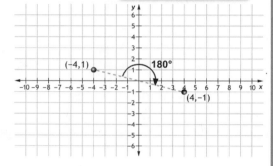

1. Rotate the point $(-4, 1)$ 180° about the origin.

> To rotate a point 180°, take the opposite of each coordinate.

SOLUTION

Take opposites of coordinates

$(x, y) \rightarrow (-x, -y)$

$(-4, 1) \rightarrow (4, -1)$

To rotate a point 180° about the origin, take the opposite of each coordinate. The point at $(-4, 1)$ rotates 180° about the origin when we take the opposite of its coordinates.

2. Rotate the figure in the diagram 180° about the origin.

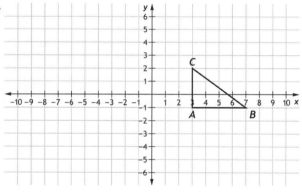

SOLUTION

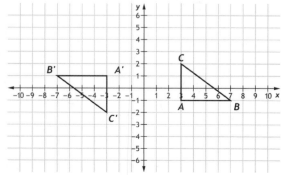

Model Problems continue . . .

3. Rotate the figure in the diagram 90° clockwise.

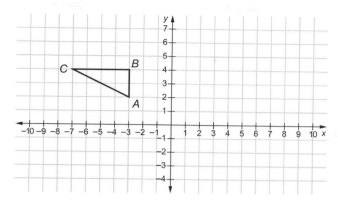

> Rotate a figure 90° clockwise by reversing the coordinates and taking the opposite of the new *y*-coordinate.

SOLUTION

Reverse *x*- and *y*-coordinates and take the opposite of new *y*-coordinate	$(x, y) \rightarrow (y, -x)$	To rotate a figure 90° clockwise, first reverse the *x*- and *y*-coordinates, then take the opposite of the new *y*-coordinate.
Point *A*	$(-3, 2) \rightarrow (2, 3)$	Rotate point *A* 90°. Reverse the *x*- and *y*-coordinates. Then take the opposite of the new *y*-coordinate.
Point *B*	$(-3, 4) \rightarrow (4, 3)$	Reverse the coordinates of point *B*, then take the opposite of -3 to get 3 as the *y*-coordinate.
Point *C*	$(-7, 4) \rightarrow (4, 7)$	Rotate point *C*, again reversing coordinates and taking the opposite of the new *y*-coordinate.

	Original (x, y)	Image (y, −x)
A	(−3,2)	(2,3)
B	(−3,4)	(4,3)
C	(−7,4)	(4,7)

Model Problems continue . . .

4. Rotate the figure in the diagram 90° counterclockwise.

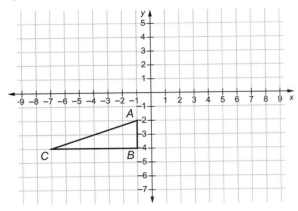

Rotate a figure 90°
counterclockwise
by reversing the
coordinates and
taking the opposite
of the new
x-coordinate.

SOLUTION

Reverse x- and
y-coordinates

To rotate a figure 90°
counterclockwise,
first reverse the x- and
y-coordinates. Then take
the opposite of the new
x-coordinate. This is
similar to clockwise 90°,
but take the opposite of
the new x-coordinate, not
the y-coordinate.

Take opposite of
new x-coordinate
$(x, y) \rightarrow (-y, x)$

Rotate A, B, and C 90°
counterclockwise. Reverse
the x- and y-coordinates
and take the opposite of
the new x-coordinate.

	Original	Image
	(x, y)	(−y, x)
A	(−1,−2)	(2,−1)
B	(−1,−4)	(4,−1)
C	(−7,−4)	(4,−7)

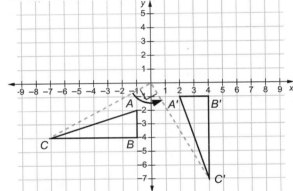

5. The segment $\overline{MZ}$ starts at $(-2, -1)$ and ends at $(-2, 6)$. It is then translated and rotated. Which of the segments described below could be the endpoints of the segment $\overline{MZ}$ after these transformations?

   A. $(-4, -2)$ and $(4, -2)$
   B. $(0, -1)$ and $(-7, -1)$
   C. $(-2, 9)$ and $(2, 9)$
   D. $(-3, -5)$ and $(3, -5)$

SOLUTION

The answer is B. The segment $\overline{MZ}$ has a length of 7, the difference of the y-coordinates; its
x-coordinates are the same. Translation and rotation are rigid motion transformations, so the segment
length must remain the same. All the line segments described in the multiple-choice section are
horizontal (since each segment's y-coordinates are the same), so their length equals the difference of
the segment's x-coordinates. Only B has a length of 7.

Model Problems continue . . .

6. Is the image the result of a 90° clockwise rotation?

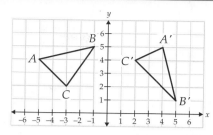

SOLUTION

Check that it is a 90° clockwise rotation	$(x, y) \rightarrow (x', y') = (y, -x)$	It looks like $\triangle A'B'C'$ may have been rotated 90° clockwise. If that is the case, the x- and y-coordinates were swapped, and the new y-coordinate is the negative of the old x-coordinate.
Check new x-coordinates	$x' = y$ $4 = 4$ $2 = 2$ $5 = 5$	The final x-coordinates were the original y-coordinates. All this is correct.
Check new y-coordinates	$y' = -x$ $5 = 5$ $4 \neq 3$ oops $1 = 1$	However, when we check the final y-coordinates, we see that the figure we have created is not a rotation. One y-coordinate is 4, and it should be 3, to be the negative of the initial x-coordinate.

To summarize:

Rotation	Original Point	Image Point
90° clockwise	(x, y)	$(y, -x)$
90° counterclockwise	(x, y)	$(-y, x)$
180° counter/clockwise	(x, y)	$(-x, -y)$

> When rotating 180°, it does not matter if the figure is rotated clockwise or counterclockwise, since it ends up in the same position.

PRACTICE

1. Which of the following figures (1, 2, or 3) can be obtained from the original figure through a rotation (not necessarily about the origin)?

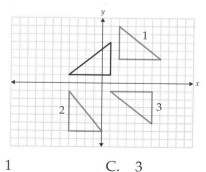

A.   1

B.   2

C.   3

D.   None of them

2. Which of the following is equivalent to rotating 67° counterclockwise?

A.   23° clockwise

B.   113° clockwise

C.   113° counterclockwise

D.   293° clockwise

Practice Problems continue . . .

3. In the regular pentagon *ABCDE*, what is the counterclockwise angle of rotation between *A* and *D* about the center of rotation? Assume the vertices of the regular pentagon *ABCDE* are written in order in a counterclockwise direction.

 A. 72°   C. 216°
 B. 144°   D. 288°

4. Which of the following coordinates describes a 180° rotation of the point $(-a, b)$ about the origin?

 A. $(-a, -b)$ C. (a, b)
 B. $(a, -b)$ D. $(b, -a)$

5. Which of the following coordinates describes a 90° counterclockwise rotation of the point $(-a, b)$ about the origin?

 A. $(-a, -b)$ C. (a, b)
 B. $(-b, -a)$ D. (b, a)

6. If you rotated a triangle to create a square, how many degrees would you rotate the triangle each time?

7. If you rotated a triangle to create a regular hexagon (6 sides), how many degrees would you rotate the triangle each time?

8. If you repeatedly rotated a triangle to create a regular decagon (10 sides), how many degrees would you rotate the triangle each time?

9. If you repeatedly rotated a triangle 40° each time to create a regular polygon, how many sides would this polygon have?

10. If you rotated a triangle 24° each time to create a regular polygon, how many sides would this polygon have?

11. If you repeatedly rotated a triangle 12° each time to create a regular polygon, how many sides would this polygon have?

12. In a 5-spoke wheel, what is the angle of rotation, in degrees counterclockwise, between spoke #2 and spoke #5? Assume the spokes are counted in increasing order in the counterclockwise direction.

13. In a 5-spoke wheel, what is the angle of rotation, in degrees counterclockwise, between spoke #1 and spoke #5? Assume the spokes are counted in increasing order in the counterclockwise direction.

14. In a 6-spoke wheel, what is the angle of rotation, in degrees clockwise, between spoke #2 and spoke #5? Assume the spokes are counted in increasing order in the counterclockwise direction.

15. In a 6-spoke wheel, what is the angle of rotation, in degrees clockwise, between spoke #1 and spoke #5? Assume the spokes are counted in increasing order in the counterclockwise direction.

16. In an 8-spoke wheel, what is the angle of rotation, in degrees counterclockwise, between spoke #2 and spoke #7? Assume the spokes are counted in increasing order in the counterclockwise direction.

17. In an 8-spoke wheel, what is the angle of rotation, in degrees counterclockwise, between spoke #2 and spoke #6? Assume the spokes are counted in increasing order in the counterclockwise direction.

18. In an 8-spoke wheel, what is the angle of rotation, in degrees clockwise, between spoke #3 and spoke #7? Assume the spokes are counted in increasing order in the counterclockwise direction.

19. Maggie states that rotations can have only two directions: left or right. What is wrong with her statement?

20. Describe in your own words the meaning of "the center of rotation."

Exercises 21–24: Determine the coordinates of the indicated vertices of the triangle rotated 180° about the origin.

21. $A(-7, 9)$, $B(9, -9)$, and $C(6, 7)$

22. $A(-2, 5)$, $B(5, -5)$, and $C(4, 3)$

23. $A(10, -8)$, $B(-4, 7)$, and $C(-1, -6)$

24. $A(4, -6)$, $B(-3, 8)$, and $C(-5, -4)$

Exercises 25–28: Determine the coordinates of the indicated vertices of the triangle rotated 90° clockwise about the origin.

25. $A(-5, 6)$, $B(6, -10)$, and $C(7, 8)$

26. $A(-7, 6)$, $B(6, -8)$, and $C(5, 4)$

27. $A(9, -6)$, $B(-6, 6)$, and $C(-2, -6)$

28. $A(5, -2)$, $B(-3, 8)$, and $C(-5, -8)$

Practice Problems continue . . .

Exercises 29–32: Determine the coordinates of the indicated vertices of the triangle rotated 90° counterclockwise about the origin.

29. $A(-6, 8)$, $B(7, -3)$, and $C(4, 4)$

30. $A(-3, 10)$, $B(5, 0)$, and $C(6, 2)$

31. $A(5, -9)$, $B(-1, 9)$, and $C(3, 9)$

32. $A(8, -8)$, $B(-9, 4)$, and $C(7, 8)$

Exercises 33–35: Sketch the resulting triangle after the indicated rotation about the origin.

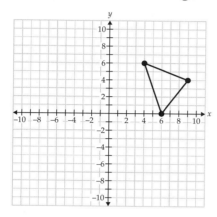

33. Rotation: 180°

34. Rotation: 90° clockwise

35. Rotation: 90° counterclockwise

Exercises 36–38: Sketch the resulting triangle after the indicated rotation about the origin.

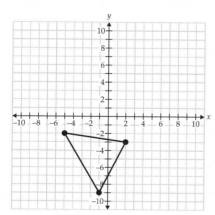

36. Rotation: 180°

37. Rotation: 90° clockwise

38. Rotation: 90° counterclockwise

Exercises 39–41: Sketch the resulting triangle after the indicated rotation about the origin.

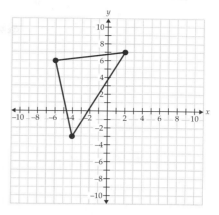

39. Rotation: 180°

40. Rotation: 90° clockwise

41. Rotation: 90° counterclockwise

42. **MP 3** Why is it necessary to specify the direction in a 90° rotation but not in a 180° rotation? Explain.

43. Using the point (a, b), show algebraically that two 90° clockwise rotations about the origin are equivalent to a 180° rotation about the origin.

44. Using the point (a, b), show algebraically that two 90° counterclockwise rotations about the origin are equivalent to a 180° rotation about the origin.

45. **MP 6** Using the previous two problems, explain in words how two 90° clockwise rotations are equivalent to two 90° counterclockwise rotations about the origin.

• Multi-Part PROBLEM Practice •

MP 1, 7, 8

a Is an example of rigid motion shown in the diagram? Explain your answer.

b The table below describes a third figure. Is it an example of rigid motion from the shaded triangle? Justify your answer.

x	14	14	17
y	-21	-18	-21

c A programmer wants to write a program that takes the segment AB of the shaded triangle in the diagram and has the segment shift down two every time it shifts one to the right. Write equations for points A and B that will cause this to occur.

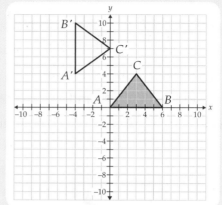

LESSON 1.6

1.6 Reflection, Rotation, and Symmetry

Suppose we reflect a figure over a line in the coordinate plane. The reflected figure and its original form an image that is symmetric about the line. The line itself is called a **line of symmetry**, or *axis of symmetry*.

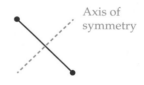

Axis of symmetry

- Two figures are **symmetrical** if they are congruent, and each point of one can be rotated or reflected to the other.

- Two points are symmetric with respect to a line if the line segment connecting them is perpendicular to the line, and they are the same distance from the line.

Reflecting an Image About an Axis

Vertical reflection

A vertical reflection flips over a horizontal axis of symmetry.

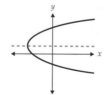

Horizontal reflection

A horizontal reflection flips over a vertical axis of symmetry.

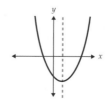

> A reflection is an image in which each point of the original figure has a symmetric point. An orange dashed line is an axis of symmetry for the first two shapes, but it is **not** an axis of symmetry for the third shape on the next page.

Not symmetric about orange dashed line

This figure is not symmetric to the axis shown because when it is flipped, the figure changes.

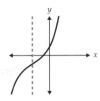

To determine if points are reflected about an axis:

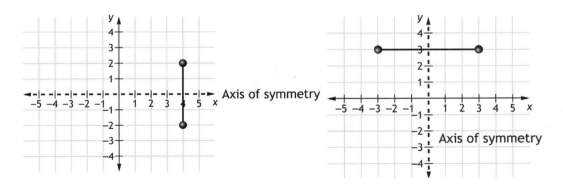

x-axis

- x-coordinates are equal
- y-coordinates are opposites

(x, y) and $(x, -y)$

For a pair of points to be symmetric with respect to the x-axis, they must have the same x-coordinate and opposite y-coordinates. In this example, you can see the y-coordinates are 2 and -2.

y-axis

- x-coordinates are opposites
- y-coordinates are equal

(x, y) and $(-x, y)$

For a pair of points to be symmetric with respect to the y-axis, they must have opposite x-coordinates and the same y-coordinate. In this example, you can see the x-coordinates are 3 and -3.

 In this activity, you reflect a line segment across the x-axis, y-axis, or both. What is the result?

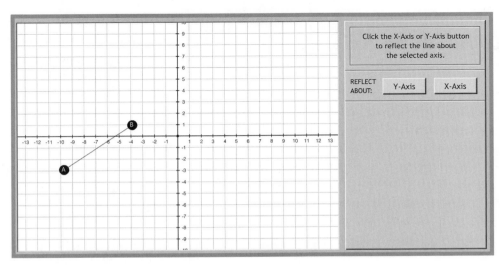

In this activity, you reflect an angle across the *x*-axis, *y*-axis, or both. What is the result?

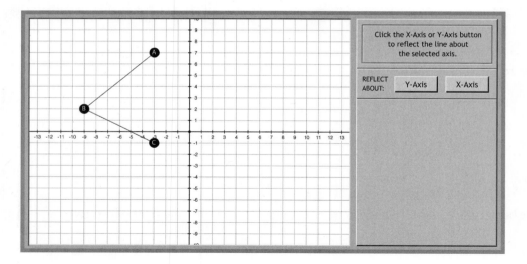

 In this activity, you determine the necessary changes to a figure's *x*- and *y*-coordinates to produce the desired reflection.

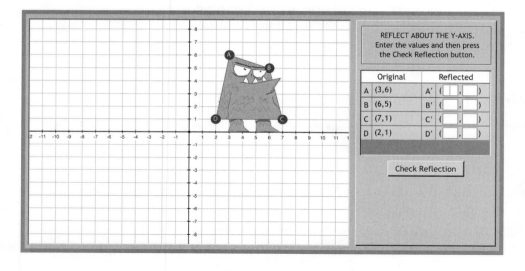

1. **MP 3** Are the figures shown in the diagram symmetric? If so, how?

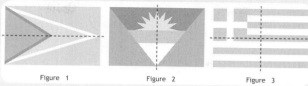

Figure 1   Figure 2   Figure 3

SOLUTION

Figure 1 is vertically symmetric. The orange line is a horizontal axis of symmetry, since it divides the figure into two congruent halves. This means they are vertically symmetric.

Figure 2 is horizontally symmetric. The orange line is a vertical axis of symmetry, since it divides the figure into two congruent halves.

Figure 3 is not vertically or horizontally symmetric. Neither orange line divides the figure into two congruent halves.

2. Reflect the point about the line $x = 2$.

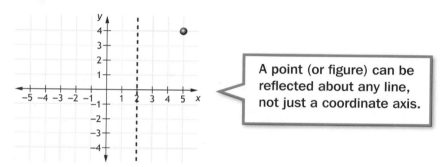

A point (or figure) can be reflected about any line, not just a coordinate axis.

SOLUTION

Identify distance from line	(5, 4)	The point is 3 to the right of the line.
Move to the line perpendicularly and continue for the same distance again	(−1, 4)	Move 3 to the line of symmetry perpendicularly and continue 3 more to the left of the line.
Draw diagram		

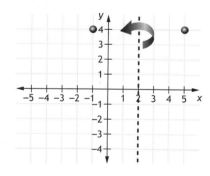

Model Problems continue . . .

3. Reflect the image about the *y*-axis.

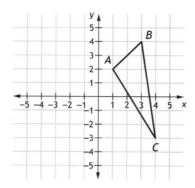

SOLUTION

Take the opposite of each *x*-coordinate $(x, y) \rightarrow (-x, y)$	To create a reflected image about the *y*-axis, take the opposite of each *x*-coordinate and keep the *y*-coordinate the same.	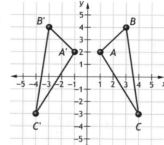

Original (x, y)	Image $(-x, y)$
A (1, 2)	A' (-1, 2)
B (3, 4)	B' (-3, 4)
C (4, -3)	C' (-4, -3)

4. Does the diagram show a reflection about the *y*-axis?

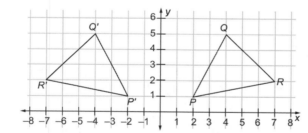

> By visual inspection, it appears this transformation is a reflection because each point on △*PQR* seems to have a matching point on △*P'Q'R'*.

SOLUTION

Check that it is a reflection	$(x, y) \rightarrow (-x, y)$	This transformation looks like it might be a reflection about the *y*-axis. In that case, the *x*-coordinates will be the opposites of one another, and the *y*-coordinates will be the same.
Check *x*-coordinates	$x \rightarrow -x$ $2 \rightarrow -2$ $4 \rightarrow -4$ $7 \rightarrow -7$	So far, so good. All the *x*-coordinates are the opposites of one another.
Check *y*-coordinates	$y \rightarrow y$ $1 \rightarrow 1$ $5 \rightarrow 5$ $2 \rightarrow 2$	This is even simpler to check: the *y*-coordinates are unchanged.
Determine congruency	Transformation was a reflection	The triangles are congruent since the transformation was a reflection.

Lines of Symmetry

A line of symmetry divides a figure into two congruent halves that are reflections of each other.

- Every point of the figure has a reflection image point in the figure: if we "pick up" a point and "flip" it to the other side of the line, it is at the same location as the other point.

The trapezoid to the right has one line of symmetry.

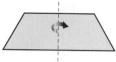

The figure to the right can be reflected about two lines.

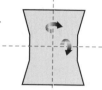

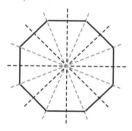

A regular octagon (one with equal length sides) has eight lines of symmetry. Four of the reflections are about diagonals that pass through the vertices. Also, the octagon can be reflected about the four lines that pass through the midpoints of its sides.

PRACTICE

1. The axis of symmetry is a _____.

  A. Value
  B. Point
  C. Line
  D. Plane

2. How many different axes of symmetry are there for a triangle with exactly two sides having equal length?

  A. 0
  B. 1
  C. 2
  D. 3

3. How many different axes of symmetry are there for a square?

  A. 0
  B. 1
  C. 2
  D. 4

4. How many different axes of symmetry are there for a circle?

  A. 0
  B. 1
  C. 17
  D. An infinite number

5. In your own words, describe the axis of reflection.

Exercises 6–9: What is the distance from P' to the x-axis?

6. Point P has coordinates $(-6, 6)$ and P' is its reflection across the x-axis.

7. Point P has coordinates $(3, 2)$ and P' is its reflection across the x-axis.

8. Point P has coordinates $(-4, -2)$ and P' is its reflection across the x-axis.

9. Point P has coordinates $(3, -1)$ and P' is its reflection across the x-axis.

Practice Problems continue . . .

Exercises 10–13: What is the distance from P' to the y-axis?

10. Point P has coordinates $(1, -8)$ and P' is its reflection across the y-axis.

11. Point P has coordinates $(9, -7)$ and P' is its reflection across the y-axis.

12. Point P has coordinates $(-8, -5)$ and P' is its reflection across the y-axis.

13. Point P has coordinates $(-4, -9)$ and P' is its reflection across the y-axis.

Exercises 14–15: Reflect the figure shown across the x-axis.

14.

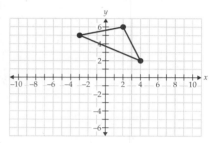

15.

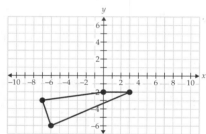

Exercises 16–17: Reflect the figure shown across the y-axis.

16.

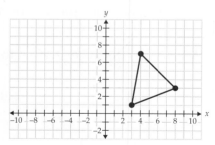

17.

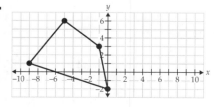

18. What are the coordinates of the reflection of the point $(0, -5)$ about the line $y = -3$?

19. What are the coordinates of the reflection of the point $(2, -7)$ about the line $y = -4$?

20. What are the coordinates of the reflection of the point $(-4, -4)$ about the line $y = 3$?

21. What are the coordinates of the reflection of the point $(-9, 6)$ about the line $x = 3$?

22. What are the coordinates of the reflection of the point $(10, 5)$ about the line $x = 5$?

23. What are the coordinates of the reflection of the point $(-1, 1)$ about the line $x = 3$?

24. Plot four vertices, $A(0, 2)$, $B(2, 7)$, $C(7, 9)$, and $D(5, 4)$, and connect them to form quadrilateral $ABCD$ on a coordinate plane. Sketch all lines of symmetry and determine the equations of these lines.

25. Plot four vertices, $A(-8, -2)$, $B(1, -2)$, $C(-2, -6)$, and $D(-5, -6)$, and connect them to form quadrilateral $ABCD$ on a coordinate plane. Sketch all lines of symmetry and determine the equations of these lines.

MP 3 Exercises 26–27: Determine whether each statement is always true, sometimes true, or always false. Justify your answer.

26. Reflections of figures preserve distances between pairs of corresponding vertices. That is, if figure A is reflected across a reflection axis to form figure A', then the distance between two vertices on A is equal to the distance between the corresponding pair of vertices on A'.

27. Reflections of polygons preserve area. That is, if figure A is reflected across a reflection axis to form figure A', then the area of A is equal to the area of A'.

28. **MP 1, 8** In the graph of the quadratic equation $y = ax^2 + bx + c$, what is the equation for the axis of symmetry? Describe how the axis of symmetry for graphs of quadratic equations is similar to the reflection axis. (Hint: Try changing the general form of the quadratic equation to vertex form.)

Practice Problems continue . . .

29. How many different axes of symmetry are there in a regular pentagon (5-sided polygon)?

30. How many different axes of symmetry are there in a regular hexagon (6-sided polygon)?

31. How many different axes of symmetry are there in a rectangle?

32. Determine the number of different lines of symmetry for an equilateral triangle.

Rotational Symmetry

If a figure has **rotational symmetry**, it can be rotated about a central point through an angle of less than 360° to perfectly overlap itself. The figure is identical with its image after rotation. Such figures can be constructed from an element that is rotated about the central point.

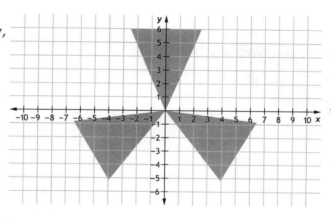

Figures like this one have rotational symmetry.

MODEL PROBLEM

If the figure in the digram has rotational symmetry, find the smallest angle of rotation that makes the image identical to the original figure.

SOLUTION

Determine the number of triangles that make up the image.

8 triangles

Divide 360° by the number of triangles to determine the smallest angle of rotation.

$$\frac{360°}{8} = 45°$$

Three-Dimensional Symmetry

Three-dimensional figures can have symmetry about a line and about a plane. A figure with rotational symmetry can be rotated about a line (through an angle smaller than 360°) so that the image perfectly overlaps the original figure. One with reflection symmetry can be divided into two congruent halves by a plane.

Rotational symmetry about a line

The square-based pyramid can be rotated about the line in 90° rotations and will perfectly overlap the original pyramid.

The equilateral-triangle-based prism can be rotated about the line in 60° rotations and will perfectly overlap the original prism.

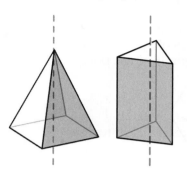

Reflection symmetry about a plane

The rectangular prism and equilateral-triangle-based pyramid can be split into two congruent halves with a plane. This means it has reflection symmetry.

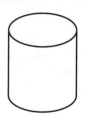

MODEL PROBLEM

Does a cylinder have reflection symmetry?

SOLUTION

Yes. A plane that contains the central axis of the cylinder will split the cylinder into two congruent halves. Also, a plane that is perpendicular to the central axis and passes through the cylinder's midpoint splits the cylinder into two congruent cylinders.

PRACTICE

1. **MP 3** Does a cube have rotational symmetry? Justify your answer.

Exercises 2–5: If the figure has rotational symmetry, find the smallest angle of rotation that makes the image identical to the original figure.

2.

3.

4.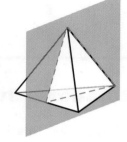

5.

Practice Problems continue . . .

Exercises 6–7: Use the diagrams on page 78 to determine if the three-dimensional figure has reflection or rotational symmetry, or both.

6. Triangular prism (a three-dimensional figure made up of two parallel triangular sides and three rectangular sides)

7. Regular tetrahedron (a three-dimensional figure made up of four equilateral triangle faces)

8. John states that the number of lines of symmetry of a two-dimensional figure is equal to the number of rotational symmetries of the figure. Is his statement true? Explain.

9. **MP 7** For a figure with rotational symmetry, the "order" of the figure is the number of distinct positions in which it is symmetric to itself as it is rotated from 0° to 360°. For example, a figure with no rotational symmetry has an order of 1, since in order to be symmetric to itself, it must be rotated 360° completely around. A figure which is rotated 180° to be symmetric to itself has an order of 2, and a figure which is rotated 120° to be symmetric has an order of 3.

a A regular polygon has an order of 9. What is the smallest angle of rotation for which the polygon has rotational symmetry?

b What is the order of a circle? Explain.

LESSON 1.7

1.7 Composition of Transformations

Order of Composite Transformations

Are transformations commutative? Does the order of rigid motions matter? We consider two cases, starting with two translations. For simplicity's sake, we translate solely a point.

> A **composition of transformations** is the result of applying two or more transformations to a figure, one after another.

Example 1: Two translations.

Translate the point $(2, -3)$ by $(4, -1)$ and $(-2, 3)$.

Translate a point at $(2, -3)$ by $(4, -1)$ and then $(-2, 3)$.

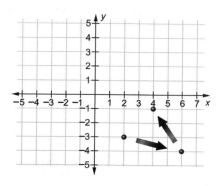

First translation:
$(2 + 4, -3 + (-1)) \rightarrow (6, -4)$

Second translation:
$(6 + (-2), -4 + 3) \rightarrow (4, -1)$

Translate a point at $(2, -3)$ by $(-2, 3)$ and then $(4, -1)$.

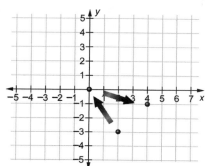

First translation:
$(2 + (-2), -3 + 3) \rightarrow (0, 0)$

Second translation:
$(0 + 4, 0 + (-1)) \rightarrow (4, -1)$

In both translations in Example 1, we end up at the same point. We have an example that shows the order of translations does not matter. If we think about the algebra involved, translation is the adding of coordinates, so we can conclude that transformations that are only translations are commutative. Why? Addition is commutative.

> **Translations are commutative.**

Example 2: Rotation and then translation.

Rotate the point $(-4, 2)$ $180°$ and translate it $(2, -1)$.

Rotate first, then translate.

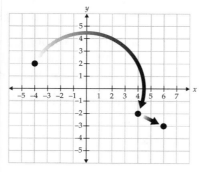

Rotation first:
$(-4, 2) \rightarrow (4, -2)$

Translation second:
$(4, -2) \rightarrow (4 + 2, -2 + (-1)) = (6, -3)$

Translate first, then rotate.

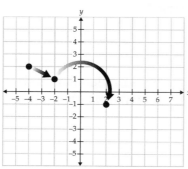

Translation first:
$(-4, 2) \rightarrow (-4 + 2, 2 + (-1)) = (-2, 1)$

Rotation second:
$(-2, 1) \rightarrow (2, -1)$

As the example shows, a composition of rotation and translation is not commutative. The point ends up at different locations depending on the order. We wrote the rotation using multiplication to show why. Does it matter whether multiplication occurs before or after addition? Yes, which is why there are rules for the order of operations. For instance, $5 \cdot 7 + 2$ does not equal $5(7 + 2)$.

> **With a translation and rotation, the order does matter.**

Glide Reflections

A **glide reflection** consists of a translation (glide) parallel to a given line followed by a reflection across that line. For example, a vertical translation and then reflection across the y-axis.

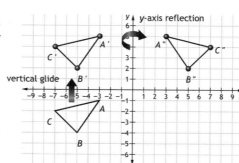

In the glide reflection to the right:

- The triangle is translated up 6. Add 6 to each y-coordinate.

- Then reflect the result across the y-axis by taking the opposite of the x-coordinates.

Parallel Reflections

We show the relationship of a pair of reflections (a composite reflection) and a translation. We start with two reflections across two parallel lines. The path of the translation is perpendicular to the parallel lines.

Reflections in parallel lines theorem

Two reflections across a pair of parallel lines is a translation.

The translation is twice the distance between the lines.

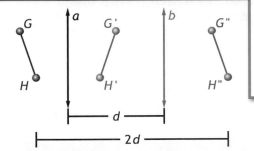

MODEL PROBLEM

How far does $\overline{DC}$ translate if it reflects across a then b?

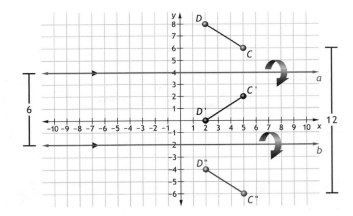

SOLUTION

Calculate the distance between a and b

$$d = |y_2 - y_1| = |4 - (-2)| = 6$$

The theorem states that the translation will be twice the distance between the lines. The difference in y-coordinates is the distance between these two lines.

Translation distance = twice distance between lines
$$= 2 \cdot 6$$
$$= 12$$

The translation is twice the distance between the lines. Though we could reflect twice, using the theorem we simply translate 12.

Composition of Transformations

Two reflections across intersecting lines is a rotation.

Two reflections across intersecting lines theorem 1

If lines a and b intersect at a point P, then a reflection in b followed by a reflection in a is the same as a rotation about point P.

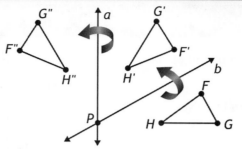

Two reflections across intersecting lines theorem 2

The amount of rotation is twice the measure of the angle between lines a and b.

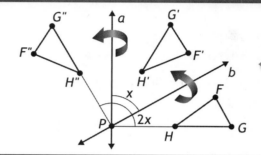

> When the intersecting lines form an angle of 90° or less, the theorem relates the angle of rotation to the angle formed by the lines.

Isometric transformations theorem

Translations, rotations, and reflections are isometric.

Composition theorem

> The composition of isometric transformations is also isometric.

Any composition of isometric transformations (translations, reflections, or rotations) is isometric. The final image is congruent with the original figure.

PRACTICE

Exercises 1–4: How far is the figure translated?

1. A figure is reflected across two parallel lines separated by 8 inches. It is reflected across one line first, and then the other.

2. A figure is reflected across two parallel lines separated by 7 inches. It is reflected across one line first, and then the other.

3. A figure is reflected across two parallel lines separated by 6 inches. It is reflected across one line first, and then the other.

4. A figure is reflected across two parallel lines separated by 10 inches. It is reflected across one line first, and then the other.

Practice Problems continue . . .

Exercises 5–8: The transformation shown is a glide reflection. Describe the specific glide and line of reflection. Note: The original figure is in orange.

5.

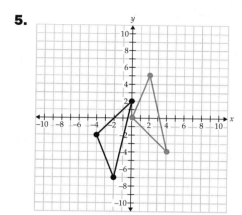

6.

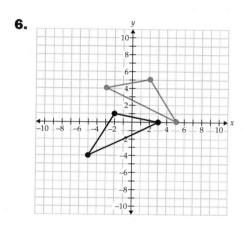

7.

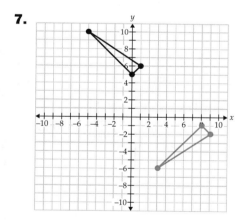

8.

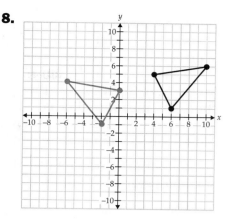

9. Does the order in which you perform multiple translations matter? Explain.

Exercises 10–21: Determine the coordinates of point P after the indicated glide reflection.

10. $P(-5, 9)$ is glided -4 units horizontally and then reflected across the x-axis.

11. $P(-1, -9)$ is glided -7 units horizontally and then reflected across the x-axis.

12. $P(1, -1)$ is glided -10 units horizontally and then reflected across the x-axis.

13. $P(8, -2)$ is glided -8 units vertically and then reflected across the y-axis.

14. $P(-3, -4)$ is glided 4 units vertically and then reflected across the y-axis.

15. $P(-3, 1)$ is glided -7 units vertically and then reflected across the y-axis.

16. $P(1, -8)$ is glided -7 units horizontally and then reflected across the line $y = -8$.

17. $P(-9, -9)$ is glided -4 units horizontally and then reflected across the line $y = -8$.

18. $P(3, -5)$ is glided -7 units horizontally and then reflected across the line $y = 6$.

19. $P(10, -2)$ is glided -8 units vertically and then reflected across the line $x = 3$.

20. $P(-7, 6)$ is glided 10 units vertically and then reflected across the line $x = 2$.

21. $P(4, -8)$ is glided -7 units vertically and then reflected across the line $x = -6$.

Practice Problems continue . . .

22. **MP 2** A figure is reflected four times, across four parallel lines that are all in the same plane. The second line is 10 inches away from the first, the third is 9 inches away from the second in the same direction, and the fourth line is 5 inches away from the third line in the same direction. How far is the figure translated?

Exercises 23–25: What is the figure's total angle of rotation about the point of intersection?

23. A figure is reflected twice across two intersecting lines that form an angle of 42°.

24. A figure is reflected twice across two intersecting lines that form an angle of 12°.

25. A figure is reflected twice across two intersecting lines that form an angle of 58°.

26. **MP 8** Suppose you have two lines, l and m, that are parallel. If you reflect a figure first across l and then across m, will the distance the figure travels be the same as if you reflected it first across m and then across l? How far does the figure travel in each case? How do you know? Sketch a labeled diagram to support your explanation.

27. Describe how multiple reflections can be applied to obtain a 180° rotation about the origin.

28. Can a glide reflection shift a point horizontally and reflect across the y-axis? Explain.

29. John is playing a game in which he tries to match up various quadrilateral blocks with pre-cut holes in a piece of wood. He has one quadrilateral in his hand that he is trying to match to a specific hole, which appears to be about the same size and shape. John has tried flipping, spinning, and moving to match up the quadrilateral with the hole, but he has not been successful. Assuming John has tried all possible combinations of flipping, spinning, and moving the piece, is this quadrilateral the correct match for the hole? Explain your reasoning.

30. In glide reflections, does gliding then reflecting produce the same result as reflecting then gliding? Explain.

31. Is a glide reflection an isometry? Explain.

• Multi-Part PROBLEM Practice •

MP 2, 3, 4 A computer has drawn the pinwheel pictured to the right.

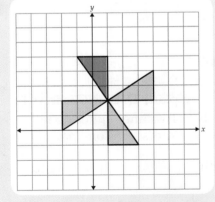

a Could rigid motion transformations have been used to take the one part of the pinwheel that is indicated, and create the other three parts? Justify your answer.

b What type of transformation would move the pinwheel so that its center would be at (6, −10) and nothing else changes?

c If the center moves to (6, −10), then how far has the pinwheel moved?

d Which of the following transformations would cause the pinwheel to move as described in part **b**? a and b represent constants. Explain your answer.

1) (x, y) yields $(-x, y)$

2) (x, y) yields $(x + a, y + b)$

3) (x, y) yields $(2ax, 2ay)$

4) (x, y) yields $(-y, -x)$

CHAPTER 1 REVIEW

1. Given the diagram below, which is a line?

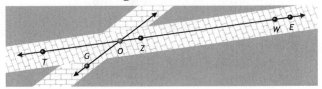

   A. $\overline{TZ}$ C. $\overrightarrow{MN}$

   B. $\overrightarrow{TZ}$ D. $\overleftrightarrow{GO}$

2. Identify a line segment in the choices below.

   A. $\overleftrightarrow{MN}$ C. $\overrightarrow{XY}$

   B. $\overline{RZ}$ D. MN

3. Identify a ray in the choices below.

   A. $\overleftrightarrow{RZ}$ C. $\overrightarrow{YX}$

   B. $\overline{RZ}$ D. $\overline{ZR}$

4. Use the choices below to determine the correct way to write a ray that begins at point H and extends in the direction through point M.

   A. $\overleftrightarrow{MH}$ C. $\overrightarrow{MH}$

   B. $\overline{HM}$ D. $\overrightarrow{HM}$

5. Which statements are true? Choose all correct answers.

   A. Two lines intersect at a plane.

   B. Three points on a line define a plane.

   C. Three points define a line.

   D. Points A and B are on line C and in plane D. Line C is in plane D.

   E. Two lines either do not intersect, or they intersect at one point.

6. Which statements could be true? Choose all correct answers.

   A. Line Z is defined by the points M and N.

   B. Line F is the intersection of planes Q and R.

   C. Lines K and L intersect at points N and P.

   D. Points A, B, and C are not on a line and they define plane X.

7. $m\angle ABC = 66°$. If $m\angle ABD$ is five times $m\angle DBC$, what is $m\angle DBC$?

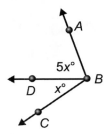

   A. $5°$

   B. $6°$

   C. $11°$

   D. $13.2°$

8. Select all sides and angles that are congruent.

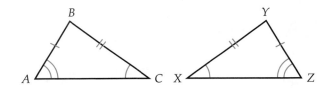

   A. $\overline{AB}$ and $\overline{YZ}$

   B. $\overline{AB}$ and $\overline{XY}$

   C. $\angle ACB$ and $\angle YXZ$

   D. $\angle ABC$ and $\angle CAB$

9. What expression below describes a $180°$ rotation of the point $(a, -b)$ about the origin?

   A. (b, a)

   B. $(b, -a)$

   C. $(-a, b)$

   D. $(-b, a)$

10. Which coordinates describe a $180°$ rotation about the origin of the triangle with vertices at $(6, 3)$, $(1, 1)$, and $(-2, 2)$?

   A. $(-6, -3)$, $(-1, -1)$, and $(2, -2)$

   B. $(6, -3)$, $(1, 1)$, and $(-2, -2)$

   C. $(-6, 3)$, $(-1, 1)$, and $(2, -2)$

Chapter Review continues . . .

11. Which of the following angles of rotation makes the image identical to the original figure?

   A. 30°

   B. 45°

   C. 60°

   D. 90°

12. What is the measure of the angle at the corner of a sheet of paper?

13. If $\overline{KL}$ is 25 units in length, how long is $\overline{KD}$?

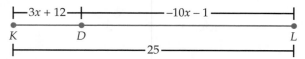

14. What is the distance between $(6, -1)$ and $(-3, -13)$?

15. What is the distance between $(3, -5)$ and $(8, 7)$?

16. Find the midpoint between $(-24, -2)$ and $(-14, -18)$.

17. Use the diagram to answer the questions.

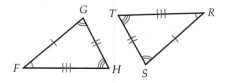

  a Which angle is congruent to $\angle R$?

  b If $GH = 8$ units, what other line segment measures 8 units?

  c Which side is congruent to $\overline{RS}$?

  d If the left-hand triangle is named $\triangle GHF$, how should the right-hand triangle be named?

  e If neither $\angle G$ nor $\angle R$ measures 80°, name an angle that could measure 80°.

  f If the perimeter of $\triangle FGH$ measures 21 inches, $FG = 7$ inches, and $TS = 5$ inches, what is the length of $\overline{FH}$?

18. **MP 7** Draw a rectangle with dimensions of 3 units by 5 units. Then, draw another rectangle that is the result of rotating the first rectangle 90 degrees clockwise. Mark all congruent parts of both rectangles.

19. Using the coordinate plane below, translate the given image 7 units up and then sketch the translated image.

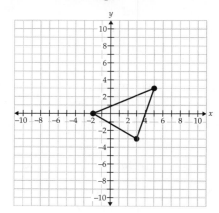

20. $\overline{AB}$ has a length of 15. It is translated -9 units in the horizontal direction and -7 units in the vertical direction. What is the length of the resulting image?

21. $\overline{AB}$ has a length of 4. It is translated 9 units in the horizontal direction and -9 units in the vertical direction. What is the length of the resulting translation?

22. Kristin is 6 miles north and 5 miles east of her home. On her drive home, she takes a detour and drives 9 miles south and 10 miles west. How far is she from her home? Round your answer to the nearest tenth. Show all steps and explain your reasoning.

23. Can the composition of translations be written as a single translation? Explain.

24. In an 8-spoke wheel, what is the angle of rotation, in degrees clockwise, between spoke #3 and spoke #5? Assume the spokes are counted in increasing order in the counterclockwise direction.

25. Using the point (a, b), show algebraically that two 180° rotations about the origin return you to the original point (a, b).

Chapter Review continues . . .

26. Using the point (a, b), show algebraically that four 90° clockwise rotations about the origin return you to the original point (a, b).

27. If you rotated a triangle to create a regular pentagon (5 sides), how many degrees would you rotate the triangle each time?

28. In a 30-spoke wheel, what is the angle of rotation, in degrees, between two adjacent spokes?

29. What are the coordinates of the reflection of the point $(-4, 1)$ across the x-axis?

30. What are the coordinates of the reflection of the point $(8, 3)$ across the x-axis?

31. What are the coordinates of the reflection of the point $(-10, -10)$ across the y-axis?

32. What are the coordinates of the reflection of the point $(-3, 6)$ across the y-axis?

33. State a rule regarding the number of lines of symmetry for any regular polygon.

34. When $\triangle FGH$ is reflected over the x-axis, it produces $\triangle PQR$. The vertices of the original triangle are located at $F(-3, 2)$, $G(4, 5)$, and $H(2, 1)$. Graph $\triangle FGH$ and $\triangle PQR$.

35. A figure is reflected four times across four intersecting lines that are all in the same plane. The second line makes a counterclockwise angle of 12° with the first, the third makes a counterclockwise angle of 32° with the second, and the fourth line makes a counterclockwise angle of 77° with the third line. What is the figure's total angle of rotation about the point of intersection?

36. **MP 3** In addition to representing a 180° rotation, the transformation $(x, y) \rightarrow (-x, -y)$ results from the composition of which two reflections? Justify your response.

37. **MP 3** Jose explains that since the reflections across two parallel lines that are x units apart make a point move a distance of $2x$ units, a single reflection across the first line would make the point move half the total distance, which is x units. Is his explanation correct? Why or why not?

38. In a 9-spoke wheel, like the one in the diagram below, the spokes are numbered consecutively in the clockwise direction from #1 through #9.

a What is the angle of rotation, in degrees clockwise, between spoke #4 and spoke #7?

b If the radius of the wheel is 14 inches, what is the length of the wheel from spoke #4 to spoke #7? Round your answer to the nearest tenth of an inch.

Chapter Content

Chapter Vocabulary

center of dilation   dilation   similar figure

diagonal   scale factor   similarity transformation

LESSON 2.1

2.1 Similar Figures

A **similar figure** is created when an object grows or shrinks by a scale factor. This process is known as **dilation**. The resulting figure has the same overall shape, but it generally has a different size. With similar figures, the ratio of each pair of corresponding sides is the same. The two shortest sides in a figure are corresponding sides, the two longest sides are corresponding sides, and so on.

> Use the similar symbol ~ to show that figures are similar.

The corresponding side lengths of similar figures are related by a scale factor. The **scale factor** is the ratio of the lengths of corresponding sides. You can multiply the length of one side of a figure by the scale factor to calculate the length of the corresponding side in the other similar figure.

> If the scale factor is 1, then dilation produces an identical figure, which is to say a congruent figure. Congruent figures are similar figures with a scale factor of 1.

If $\triangle ABC \sim \triangle DEF$, then:

Corresponding sides form a proportion: $\dfrac{AB}{DE} = \dfrac{BC}{EF} = \dfrac{AC}{DF}$

Corresponding angles are congruent: $\angle A \cong \angle D$, $\angle B \cong \angle E$, and $\angle C \cong \angle F$

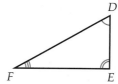

MODEL PROBLEMS

1. $\triangle ABC \sim \triangle DEF$. What is the length of $\overline{ED}$?

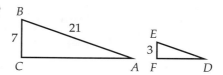

SOLUTION

Write proportion

$$\frac{ED}{BA} = \frac{EF}{BC}$$

$$\frac{ED}{21} = \frac{3}{7}$$

$\overline{ED}$ and $\overline{BA}$ are corresponding sides of the figures. Another pair of corresponding sides is $\overline{BC}$ and $\overline{EF}$. Write their lengths as ratios. These ratios equal our scale factor. Setting them equal to each other creates a proportion in which we can solve for the unknown side length. Notice how EF and ED are both on top of their ratios, because they are side lengths from the same triangle. Substitute the known segment lengths.

Solve proportion

$$21 \cdot \frac{ED}{21} = 21 \cdot \frac{3}{7}$$

$$ED = 9$$

ED equals 9.

Model Problems continue . . .

2. Which angles are congruent? The triangles are similar: $\triangle DEF \sim \triangle RQP$.

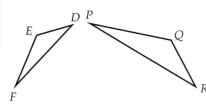

By determining corresponding sides, you can determine which angles are congruent.

SOLUTION

Identify corresponding sides	Longest sides: $\overline{FD}$ and $\overline{PR}$	Identify shortest, longest, and middle length sides.
	Shortest sides: $\overline{DE}$ and $\overline{RQ}$	
	Middle sides: $\overline{EF}$ and $\overline{QP}$	
Identify congruent angles using corresponding sides	$\angle D \cong \angle R$ $\angle F \cong \angle P$ $\angle E \cong \angle Q$	When a pair of sides of one triangle correspond to a pair of sides of the other, the angles between the pairs are congruent.

3. What is the length of $\overline{FE}$? The triangles are similar.

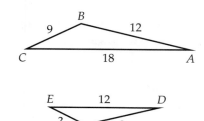

With a similarity statement such as $\triangle ABC \sim \triangle DEF$, corresponding angles must be written in order.

SOLUTION

Identify corresponding sides	$\overline{AC}$ and $\overline{DE}$ are longest $\overline{AB}$ and $\overline{DF}$ are medium $\overline{BC}$ and $\overline{FE}$ are shortest	To calculate *FE*, determine the corresponding sides of these similar triangles. Write down the longest, medium, and shortest sides.
Write proportion	$\dfrac{FE}{BC} = \dfrac{DE}{AC}$	Write a proportion. On the left is the ratio of the shortest sides. On the right are the longest sides. The ratio of the medium sides on the right could also have been used.
Substitute and solve	$\dfrac{FE}{9} = \dfrac{12}{18}$ $FE = 9 \cdot \dfrac{12}{18}$ $FE = 6$	Substitute and solve.

Model Problems continue . . .

4. An equilateral triangle (one with three equal angles) is dilated by a scale factor of 0.75. The resulting triangle

   A. Has shorter sides but angles of the same measure.

   B. Has shorter sides and angles of smaller measure.

   C. Has longer sides but angles of the same measure.

   D. Has longer sides and angles of greater measure.

SOLUTION

The answer is A. The length of each side is multiplied by the 0.75 scale factor, creating shorter sides. Dilation does not change the measure of angles.

PRACTICE

1. Triangles *ABC* and *DEF* are similar. $AB = 15$ cm, $BC = 18$ cm, and $EF = 6$ cm. What is the length of $\overline{DE}$?

   A.   4 cm

   B.   5 cm

   C.   6 cm

   D.   7 cm

2. $\triangle ABC \sim \triangle FDE$. What is the length of $\overline{DE}$?

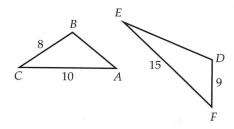

3. $\triangle ABC \sim \triangle XYZ$. What is the length of $\overline{XY}$?

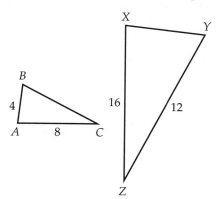

4. $\triangle XYZ \sim \triangle MNP$. What is the length of $\overline{YZ}$?

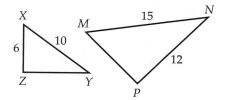

5. $\triangle ABC \sim \triangle DEF$. What is the length of $\overline{DF}$?

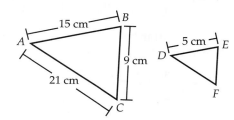

6. $\triangle ABC \sim \triangle DEF$. If $AB = 16$ in, $DE = 12$ in, and $BC = 24$ in, what is the length of $\overline{EF}$?

7. $\triangle ABC \sim \triangle DEF$. If $AC = 28$ cm, $DF = 24$ cm, and $DE = 12$ cm, what is the length of $\overline{AB}$?

8. $\triangle ABC \sim \triangle DEF$. If $AB = 14$ in, $DE = 42$ in, and $AC = 12$ in, what is the length of $\overline{DF}$?

9. $\triangle RST \sim \triangle UVW$. If $ST = 36$ cm, $VW = 18$ cm, and $UV = 45$ cm, what is the length of $\overline{RS}$?

10. The ratio of the sides of two similar triangles is 1.5 : 1. If a side in the smaller triangle is 6 inches, what is the length of the corresponding side in the larger triangle in inches?

Practice Problems continue . . .

11. The ratio of the sides of two similar triangles is $\frac{2}{5}$. If a side in the larger triangle is 15 meters, what is the length of the corresponding side in the smaller triangle in meters?

12. Triangle ABC is similar to triangle DEF. In triangle ABC, $\angle A$ measures $67°$, $\angle B$ measures $102°$, and $\angle C$ measures $11°$. What is the measure of $\angle D$?

13. Given similar triangles RST and UVW, write the proportion that relates the corresponding side lengths of the triangles.

14. The lengths of the sides of a triangle have the ratio $3 : 4 : 6$. If the perimeter of the triangle is 52 cm, what are the lengths of the sides, from smallest to largest?

15. The lengths of the sides of a triangle have the ratio $2 : 3 : 4$. If the perimeter of the triangle is 108 inches, what are the lengths of the sides, from smallest to largest?

16. The ratio of the lengths of the sides of a triangle is $6 : 7 : 8$. If the perimeter of the triangle is 105 inches, what are the lengths of the sides, from smallest to largest?

17. Given the similar triangles below, what is the length of $\overline{DF}$?

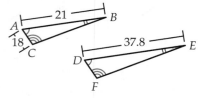

18. Given the similar triangles below, what is the length of $\overline{EF}$?

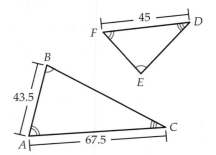

19. Draw and label the sides and angles of two similar triangles.

20. Draw and label a triangle with side lengths adhering to the ratio $4 : 5 : 6$.

21. Draw and label a triangle with side lengths adhering to the ratio $5 : 6 : 7$.

22. **MP 2** Robert builds a right triangular brace for a shelf unit. The brace has side lengths of 3 inches, 4 inches, and 5 inches. He must build another, larger, right triangular brace that is similar to this one and related by a scale factor of 2. What are the side lengths of the new right triangular brace?

23. **MP 8** A novelty shop has two similar, triangular photo frames. The smaller photo frame has sides of 4 inches, 6 inches, and 8 inches. The sides of the larger photo frame are 10 inches, 15 inches, and 20 inches. What scale factor is used to obtain the dimensions of the larger frame?

24. Mandy plans to tile her kitchen floor using triangular tiles. The home supply store offers two sizes of triangular tiles in the color she desires. The triangular tiles are similar in shape. The sides of the smaller tile are 11 inches, 11 inches, and 13 inches. If the larger tile is related to the smaller tile by a scale factor of 1.5, what are the side lengths of the larger tile?

25. A triangle has side lengths that adhere to the ratio $2 : 3 : 4$. If the perimeter of the triangle is 117 inches, what is the length of the longest side? Show all steps and explain your reasoning.

2.2 Dilation and Similar Figures

Not all transformations are rigid motion. Dilation is *not* rigid motion, since dimensions change. For instance, if you enlarge (dilate) a photographic image, it is not rigid motion since the lengths of the sides change. The resulting image is <u>not</u> congruent with the original figure.

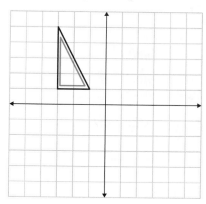

> Dilation is a transformation that does *not* produce a congruent figure. Reflections, rotations, and translations are the transformations that produce congruent figures. A dilation is *not* isometric, while reflections, rotations, and translations are isometric.

Dilation and Proportions

Dilation is defined by:

Proportional shrinking

- Dilation can mean a figure is made smaller. For instance, we can proportionally reduce the lengths of the sides of a figure so that the ratio of the original image to the new image is 2 : 1. The figures are no longer congruent, but they remain similar.

- All the lengths of the shrunken rectangle in the figure to the right are $\frac{1}{2}$ as big as the original figure.

- $\dfrac{A'B'}{AB} = \dfrac{B'C'}{BC} = \dfrac{C'D'}{CD} = \dfrac{D'A'}{DA} = \dfrac{1}{2}$

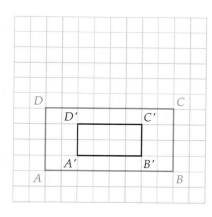

> The numbers $\frac{1}{2}$ and 3 are each a scale factor, describing the ratio of an image's lengths to the original figure's lengths. This constant can be represented by *k*, the constant of proportionality.

Proportional expanding

- Dilation can mean expansion as well. The length of each side of the new figure is three times the length of its corresponding side in the original figure.

- On the right, we show a square when it is expanded; each side is three times as long as in the original image.

- $\dfrac{E'F'}{EF} = \dfrac{F'G'}{FG} = \dfrac{G'H'}{GH} = \dfrac{H'E'}{HE} = \dfrac{3}{1}$

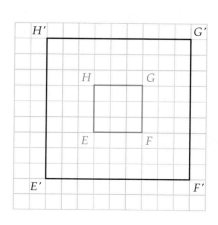

In this activity, you dilate a line segment by changing the scale factor, constant *k*. Is the result congruent? How does *k* relate to the distance between the origin and the resulting segment's endpoints?

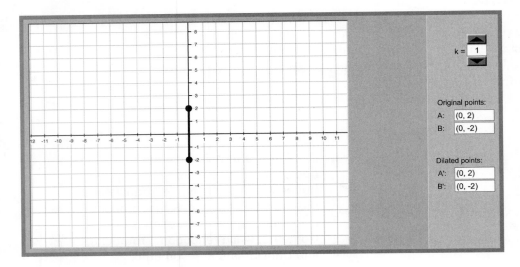

 In this activity, you see how dilation changes a horizontal line segment.

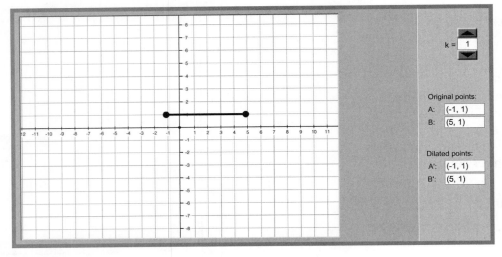

Dilation and Angles

Dilation does not change the measure of angles. We illustrate this below with similar triangles *ABC* and *DEF*. The two angles, ∠*BCA* and ∠*EFD*, are one example of a pair of congruent angles.

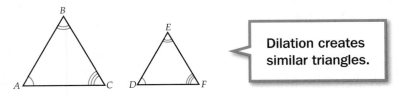

Dilation creates similar triangles.

MODEL PROBLEMS

1. Dilate $\overline{AB}$ by a scale factor of $\frac{3}{2}$.

SOLUTION

Scale factor is $\frac{3}{2}$ $\qquad$ $k = \dfrac{A'B'}{AB} = \dfrac{3}{2}$

Calculate $A'B'$ $\qquad$ $A'B' = k(AB)$

$\qquad\qquad\qquad A'B' = \dfrac{3}{2}(6)$

$\qquad\qquad\qquad A'B' = 9$

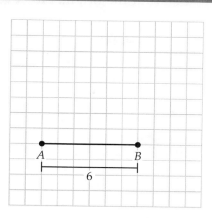

2. **MP 7** Identify which two triangles are similar.

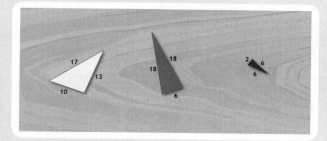

SOLUTION

First and second triangles:
$\dfrac{10}{6} \overset{?}{=} \dfrac{13}{18} \overset{?}{=} \dfrac{17}{18} \rightarrow \dfrac{5}{3} \neq \dfrac{13}{18} \neq \dfrac{17}{18}$

Similar triangles have the same scale factor between each corresponding pair of sides.

First and third triangles:
$\dfrac{10}{2} \overset{?}{=} \dfrac{13}{6} \overset{?}{=} \dfrac{17}{6} \rightarrow 5 \neq \dfrac{13}{6} \neq \dfrac{17}{6}$

Examine the ratios between the shortest sides, the middle sides, and longest sides for each triangle and reduce the fractions to see if the scale factor is the same.

Second and third triangles:
$\dfrac{6}{2} \overset{?}{=} \dfrac{18}{6} \overset{?}{=} \dfrac{18}{6} \rightarrow 3 = 3 = 3$

The second and third triangles are similar because the scale factor is the same.

Centers of Dilation

A figure on a coordinate plane is dilated about a center, called a **center of dilation**. When asked to dilate a figure on a coordinate plane, you are being asked to dilate with the origin as the center of dilation, unless you are told another dilation center.

When the center of dilation is the origin and at the figure's center, the figure's vertices are moved along rays emanating from (0, 0). Dilation pushes the vertices *away* from the origin if the scale factor is greater than 1 and *toward* the origin if the scale factor is less than 1.

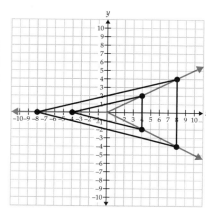

When the center of dilation is the origin, but **not** at the figure's center, the vertices are still moved along rays that start at the origin. However, because the center of dilation is not at the center of the figure, the image does not shrink or expand around the original figure.

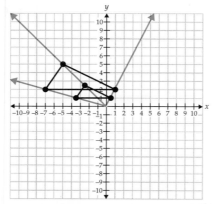

 In this activity, you see how a line changes by adjusting the scale factor. How does *k* relate to the distance between the origin and the points on the line (example: *y*-intercept)? How is the dilation of a line different from the dilation of a line segment?

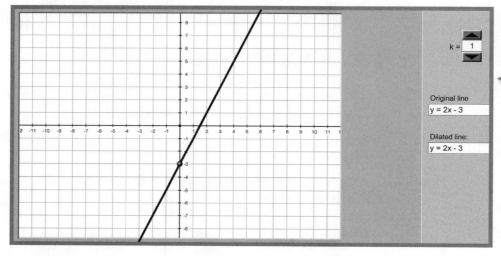

When the scale factor is less than one, the original figure is shrinking. When the scale factor is greater than one, the original figure is expanding.

 In this activity, you see how dilation changes another line which also does not pass through the origin.

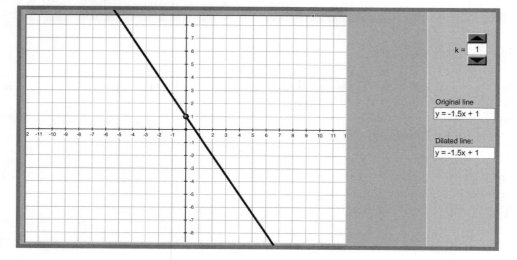

In this activity, you see the dilation of a line which passes through the origin. What is the result?

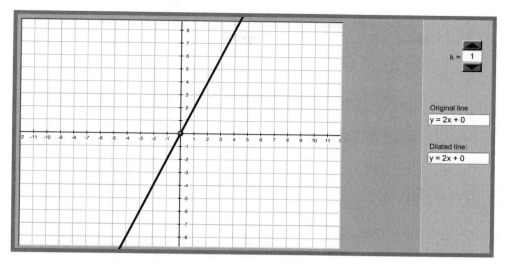

MODEL PROBLEMS

1. **MP 8** Calculate the scale factor of a line and its dilated image by using the two pairs of points that are shown. The center of dilation is the origin.

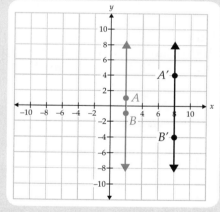

SOLUTION

Calculate lengths between corresponding points

$$AB = |y_2 - y_1| = |-1-1| = 2$$
$$A'B' = |y_2 - y_1| = |-4-4| = 8$$

Calculate ratio

$$\frac{A'B'}{AB} = \frac{8}{2} = 4$$

Model Problems continue . . .

2. In the dilation shown in the diagram, what is the scale factor? The center of dilation is (3, 1).

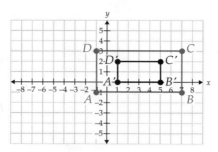

In this problem, the center of dilation is at the center of the figure.

SOLUTION

Calculate lengths of corresponding sides

$$AB = |x_2 - x_1| = |-1 - 7| = 8$$
$$A'B' = |x_2 - x_1| = |1 - 5| = 4$$

Calculate the lengths of a pair of corresponding sides. Their lengths are the differences in their x-coordinates since they are horizontal segments.

Calculate ratio to find scale factor

$$\frac{A'B'}{AB} = \frac{4}{8} = \frac{1}{2}$$

Calculate the ratio of the dilated figure to the original figure.

3. Dilate a triangle with vertices at (4, 2), (−4, 0), and (4, −2) using a scale factor of 2 and given the center of dilation is the origin.

SOLUTION

Dilation scale factor is 2

scale factor $= k = 2$
$(x, y) \rightarrow (kx, ky)$
$(4, 2) \rightarrow (8, 4)$

Dilate the triangle by a scale factor of 2, so multiply each coordinate of the vertex by 2. (4, 2) dilates to (8, 4).

Dilate other vertices

$(-4, 0) \rightarrow (-8, 0)$
$(4, -2) \rightarrow (8, -4)$

Dilate the other vertices along their respective lines.

Connect dilated vertices

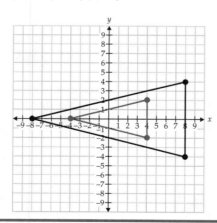

To complete the dilation of the triangle, connect the dilated vertices.

Model Problems continue . . .

4. Dilate a triangle with vertices at $(1, 2)$, $(-7, 2)$, and $(-5, 5)$ using a dilation scale factor of $\frac{1}{2}$.

SOLUTION

Dilation scale factor is $\frac{1}{2}$

$$\text{scale factor} = k = \frac{1}{2}$$
$$(x, y) \rightarrow (kx, ky)$$
$$(1, 2) \rightarrow (0.5, 1)$$

Dilate $(1, 2)$, so multiply each coordinate of the vertex by $\frac{1}{2}$.

Dilate other vertices

$$(-7, 2) \rightarrow (-3.5, 1)$$
$$(-5, 5) \rightarrow (-2.5, 2.5)$$

Dilate the other vertices along their respective lines, and connect them to finish our dilation.

Figure does not enclose image

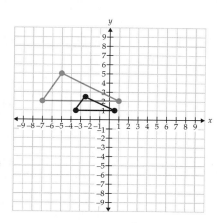

Since the center of dilation is not inside the figure, the dilated image is not totally enclosed in the figure.

5. **MP 2** The graphics of a video game need to be rescaled. The image shown is part of the original graphics—each square has a side length of 4 pixels.

a If each square now has a side length of 6 pixels, what will the height and base of the resized image be, in pixels?

b How does the number of pixels in the resized picture change from the original?

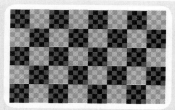

SOLUTION

a Change scale from 4 pixels to 6

$$\frac{6 \text{ new}}{4 \text{ original}}$$

State the ratio.

> We use ratios to rescale the image and calculate its new pixel dimensions.

Write, solve proportion

$$\frac{6 \text{ new}}{4 \text{ original}} = \frac{y}{20}, \text{ so } y = 30$$

Write and solve the proportion for the height. The original image's height is 20 pixels. Solve for y, the new number of pixels that makes up the height.

Write, solve proportion

$$\frac{6 \text{ new}}{4 \text{ original}} = \frac{x}{32}, \text{ so } x = 48$$

Do the same for the base. 32 is the original number of pixels in the base, and x is our new number of pixels in the base.

New height and base of image

height = 30 pixels
base = 48 pixels

b The number of pixels increases from 640 to 1440, which is an increase by a factor of $\frac{9}{4}$, or $\left(\frac{6}{4}\right)^2$.

PRACTICE

1. Calculate the scale factor for the dilation shown. Note: The original figure is in orange.

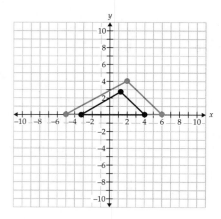

   A. $\dfrac{1}{3}$ C. $\dfrac{2}{3}$

   B. $\dfrac{1}{2}$ D. $\dfrac{3}{2}$

2. Triangle ABC is dilated to form triangle $A'B'C'$. If $\dfrac{AB}{A'B'} = 7$, what is $\dfrac{B'C'}{BC}$?

   A. $\dfrac{1}{7}$

   B. 7

   C. 49

   D. Not enough information given to know

3. The vertex B of $\triangle ABC$ is at $(-4, 2)$. If the triangle is dilated by a scale factor of 3, with the center of dilation at the origin, what are the coordinates of B'?

Exercises 4–5: Calculate the scale factor. Note: The original figure is in orange.

4.

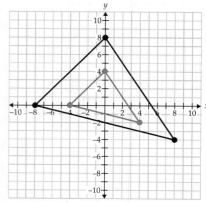

5.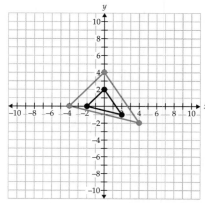

Exercises 6–9: Triangle ABC is dilated to form triangle $A'B'C'$.

6. If $\dfrac{A'C'}{AC} = 3$, what is $\dfrac{A'B'}{AB}$?

7. If $\dfrac{A'C'}{AC} = 8.5$, what is $\dfrac{A'B'}{AB}$?

8. If $\dfrac{BC}{B'C'} = 9$, what is $\dfrac{A'C'}{AC}$?

9. If $\dfrac{BC}{B'C'} = 3$, what is $\dfrac{A'C'}{AC}$?

Exercises 10–17: Given the vertices of a triangle and the scale factor, find the vertices of the dilated image. The center of dilation is the origin.

10. $A(0, 3)$, $B(2, -7)$, and $C(4, 4)$ with a scale factor of 5

11. $A(-7, 7)$, $B(8, -4)$, and $C(8, 8)$ with a scale factor of 3

12. $A(-7, 8)$, $B(7, -5)$, and $C(8, 10)$ with a scale factor of 4

13. $A(-8, 6)$, $B(2, -9)$, and $C(7, 8)$ with a scale factor of 3

14. $A(-1, 1.75)$, $B(-0.5, -2)$, and $C(1.75, 2.25)$ with a scale factor of 4

15. $A(-2.5, 1.5)$, $B(3, -2.5)$, and $C(0.5, 2)$ with a scale factor of 2

16. $A(-0.75, 0.5)$, $B(1.25, -1.5)$, and $C(0.5, 1.25)$ with a scale factor of 4

17. $A(-2, 2.5)$, $B(1.75, -2)$, and $C(2, 0.5)$ with a scale factor of 4

Practice Problems continue . . .

18. Figure *A* is dilated by a scale factor of 7 to form figure *B*, which is then dilated by a scale factor of $\frac{5}{6}$ to form figure *C*. What is the scale factor that dilates figure *A* to figure *C*?

19. The scale factor of a figure and its dilated image is 2.5. Is the figure shrinking or expanding? Explain.

20. On a copy machine, a document is being resized to 105% of its original size. What is the scale factor of this dilation, expressed as a decimal?

21. Kerry wants to enlarge an old rectangular picture to make both the length and width 2 times as large as they were originally. If the area of her original picture is 24 in^2, what is the area of the enlargement?

22. **MP 2** Karissa currently owns a rectangular pig pen that is 16 feet by 24 feet. She needs to increase the size to 80 feet by 120 feet. By what scale factor is Karissa increasing the dimensions of the pen?

23. Fabius is buying some land that is adjacent to his current property. This purchase will proportionally increase the length and width of his original land, which measures 75 meters by 35 meters. If the area of his old and new holdings together will be 9 times larger than his current land, what are the dimensions of Fabius's land after his purchase?

24. **MP 3** Dilate the figure below by a factor of 2. The center of dilation is the origin. Do the equations of the lines containing the sides of the triangle change? If so, describe in general how they change, using the concepts of slope and intercept.

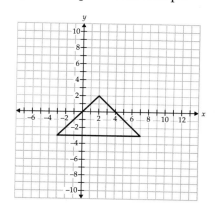

• Multi-Part PROBLEM Practice •

MP 2, 3, 4 A toy engineer, Joan, is asked to change the design in the diagram so that the roof is the length shown in the final design. She uses strips of plastic that are one centimeter long, so her design must be to the nearest centimeter. How many strips should Joan use in each case? If forced to choose, Joan will make the design slightly too long rather than slightly too short.

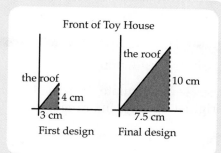

a The toy engineer wants to confirm the triangles formed by the roofs are similar. Are they? Justify her answer. How many strips of plastic should she use in the final design for the roof?

b Joan is then told by the head designer: "I'm sorry, Joan. I want the area of the front of the house to quadruple while still being a similar triangle to the original design, instead of the original change in design." How many strips of plastic will Joan now specify in her design for the roof? If forced to choose, Joan will make the design slightly too long rather than slightly too short.

2.3 Similarity, Polygons, and Circles

Similarity and Polygons

Similar polygons have the same shape but typically different sizes. Their angles are congruent and the lengths of their corresponding sides are proportional.

If *ABCD* ~ *EFGH*, then:

Corresponding angles are congruent:
$\angle A \cong \angle E$, $\angle B \cong \angle F$ and $\angle C \cong \angle G$, $\angle D \cong \angle H$

Corresponding sides are proportional:

$$\frac{AB}{EF} = \frac{BC}{FG} = \frac{CD}{GH} = \frac{DA}{HE}$$

Similarity and Circles

All circles are similar figures. In circles, all angles are congruent because circles have a 360° angle. All lengths are proportional because radii and circumferences are proportional.

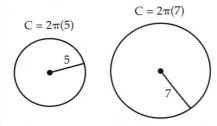

 In this activity, you calculate the height of a pyramid and the Eiffel Tower with a ruler and similar triangles. It's a method you can use on a nearby building where you live.

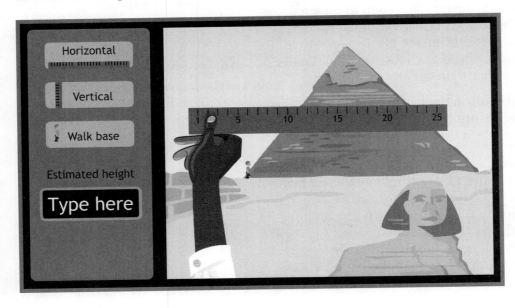

In this activity, you calculate the height of a building and a mountain using a measuring staff and your understanding of similar polygons.

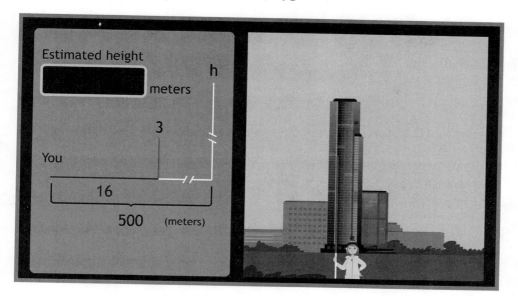

Estimated height

[ ] meters

h

3

You

16

500 (meters)

MODEL PROBLEMS

1. The two rectangular swimming pools are similar. How far is it diagonally across each pool?

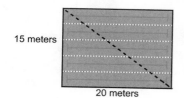

15 meters

20 meters

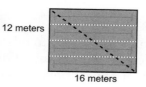

12 meters

16 meters

> When two polygons are similar, the ratios of their corresponding sides are proportional. As discussed before, this ratio is known as the scale factor. A **diagonal** connects two non-adjacent vertices. The diagonals of the two similar rectangles have the same scale factor.

SOLUTION

Calculate diagonal of longer pool using the Pythagorean theorem

$$c^2 = a^2 + b^2$$
$$c^2 = 15^2 + 20^2$$
$$c = \sqrt{625} = 25 \text{ meters}$$

To find the diagonal length across the longer pool, use the Pythagorean theorem. Substitute the width and length of the larger pool. Calculate c. The diagonal distance across the longer pool is 25 meters.

Since pools are similar, diagonals are proportional

$$\frac{\text{diagonal shorter pool}}{\text{diagonal longer pool}} = \frac{\text{width shorter pool}}{\text{width longer pool}}$$

$$\frac{\text{diagonal shorter pool}}{25} = \frac{12}{15}$$

$$\text{diagonal shorter pool} = \left(\frac{12}{15}\right) 25 = 20 \text{ meters}$$

Since the polygons are similar, their diagonals will be proportional. Use the two widths for a ratio of known lengths and solve.

Model Problems continue . . .

2. **MP 2, 4** A junior high school wants to build a basketball court that is similar to high school basketball courts, which are 84 feet by 50 feet. However, the junior high only has room for a court that is 42 feet wide. How long should the court be, to the nearest foot?

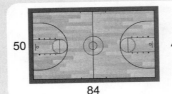 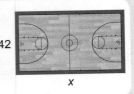

SOLUTION

Calculate length	$\dfrac{x}{84} = \dfrac{42}{50}$	They want a similar court, so the corresponding sides will be proportional. Use x to represent the length of the junior high school court. Write a ratio for the two corresponding widths.
Solve	$x = \dfrac{42}{50} \cdot 84$ $x \cong 71 \text{ feet}$	Multiply both sides by 84, and then round to the nearest foot. The court should be 71 feet long.

3. **MP 2, 4**

   a Draw a scale diagram of the building in the diagram. Hints: You want the building's height to span around 30 boxes on your graph paper. Use the ratio 50 feet is equal to 1 grid box.

   b If the skyscraper had an addition built that made its width 400 feet instead of 300, how many boxes wide should the scale drawing be?

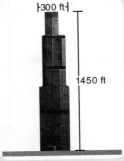

SOLUTION

a Calculate scale	$\dfrac{1450 \text{ feet}}{30 \text{ grid boxes}} \approx \dfrac{48 \text{ feet}}{1 \text{ grid box}}$	To calculate a scale to relate a box to a number of feet, divide the height of the building by the number of grid boxes. Use 30 grid boxes, since we want to keep a bit of border above and below.
State ratio	$50 \text{ feet} = 1 \text{ grid box}$	Write the ratio we will use for the number of feet that a grid box will represent. Round 48 up to 50 feet just to have an easier number to remember.
Write, solve proportion for height	$\dfrac{y \text{ grid boxes}}{1450 \text{ feet}} = \dfrac{1 \text{ grid box}}{50 \text{ feet}}$ $y = 29 \text{ grid boxes}$	Calculate how many grid boxes we need to draw the vertical figure. The building is 1,450 feet tall. Write a proportion, using the ratio of grid boxes to feet from our scale. Solve the proportion.
Write, solve proportion for width	$\dfrac{x \text{ grid boxes}}{300 \text{ feet}} = \dfrac{1 \text{ grid box}}{50 \text{ feet}}$ $x = 6 \text{ grid boxes}$	Do the same for the horizontal dimension.
Create a sketch.	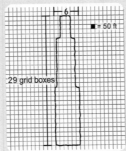	Sketch the building, estimating the narrower floors.

Model Problems continue . . .

b State ratio $\dfrac{1 \text{ grid box}}{50 \text{ feet}}$

We want to know how many grid boxes we'd need to draw the building if an addition made it 400 feet wide. Determine the ratio needed to solve the problem.

Solve $\dfrac{x \text{ grid boxes}}{400 \text{ feet}} = \dfrac{1 \text{ grid box}}{50 \text{ feet}}$

$x = 8$ grid boxes

Set up and solve the proportion.

PRACTICE

1. The vertex P of a regular hexagon has the coordinates $(-8, 20)$. If the hexagon is dilated by a factor of $\dfrac{1}{4}$, where is P'? The center of dilation is the origin.

  A. $(-2, 5)$ C. $(-32, 80)$

  B. $(2, -5)$ D. $(32, -80)$

2. Two rectangles are similar. The smaller rectangle has sides of length 15 cm and 24 cm. If the larger rectangle is related to the smaller rectangle by a scale factor of 1.2, what are the dimensions of the larger rectangle?

  A.   12.5 cm, 20 cm

  B.   17 cm, 26 cm

  C.   18 cm, 18.8 cm

  D.   18 cm, 28.8 cm

3. The ratio of the areas of two squares is $1 : 4$. If the area of the smaller square is 25 square units, what is the length of each side of the larger square?

  A.   2.5 units   C.   7.5 units

  B.   5 units   D.   10 units

4. Two similar pentagons are shown below. What are FG, HI, IJ, and FJ?

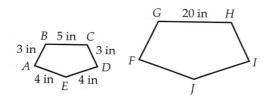

5. Given the similar quadrilaterals $ABCD$ and $EFGH$ below, write the four pairs of congruent angles.

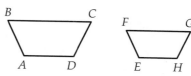

6. Given the similar trapezoids $ABCD$ and $EFGH$ below, identify the side that is proportional to $\overline{BC}$.

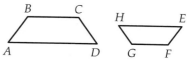

7. The rectangles shown below are similar. What is the height of the smaller rectangle?

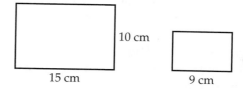

8. Similar parallelograms $ABCD$ and $EFGH$ are shown. What is the length of $\overline{GH}$?

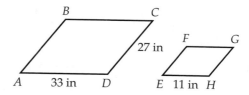

9. The vertex B of an octagon is located at $(24, -16)$. The octagon is dilated by a factor of 0.25, with the center of dilation at the origin. Where is B'?

Practice Problems continue . . .

Exercises 10–11: Calculate the scale factor. The original figure is highlighted in orange.

10.

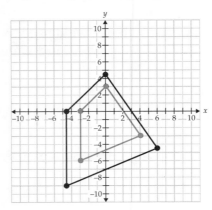

11.

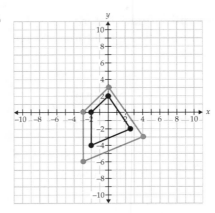

12. Two rectangles are similar. The length and width of the first rectangle are 24 cm and 18 cm, respectively. If the width of the second rectangle is 45 cm, what is the length of the second rectangle?

13. Two rectangles are similar. The width of the smaller rectangle is 6 centimeters. If the width of the larger rectangle is 8 centimeters and its height is 2.5 centimeters, what is the height of the smaller rectangle in centimeters?

14. Two squares are similar. The smaller square has side lengths of 3 inches. The larger square is related to the smaller square by a scale factor of 4.5. What is the measure of each side of the larger square?

15. The corresponding sides of two rectangular swimming pools are 66 feet and 44 feet. If the perimeter of the larger pool is 198 feet, what is the perimeter of the smaller pool?

16. Two rectangles are similar, with their widths corresponding. The width of the larger rectangle is 24, and the width of the smaller rectangle is 12. If the height of the smaller rectangle is 5, what is the height of the larger rectangle?

17. Two rectangles have a scale factor of 3. The smaller rectangle has a width of 9 and a height of 12. What is the length of the larger rectangle's diagonal?

18. Two rectangles have a scale factor of 6. The larger rectangle has a width of 30 and a height of 72. What is the length of the smaller rectangle's diagonal?

19. Two rectangles have a scale factor of 4. The smaller rectangle has a width of 6 and a height of 8. What is the length of the larger rectangle's diagonal?

20. The corresponding sides of two similar pentagons (5-sided figures) have a scale factor of 4. If the smaller pentagon has a perimeter of 7, what is the perimeter of the larger pentagon?

21. The corresponding sides of two similar octagons (8-sided figures) have a scale factor of 0.4. If the larger octagon has a perimeter of 20, what is the perimeter of the smaller octagon?

22. Quadrilaterals $ABCD$ and $EFGH$ are similar. If $AB = 9$ in, $BC = 13$ in, $CD = 7$ in, $AD = 11$ in, and $EF = 18$ in, what are FG, GH, and EH?

23. Rectangles $ABCD$ and $EFGH$ are similar.

   a If $AB = 27$ cm, $AD = 36$ cm, and $EH = 3$ cm, what is the length of $\overline{EF}$?

   b If $AD = 29$ cm, $CD = 18$ cm, and $GH = 14.4$ cm, what is EH? What is the scale factor used to obtain the measurements of rectangle $EFGH$, given the measurements of rectangle $ABCD$?

   c If $CD = 14$ in, $AD = 20$ in, and $FG = 28$ in, what is the length of $\overline{GH}$? What is the scale factor used to obtain the measurements of rectangle $EFGH$, given the measurements of rectangle $ABCD$?

Practice Problems continue . . .

Practice Problems continued . . .

24. $ABCD \sim EFGH$. If $AD = 30$ cm, $EH = 7.5$ cm, and $CD = 8$ cm, what is GH?

25. Two similar pentagons are related by a scale factor of 2. If the smaller pentagon has sides of 4 cm, 8 cm, 6 cm, 3 cm, and 2 cm, what are the side lengths of the larger pentagon? List the lengths in the order of the corresponding sides given.

26. **MP 3** Laney states, "All rectangles are similar because they all have four right angles." Is she correct? Why or why not?

27. **MP 3, 6** $\triangle MAP$ has vertices located at $M(a, b)$, $A(0, 0)$, and $P(0, c)$. $\triangle QST$ has vertices located at $Q(3a, 3b)$, $S(0, 0)$, and $T(0, 3c)$. Show that $\triangle MAP \sim \triangle QST$.

Similar Polygons and Area

If two polygons are similar, their areas have a special relationship involving the ratio between the squares of their corresponding sides.

Similar polygons area theorem

If two polygons are similar, then the ratio of their areas is equal to the ratio of the squared lengths of any pair of corresponding sides.

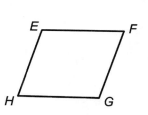

If $ABCD \sim EFGH$, then $\dfrac{\text{area of } ABCD}{\text{area of } EFGH} = \dfrac{(AB)^2}{(EF)^2} = \dfrac{(BC)^2}{(FG)^2} = \dfrac{(CD)^2}{(GH)^2} = \dfrac{(DA)^2}{(HE)^2}$.

MODEL PROBLEMS

1. What is the area of triangle XYZ? $\triangle FMN \sim \triangle XYZ$.

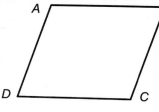

SOLUTION

Write proportion

$\dfrac{\text{area } \triangle XYZ}{\text{area } \triangle FMN} = \dfrac{(\text{length of a side})^2}{(\text{length of corresponding side})^2}$

We write a proportion saying that the areas of the triangles are proportional to the squares of the lengths of corresponding sides.

Substitute

$\dfrac{\text{area } \triangle XYZ}{72} = \dfrac{(9)^2}{(12)^2}$

Substitute the area we were told, and the lengths of the corresponding sides.

Solve

$\text{area } \triangle XYZ = (72)\dfrac{81}{144}$

$\text{area } \triangle XYZ = 40.5$

To solve the equation, square the numbers, and multiply both sides by 72.

Model Problems continue . . .

2. **MP 2, 4** A photographer wants to shrink a rectangular mural that is 120 inches by 40 inches to a similarly shaped photograph with an area of 75 square inches. What will the height of the photograph be?

SOLUTION

We take advantage of the fact that the ratio of the areas is proportional to the squares of the corresponding sides.

Write proportion

$$\frac{(\text{length of a side})^2}{(\text{length of corresponding side})^2} = \frac{\text{area figure}}{\text{area similar figure}}$$

Write a proportion saying that the areas of the mural and photo are proportional to the squares of the lengths of corresponding sides.

$$\frac{(\text{height photograph})^2}{(\text{height mural})^2} = \frac{\text{area photo}}{\text{area mural}}$$

We were told the desired area of the photograph. The area of the rectangle equals the product of its base and height.

Solve for photograph height

$$(\text{height photograph})^2 = (\text{height mural})^2 \cdot \frac{\text{area photo}}{\text{area mural}}$$

Solve for photograph height.

$$\text{height photograph} = \text{height mural} \cdot \sqrt{\frac{\text{area photo}}{\text{area mural}}}$$

Substitute, evaluate

$$\text{height photograph} = 40\sqrt{\frac{75}{(120)(40)}}$$

Substitute the height of the mural.

$$\text{height photograph} = 5 \text{ inches}$$

PRACTICE

1. A pediatrician's office has two doors that are similar rectangles: one for adults and one for children. The larger door has a base of 4 ft and a height of 6.5 ft. The smaller door has a base of 3 ft. Which of the following best represents the length of a diagonal on the smaller door?

A. 3.9 ft   C. 5.1 ft
B. 4.5 ft   D. 5.7 ft

2. $\triangle ABC \sim \triangle DEF$. $AB = 8$ inches, $DE = 10$ inches, and the area of $\triangle ABC$ is 56 square inches. What is the area of $\triangle DEF$?

A. 44.8 in²   C. 87.5 in²
B. 70 in²   D. 90.5 in²

3. Jamie chooses a rectangular tile with a length of 12 inches and a width of 8 inches. Her husband chooses a rectangular tile that is similar, with a corresponding length of 14 inches. What is the width of the tile her husband chooses, to the nearest tenth?

4. Shawna states, "The ratio of the areas of two similar polygons is equal to the ratio of their corresponding sides." Is she correct? Explain.

5. Write a word problem that involves finding at least one dimension of a similar polygon within a real-world context.

Practice Problems continue . . .

6. $\triangle ABC \sim \triangle DEF$. $AB = 5$, $EF = 21$, and the altitude of $\triangle ABC = 4$. The altitudes bisect (divide in half) the bottom sides of the triangles. Calculate the altitude of $\triangle DEF$.

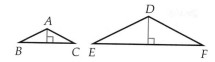

8. Two pieces of wall art are similar rectangles and have areas of 340 square inches and 380 square inches, respectively. The smaller piece has a width of 36 inches. What is the corresponding width for the larger piece of wall art? Round the width to the nearest inch.

7. Circle O has a circumference of 8π. Circle O' has a circumference of 4π. What is the ratio of the area of circle O to the area of circle O'?

LESSON 2.4

2.4 Similarity and Transformations

When dilation and rigid motion are combined, this is called a **similarity transformation**. The figure to the right undergoes a composition of transformations—three, in fact. All three figures are similar. Any combination of rigid motion and dilation transformations creates a similar figure.

> When transformations include both a dilation and rigid motion, the resulting figure is similar but not congruent.

Transformation 1: Translate the figure to the right by adding 5 to each x-coordinate.

Transformation 2: Reflect the triangle by taking the opposite of its y-coordinates.

Transformation 3: Dilate the figure by a factor of 1.5 by multiplying each coordinate by 1.5.

MODEL PROBLEMS

1. The point $(4, 10)$ is a vertex of a triangle. The triangle is reflected about the y-axis, dilated by a factor of 2 with the origin as the center of dilation, and then translated up 5. What are the final coordinates of this vertex?

SOLUTION

Reflect about the y-axis	$(-4, 10)$	The first transformation is to reflect this point about the y-axis. Take the opposite of its x-coordinate.
Dilate by a factor of 2	$(-8, 20)$	The point is part of a triangle being dilated with the origin as center of dilation. The dilation factor is 2. Multiply each coordinate by 2.
Translate up 5	$(-8, 25)$	To translate the point up 5, add 5 to its y-coordinate.

Model Problems continue . . .

2. A transformation changes the size of a figure but maintains its shape. The transformation

A. Must be a form of rigid motion.
B. Must be a dilation.
C. Could be a rigid motion transformation or dilation.
D. Cannot be a rigid motion transformation or dilation.

SOLUTION

The answer is B. Rigid motion transformations do not change the size of figures. Dilation maintains the shape of a figure but changes its size.

PRACTICE

1. The point $(-4, 7)$ is a vertex of some figure. If the figure is rotated 90° counterclockwise, reflected across the x-axis, and then dilated by a factor of 3, what are the new coordinates of this point after the transformations? The centers of rotation and dilation are the origin.

   A. $(-21, -12)$
   B. $(-21, 12)$
   C. $(21, -12)$
   D. $(21, 12)$

2. Which of the following transformations is not an isometry?

   A. Translation
   B. Rotation
   C. Reflection
   D. Dilation

Exercises 3–16: What are the coordinates of the vertex after the transformations? The center of both rotation and dilation for each of the following problems is the origin.

3. The point $(-6, -3)$ is a vertex of a figure. The figure is reflected across the x-axis, dilated by a factor of 4, and then translated 5 units horizontally.

4. The point $(10, -3)$ is a vertex of a figure. The figure is reflected across the x-axis, dilated by a factor of 4, and then translated -3 units horizontally.

5. The point $(1, 7)$ is a vertex of a figure. The figure is reflected across the y-axis, dilated by a factor of 3, and then translated 10 units vertically.

6. The point $(10, -9)$ is a vertex of a figure. The figure is reflected across the y-axis, dilated by a factor of 5, and then translated -5 units vertically.

7. The point $(-4, -6)$ is a vertex of a figure. The figure is translated -3 units horizontally, rotated 90° counterclockwise, and dilated by a factor of 5.

8. The point $(6, 1)$ is a vertex of a figure. The figure is translated -9 units horizontally, rotated 90° counterclockwise, and dilated by a factor of 4.

9. The point $(9, -6)$ is a vertex of a figure. The figure is translated 9 units up, rotated 90° clockwise, and dilated by a factor of 5.

10. The point $(-4, -1)$ is a vertex of a figure. The figure is translated 2 units up, rotated 90° clockwise, and dilated by a factor of 4.

11. The point $(-6, 8)$ is a vertex of a figure. The figure is rotated 180°, dilated by a factor of 3, and then translated 7 units horizontally and 5 units vertically.

12. The point $(-3, -1)$ is a vertex of a figure. The figure is rotated 180°, dilated by a factor of 3, and then translated -9 units horizontally and -3 units vertically.

Practice Problems continue . . .

13. The point $(-1, -8)$ is a vertex of a figure. The figure is reflected across the x-axis, rotated 90° counterclockwise, dilated by a factor of 2, and then translated -7 units horizontally and 7 units vertically.

14. The point $(7, -7)$ is a vertex of a figure. The figure is reflected across the x-axis, rotated 90° counterclockwise, dilated by a factor of 4, and then translated 3 units horizontally and -6 units vertically.

15. The point $(3, -4)$ is a vertex of a figure. The figure is reflected across the x-axis, rotated 90° counterclockwise, dilated by a factor of 4, and then translated -8 units horizontally and -7 units vertically.

16. The point $(9, 2)$ is a vertex of a figure. The figure is dilated by a factor of 3, translated 2 units horizontally and 8 units vertically, rotated 90° clockwise, and then reflected across the y-axis.

MP 5, 7 Exercises 17–20: Sketch the resulting triangle after the transformations. State whether the resulting figure is similar, congruent, or both. Explain your reasoning.

17. Rotated 90° clockwise; translated 5 units vertically

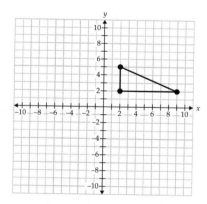

18. Rotated 90° counterclockwise; translated 3 units horizontally; dilated by a factor of 2

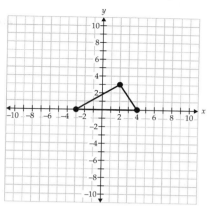

19. Dilated by a factor of 2; reflected across the y-axis; translated 4 units vertically

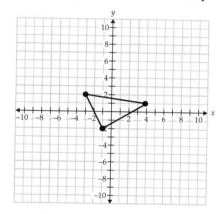

20. Translated -2 units vertically; dilated by a factor of $\frac{1}{2}$; reflected across the y-axis

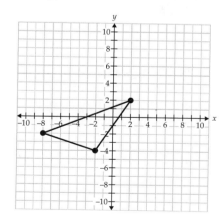

• Multi-Part PROBLEM Practice •

MP 3 Winnifred is correcting Ted's homework. He was asked to describe the actions required to complete the two transformations in the diagram. The original figure is highlighted in orange.

Ted wrote: "The figure is first dilated. Since its area is now $\frac{1}{4}$ of what it was at first, the scale factor is 1 : 4, and each angle also is scaled by $\frac{1}{4}$. The rectangle is then translated."

a Should Winnifred agree or disagree with each of Ted's statements? Explain.

b What expressions should she write?

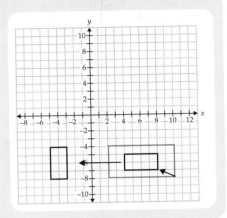

CHAPTER 2 REVIEW

1. A triangle is translated and then dilated with a scale factor of 11. The resulting triangle

   A. Has the same shape but is larger and in a different location.

   B. Has a different shape and different size.

   C. Is in a different location but has the same shape and size.

   D. Has the same shape and cannot be both translated and dilated.

2. A square initially has an area of A, and after dilation, its area is 64% of its original area. The scale factor of the dilation is:

   A. 0.64   C. 0.8

   B. 0.4096   D. None of the above

3. $\triangle ABC \sim \triangle GHI$. Which of the following angle pairs are congruent? Choose all that apply.

   A. $\angle A$ and $\angle I$ D. $\angle A$ and $\angle G$

   B. $\angle B$ and $\angle H$ E. $\angle C$ and $\angle I$

   C. $\angle C$ and $\angle G$

4. $\triangle ABC \sim \triangle DEF$. What is the length of $\overline{EF}$?

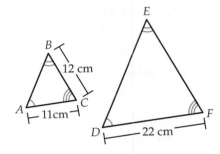

5. A carpenter builds a desktop in the shape of a triangle. The lengths of the sides of the desktop are in the ratio 1 : 2 : 2.5. If the perimeter of the desktop is 192.5 inches, what are the lengths of the sides of the desktop?

6. In the following diagram, $\triangle ABC \sim \triangle DEF$.

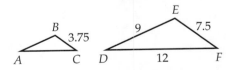

   a What is the length of $\overline{AC}$?

   b What is the length of $\overline{AB}$?

Chapter Review continues . . .

7. $\triangle ABC \sim \triangle DEF$. What is the length of $\overline{AC}$?

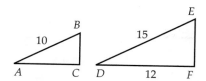

8. $\triangle ABC \sim \triangle DEF$. What is the length of $\overline{EF}$?

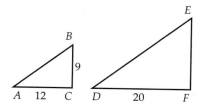

9. The coordinates of vertex X of triangle XYZ are $(-7, -9)$. Find the coordinates of X' if the triangle is dilated by a scale factor of 8 and center of dilation is the origin.

10. The coordinates of vertex X of triangle XYZ are $(-5, -5)$. Find the coordinates of X' if the triangle is dilated by a scale factor of 5 and center of dilation is the origin.

11. The coordinates of vertex X of triangle XYZ are $(-7, 3)$. Find the coordinates of X' if the triangle is dilated by a scale factor of 6 and the center of dilation is the origin.

Exercises 12–15: Sketch the dilation of the triangle with the indicated scale factor. The center of dilation is the origin.

12. Scale factor of 3

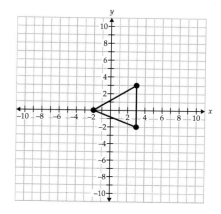

13. Scale factor of $\frac{1}{2}$

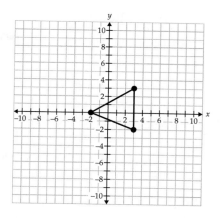

14. Scale factor of $\frac{3}{2}$

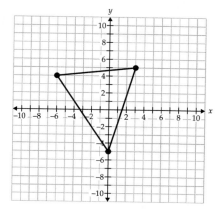

15. Scale factor of $\frac{1}{3}$

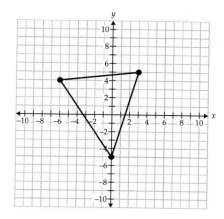

Chapter Review continues . . .

16. Figure *A* is dilated by a scale factor of 7 to form figure *B*, which is then dilated by a scale factor of $\frac{7}{8}$ to form figure *C*. What is the scale factor that dilates figure *A* to figure *C*?

17. **MP 4** Rayna looked through a microscope at a princess-cut diamond with a rectangular face that was 0.8 cm by 0.7 cm. She noticed that the magnification resulted in the diamond's area looking 100 times larger. What are the apparent dimensions of the diamond's face after the magnification?

18. **MP 3, 6** Triangle *ABC* is transformed to form triangle *A′B′C′*. Josh calculates the ratio $\frac{A'B'}{AB}$ and finds that it is equal to 6. He then states that triangle *A′B′C′* is a dilation of triangle *ABC* with a scale factor of 6. Is his reasoning sufficient? Explain.

19. How can you tell from the scale factor whether the dilation of a figure will expand or shrink it?

20. Explain why dilations do not necessarily produce congruence.

21. Describe in words the dilated image of a circle having radius 3 and centered at $(-2, 5)$ if the circle is dilated by a scale factor of 3. The center of dilation is the origin. Is the result a similar figure?

22. What is the scale factor of the dilation below? The original figure is highlighted in orange.

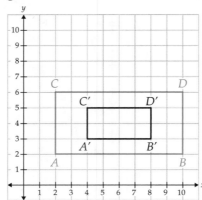

23. $\triangle ABC$ is dilated by a factor of 2. $m\angle A = 30°$. What is $m\angle A'$?

24. Given the similar trapezoids shown below, what are the lengths of the two bases of the smaller trapezoid?

25. The two shapes below are similar. What is the scale factor you must apply to the figure on the left to get the figure on the right?

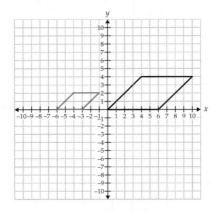

26. The ratio of the side lengths of two similar squares is 1 : 3. If the smaller square has side lengths of 9 cm, what is the length of each side of the larger square?

27. **MP 4** A restaurant owner wishes to install a new flat-screen television with the same aspect ratio, or the ratio of width to height, as the current one. The current one is 56 inches wide by 42 inches tall. If the new one needs to have a height of 45 inches, what must its width be?

28. The point $(-12, 8)$ is one of the vertices of a rhombus. The center of dilation is the origin. The rhombus is dilated by a factor of $\frac{1}{4}$, then it is reflected across the *x*-axis. Finally, it is translated right 5 and up 2. What is the final location of the vertex? Show all steps and explain your reasoning.

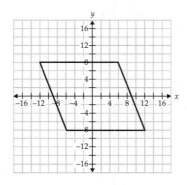

1. How should the angle be written?

A. $\angle PQR$

B. $\angle RQP$

C. $\angle QRP$

D. $\angle P$

2. Which choice below names JK as a line segment?

A. $\overleftrightarrow{JK}$

B. $\overrightarrow{JK}$

C. $\overline{JK}$

D. JK

3. If $m\angle L = 217°$, what quadrant is it in?

A. Quadrant I

B. Quadrant II

C. Quadrant III

D. Quadrant IV

4. What are the vertices of the reflection of the figure about the y-axis?

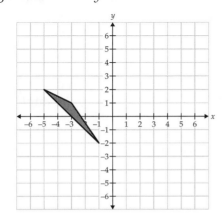

A. $(5, 2)$, $(3, 1)$, and $(1, -2)$

B. $(-5, -2)$, $(-3, -1)$, and $(-1, 2)$

C. $(5, -2)$, $(3, -1)$, and $(1, 2)$

D. $(-2, 5)$, $(-1, 3)$, and $(2, 1)$

5. $\angle XYZ$ measures 41°. It is rotated 2°. After the rotation, its measure is

A. 43° if the rotation is clockwise, 39° if the rotation is counterclockwise.

B. 39° if the rotation is clockwise, 443° if the rotation is counterclockwise.

C. 41°

D. 82°

6. Which of the following is the reflection of the point $(-4, 7)$ across the line $x = 1$?

A. $(-4, -7)$

B. $(-4, -5)$

C. $(4, 7)$

D. $(6, 7)$

7. Two lines are not parallel. This means

A. They cannot be in the same plane.

B. They must intersect.

C. The two lines must define a plane.

D. They may or may not be in same plane.

8. A triangle is dilated by a scale factor of 1.5 and then by a scale factor of 0.8. The resulting figure is

A. No longer a triangle.

B. Larger.

C. Smaller.

D. The same size.

9. A parallelogram (a four-sided figure with sides that are parallel) is reflected, rotated, reflected again, and then translated. The resulting figure is

A. Not a parallelogram.

B. A parallelogram that is larger.

C. A parallelogram that is smaller.

D. A parallelogram of the same shape and size.

10. What are the coordinates of the reflection of the point $(-4, -2)$ about the y-axis?

11. $\angle ABC$ is divided by a line containing point D. Given that the measure of $\angle ABD$ is four times as large as that of $\angle CBD$, and the product of the measures of these two angles is 169, what is the exact measure of $\angle ABC$?

12. **MP 1** You have an unlimited number of $17°$ and $13°$ angles. You can add or subtract these angles to make new angles of different sizes. For example, you can add a $17°$ angle and a $13°$ angle to make a $30°$ angle, or subtract a $13°$ angle from a $17°$ angle to make a $4°$ angle. Explain how you can use these angles to create an angle with a measure of $29°$.

13. $\triangle ABC \sim \triangle DEF$. What is the length of $\overline{EF}$?

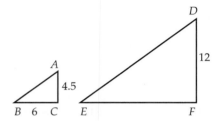

14. The two triangles shown below are similar and drawn so corresponding sides are in the same locations. What is the value of a?

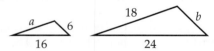

15. The coordinates of vertex X of triangle XYZ are $(-1, -5)$. Find the coordinates of X' if the triangle is dilated by a scale factor of 5 and if the center of dilation is the origin.

16. The coordinates of vertex X of triangle XYZ are $(6, 0)$. Find the coordinates of X' if the triangle is dilated by a scale factor of 6 and if the center of dilation is the origin.

17. The coordinates of vertex X of triangle XYZ are $(-7, 6)$. Find the coordinates of X' if the triangle is dilated by a scale factor of 6 and the center of dilation is the origin.

18. Write the possible side lengths of a triangle that is similar to the one shown below.

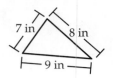

19. Graph $\triangle QUA$, which has vertices at $Q(-2, 1)$, $U(1, 5)$, and $A(3, 1)$. Then, graph $\triangle EGO$, which is the result of a rigid motion transformation of $\triangle QUA$. Label the vertices of both triangles.

20. Use the compass rose to answer the following questions.

   a If the compass rose continues to point in the same direction but is found in a different location on the page, what type of rigid motion has occurred?

   b If the compass rose is moved in a single transformation such that N and S exchange positions and E and W exchange positions, what type of transformation has occurred?

   c If the area of the black sections of the compass rose is to be increased by a factor of 4, what type of transformation has occurred, and by what amount?

Exercises 21–22: What is the distance from P to P'?

21. Point P has coordinates $(6, -3)$ and P' is its reflection across the line $x = -2$.

22. Point P has coordinates $(8, -6)$ and P' is its reflection across the line $x = -1$.

23. **a** Do dilations change the interior angles of a figure? Explain.

   b Does any transformation discussed so far change the measures of the angles of a triangle?

24. Point H lies on $\overline{BK}$. BK is 84 and BH is 8. What is HK?

25. You want to move a figure 3 to the left and up 2. What constants do you add to the coordinates of each point?

26. $\triangle ABC \cong \triangle ZYX$. If $m\angle B = 80°$ and $m\angle C = 10°$, what does Z equal?
Hint: Consider what angle Z corresponds to in $\triangle ABC$.

27. The ratio of the perimeter of one equilateral triangle to the perimeter of another equilateral triangle is 1 : 4. How many of the smaller triangles would fit inside the larger triangle with no overlap or uncovered space?

28. Triangle ABC is dilated to form triangle $A'B'C'$. Sophia calculates the ratio $\dfrac{AB}{A'B'}$ to be 5 and states that the scale factor for this dilation is 5. Is Sophia correct? Explain.

29. **MP 5, 7** Triangle ABC has vertices at $(1, 4)$, $(5, -1)$, and $(-2, -7)$.

a Graph the triangle.

b Name a transformation that produces a figure that is both congruent and similar. Describe the transformation and give the coordinates of the new triangle. Draw the new triangle on the same coordinate axis as the original.

c Name a transformation that produces a figure that is not congruent but similar. Describe the transformation and give the coordinates of the new triangle. Draw the new triangle on the same coordinate axis as your other two.

Chapter 3 Reasoning

Chapter Content

Chapter Vocabulary

adjacent angle	counterexample	inverse
biconditional	deductive reasoning	linear pair
complementary angles	definition	negation
conclusion	fractal	proof
conditional statement	given	reason
conjecture	hypothesis	supplementary angle
contrapositive	inductive reasoning	vertical angles
converse		

LESSON 3.1

3.1 Inductive Reasoning

Inductive reasoning, or simply, *induction*, is a way to decide if something is true or false. It is based on drawing **conclusions** from a consistent pattern. Inductive reasoning is different from deductive reasoning, which is making an argument one step at a time to reach a conclusion.

We use inductive reasoning to predict how many bacteria there will be in the next squares.

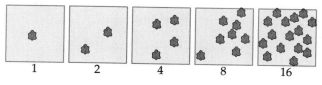

The bacteria double in number in each square. The pattern is 1, 2, 4, 8, 16. If asked to predict how many bacteria are in the next squares, we would guess 32, 64, 128, and so on.

Finding Patterns in Numbers

Patterns can be found in numbers. Look for the difference between the numbers and see if you find a pattern there.

> A chart can be a good way to note a pattern and determine the next number in the sequence.

Example 1

What is the next number in the pattern 2, 5, 8, 11, …?

Calculate the differences between the numbers and look for the pattern there	The difference between each pair of adjacent numbers is 3.

Apply pattern	$11 + 3 = 14$
	The next number is 14.

Example 2

What is the next number in the pattern 3, 4, 6, 9, 13, …?

Calculate the differences between the numbers and look for the pattern there

Each difference is one greater than the prior difference.

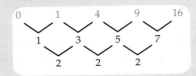

Apply pattern

$13 + 5 = 18$

The next number is 18.

MODEL PROBLEM

MP 1, 7 **a** What is the pattern in the differences between the squares of numbers?

b Suppose you could not directly calculate the square of 10. Based on the pattern you observed in part **a** regarding the differences between squares of numbers, what would you expect for the difference $10^2 - 9^2$?

SOLUTION

a We look for a pattern in the squares of numbers.

Calculate the differences between the numbers

To decide the next number in the pattern, we calculate the differences between the numbers.

Look for the pattern there

Each difference is two greater than the prior difference.

We can apply the rule: $7^2 = 49$, $8^2 = 64$, $9^2 = 81$. The differences are 15 and 17.

b The difference between the squares of 8 and 7 was 15. The difference between the squares of 9 and 8 was 17. Each difference was 2 greater than the one before. The difference between the squares of 10 and 9, based on this pattern, is expected to be 19.

Finding Patterns in Figures

Patterns can be shown visually. The diagram shows a figure called a Sierpinski triangle. Though it is a bit harder than what you may be asked to draw, it is a famous pattern since it is a fractal. A **fractal** is a pattern that is repeated at every scale (so that if you zoom in, you are seeing the same pattern you would see at a distance).

Example

What would the fourth triangle look like?

Sometimes analyzing a sequence can help you determine a pattern.

Look for the pattern   The pattern is that each black triangle has a white triangle placed in it.

Apply the pattern

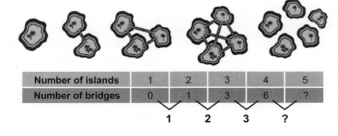

We show another three more triangles of the pattern. You can see how the pattern stays the same if you look closer. For instance, the third triangle is one of the three triangles that forms the fourth triangle.

MODEL PROBLEM

How many bridges can connect the islands as one island is added each time?

SOLUTION

Create a table

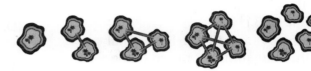

Number of islands	1	2	3	4	5
Number of bridges	0	1	3	6	?

       1   2   3   ?

We are asked how many bridges can connect 5 islands. The diagram might be fairly difficult. Start by writing down the number of bridges that are shown. The picture shows groups of 1, 2, 3, and 4 islands and the bridges connecting the islands in each group.

Apply pattern $6 + 4 = 10$ Now calculate the differences of the differences. The pattern seems clear: Each time the difference is one more than the prior one. Since the last difference is 3, we predict the next one is 4, and we add 4. If we count closely in the diagram, we can see this is true.

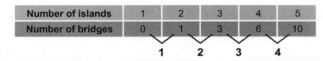

Number of islands	1	2	3	4	5
Number of bridges	0	1	3	6	10

       1   2   3   4

Counterexamples

A conclusion reached by inductive reasoning may be false. For this reason, a conclusion reached by inductive reasoning is called a **conjecture**. It remains to be proven true.

For instance, perhaps someone says: "All odd numbers are prime. 3 is prime, 5 and 7 are prime—you see, all odd numbers are prime." But 9, an odd number, is not prime, nor is 15. This is a **counterexample**—an example that proves a conjecture false. The person considered a few cases, but the pattern did not hold. The numbers 9 and 15 are counterexamples to the conjecture that all odd numbers are prime.

PRACTICE

1. Which of the following statements is an example of inductive reasoning? Note that not all of the conclusions are necessarily true.

   A. The numbers 6 and 12 are divisible by 3; thus, all multiples of 6 are divisible by 3.

   B. The numbers 8 and 16 are not divisible by 3; thus, no multiples of 8 are divisible by 3.

   C. The values 7^0 and 24^0 are both equal to 1; thus, any number raised to the 0 is 1.

   D. All of the above.

2. Which of the following is a counterexample for the statement "All even numbers are divisible by 4"?

   A. 8 is divisible by 4.

   B. 10 is not divisible by 4.

   C. 13 is not divisible by 4.

   D. 16 is divisible by 4.

3. Which of the following is a counterexample for the statement "All mammals have four legs"?

   A. A dog is a mammal that has four legs.

   B. A human is a mammal that does not have four legs.

   C. A reptile is not a mammal but has four legs.

   D. A salmon is not a mammal and does not have four legs.

4. Meng skims a table of prime numbers and concludes that all prime numbers are odd. Which of the following would be a valid counterexample to prove that his conjecture is false?

   A. 7 is an odd number, and it is prime.

   B. 25 is an odd number, and it is not prime.

   C. 2 is an even number, and it is prime.

   D. 46 is an even number, and it is not prime.

5. Tabetha says, "All parallelograms have 2 acute angles and 2 obtuse angles." Which of the following would be a valid counterexample to prove that her conjecture is false?

   A. Some rhombuses also have 2 acute angles and 2 obtuse angles.

   B. A rectangle is a parallelogram, and it has 4 right angles.

   C. A square is a rhombus, and it has 4 right angles.

   D. A rectangle is a parallelogram, and it has 2 pairs of congruent sides.

6. Sebastian says, "All rhombuses have 2 acute angles and 2 obtuse angles." Which of the following would be a valid counterexample to prove that his conjecture is false?

   A. A square is a rhombus, and it has 4 right angles.

   B. A rectangle is a rhombus, and it has 4 right angles.

   C. A rhombus does not always have 2 acute angles and 2 obtuse angles.

   D. A rhombus has 4 congruent sides, so it doesn't have to have acute angles.

Practice Problems continue . . .

Practice Problems continued . . .

MP 7 Exercises 7–12: Make a conjecture for the next term in the sequence.

7. $-9, -4, 1, 6, \dots$

8. $-7, 3, 13, 23, \dots$

9. $0, 12, 24, 36, \dots$

10. $0, 5, 10, 15, \dots$

11. $400, 576, 784, 1024, \dots$

12. $-1, 2, 23, 80, 191, \dots$

13. Consider the sequence 3, 4, 6, 9, 13, 18 … What is the next number in the sequence?

14. Fibonacci's sequence begins as follows: 1, 1, 2, 3, 5, 8… What is the next number in the sequence?

15. A famous mathematical series from Zeno's dichotomy begins as follows: $\dfrac{1}{2} + \dfrac{1}{4} + \dfrac{1}{8}, \dots$ What is the next number in the series?

16. A sequence begins as follows: 1, 7, 13, 19, 25, … What is the next number in the sequence?

Exercises 17–20: Find a counterexample for the following statements.

17. $a - b \leq a$

18. $\dfrac{x}{z} + \dfrac{y}{z} = \dfrac{x + y}{2z}$ for any $z \neq 0$

19. $a^2 > a$

20. All numbers are greater than 0 and less than or equal to 1.

21. Use the diagram to answer the following questions.

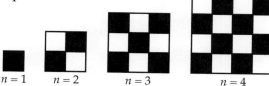

$n = 1$ $n = 2$ $n = 3$ $n = 4$

a There is 1 square for $n = 1$, 5 squares for $n = 2$, and 14 squares for $n = 3$. How many squares are there for $n = 4$?

b Sketch the squares for $n = 5$.

c How many squares are there for $n = 5$?

d How many squares are there for $n = 10$?

e Suppose a diagram contains 1,015 squares. Make a well-justified conjecture for the value of n.

22. Use the diagram to answer the following questions.

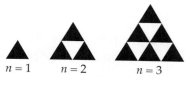

$n = 1$ $n = 2$ $n = 3$

a There is 1 triangle for $n = 1$ and 5 triangles for $n = 2$. How many triangles are there for $n = 3$?

b Sketch the triangles for $n = 4$.

c How many triangles are there for $n = 4$?

d Make a well-justified conjecture for the number of triangles contained in the figure when $n = 12$.

23. The diagram represents the first 3 iterations of the Koch curve. Use the diagram to answer the following questions.

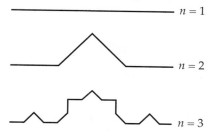

$n = 1$

$n = 2$

$n = 3$

a Sketch the Koch curve for $n = 4$.

b The number of segments in the Koch curve for $n = 1$ is 1 and for $n = 2$ is 4. What is the number of segments for $n = 4$?

c The length of each segment in the Koch curve for $n = 1$ is 1 and for $n = 2$ is $\dfrac{1}{3}$. What is the length of each segment for $n = 3$? Then use inductive reasoning to make a conjecture for the length of each segment for $n = 4$.

d The length of the Koch curve is 1 for $n = 1$ and $\dfrac{4}{3}$ for $n = 2$. What is the length of the Koch curve for $n = 3$ and $n = 4$?

e Make a conjecture about the length of the Koch curve as n goes to infinity.

MP 2, 4, 7 A machine produces rectangular cardboard boxes like the one on the right. Unfortunately, the machine is not working perfectly, so although the first box is the correct size, the other ones vary from that size. The table shows the dimensions of 9 boxes that the machine produced in sequence.

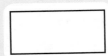

Box number	Height	Width
1	50.0	100
2	49.5	98.9
3	49	98.0
4	49.4	99.1
5	50.1	100.1
6	50.9	100.9
7	50.2	99.9
8	49.6	99.0
9	49.1	98.1

a Describe the relationship of change as it relates to height and width.

b Would the change in width in just the first six boxes best fit a linear or quadratic model? Explain your choice.

c How would the rate of change in the area compare to the rate of change in the height?

d Assuming that the pattern above continues, would you expect a box with dimensions of 50.8 by 100.9 to be box 12 or box 15? Explain your reasoning.

LESSON 3.2

3.2 Conditional Statements

Many mathematical statements are written in the form "If A, then B." Statements in this form are called **conditional statements**.

> A conditional statement is written in "if A, then B" form. Part A is the **hypothesis**; part B is the conclusion.
>
> - An example of a conditional statement is "If m is even, then $m + 1$ is odd."
> - The hypothesis is "If m is even" and the conclusion is "$m + 1$ is odd."

For a conditional statement to be true, the statement must *always* be true, not just true sometimes. We provide an example of a conditional that is always true, and one that is only sometimes true, so it is considered false.

For example:

- If it is a kitten, then it is a cat. → True
- If it flies, then it is a bird. → False; some flying animals are birds, but not all, so the conditional is false.

The order of the hypothesis and conclusion is very important, because switching them changes the meaning of the statement. Not all conditionals are reversible.

For example:

- If it's a carrot, then it's a vegetable. → True
- If it's a vegetable, then it's a carrot. → False; this statement is false, since the conclusion is not always true.

A conditional statement is not always written as a formal "If *A*, then *B*." You will need to recognize different forms of conditional statements and transform statements with words like "all" and "never" into conditional statements.

> **Statements can be true or false.**

Statement	Written as a conditional statement
All mammals have warm blood.	If it is a mammal, then it has warm blood.
Parallel lines never intersect.	If two lines are parallel, then they do not intersect.
Kittens are cats.	If it is a kitten, then it is a cat.

MODEL PROBLEM

Use the diagram to determine whether each statement is true or false, and then rewrite the statement as a conditional statement.

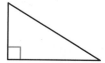

a The figure is a triangle.
b All of its angles are right angles.
c Its angles sum to 180°.

SOLUTION

a True. If a figure is a three-sided polygon, then it is a triangle.
b False. If a figure is a triangle, then all of its angles are right angles.
c True. If a figure is a triangle, then its angles sum to 180°.

The figure in the diagram is a three-sided polygon, which means it is a triangle and its angles sum to 180°, but its angles are not all right angles.

Applying Conditional Statements

With a <u>true</u> conditional statement, if *A* is true, then *B*, the conclusion must <u>always</u> be true. There can also be conditionals with a false hypothesis, but they are not the focus of this book.

> **For true conditionals:**
>
> If *A* is true, then B must be true.
> If *A* is false, then B may be true or false.

A **negation** is the opposite of a statement. "The cat is not black" is the negation of "The cat is black." To write the negation of a sentence that contains a "not," remove the "not." The negation of "The sky is not falling" is "The sky is falling."

We show examples of other types of conditionals, including converse, inverse, and contrapositive:

Types of Statements	Example
Conditional	*If you are taking a nap,* then you are sleeping.
Converse • Reverse hypothesis and conclusion	If you are sleeping, then *you are taking a nap.*
Inverse • Negation of hypothesis and conclusion	*If you* are **not** *taking a nap,* then you are **not** sleeping.
Contrapositive • Inverse of converse	If you are **not** sleeping, then *you are* **not** *taking a nap.*

Be careful. Some of the changes to conditional statements described above can change a statement from true to false. Even if a conditional is true, its converse or inverse may or may not be true. For instance, "If you like banana pudding, then you like bananas" does not mean that if you like bananas, then you like banana pudding. However, if a statement is true, its contrapositive is true as well.

A **biconditional** is a statement that can be written in the "if and only if" form. For example: "A number is negative <u>if and only if</u> it is to the left of the origin on the number line."

When a conditional *and* its converse are true, then it can be written as a biconditional. Biconditionals are also **definitions**.

For instance:

> When a conditional and its converse are true, the statement can be written as a biconditional or a definition.

Conditional	If a number is to the left of the origin, then it is negative.	True
Converse	If a number is negative, then it is to the left of the origin.	True

- Written as a *biconditional*: "A number is negative if and only if it is to the left of the origin."
- Written as a *definition*: "Negative numbers are to the left of the origin."

1. a Write the converse, inverse, and contrapositive of the conditional statement "If you are a professional soccer player, then you are an athlete." Indicate which statements are true or false.

b If a biconditional exists, write the biconditional.

SOLUTION

a

Conditional	If you are a professional soccer player, then you are an athlete.	True
Converse	If you are an athlete, then you are a professional soccer player.	False
Inverse	If you are not a professional soccer player, then you are not an athlete.	False
Contrapositive	If you are not an athlete, then you are not a professional soccer player.	True

b The conditional and its converse are not both true, so it is not a biconditional.

2. a Write the converse, inverse, and contrapositive of the conditional statement "If a polygon has three sides, then it is a triangle." Indicate which statements are true or false.

b If a biconditional exists, write the biconditional.

SOLUTION

a

Conditional	If a polygon has three sides, then it is a triangle.	True
Converse	If it is a triangle, then it is a polygon with three sides.	True
Inverse	If a polygon does not have three sides, then it is not a triangle.	True
Contrapositive	If it is not a triangle, then the polygon does not have three sides.	True

b Both the conditional and converse are true, so a biconditional exists. A polygon is a triangle if and only if it has three sides.

3. If *K* is true, then *N* is also true. It must be true that

A. If *N* is true, then *K* is true.
B. If *K* is false, then *N* is also false.
C. Both *K* and *N* are true.
D. None of the above.

SOLUTION

The answer is D. Answer A is an example of a converse statement, and converse statements are not always true. B is incorrect, since inverses need not be true. C is false, since nothing requires *K* to be true. So the answer by elimination is D.

PRACTICE

Exercises 1–2: Use the following statement to answer the problems: "If you live on the east side of Bank Street, then your house number is even."

1. If Erica lives on the east side of Bank Street, then what can you say about her address?

    A.   Erica's house number is even.

    B.   Erica's house number is odd.

    C.   We cannot tell from this information whether Erica's house number is even or odd.

2. If Candace lives on Bank Street, then what can you say about her address?

    A.   Candace's house number is even.

    B.   Candace's house number is odd.

    C.   We cannot tell from this information whether Candace's house number is even or odd.

3. Which of these is the converse of, "If you can run a marathon, you are an athlete"?

    A.   If you are an athlete, you can run a marathon.

    B.   If you cannot run a marathon, you are not an athlete.

    C.   If you are not an athlete, you cannot run a marathon.

    D.   If you can run a marathon, you are an athlete.

4. Which of these is the inverse of, "If an animal is a bird, then it hatches from an egg"?

    A.   If an animal does not hatch from an egg, it is not a bird.

    B.   If an animal is a bird, then it hatches from an egg.

    C.   If an animal hatches from an egg, then it is a bird.

    D.   If an animal is not a bird, it does not hatch from an egg.

5. Which of these is the contrapositive of, "If a recipe is for a cake, then it contains sugar"?

    A.   If a recipe contains sugar, then it is for a cake.

    B.   If a recipe is for a cake, then it contains sugar.

    C.   If a recipe does not contain sugar, then it is not for a cake.

    D.   If a recipe is not for a cake, then it does not contain sugar.

6. Which is the contrapositive of, "If a number is even, then it is divisible by two"?

    A.   If a number is divisible by two, then it is not even.

    B.   If a number is not even, then it is not divisible by two.

    C.   If a number is not divisible by two, then it is not even.

7. Which is the converse of, "If a number is even, then it is divisible by two"?

    A.   If a number is divisible by two, then it is even.

    B.   If a number is divisible by two, then it is not even.

    C.   If a number is not divisible by two, then it is not even.

8. The statement: "A horse has four legs" is equivalent to

    A.   If it has four legs, then it is a horse.

    B.   If it is a horse, then it has four legs.

    C.   Any animal with four legs is a horse.

Exercises 9–12: Write an equivalent conditional statement in the form "If *A*, then *B*" for the following statements.

9. All squares are rectangles.

10. All dogs chase cats.

11. All liquids are consumable.

12. No vegans eat meat.

Practice Problems continue . . .

Exercises 13–16: Determine whether each statement is true or false. If it is false, give a counterexample.

13. If you are playing a sport, then you are using a ball.

14. If you exercise daily, then you are burning calories.

15. All jobs are paid by a yearly salary.

16. All moving vehicles have four tires.

MP 3 **Exercises 17–21:** Write the converse of each statement and determine whether the converse is a true or false statement. Justify your answer.

17. If you drink alcohol, then you are at least 21 years old.

18. If you have never lost a match in tennis, then your winning percentage in tennis is 100%.

19. If it's June, then it is hot.

20. If one is in a school setting, then learning is taking place.

21. If the sum of two numbers is greater than 10, then at least one of the numbers is greater than 5.

Exercises 22–25: Write the contrapositive for the given conditional statement.

22. If an item is electronic, then it must be placed away from liquids.

23. If I am determined, then I will be successful.

24. If it is snowing, then school is not in session.

25. If I am eating, then I am hungry.

MP 3 **Exercises 26–29:** Determine whether the given biconditional is true or false. Justify your answer.

26. It will rain tomorrow if and only if it rains today.

27. At standard pressure, water freezes if and only if its temperature is at or below 32° F (0° C).

28. A person snores if and only if he or she is sleeping.

29. The cost of products increases if and only if inflation increases.

Exercises 30–34: Use the following conditional statement to answer each question: "If the figure is a triangle, then its interior angles sum to 180°."

30. Write the converse statement and determine whether it is true or false.

31. Write the inverse statement and determine whether it is true or false.

32. Write the contrapositive statement and determine whether it is true or false.

33. Combine the conditional and converse statements to write the biconditional statement. Then determine whether it is true or false.

34. Can this statement be converted into a definition? If so, write the definition for a triangle. If not, explain why not.

35. **MP 3** Let's consider the conditional statement "If it is raining, then it is cloudy" to be a true statement.

   a In your own words, explain how the converse statement is different from the conditional statement.

   b In your own words, explain how the contrapositive statement is equivalent to the conditional statement.

   c If we switched the hypothesis and conclusion of "All squares have four right angles" as a conditional statement, would the statement be true or false? Explain.

3.3 Deductive Reasoning

In Lesson 3.1, we introduced inductive reasoning, which is the process of deciding if something is true or false based on conclusions drawn from a specific pattern. This type of reasoning is different from **deductive reasoning**, where we start with a true claim and then systemically build a valid argument, based on previously known true statements, that ends with a logical conclusion. You have built arguments based on deductive reasoning throughout your mathematical career. In this lesson and the next, we formalize the language of these arguments as "proofs" and provide practice with simple proofs to familiarize you with the process.

Proof and Its Origins

It is believed that mathematical proof as we know it was formalized by the famous Greek geometer Euclid of Alexandria, who lived from about 365 BCE to 300 BCE. He published a series of books, called *Elements*, which were composed of his original works as well as his interpretations of works that came before him. Although the *Elements* contain treatises on many parts of mathematics, Euclid is best known for *Elements I*, which focuses on geometry. In that book, he formalized definitions and an axiomatic system of geometry, where deductive reasoning is used to draw logical conclusions. We now call this deductive reasoning a proof.

A mathematical **proof** is a sequence of statements, such as a **given**, an axiom, a postulate, a theorem, or is somehow deduced from previously established statements, which establishes the truth of a mathematical statement. As we learn to write proofs, we must give a **reason**, or justification, for each step of the proof. For example, suppose that we want to prove two angles, as shown in the box below, have the same measure.

> A proof starts with a *given*, something you are told is true, including information you see in a marked diagram.

Now, you might be thinking, "Well, of course they have the same measure! They look exactly alike." Yes, that is true, but in mathematics, it is not enough that something appears to be true on a diagram. You must prove it. To do so, we write a two-column proof, starting with the given information. Note that there are other methods of writing proofs, which will be addressed later.

Given: $\angle A$ is a right angle; $\angle B$ is a right angle
Prove: $\angle A$ has the same measure as $\angle B$

> This proof is a bit trivial, but it provides the basic structure of an argument based on deductive reasoning. In the model problems, we look at more substantive proofs.

Statement	Reason
$\angle A$ is a right angle	Given
$\angle B$ is a right angle	Given
$m\angle A = 90°$	Measure of a right angle is 90°
$m\angle B = 90°$	Measure of a right angle is 90°
$\angle A$ has the same measure as $\angle B$	Both angles have the same measure

MODEL PROBLEMS

1. **MP 1, 3, 6** Show that $AB = AC - BC$, if B is between A and C on a line segment using the segment addition postulate.

Segment addition postulate

If B is between A and C on a line segment, then $AB + BC = AC$.

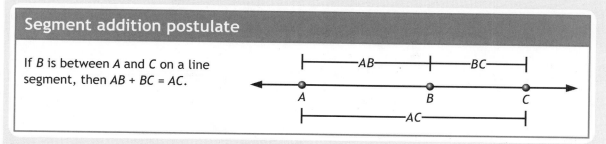

SOLUTION

Statement	Reason
B is between A and C	Given from diagram
$AB + BC = AC$	Segment addition postulate
$AB + BC - BC = AC - BC$	Addition property of equality
$AB = AC - BC$	Additive inverse

2. **MP 2, 4, 6** A rocket is launched with a starting velocity of 5 miles per second. If it accelerates at the rate of 4 miles per second squared, what is the rocket's velocity after 7 seconds? Show the algebraic reasoning required to answer this question. The definition of acceleration is

$$\text{acceleration} = \frac{\text{final velocity} - \text{starting velocity}}{\text{time}}.$$

SOLUTION

Statement	Reason	
$\text{acceleration} = \dfrac{\text{final velocity} - \text{starting velocity}}{\text{time}}$	Given	The definition of acceleration was given.
$\text{time} \cdot \text{acceleration} = \text{final velocity} - \text{starting velocity}$	Multiplication property of equality	Solve for the final velocity to calculate its value. Multiply both sides by time.
$\text{final velocity} = \text{time} \cdot \text{acceleration} + \text{starting velocity}$	Addition property of equality	Use the addition property of equality to solve for the final velocity. Use the symmetry property to switch final velocity to the left side.
$\text{final velocity} = 7 \cdot 4 + 5$ $\text{final velocity} = 33$ miles per second	Substitution property	Use the substitution property to substitute and then evaluate.

Model Problems continue . . .

3. **MP 1, 8** $m\angle CAB$ is three times $m\angle DAC$. If $m\angle DAB$ is 52°, what is $m\angle CAB$?

SOLUTION

Statement	Reason	
$m\angle DAB = 52°$	Given	Stated in problem.
$m\angle CAB + m\angle DAC = 52°$	Angle sum postulate	The angle sum postulate says we can sum the two angles.
$3x + x = 52°$ $4x = 52°$	Substitution property	Substitute $3x$ for $m\angle CAB$ and x for $m\angle DAC$ and combine like terms.
$\dfrac{4x}{4} = \dfrac{52°}{4}$ $x = 13°$	Multiplication property of equality	Use the multiplication property of equality to solve for x. $m\angle DAC$ is equal to 13°.
$m\angle CAB = 3x$ $m\angle CAB = 3 \cdot 13$ $m\angle CAB = 39°$	Substitution property	Use the expression for $m\angle CAB$ and substitute. The measure of $\angle CAB$ is three times the measure of $\angle DAC$.

In this activity, apply deductive reasoning to a geometric proof.

PROVE

AC = BD

GIVEN

A, B, C and D are on a segment

AB = CD

Statements	Reasons	Choose tiles for your proof	
		AB = CD	Segment addition postulate
		AC = AB + BC	Segment addition postulate
		BD = CD + BC	Given
		AC = CD + BC	Substitution property
		A, B, C and D are on a segment	Given
		AC = BD	Transitive property of equality

CHECK YOUR PROOF **RESET TILES**

PRACTICE

1. What clues might help you deduce that your dog is hungry?

   I.   He follows you around the house.
   II. He whines next to his food bowl.
   III. He chews on anything in sight.
   IV. His tail won't stop wagging.

   A. I and III
   B. II and IV
   C. I, II, and III
   D. II only

2. Deductive reasoning is best described as

   A. Generalizing based on a few examples.
   B. Using logic to prove something.
   C. Drawing a conclusion based on collected data.

3. **MP 3, 6** Which is the first mistake made in the following proof?

Statement	Reason
$-2(5 - x) + 1 = 4x$	Given
Step 1: $-2(5 - x) = 4x - 1$	Addition property of equality
Step 2: $(5 - x) = -2x - 1$	Multiplication property of equality
Step 3: $-x = -2x - 6$	Addition property of equality
Step 4: $-3x = -6$	Addition property of equality
Step 5: $x = 3$	Multiplication property of equality

   A. Step 2
   B. Step 3
   C. Step 4
   D. Step 5

4. Sarah attends high school with Carolyn. Sarah also attends high school with Beth. If Sarah attends only one high school, what conclusion can be drawn?

   A. Sarah attends two high schools.
   B. Carolyn and Beth attend different high schools.
   C. Carolyn and Beth attend the same high school.
   D. No conclusion can be drawn from the given information.

5. A scientist concludes that a certain type of rod will conduct electricity. What are the statements that, if true, she will need to support her conclusion? Choose all that apply.

   A. The rod is made of copper.
   B. Two plus two equals four.
   C. The last 3 rods studied conducted electricity.
   D. Copper conducts electricity.

6. Sherlock Holmes, always correct, muttered: "If a man has no servants, his shirts are wrinkled. If a man has lost his job, he has no servants." Sherlock would conclude

   A. If a man has no servants, he has lost his job.
   B. If a man has lost his job, his shirts are wrinkled.
   C. A man with servants has no wrinkled shirts.
   D. A man with a job has servants.

7. **MP 3, 6** Keara states that if the ratios $\dfrac{a}{b}$ and $\dfrac{m}{n}$ are equal, then it must be true that $a = m$ and $b = n$. Is her statement correct? Explain.

8. Is the expression $(5a \cdot b) + (4a \cdot c)$ equivalent to the expression $(c \cdot 4a) + (b \cdot 5a)$? Explain your reasoning.

MP 6 Exercises 9–12: Use a two-column proof to solve the equation. Refer to the properties on page 5 as needed to answer these questions.

9. $2x = 6(2 + x)$

Practice Problems continue . . .

10. $4x = 2(9 - x)$

11. $-7x = 2(1 - 3x)$

12. $-2(2 - 3x) = 10 - x$

MP 6 Exercises 13–15: Use the diagram below and the theorems you've learned thus far to create a two-column proof to find the value of x.

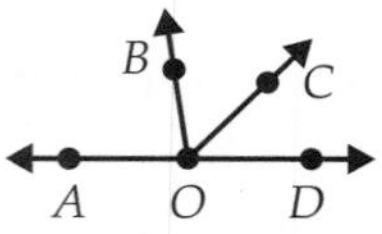

13. $m\angle AOB = x + 45°$; $m\angle BOC = 2x - 17°$; $m\angle COD = x$

14. $m\angle AOB = 5x$; $m\angle BOC = 3x$; $m\angle COD = 2(x + 20°)$

15. $m\angle AOB = 3x - 41°$; $m\angle BOC = x$; $m\angle COD = 2x - 19°$

16. Teresa orders a vase from a website. If the vase is cracked, then she will return it. If the vase is dropped during shipping, it will crack. What can you conclude?

17. Write a conditional statement of the form "If A, then B. If B, then C. If C, then D." Then make the conclusion "If A, then D."

18. Suppose we have the true biconditionals "A if and only if B" and "B if and only if C." Is the biconditional "A if and only if C" also true? Explain.

LESSON 3.4

3.4 Reasoning in Geometry

Angles and Their Relationships

Complementary angles are two angles that sum to 90°. **Adjacent angles** are two angles that share a common side and vertex. We show how two adjacent angles can sum to a complementary angle. If complementary angles are adjacent, they form a right angle, as the bracket shown below indicates.

> Complementary angles sum to 90°. Supplementary angles sum to 180°.

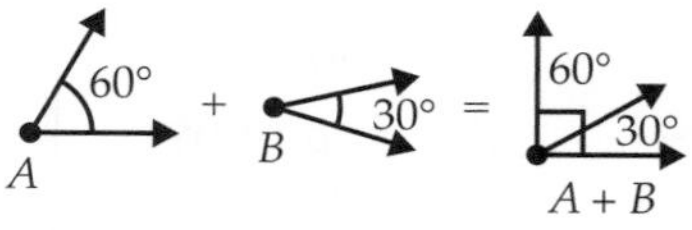

If two angles sum to 180°, they are **supplementary angles**. If they are adjacent, their rays form a line, and they are called a **linear pair**, or linear angles.

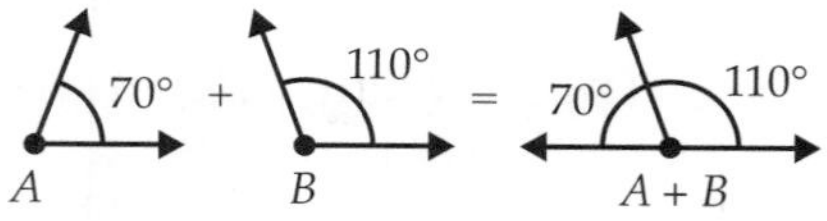

Vertical Angles

Vertical angles are a pair of angles, opposite from one another, formed by two intersecting lines. You can see why vertical angles are also called opposite angles in the diagram. Vertical angles have the same measure—they are congruent. (Their congruence is a theorem we prove later.)

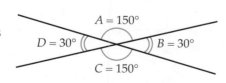

- A and C are vertical angles. They are congruent; $m\angle A = m\angle C = 150°$.
- B and D are vertical angles. They are congruent; $m\angle B = m\angle D = 30°$.

1. Show $m\angle ABC = 18°$.

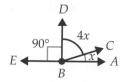

SOLUTION

Given in diagram	$m\angle EBD = 90°$	$\angle EBD$ is shown to be a right angle with the bracket symbol. This means it is 90°.
Supplementary angle	$m\angle DBA = 90°$	Since angles $\angle EBD$ and $\angle DBA$ are supplementary, angle $m\angle DBA$ is also 90°.
Angle addition postulate	$m\angle CBD + m\angle ABC = m\angle DBA$	
Substitute and evaluate	$m\angle CBD + m\angle ABC = 90°$ $4x + x = 90°$ $5x = 90°$	Substitute the value we found for $m\angle DBA$. $m\angle CBD$ is 4 times $m\angle ABC$. Use that expression, substitute and evaluate.
Multiplication property of equality	$x = 18°$	
Write solution	$4x = m\angle CBD$ $4x = 4(18°) = 72°$ $m\angle ABC = 18°$ $m\angle CBD = 72°$	State the measures of the two angles.

2. $m\angle A$ is four times $m\angle B$. Show $m\angle D = 36°$.

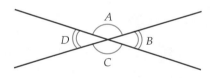

SOLUTION

Supplementary angles sum to 180°	$m\angle A + m\angle B = 180°$	To calculate $m\angle D$, we will calculate $m\angle B$, since B is a vertical angle with D. Since A and B are supplementary, they sum to 180°.
Write relationship of A and B	$m\angle A = 4(m\angle B)$	The problem states that $m\angle A$ is four times $m\angle B$. Write this as an equation.
Replace $m\angle A$ with $4\angle B$	$m\angle A + m\angle B = 180°$ $4(m\angle B) + m\angle B = 180°$	Replace $m\angle A$ with $4\angle B$.
Solve	$5(m\angle B) = 180°$ $m\angle B = 36°$	Solve the equation. Combine the like terms, $4m\angle B$ and $m\angle B$, which equals $5m\angle B$. Then divide each side of the equation by 5.
	$m\angle D = m\angle B = 36°$	Since B and D are vertical angles, they have equal measures. $m\angle D$ equals 36°.

Model Problems continue . . .

3. **MP 7** What are the measures of angles *E*, *F*, and *G*? Solve the problem using two different methods.

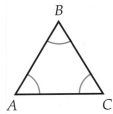

SOLUTION

Method 1

Start with vertical angles	$m\angle F = m\angle D = 30°$	*F* and *D* are vertical angles. This means they are congruent.
Use supplementary angle relationship	$m\angle D + m\angle E = 180°$ $30° + m\angle E = 180°$ $m\angle E = 150°$	*D* and *E* are supplementary angles, so they sum to 180°. Substitute for *D*. Solve for $m\angle E$. It equals 150°.
Use vertical angles again	$m\angle G = m\angle E = 150°$	Since *G* and *E* are vertical angles, they are congruent.

Method 2

Another way to solve this problem is to simply use the relationship of supplementary angles.

Start with supplementary angle relationship	$m\angle D + m\angle E = 180°$ $30° + m\angle E = 180°$ $m\angle E = 150°$	As above, solve for $m\angle E$. It equals 150°.
Use supplementary angles again	$m\angle E + m\angle F = 180°$ $150° + m\angle F = 180°$ $m\angle F = 30°$	Use the fact that these two angles are supplementary.
And again	$m\angle F + m\angle G = 180°$ $30° + m\angle G = 180°$ $m\angle G = 150°$	And once again, use the relationship of supplementary angles.

Properties of Equality and Congruence

Below are some properties that we used in algebra, and we show how they relate to geometry. We will use these properties often in proofs. Although the transitive property of equality may seem obvious to you, such properties come in handy. Transitive means that a value "transfers" from one number to another. "It's obvious" is not a reason accepted in geometry proofs!

Transitive Properties of Equality

For real numbers	If $a = b$ and $b = c$, then $a = c$.
Lengths • For segments $\overline{AB}$, $\overline{BC}$, and $\overline{CD}$	If $AB = BC$ and $BC = CD$, then $AB = CD$.
Angle measures	If $m\angle A = m\angle B$ and $m\angle B = m\angle C$, then $m\angle A = m\angle C$.

Transitive Properties of Congruence

| Segments | If $\overline{AB} \cong \overline{BC}$ and $\overline{BC} \cong \overline{CD}$, then $\overline{AB} \cong \overline{CD}$. |
| Angles | If $\angle A \cong \angle B$ and $\angle B \cong \angle C$, then $\angle A \cong \angle C$. |

> The transitive property of congruence parallels algebraic properties, such as the statement, if $a = b$ and $b = c$, then $a = c$.

Symmetric Properties of Equality

For real numbers	If $a = b$, then $b = a$.
Lengths • For segments $\overline{AB}$ and $\overline{BC}$	If $AB = BC$, then $BC = AB$.
Angle measures	If $m\angle A = m\angle B$, then $m\angle B = m\angle A$.

Symmetric Properties of Congruence

Segments	If $\overline{AB} \cong \overline{BC}$, then $\overline{BC} \cong \overline{AB}$.
Angles	If $\angle A \cong \angle B$, then $\angle B \cong \angle A$.

Reflexive Properties of Equality

For real numbers	$a = a$
Lengths • For segments $\overline{AB}$	$AB = AB$
Angle measures	$m\angle A = m\angle A$

Reflexive Properties of Congruence

Segments	$\overline{AB} \cong \overline{AB}$
Angles	$\angle A \cong \angle A$

 In this activity, prove the Congruent Complements Theorem, that $A = C$.

PROVE

$A \approx C$

Statements	Reasons	Choose tiles for your proof	
		$A + B = 180°$	Sum of complementary angles
		$A + B = 90°$	Sum of complementary angles
		$B + C = 90°$	Addition property of equality
		$A + B = B + C$	Transitive property of equality
		$A \approx C$	Diagram
		A and B are complementary angles	Diagram
		B and C are complementary angles	Sum of supplementary angles
			Reflexive property of congruence

CHECK YOUR PROOF   RESET TILES

Proving Relationships About Angles

There are some theorems and postulates about angles and their relationships that are frequently used in geometry. We state and prove several of them to demonstrate how theorems can be proven.

Congruent supplements theorem

If two angles are supplementary to the same angle, then they are congruent.

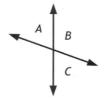

If ∠A and ∠C are both supplementary to ∠B, then ∠A ≅ ∠C.

Congruent complements theorem

If two angles are complementary to the same angle, then they are congruent.

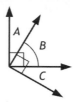

If ∠A and ∠C are both complementary to ∠B, then ∠A ≅ ∠C.

Linear pair postulate

If two angles form a linear pair, then their measures sum to 180°.

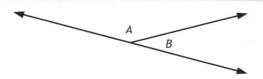

If ∠A and ∠B form a linear pair, then $m\angle A + m\angle B = 180°$.

Vertical angles theorem

If two angles are pairs of vertical angles, then they are congruent.

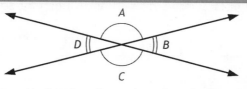

If ∠A and ∠C, and ∠B and ∠D are vertical angles, then ∠A ≅ ∠C, and ∠B ≅ ∠D.

We do a short proof of the congruent supplements theorem to show again a format we will often use, with statements in the left-hand column and reasons in the right-hand column.

Prove: $m\angle A = m\angle C$

Statement	Reason
A and B are supplementary B and C are supplementary	Diagram
$m\angle A + m\angle B = 180°$ $m\angle B + m\angle C = 180°$	Definition of supplementary angles
$m\angle A + m\angle B = m\angle B + m\angle C$	Transitive property of equality
$m\angle A = m\angle C$	Addition property of equality

MODEL PROBLEMS

1. **MP 3, 6** Prove: $m\angle A = m\angle C$

SOLUTION

Statement	Reason
A and B are complementary angles	Diagram
B and C are complementary angles	Diagram
$m\angle A + m\angle B = 90°$	Sum of complementary angles
$m\angle B + m\angle C = 90°$	Sum of complementary angles
$m\angle A + m\angle B = m\angle B + m\angle C$	Transitive property of equality
$m\angle A = m\angle C$	Addition property of equality

2. **MP 3, 6** Prove the vertical angles theorem by showing that angles A and C are congruent.

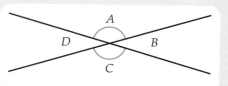

SOLUTION

Statement	Reason
A and C are vertical angles	Diagram
A and B are supplementary	Linear pair postulate
B and C are supplementary	Linear pair postulate
A and C are congruent	Congruent supplements theorem

Model Problems continue . . .

3. Angles Z and P are supplementary angles on a line. Angles Z and N are vertical angles. This means that angles P and N are

  A. Also vertical angles.   C. Supplementary.
  B. Congruent.   D. None of the above.

SOLUTION

Drawing a diagram is a good way to answer some multiple-choice questions. Angles P and N are a linear pair; this means they are supplementary. They are not vertical angles, and they need not be congruent, so answers A and B are false. The answer is C.

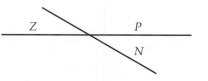

4. Show the linear pair postulate is true using the diagram to the right.

  Given: $\angle A$ and $\angle B$ form a linear pair.

  Prove: $m\angle A + m\angle B = 180°$

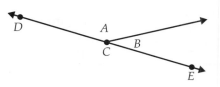

SOLUTION

Statement	Reason
$\angle A$ and $\angle B$ form a linear pair	Given
$\overrightarrow{CD}$ and $\overrightarrow{CE}$ are opposite rays	Definition of opposite rays
$\angle DCE$ is a straight angle	Definition of a straight angle
$m\angle A + m\angle B = m\angle DCE$	Angle addition postulate
$m\angle A + m\angle B = 180°$	Substitution

5. Given: $m\angle B \cong m\angle C$
   Prove: $m\angle A \cong m\angle D$

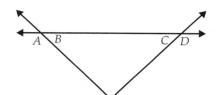

SOLUTION

Statement	Reason
$m\angle B \cong m\angle C$	Given
$\angle A$ and $\angle B$ are a linear pair	Definition of linear pair
$\angle C$ and $\angle D$ are a linear pair	Definition of linear pair
$m\angle A + m\angle B = 180°$	Linear pair postulate
$m\angle C + m\angle D = 180°$	Linear pair postulate
$m\angle A + m\angle B = m\angle C + m\angle D$	Substitution
$m\angle A + m\angle B = m\angle B + m\angle D$	Substitution
$m\angle A = m\angle D$	Subtraction property of equality

1. The measure of ∠D is eight times m∠F. What is m∠E?

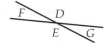

   A. 20°
   B. 40°
   C. 140°
   D. 160°

2. Angles R and S are complementary. If m∠R = 32°, what is m∠S?

   A. 13°
   B. 58°
   C. 113°
   D. 148°

3. What can be concluded from m∠A = m∠B = 90°?

   A. A and B are complementary angles.
   B. A and B are supplementary angles.
   C. A and B are vertical angles.
   D. None of the above.

4. ∠BAC is a straight angle formed by the adjacent angles ∠DAB and ∠DAC. m∠DAC is five times m∠DAB. What is m∠DAC?

   A. 30°
   B. 45°
   C. 120°
   D. 150°

5. Angles A and B are complementary. If m∠B = 39°, what is m∠A?

6. Angles C and D are supplementary. If m∠C = 126°, what is m∠D?

7. ∠BAC is a right angle formed by the adjacent angles ∠BAD and ∠DAC. The measure of ∠BAD is two times m∠DAC. What is m∠DAC?

8. ∠ABC and ∠CBD are supplementary. The measure of ∠ABC is 11 times m∠CBD. What is m∠ABC?

9. What is the sum of m∠DAC and m∠BAD?

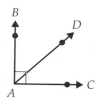

10. What is the sum of m∠BAD and m∠BAC?

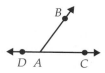

11. The measure of ∠DAB is three times m∠DAC. What is m∠DAB? What is m∠DAC?

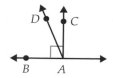

12. The measure of ∠ABC is four times m∠CBD. What is m∠ABC? What is m∠CBD?

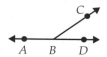

13. What is m∠DAB?

14. What is m∠DAC?

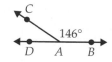

15. Angles A and C are vertical angles. If m∠A = 72°, what is m∠C?

16. Angles A and C are vertical angles. Angle A is supplementary to angle B. If m∠B = 38°, what is m∠C?

Practice Problems continue . . .

17. Name the angle that forms a vertical angle with angle *B*.

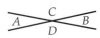

18. **MP 2, 4** A carpenter fits together two pieces of wood to form a tabletop. The wood pieces can be placed such that two adjacent angles are supplementary. If one of the adjacent angles measures 78°, what is the measure of the other adjacent angle?

19. **MP 2, 4** Hannah is making an art collage. She cuts a rectangular portrait along a diagonal line, drawn through the bottom left corner. One of the adjacent angles formed at the bottom left corner measures 50°. What is the measure of the other adjacent angle?

20. **MP 2, 4** The bottom of a chair has two intersecting, steel, cylindrical bars acting as cross-bracing. The bars form vertical angles. If the measure of one of the angles is 110°, what is the measure of its opposite angle? What are the measures of the other two angles?

21. **MP 2, 4** An architect designs a skylight. Each square windowpane has a diagonal, drawn from one corner to the opposite corner. The diagonal divides the angle of each corner into two angles of equal measure. What is the measure of the angle on either side of the diagonal?

22. Draw a pair of supplementary angles. Then, draw a pair of complementary angles. Label all angle measures.

23. Draw a diagram that includes complementary and supplementary angles. Label one angle measure and solve for all other angle measures.

24. If ∠*R* is supplementary to a 47° angle and ∠*S* is supplementary to a 56° angle, could they be vertical angles? Explain.

25. *X* is supplementary to a 135° angle, and *Y* is supplementary to a 125° angle. Could they be vertical angles? Why or why not?

26. *M* is supplementary to a 25° angle, and $m\angle N = 155°$. Could they be vertical angles? Why or why not?

27. Two lines cross, forming ∠*A*, ∠*B*, ∠*C*, and ∠*D*. ∠*A* and ∠*C* are vertical angles. If the measure of $\angle C = x^2 + 3x$ and the measure of $\angle B = 8x$, what is the measure of ∠*A*?

Exercises 28–31: Suppose angles *A* and *B* are a linear pair. Given the relationships below, find the measure of angles *A* and *B*. Round your answers to the nearest tenth of a degree.

28. $m\angle A = 5x + 15°$; $m\angle B = 8x + 28°$

29. $m\angle A = 4x + 14°$; $m\angle B = 9x + 24°$

30. $m\angle A = 4x + 16°$; $m\angle B = 5x + 10°$

31. $m\angle A = 3x + 7°$; $m\angle B = 5x + 20°$

32. A straight angle is cut into *x* congruent angles, where *x* is an integer greater than or equal to 2. Write an expression that can be used to find the total angle measure, in degrees, of any number *y* of these congruent angles. Assume $x > y$.

33. "Two parallel lines never intersect" is accepted without proof. Is this a postulate or a theorem? Explain.

34. Scientists once accepted without proof that the speed of light is not constant. For these scientists, was the belief that the speed of light could change a postulate or a theorem? Explain.

35. Prove the vertical angles theorem.
Given: Lines *k* and *m* intersect.
Prove: ∠*A* ≅ ∠*C*

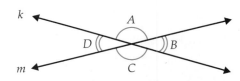

36. Given: $m\angle 1 \cong m\angle 3$; $m\angle 2 \cong m\angle 4$
Prove: $m\angle YXZ \cong m\angle BAC$

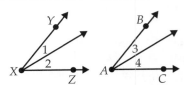

MP 1, 3, 6, 7

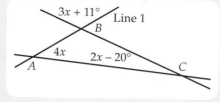

a What is the measure of angle *BCA* ? List all the steps used to determine the angle, and explain your reasoning for each step. The diagram is *not* drawn to scale.

b Line 1 is rotated 20° clockwise. Point *B* is the center of rotation. Write an algebraic expression for the angle described in the diagram as $3x + 11°$ after the rotation.

c If a rotation was applied that would increase the slope of line 1, write an expression that could replace $3x + 11°$. Justify your response.

CHAPTER 3 REVIEW

1. James says: "$\sqrt[3]{-8}$ is -2, $\sqrt[3]{-512}$ is -8. The cube roots of negative numbers must all be negative." What kind of reasoning is this?

   A. Deductive

   B. Inductive

   C. Not enough information

2. Johann says, "All rectangles have 2 pairs of congruent sides with different lengths." Which of the following would be a valid counterexample to prove that his conjecture is false?

   A. A rectangle is a parallelogram, and it has 2 pairs of parallel sides.

   B. A rectangle is a parallelogram, and it has 4 right angles.

   C. A square is a rhombus, and it has 2 pairs of congruent sides with the same length.

   D. A square is a rectangle, and it has 2 pairs of congruent sides with the same length.

3. Which of the following is a correct way to write "All math books are fun to read" as a conditional statement?

   A. Some math books are fun to read.

   B. If it is a math book, then it is fun to read.

   C. If it is fun to read, it must be a math book.

4. Which of the following is a correct way to write "All squares have four right angles" as a conditional statement?

   A. If it has four right angles, then it is a square.

   B. If it is a square, then it has four right angles.

   C. If it has four sides, then it is a square and has four right angles.

5. Which is the converse of "If you do not like ice cream, you do not like dessert"?

   A. If you like dessert, you like ice cream.

   B. If you do not like ice cream, you do not like dessert.

   C. If you like ice cream, you like dessert.

   D. If you do not like dessert, you do not like ice cream.

6. Which is the contrapositive of "If you do not like ice cream, you do not like dessert"?

   A. If you like dessert, you like ice cream.

   B. If you do not like ice cream, you do not like dessert.

   C. If you like ice cream, you like dessert.

   D. The best flavor of ice cream is mint chocolate chip.

Chapter Review continues . . .

7. Which is the inverse of, "If a number is even, then it is divisible by two"?

    A. If a number is divisible by two, then it is not even.

    B. If a number is not even, then it is not divisible by two.

    C. If a number is not divisible by two, then it is not even.

8. Equilateral triangles have 3 congruent sides. Which two conditional statements, when taken together as true, are equivalent to that definition? Select the two.

    A. If it is an equilateral triangle, then it has 3 congruent sides.

    B. If it doesn't have 3 congruent sides, then it's not an equilateral triangle.

    C. If it's not an equilateral triangle, then it doesn't have 3 congruent sides.

    D. If a triangle has 3 congruent sides, then it is an equilateral triangle.

9. Angles X and Y are both supplementary and congruent. This means they must be

    A. Vertical angles.

    B. Acute angles.

    C. Right angles.

    D. Complementary angles.

10. Angles K and P are supplementary angles. Which equation must be true?

    A. $m\angle K - m\angle P = 180°$

    B. $m\angle K = 180° - m\angle P$

    C. $m\angle K + m\angle P = 90°$

    D. $m\angle K - m\angle P = 90°$

11. If you advertise a garage sale, at least 25 buyers will come. What additional statement is needed to conclude that if you advertise a garage sale, you will make $100?

    A. If you make $100, you must have advertised your garage sale.

    B. If you make $100, at least 25 buyers came.

    C. If at least 25 buyers come, you will make $100.

12. `MP 2, 3, 4, 5`

Hours of tennis practice each week	Winning percentage on matches
0	18%
5	42%
10	63%
15	71%
20	76%

From the data in the table,

    a Make a conjecture about how a tennis player's winning percentage depends on the number of hours practiced per week.

    b Plot the points on a graph and sketch a best-fit line.

    c Find a linear equation for the line.

    d Does your graph support your conjecture? Explain.

Exercises 13–18: Determine whether each of the following statements is an example of inductive or deductive reasoning.

13. It rained every Saturday of this past month; therefore, it will rain this upcoming Saturday.

14. Only triangles have 3 sides. A shape has 3 sides; therefore, the shape is a triangle.

15. Of the 20 whales hunted in the last year, all were hunted by Logan. A whale was hunted yesterday; therefore, Logan must have hunted it.

16. Only non-vertical lines are of the form $y = mx + b$; therefore, $y = 4x - 1$ is a non-vertical line.

17. All games are fun. Basketball is a game; therefore, basketball is fun.

18. Claire claims that $a + b > a$ since $4 + 2 > 4$ and $7 + 1 > 7$.

19. Bernard says, "725 ends with a five. All numbers divisible by five either end in a zero or a five. 725 must be divisible by five." What kind of reasoning is this? Justify your answer.

Chapter Review continues . . .

20. Explain why the following two-column proof is incorrect, and then write the correct algebraic proof.

Statement	Reason
$4(5 - x) + 3 = 8$	Given
$5 - x + 3 = 2$	Multiplication property of equality
$8 - x = 2$	Simplify
$-x = -6$	Addition property of equality
$x = 6$	Multiplication property of equality

21. What are $m\angle B$, $m\angle C$, and $m\angle D$?

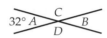

22. The measure of $\angle C$ is three times $m\angle A$. What is $m\angle B$?

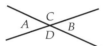

23. What is $m\angle D$?

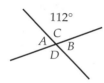

24. Find $m\angle ABE$, $m\angle ABD$, and $m\angle EBC$.

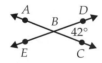

25. If A and B are complementary angles and $m\angle A = 37°$, what is the measure of angle B?

26. If A and B are complementary angles and $m\angle A = 33°$, what is the measure of angle B?

Exercises 27–30: Suppose A and B are complementary angles. Given the relationships below, find the measures of angles A and B. Round your answers to the nearest tenth of a degree.

27. $m\angle A = 7x + 3°$; $m\angle B = 2x + 10°$

28. $m\angle A = 3x + 6°$; $m\angle B = 5x + 19°$

29. $m\angle A = 4x + 5°$; $m\angle B = 5x + 2°$

30. $m\angle A = 3x + 18°$; $m\angle B = 6x + 5°$

Exercises 31–36: Determine whether the following statement is true or false. Justify your answer.

31. If A and B are complementary angles, then both A and B are acute angles. Assume no angles have a measure of $0°$.

32. If A and B are supplementary angles, then both A and B are obtuse angles. Assume no angles have a measure of $0°$.

33. If two angles form a linear pair, then they are supplementary angles.

34. If two angles are supplementary angles, then they form a linear pair.

35. How many linear pairs are formed when two non-parallel lines intersect?

36. How many linear pairs are formed when three non-parallel lines intersect at one point?

1. If P is true, then Q is true. Q is true. This means that

A. P must be true.

B. P must be false.

C. P may be true or may be false.

D. None of the above.

2. The line $y = ax + d$ is translated upward by 2 units. The translated line is described by the equation:

A. $y = (a + 2)x + d$ C. $y = ax + d + 2$

B. $y = 2x + d$ D. $y = ax + 2d$

3. $m\angle ABC = 87°$. If $m\angle ABD$ is twice $m\angle DBC$, what is $m\angle DBC$?

A. $2°$ C. $29°$

B. $17°$ D. $43.5°$

4. Which of the following is a correct way to write "All planets have elliptical orbits" as a conditional statement?

A. If something is moving in elliptical orbit, then it is a planet.

B. Only planets move in elliptical orbits.

C. If it is a planet, then it is in an elliptical orbit.

5. If you are at an altitude of over 26,000 feet, you are in the climbing Death Zone. If you are in the Death Zone, you have brain cells dying. One can conclude

A. If you have brain cells dying, you are at an altitude of over 26,000 feet.

B. If you are at an altitude of over 26,000 feet, you have brain cells dying.

C. If you are climbing in the Death Zone, you are at an altitude of over 26,000 feet.

6. If $\overline{AB} \cong \overline{BC}$ and $\overline{BC} \cong \overline{CD}$, then which of these statements must be true? The points do not necessarily lie on the same line. Choose all that apply.

A. $\overline{AB} \cong \overline{CD}$ C. $AC = BD$

B. $\overline{AC} \cong \overline{BD}$ D. $AB = AB$

7. $\angle A$ is complementary to $\angle B$. $\angle B$ is complementary to $\angle C$. $m\angle C = 25°$. What is $m\angle A$?

A. $10°$ C. $65°$

B. $25°$ D. $90°$

8. Are these two triangles congruent?

A. Yes

B. No

C. Cannot tell

9. Select all sides and angles that are congruent.

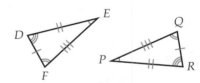

A. $\angle D \cong \angle R$ C. $\overline{EF} \cong \overline{PQ}$

B. $\angle E \cong \angle Q$ D. $\overline{FD} \cong \overline{QR}$

10. Select all sides and angles that are congruent.

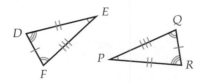

A. $\angle F \cong \angle R$ C. $\overline{DE} \cong \overline{PQ}$

B. $\angle F \cong \angle P$ D. $\overline{DE} \cong \overline{RP}$

11. Provide the dimensions of two similar right triangles that are related by a scale factor of 4.

12. Two rectangles are similar. The length of a side of the larger rectangle is 8 times the length of a corresponding side of the smaller rectangle. By what factor is the area of the larger rectangle greater than the area of the smaller rectangle?

13. **MP 6** Two rectangles are similar. The length of a side in the larger rectangle is *a* times the length of a corresponding side in the smaller rectangle. Algebraically prove the ratio of the perimeter of the larger rectangle to the perimeter of the smaller rectangle is *a* : 1.

14. $\triangle ABC \sim \triangle DEF$. Calculate the altitude of $\triangle DEF$. The altitude bisects (divides in half) the base of each triangle.

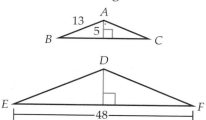

15. Two rectangles are similar, with their widths corresponding. The width of the larger rectangle is 18; the width of the smaller rectangle is 12. If the height of the smaller rectangle is 6, what is the height of the larger rectangle?

16. Two rectangles are similar, with their widths corresponding. The width of the larger rectangle is 24; the width of the smaller rectangle is 18. If the height of the taller rectangle is 36, what is the height of the smaller rectangle?

17. Using a two-column proof, show that if two congruent angles *A* and *B* form a linear pair, then *A* and *B* are right angles.

18. Two intersecting lines form two pairs of vertical angles: $\angle A$ and $\angle C$, and $\angle B$ and $\angle D$. $m\angle A$ can be represented by the expression $2x - 9$. $m\angle C$ can be represented by the expression $42 - y$. Finally, $m\angle B$ can be represented by the expression $4x + 9y$. What is $m\angle A$?

19. $\angle B$ shares one side with $\angle A$, with which it is supplementary. $\angle B$ shares its other side with $\angle C$, with which it is complementary. If the sum of the measures of $\angle A$ and $\angle C$ is 140°, what is the measure of $\angle B$?

20. Amy states, "Vertical angles are adjacent angles." Is she correct? Explain.

21. $\angle A$ is supplementary to a 143° angle, and $\angle B$ is supplementary to a 136° angle. What are $m\angle A$ and $m\angle B$?

22. $\angle R$ and $\angle S$ are vertical angles. $\angle S$ is supplementary to a 25° angle. What is $m\angle R$?

23. The point $(5, -8)$ is a vertex of a figure. The figure is dilated by a factor of 3, translated 8 units horizontally and 6 units vertically, rotated 90° clockwise, and then reflected across the *y*-axis. The origin is the center of dilation and rotation. What are the coordinates of this vertex after the transformations?

24. The point $(-5, 10)$ is a vertex of a figure. The figure is dilated by a factor of 2, translated 3 units horizontally and -5 units vertically, rotated 90° clockwise, and then reflected across the *y*-axis. The origin is the center of dilation and rotation. What are the coordinates of this vertex after the transformations?

25. Given two similar quadrilaterals, what is the scale factor relating *ABCD* to *EFGH*? Figure *ABCD* is the original figure. What is the length of $\overline{FG}$?

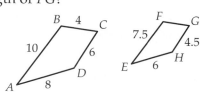

26. Two similar trapezoids are shown. What are the lengths of $\overline{EF}$, $\overline{FG}$, and $\overline{EH}$? What is the perimeter of *EFGH*?

27. $\triangle ABC$ is dilated to form $\triangle XYZ$. $\dfrac{XY}{AB} = 4$. What is $\dfrac{XZ}{AC}$?

28. $\triangle LMN$ is dilated to form $\triangle OPQ$. $\dfrac{OP}{LM} = 3$. What is $\dfrac{PQ}{MN}$?

29. What is the scale factor of the dilation from *ABCD* to *A'B'C'D'*?

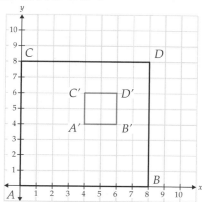

Chapter 4
Parallel and Perpendicular Lines

Chapter Content

Chapter Vocabulary

alternate exterior angle	coplanar	parallel
alternate interior angle	corollary	perpendicular bisector
auxiliary line	exterior angle	skew line
consecutive interior angle	interior angle	transversal

LESSON 4.1

4.1 Parallel Lines and Angles

Parallel and Perpendicular Lines

Two **coplanar** lines that never intersect are called parallel lines.

- In the diagram to the right, lines *a* and *b* are **parallel**, which is written $a \parallel b$.

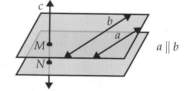

If two lines are not in the same plane and they never intersect, they are called **skew lines**.

- Lines *b* and *c* in the diagram to the right are skew lines.

Two planes that do not intersect are parallel planes.

> Lines are coplanar if they exist in the same plane.

- The planes *M* and *N* are parallel, which is expressed as $M \parallel N$.

With parallel lines defined, we can state the parallel postulate.

Parallel postulate

Given a line and a point not on the line, one, and only one, line parallel to the given line can be drawn through the point.

If *P* is not on *a*, then only one line *b* passes through *P* and is parallel to *a*.

Given a point not on a line, there exists only one line that passes through that point and is perpendicular to the first line.

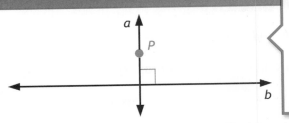

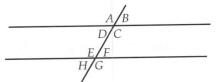

Similar to the case for parallel lines, there is also a unique perpendicular line through a given point.

If P is not on b, then only one line a that passes through P is perpendicular to b.

Corresponding Angles

We now investigate the various postulates and theorems that result from intersecting a pair of parallel lines with a transversal. A **transversal** is a line that intersects two other lines. Corresponding angles are formed by a transversal and located at the same position relative to the transversal. In other words, they are at the same location of each intersection, such as above a line and to the left of the transversal. In the diagram, the corresponding angles are the pairs A and E, B and F, C and G, and D and H.

Corresponding angles postulate

If a transversal intersects parallel lines, then all the pairs of corresponding angles are congruent.

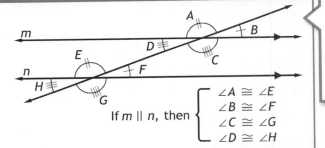

The converse of the corresponding angles postulate is also true.

If $m \parallel n$, then
$$\angle A \cong \angle E$$
$$\angle B \cong \angle F$$
$$\angle C \cong \angle G$$
$$\angle D \cong \angle H$$

MODEL PROBLEMS

1. A pair of corresponding angles created by a transversal and two lines have measures described by the expressions $2x + 3$ and $3x - 11$. If $x = 14$, the lines must be

   A. Parallel.
   B. Perpendicular.
   C. Neither parallel nor perpendicular.
   D. Not planar.

SOLUTION

The answer is A. Evaluating the expressions with $x = 14$, the result is 31 in both cases. The angles are congruent, and with congruent corresponding angles, the lines must be parallel.

Model Problems continue . . .

2. What is $m\angle H$?

SOLUTION

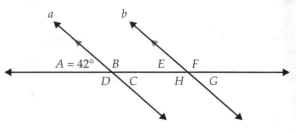

a and b are parallel lines. Angle H is a corresponding angle with D, so if we can calculate $m\angle D$, we know $m\angle H$, since the angles are congruent.

A and D are supplementary	$m\angle A + m\angle D = 180°$	A and D are linear angles, which means they are supplementary and sum to 180°. Substitute for $m\angle A$ and solve.
	$42° + m\angle D = 180°$	
	$m\angle D = 138°$	
D and H are congruent	$m\angle H = m\angle D = 138°$	The two angles are corresponding angles and the lines are parallel, so $m\angle H = m\angle D = 138°$.

Alternate Interior and Exterior Angles

A transversal crosses two lines. **Alternate interior angles** are *inside the parallel lines* on opposite sides of the transversal. C and E are alternate interior angles, as are D and F. They are interior to (inside) the parallel lines and on alternate (different) sides of the transversal.

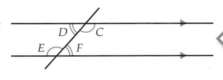

> The pair of orange arrowheads indicate parallel lines.

Alternate interior angles theorem

If a transversal intersects parallel lines, then all of the pairs of alternate interior angles are congruent.

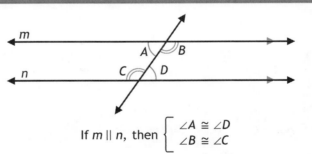

If $m \parallel n$, then $\begin{cases} \angle A \cong \angle D \\ \angle B \cong \angle C \end{cases}$

Alternate exterior angles are *outside the parallel lines*, on opposite sides of the transversal. A and G are alternate exterior angles, as are B and H. They are exterior to (outside) the parallel lines and on alternate (different) sides of the transversal.

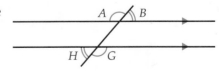

Alternate exterior angles theorem

If a transversal intersects parallel lines, then all of the pairs of alternate exterior angles are congruent.

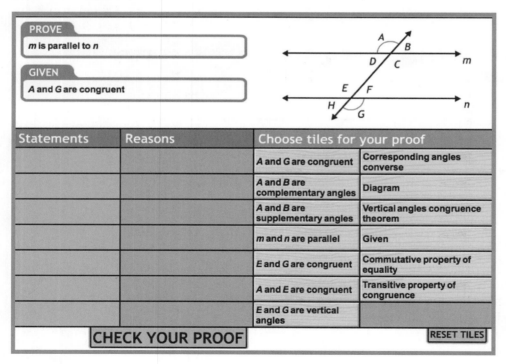

If $m \parallel n$, then
$$\begin{cases} \angle A \cong \angle D \\ \angle B \cong \angle C \end{cases}$$

Instead of stating that corresponding angles are congruent (when a transversal intersects parallel lines) as a postulate, we could state it as a theorem. To do this, assume that the alternate exterior angles theorem is a postulate. We use a paragraph proof to prove the theorem.

Paragraph Proof

With alternate exterior angles stated as a postulate, we have one set of angles shown to be congruent. Alternate interior angles would then be congruent too, since they are vertical angles to the alternate exterior angles, and vertical angles are congruent. The other pairs of corresponding angles would have to be congruent since they are supplementary to congruent angles.

In this activity, prove the alternate exterior angles theorem converse by proving that lines m and n are parallel.

PROVE

m is parallel to n

GIVEN

A and G are congruent

Statements	Reasons	Choose tiles for your proof	
		A and G are congruent	Corresponding angles converse
		A and B are complementary angles	Diagram
		A and B are supplementary angles	Vertical angles congruence theorem
		m and n are parallel	Given
		E and G are congruent	Commutative property of equality
		A and E are congruent	Transitive property of congruence
		E and G are vertical angles	

CHECK YOUR PROOF   RESET TILES

MODEL PROBLEMS

1. **MP 7** In the diagram, angles A and F have no direct relationship. What is $m\angle F$?

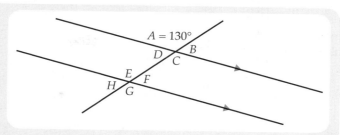

SOLUTION

Look for angle that relates to F	Start the problem by looking for an angle with a known relationship to F. For instance, B and F are corresponding angles, so if B is known, then F can be calculated.

A and B are supplementary	$m\angle A + m\angle B = 180°$ $130° + m\angle B = 180°$ $m\angle B = 50°$	A and B are supplementary angles. Use an equation that says the angles sum to 180° and solve for $m\angle B$.
B and F are corresponding angles	$\angle B \cong \angle F$ $m\angle B = m\angle F = 50°$	Since the two angles are congruent, they have the same measure.

2. **MP 1** $m\angle A$ is 50% greater than $m\angle D$. What is $m\angle F$?

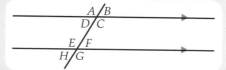

SOLUTION

Relationship of A and D	$m\angle A = 1.5(m\angle D)$	$m\angle A$ is 50% greater than $m\angle D$. This means $m\angle A$ equals 1.5 times $m\angle D$.
Calculate D	$m\angle A + m\angle D = 180°$	Angles A and D are supplementary, so they sum to 180°.
Write equation	$1.5(m\angle D) + m\angle D = 180°$	Replace $m\angle A$ with $1.5m\angle D$.
Solve	$2.5(m\angle D) = 180°$ $m\angle D = 72°$	Solve for $m\angle D$ by combining like terms, and then dividing both sides by 2.5.
D and F are alternate interior angles	$\angle F \cong \angle D$ $m\angle F = m\angle D = 72°$	D and F are congruent since they are alternate interior angles.

Consecutive Interior Angles

Consecutive interior angles are angles on the same side of the transversal and between the lines. In the diagram, D and E are consecutive interior angles, and C and F are consecutive interior angles.

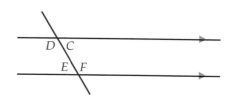

Consecutive interior angles theorem

If a transversal intersects parallel lines, then all pairs of consecutive interior angles are supplementary.

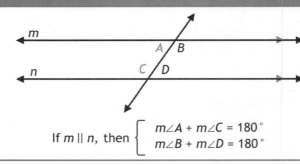

If $m \parallel n$, then $\begin{cases} m\angle A + m\angle C = 180° \\ m\angle B + m\angle D = 180° \end{cases}$

> The consecutive interior angles theorem is also known as the same side interior angles theorem.

MODEL PROBLEMS

1. What is $m\angle E$?

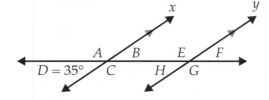

SOLUTION

Look for a relationship between E and D. B is the connection between D and E.

Vertical angles $m\angle B = m\angle D = 35°$ Angles B and D are vertical angles, and therefore congruent.

Consecutive interior angles are supplementary

$m\angle B + m\angle E = 180°$

$m\angle D + m\angle E = 180°$

Substitute D for B in the relationship of consecutive interior angles.

Solve $35° + m\angle E = 180°$ Complete the calculation.

$m\angle E = 145°$

2. Prove the converse of the corresponding angles postulate: If two lines and a transversal form corresponding angles that are congruent, then the lines are parallel.

Prove: $a \parallel b$
Given: $\angle D \cong \angle H$

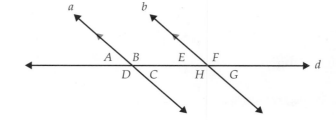

SOLUTION

Statement	Reason
$\angle D \cong \angle H$	Given
$m\angle D + m\angle C = 180°$	Angles D and C are a linear pair
$m\angle H + m\angle C = 180°$	Substitution
$a \parallel b$	Consecutive interior angles theorem

PRACTICE

1. Non-coplanar lines that never intersect are called

   A. Parallel.
   B. Perpendicular.
   C. Transversal.
   D. Skew.

2. Lines j and k are skew. Which of these is true? Choose all that apply.

   A. j and k intersect.
   B. j and k do not intersect.
   C. j and k are in the same plane.
   D. j and k are in different planes.
   E. j and k are parallel.

3. On a plane, point A doesn't lie on the line a. Three new lines are drawn through point A. How many of these lines could intersect a?

   A. Only one
   B. Only two
   C. All three
   D. Zero

4. On a plane, point A doesn't lie on line b. Three new, distinct lines are drawn through point A. How many of these lines could be perpendicular to line b?

   A. One could be
   B. One or two could be
   C. All three could be

5. Point A is not on line j. How many lines pass through A and are perpendicular to j?

   A. 0   C. 2
   B. 1   D. An infinite number

6. Which of these are pairs of corresponding angles? Choose all that apply.

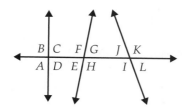

   A. A and B D. A and H
   B. A and C E. A and I
   C. A and E

7. $\angle 3 + \angle 5 = 148°$. Determine the measure of $\angle 2$.

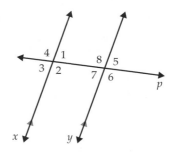

   A. 32°   C. 74°
   B. 106°   D. 148°

8. Angles A and G are

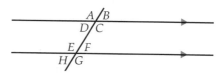

   A. Consecutive interior angles.
   B. Alternate interior angles.
   C. Alternate exterior angles.
   D. Corresponding angles.

9. Choose all true statements that apply to the diagram below.

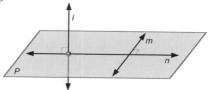

   A. Lines l and m are skew lines.
   B. Lines l and m are perpendicular.
   C. Lines l and n are perpendicular.
   D. Lines l, m, and n are in the same plane, P.
   E. Lines m and n are skew lines.
   F. Lines m and n are perpendicular.
   G. Lines l and n are parallel.
   H. Lines m and n are in the same plane, P.

Practice Problems continue . . .

10. The lines *m* and *n* are intersected by a transversal *d*. List all pairs of corresponding angles formed in the diagram below.

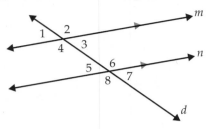

11. In the diagram below, if $m\angle 6 = 100°$, what is the measure of $\angle 2$?

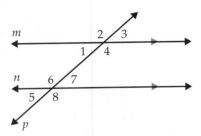

12. The lines *IJ* and *KL* are parallel. Use the diagram below to answer the questions.

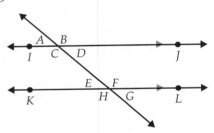

   a List all the pairs of alternate interior angles.

   b List all the pairs of alternate exterior angles.

   c If $m\angle D = 40°$, what is the measure of $\angle E$?

   d If $m\angle B = 145°$, what is the measure of $\angle H$?

13. **MP 2** When two parallel lines are intersected by a transversal, one of the angles formed is equal to 150°. Make a sketch, labeling all the angles formed. Then find the measures of all the angles in your diagram.

14. $m\angle FPM = 34°$. Find the measure of $\angle NMP$.

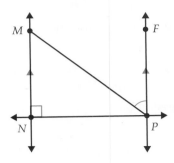

15. Lines *x* and *y* are parallel. If $m\angle C = 120°$, what is $m\angle F$?

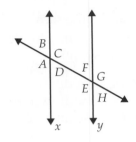

16. **MP 2, 3** The lines *a*, *b*, *c*, and *p* are coplanar. *a* is perpendicular to *p*, *b* is perpendicular to *p*, and *c* intersects *a*. Do lines *b* and *c* intersect? Make a sketch and explain your answer.

17. **MP 2, 4** 5th and 10th Avenues are parallel; K Street runs parallel to J Street. Lincoln Way is perpendicular to 10th Avenue. K Street and Lincoln Way make an angle of 39°, and 5th Avenue and J Street make an angle of 129°.

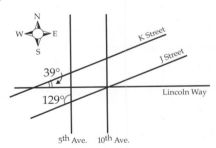

   a Amid is going northeast on J Street and turning left on Lincoln Way. By what angle does he need to turn?

   b Rachel goes north on 10th Avenue and needs to turn right onto K Street. By what angle does she need to turn?

Practice Problems continue . . .

Practice Problems continued . . .

18. **MP 3** In the diagram below, line *m* intersects the sides of the angle *M* at the points *A* and *B*. Can both $\overrightarrow{MA}$ and $\overrightarrow{MB}$ be perpendicular to line *m*? Use the perpendicular postulate to explain your answer.

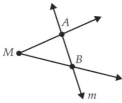

19. **MP 3** $m\angle 2 + m\angle 8 = 46°$. Find the measures of all angles in the diagram below. Show your work.

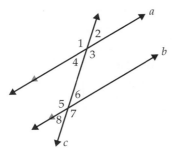

Exercises 20–22: Lines *x* and *y* are parallel.

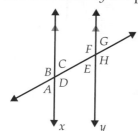

20. $m\angle B$ is 4 times $m\angle A$. What is $m\angle F$?

21. $m\angle B$ is 3 times $m\angle A$. What is $m\angle F$?

22. List all pairs of consecutive interior angles.

23. The parallel lines *a* and *b* are intersected by a transversal *c*.

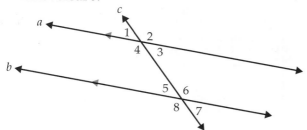

   a If $\angle 2 = 108°$, what is the measure of $\angle 5$?
   b If $\angle 3 = 45°$, what is the measure of $\angle 8$?
   c If $\angle 1 = 82°$, what is the measure of $\angle 6$?
   d If $\angle 7 = 29°$, what is the measure of $\angle 1$?

24.

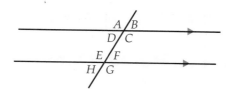

   a What is $m\angle C$, if $m\angle F = 110°$?
   b Calculate the sum of $m\angle D$ and $m\angle E$.

25. **MP 3** The lines *a* and *b* intersect. Selena says she can draw a third line, *c*, that is parallel to both *a* and *b*. Is Selena right? Explain why or why not.

26. In a triangle *ABC*, how many lines passing through the point *C* can be drawn so they are parallel to the side $\overline{AB}$? Make a sketch and use the parallel postulate to explain your answer.

27. Lines *a*, *b*, and *c* are coplanar. The lines *a* and *b* are both perpendicular to line *c*. Show that *a* is parallel to *b*. Make a sketch to explain your answer. Hint: Suppose that line *a* is not parallel to line *b*, and use the perpendicular postulate to show that this leads to a contradiction.

28. **MP 3, 4** The system of three weights is balanced as shown. All vertical strings are parallel. Show that $m\angle A + m\angle B = m\angle C$.

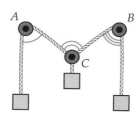

Exercises 29–32: Use the diagram below to answer the questions.

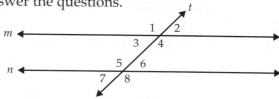

29. Prove: $\angle 3 \cong \angle 6$; $\angle 4 \cong \angle 5$
   Given: $m \parallel n$

30. Prove: $m \parallel n$
   Given: $\angle 3 \cong \angle 6$

31. Prove: $m\angle 3 + m\angle 5 = 180°$;
   $m\angle 4 + m\angle 6 = 180°$
   Given: $m \parallel n$

32. Prove: $m \parallel n$
   Given: $m\angle 3 + m\angle 5 = 180°$

4.2 More on Parallel Lines and Angles

Angle Relationships

We prove alternate exterior angles are congruent when a transversal intersects two parallel lines.

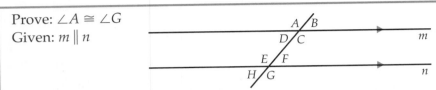

	Prove: $\angle A \cong \angle G$ Given: $m \parallel n$		

Statement	Reason	
$m \parallel n$	Given	We were told that m and n are parallel.
$\angle A \cong \angle E$	Corresponding angles postulate	Since A and E are corresponding angles, the corresponding angles postulate says they are congruent.
$\angle E \cong \angle G$	Vertical angles congruence theorem	Since E and G are vertical angles, they are congruent.
$\angle A \cong \angle G$	Transitive property of congruence	The transitive property of congruence tells us that if $\angle A \cong \angle E$ and $\angle E \cong \angle G$, then $\angle A \cong \angle G$.

 In this activity, you prove the alternate interior angles theorem.

PROVE			Choose tiles for your proof	
$D \cong F$				
GIVEN				
m is parallel to n				

Statements	Reasons	Choose tiles for your proof	
		D is congruent to F	commutative property of equality
		m and n are parallel	given
		H and F are vertical angles	vertical angles theorem
		D and H are corresponding angles	corresponding angles postulate
		H is congruent to F	diagram
		A and B are complementary angles	transitive property of congruence
		D is congruent to H	diagram
		A and B are supplementary angles	

CHECK YOUR PROOF   RESET TILES

MODEL PROBLEM

Find the measures of all the angles. The measure of angle G is 65°. Show two different ways to solve for the angles.

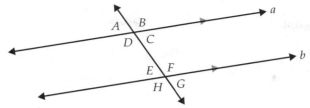

SOLUTION

Method 1

Calculate corresponding angles	$m\angle C = m\angle G = 65°$	$\angle C$ and $\angle G$ are corresponding, so they are congruent.
Calculate supplementary angles	$m\angle C + m\angle D = 180°$ $65° + m\angle D = 180°$ $m\angle D = 115°$	$\angle C$ and $\angle D$ are supplementary, so calculate $m\angle D$.
Calculate supplementary angles	$m\angle G + m\angle H = 180°$ $65° + m\angle H = 180°$ $m\angle H = 115°$	Calculate another angle using a supplementary angle.
Calculate vertical angles	$m\angle A = m\angle C = m\angle E = m\angle G = 65°$ $m\angle B = m\angle D = m\angle F = m\angle H = 115°$	Fill in the other angles.

Method 2

Use alternate exterior angles	$m\angle G = m\angle A = 65°$	$\angle G$ and $\angle A$ are alternate exterior angles, so they are congruent.
Use vertical angles	$m\angle A = m\angle C = 65°$ $m\angle E = m\angle G = 65°$	There are two pairs of vertical angles.
Use supplementary angles	$m\angle A + m\angle B = 180°$ $m\angle C + m\angle D = 180°$ $m\angle E + m\angle F = 180°$ $m\angle G + m\angle H = 180°$	Use four pairs of supplementary angles.
Calculate supplementary angles	$65° + m\angle B = 180°$ $m\angle B = 115°$ $m\angle B = m\angle D = m\angle F = m\angle H = 115°$	We show how we calculate one angle. The remaining angles would be calculated the same way.

Parallel Lines and Angles

Earlier, we stated a postulate: If two parallel lines are intersected by a transversal, then the corresponding angles are congruent. The converse is true: If the corresponding angles are congruent, then the lines are parallel. Since converses are not always true, we must carefully determine their validity.

Corresponding angles postulate converse

If the lines intersected by a transversal form congruent corresponding angles, then the lines intersected by the transversal are parallel.

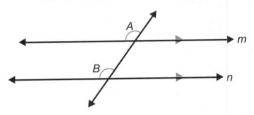

If ∠A is ≅ ∠B, then m∥n.

This postulate lets us write a series of theorem converses:

Angle and parallel line theorem converses

Alternate interior angles converse
If alternate interior angles are congruent, then the lines intersected by the transversal are parallel.

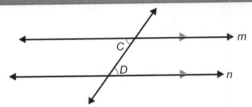

If ∠C ≅ ∠D, then m∥n.

Alternate exterior angles converse
If alternate exterior angles are congruent, then the lines intersected by the transversal are parallel.

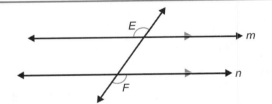

If ∠E ≅ ∠F, then m∥n.

Consecutive interior angles converse
If consecutive interior angles are supplementary, then the lines intersected by the transversal are parallel.

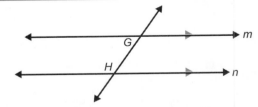

If m∠G + m∠H = 180°, then m ∥ n.

MODEL PROBLEMS

1. **MP 3, 6**

   a If $\angle C \cong \angle F$, which lines must be parallel? Explain.

   b If $\angle B \cong \angle D$, which lines must be parallel? Explain.

   c If $m\angle B + m\angle F = 180°$, which lines must be parallel?

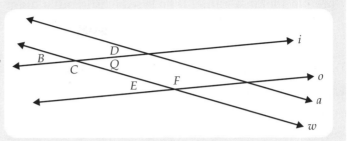

SOLUTION

a $i \parallel o$ because of the alternate interior angles theorem converse. This is a pair of alternate interior angles, with line w being the transversal. Since the angles are congruent, the lines the transversal intersects are parallel: $i \parallel o$.

b $w \parallel a$ because of the corresponding angles theorem converse. This is a pair of corresponding angles, with line i being the transversal. Since the angles are congruent, the lines the transversal intersects are parallel: $w \parallel a$.

c Since $m\angle B + m\angle F = 180°$ then lines i and o must be parallel, because angle B is a vertical angle with angle Q that is a consecutive interior angle to F, making F and Q supplementary.

2. **MP 6** What do the angle measures have to equal for the lines to be parallel?

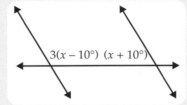

SOLUTION

If the lines are parallel, the angles must be supplementary	$3(x - 10°) + (x + 10°) = 180°$	The two angles whose measures are given by algebraic expressions are consectuve interior angles. Their measures must sum to 180° if the lines are parallel.
Solve equation	$3x - 30° + x + 10° = 180°$ $4x - 20° = 180°$ $x = 50°$	Distribute the 3. Combine like terms, and then solve for x.
Use value of x in expressions	$3(x - 10°) = 3(50° - 10°) = 120°$ $x + 10° = 50° + 10° = 60°$ Angle measures = 120° and 60°	Substitute the value of x into the expressions for the angles. Check the calculations: The angle measures sum to 180°.

Model Problems continue . . .

3. **MP 2, 5, 7** A designer is trying to ensure that levels 1 and 2 are parallel in a game. If he is sketching out a diagram for the factory, how might he do so?

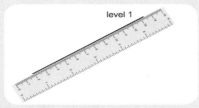

SOLUTION

Construct level 1 using a straightedge

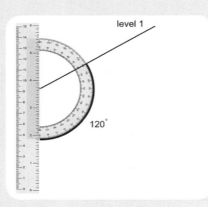

The designer can use a postulate concerning corresponding angles and parallel lines, as well as a protractor and straightedge. Use the straightedge—a ruler, in this case—to draw a line segment that represents level 1.

Construct an angle using a protractor

Place the straightedge to the left of level 1 and measure the angle with a protractor. This particular angle is 120°.

Construct a corresponding angle using a protractor

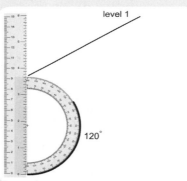

Move the protractor down along the straightedge, and measure a corresponding angle of 120°.

Construct level 2 using the corresponding angles postulate converse

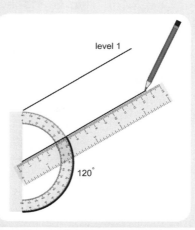

Using a straightedge, construct level 2 at the 120° mark on the protractor. Since the corresponding angles are congruent, the levels are parallel.

PRACTICE

1. If $m\angle 1 = 146°$, what must the sum of the angles 4 and 6 be so the lines a and b are parallel?

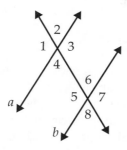

A. 17° C. 68°

B. 34° D. 146°

2. What is the measure of angle F?

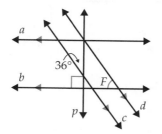

A. 36° C. 126°

B. 54° D. 144°

3. Two lines are intersected by a transversal. Which of the following conditions must be true so the lines are parallel?

I. Alternate interior angles are congruent.

II. The sum of corresponding angles is 180°.

III. Interior consecutive angles are congruent.

IV. Interior consecutive angles are supplementary.

A. I only

B. I and III only

C. I and II and IV only

D. I and IV only

4. If the lines a and b are parallel, and $m\angle 3$ is 40% greater than $m\angle 4$, what is $m\angle 8$?

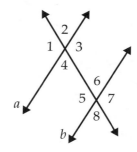

A. 74° C. 105°

B. 75° D. 106°

5. In the diagram below, the lines a, b, and c are intersected by a transversal d. Which lines must be parallel? The diagram is not drawn to scale.

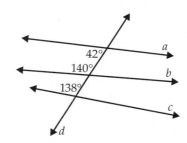

A. a and b

B. a and c

C. b and c

D. None of the above

6. Two parallel lines are intersected by a transversal. One of the angles formed is 70°. Can any of the other angles be equal to 30°?

A. Yes

B. No

C. Not enough information to decide

Practice Problems continue . . .

7. In the diagram below, $m\angle3 = m\angle4 = 128°$, $m\angle5 = 52°$. Which lines must be parallel? The diagram is not drawn to scale.

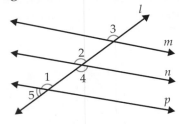

A. *m* and *n* only
B. *n* and *p* only
C. *m*, *n*, and *p* are all parallel
D. No parallel lines on the diagram

8. According to the congruent angles marked in the diagram below, which lines must be parallel?

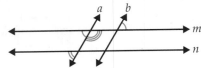

A. *a* and *b*
B. *m* and *n*
C. All of the above
D. None of the above

9. According to the congruent angles marked in the diagram below, which lines must be parallel?

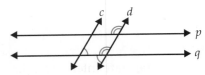

A. *c* and *d*
B. *p* and *q*
C. All of the above
D. None of the above

10. Suppose $m\angle G$ is known. Which of the following techniques could be used to find $m\angle A$? Choose all that apply.

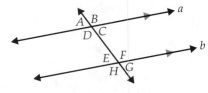

A. Alternate exterior angles to find *A*.
B. Vertical angles to find *E*, then corresponding angles to find *A*.
C. Alternate interior angles to find *F*, then vertical angles to find *A*.
D. Consecutive interior angles to find *D*, then corresponding angles to find *A*.

Exercises 11–12: Solve for *x*.

11.

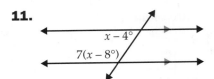

12.

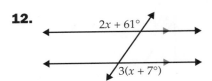

Exercises 13–16: In the diagram, the lines *x* and *y* are parallel.

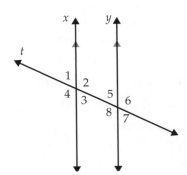

13. If $m\angle4 = 124°$, find all other angles.

14. If $m\angle6 + m\angle4 = 250°$, find $m\angle7$.

15. If $m\angle3$ is 72° less than $m\angle8$, find $m\angle2$.

16. If $m\angle6$ is 5 times $m\angle1$, find $m\angle4$.

Practice Problems continue . . .

Exercises 17–20: Use the diagram to answer the questions.

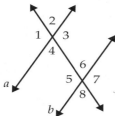

17. $m\angle 2 = 45°$ and $m\angle 7$ is three times $m\angle 4$. Are the lines a and b parallel? Why or why not?

18. $\angle 2$ measures 68°. What must the measure of angle 5 be so the lines a and b are parallel?

19. $\angle 3$ measures 100°. What must the measure of angle 8 be so the lines a and b are parallel?

20. If $m\angle 1 = x + 1$ and $m\angle 6 = 2x + 2$, what must $m\angle 5$ be so the lines a and b are parallel?

21. **MP 3** Using the diagram, prove the alternate interior angles theorem converse.

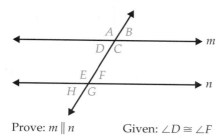

Prove: $m \parallel n$ Given: $\angle D \cong \angle F$

22. Explain how you would prove that if the alternate interior angles formed by two lines and a transversal are not congruent, then the two lines intersect.

23. Are lines m and n parallel? Justify your answer.

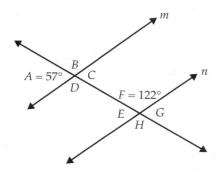

24. **MP 2, 3** $\angle ABC$ is equal to 60°. $\angle BCD$ is equal to 120°. Dilmah made a sketch and said $\overleftrightarrow{AB}$ and $\overleftrightarrow{CD}$ must be parallel, since $120° + 60° = 180°$. Toshi also sketched the angles and said $\overleftrightarrow{AB}$ and $\overleftrightarrow{CD}$ intersect. Try to create both the sketches Dilmah and Toshi could have made and explain who is right.

25. **MP 2, 4** The sketch shows Jen's favorite chair from the side. The black segments represent the backrest, seat, and one of the legs of the chair. The gray segments represent one of the chair's arms.

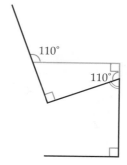

a Are the chair's arms parallel to the chair's seat? Why or why not?

b Jen likes to sit with her arms parallel to her thighs, so she decides to put a pillow under her hands. Finding the angle by which she needs to raise her arms will help Jen to figure out how thick the pillow should be. What must that angle be?

26. Two parallel lines are intersected by a transversal. Prove that angle bisectors (lines dividing an angle into two adjacent congruent angles) of the alternate interior angles are parallel to each other. Make a sketch and label the angles, referring to them in your proof.

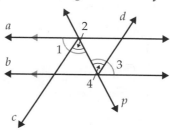

Practice Problems continue . . .

27. Prove the alternate exterior angles postulate converse: If alternate exterior angles are congruent, then the lines intersected by the transversal are parallel.

Prove: $m \parallel n$
Given: $\angle 1 \cong \angle 8$

28. Using the diagram provided and the knowledge that $\angle 3 \cong \angle 10$ and $\angle 1 \cong \angle 6$, prove that $\angle 15 \cong \angle 13$. Hint: First prove line a is parallel to line b. Then prove line c is parallel to line d.

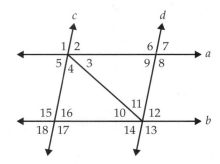

• Multi-Part PROBLEM Practice •

MP 2, 4 Use the diagram to answer the questions. 136th Avenue is parallel to 130th Avenue.

a Is Jefferson Boulevard parallel to 136th Avenue? Why or why not?

b A lightrail track is planned to be built south from the intersection of Jefferson Boulevard and Sunset Way. What should the measure of the acute angle between the train route and Sunset Way be so the tracks run parallel to 136th Avenue?

c What would be the measure of the acute angle between the lightrail route and Lark Street?

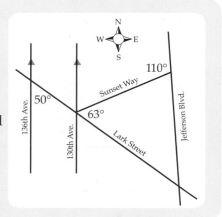

LESSON 4.3

4.3 Perpendicular Lines

Pairs of Perpendicular Lines

In this lesson, we build on our knowledge of theorems related to parallel and perpendicular lines.

Perpendicular lines and right angles theorem

If two lines are perpendicular, then they intersect to form four right angles.

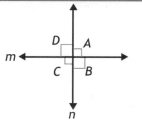

If $m \perp n$, then $\angle A$, $\angle B$, $\angle C$, and $\angle D$ are right angles.

This is a theorem about perpendicular lines and their relationship to right angles. The symbol for perpendicular lines is an upside-down T: $\perp$

Lines perpendicular to a transversal theorem

If two lines in a plane are perpendicular to the same line, then they are parallel to one another.

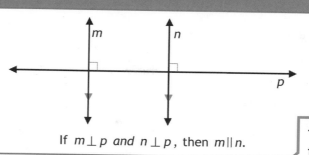

If $m \perp p$ and $n \perp p$, then $m \| n$.

These two theorems are about perpendicular transversals.

Perpendicular transversal theorem

If a transversal is perpendicular to one of a pair of parallel lines, then it is perpendicular to the other parallel line.

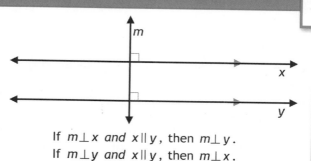

If $m \perp x$ and $x \| y$, then $m \perp y$.
If $m \perp y$ and $x \| y$, then $m \perp x$.

Prove: $m \perp y$

We prove the perpendicular transversal theorem.

Statement	Reason	
$x \| y$ $m \perp x$	Diagram	The diagram tells us that lines x and y are parallel, and that line m is perpendicular to line x.
$m\angle A = 90°$	Definition of perpendicular lines	By the definition of perpendicular lines, we know that $\angle A$ is a right angle, and therefore its measure must be 90°.
$m\angle A = m\angle B = 90°$	Angles A and B are corresponding angles $\angle A \cong \angle B$ $m\angle A = m\angle B = 90°$	Angles A and B are congruent, because they are corresponding angles of parallel lines. So they have the same measure, 90°.
$\angle B$ is a right angle	Definition of right angle	Since angle B has a measure of 90°, angle B is a right angle by definition.
$m \perp y$	Definition of perpendicular lines	Finally, by definition of perpendicular lines, line m is perpendicular to line y, and we have proved our theorem.

1. **a** Is p parallel to q?

   b Is p perpendicular to r?

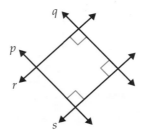

SOLUTION

a Yes, because of the lines perpendicular to a transversal theorem. The theorem states that if two lines (such as lines p and q) are perpendicular to the same line (such as line s), then they are parallel to each other.

b Yes, because of the perpendicular transversal theorem. The theorem states that if two lines (such as r and s) are perpendicular to one of a pair of parallel lines (line q), then they are perpendicular to the other (line p).

2. Prove: $o \perp m$

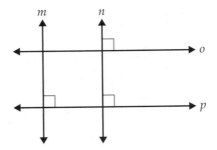

SOLUTION

Statement	Reason	
$p \perp m$	Diagram	This is shown in the diagram.
$o \parallel p$	Lines perpendicular to a transversal theorem	Two lines, o and p, perpendicular to the same line, n, are parallel.
$o \perp m$	Perpendicular transversal theorem	Since m is perpendicular to p, one of two parallel lines, m is also perpendicular to o, the other parallel line.

Construction: Perpendicular and Parallel Lines

We construct a **perpendicular bisector**, a perpendicular line that divides a line segment in half. To do so, we do two things at the same time.

(1) We construct a line perpendicular to our original line using a compass and a straightedge.

(2) We bisect (divide into two equal parts) the line segment defined by the two points on the line in the first step.

Constructing a perpendicular line with a compass:

1. Start with two points on line.

2. Draw an arc. Keep the compass wider than distance halfway between the points. Put one end of the compass on a point and draw an arc with the other.

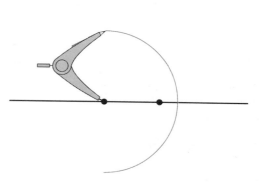

3. Draw another arc from second point. Keep compass open same amount.

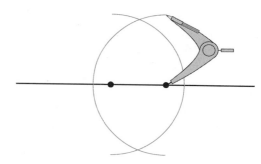

4. Connect intersection points of arc. Use a straightedge.

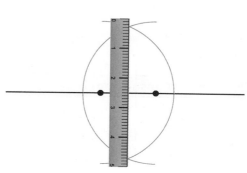

We can also construct a line that is perpendicular to our original line and that passes through a given point not on the original line:

1. Place compass at point. Draw arc through line.

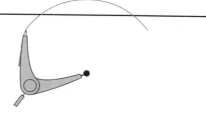

2. Mark two intersection points. Create two arcs using points on line. Follow same steps as shown above.

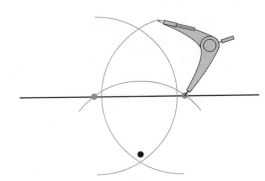

3. Connect intersection points of arcs. Use a straightedge.

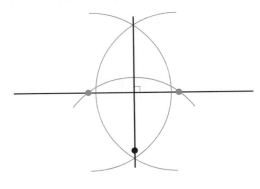

Why did the construction above create perpendicular lines? (We added to our construction diagram for our proof.)

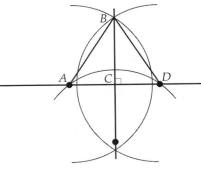

An intersecting line that forms right angles is perpendicular to another line, so this proof explains the geometry behind the construction.

Statement	Reason	
$\overline{AC} \cong \overline{DC}$ and $\overline{AB} \cong \overline{DB}$	Each pair was drawn with same compass setting	Both pairs of segments are congruent.
$\overline{BC} \cong \overline{BC}$	Reflexive property	The two triangles share this side.
$\triangle ABC \cong \triangle DBC$	SSS congruence	The triangles have three pairs of congruent sides. (We discuss SSS in depth in the next chapter.)
$\angle ACB \cong \angle DCB$	Definition of congruence	They are two corresponding angles in congruent triangles.
$\angle ACB$, $\angle DCB$ are right angles	They are linear pair and congruent.	The measures of linear pair angles sum to 180° and the angles are congruent. Only 90° angles match this description.

We want to use construction to create two parallel lines. To do this, we start by constructing two perpendicular lines.

1. Start with a perpendicular line. Follow the same steps as shown above.

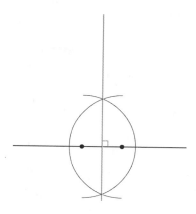

2. Construct another perpendicular line. Line is parallel to original line.

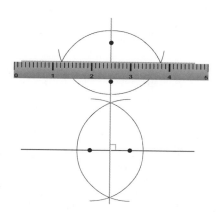

Finally, we construct a parallel line through a point, C:

1. Connect point C and line using straightedge. Lines intersect at D.

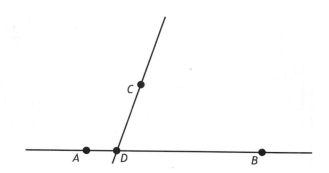

2. Create two arcs. Set compass width greater than halfway between points C and D, but smaller than the distance between C and D. Draw arcs with compass placed at C and D.

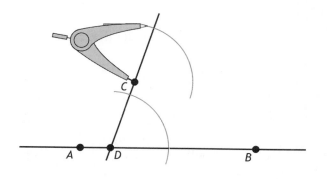

3. Draw two small arcs. Set compass width to lower previously drawn arc. Draw arcs with compass placed at intersection points of the previously drawn arcs and the construction line. Label intersection point *E*.

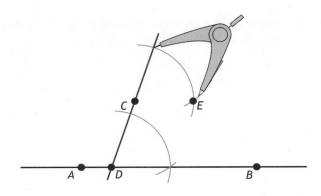

4. Draw parallel line, $\overleftrightarrow{CE}$. Use a straightedge.

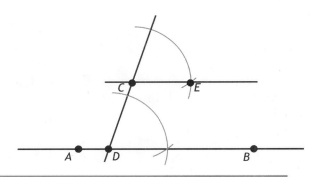

Why does the above construction create a parallel line?

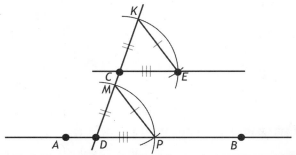

Statement	Reason	
$\overline{KC} \cong \overline{MD}$ and $\overline{CE} \cong \overline{DP}$ and $\overline{KE} \cong \overline{MP}$	Each pair was drawn with same compass setting	Each connects points drawn with same compass setting.
$\triangle KCD \cong \triangle MDP$	SSS congruence	Three pairs of corresponding sides are congruent. (We discuss SSS in depth in the next chapter.)
$\angle KCE \cong \angle MDP$	Definition of congruence	They are two corresponding angles in congruent triangles.
$\overline{CD}$ is a transversal	Diagram	Given in the diagram.
$\angle KCE$ and $\angle MDP$ are corresponding angles	Diagram	They occupy corresponding positions relative to the lines.
Lines are parallel	Corresponding angles are congruent	Since the corresponding angles are congruent, the lines must be parallel.

Distance and Perpendicular Lines

The distance between a point and a line is the shortest distance between the point and the line. That distance is the length of the perpendicular segment from the point to the line.

MODEL PROBLEM

What is the distance between the point and the line?

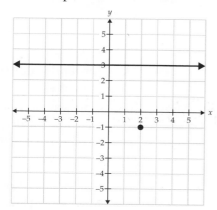

SOLUTION

Draw perpendicular segment

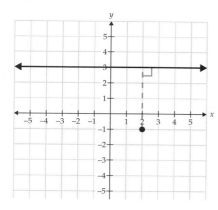

Use ruler postulate

$$\text{distance} = |y_2 - y_1|$$
$$\text{distance} = |-1 - 3| = 4$$

PRACTICE

1. Lines a and b are parallel. Line c forms an angle of 91° with line a. Choose the true statement.

   A. b is parallel to c.
   B. c is perpendicular to b.
   C. None of the above.

2. If the angle between the lines a and b is 89°, and c is parallel to b, then

   A. a is perpendicular to c.
   B. c is parallel to a.
   C. b is perpendicular to a.
   D. None of the above.

Practice Problems continue . . .

3. Which two lines must be parallel?

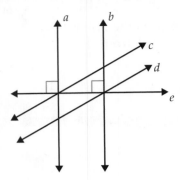

A. *c* and *d*

B. *a* and *e*

C. *a* and *b*

4. What is the distance between point *M* and line *c*?

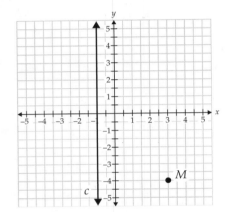

A. 3

B. 4

C. 5

D. −4

5. If line *c* is perpendicular to one of a pair of perpendicular lines, and all lines are coplanar, then

A. *c* is perpendicular to the other line of the pair.

B. *c* is parallel to the other line of the pair.

C. *c* is parallel to both lines.

D. None of the above.

6. If point *P* is 8 units away from the *y*-axis, which of these coordinates may represent the point *P*?

A. (2, 8)   C. (−8, 3)

B. (−6, −8)   D. (4, 4)

7. How do we know that lines *g* and *h* are parallel?

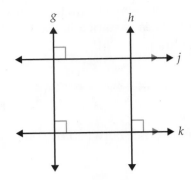

A. Given in the diagram

B. Perpendicular transversal theorem: *g* and *h* perpendicular to *j*

C. Lines perpendicular to a transversal theorem: *g* and *h* perpendicular to *k*

D. Perpendicular transversal theorem: *g* and *h* perpendicular to *k*

8. Lines *m* and *n* are perpendicular. Which of the following statements must be true? Choose all that apply.

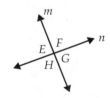

A. Angles *E*, *F*, *G*, and *H* are right angles.

B. $\angle E \cong \angle F$

C. Angles *E* and *F* are supplementary angles.

D. Angles *E* and *G* are vertical angles.

9. What is the distance between the point and the line?

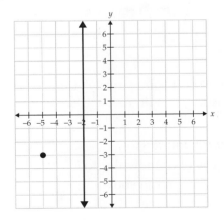

Practice Problems continue . . .

10. **MP 3** Given that $m \parallel n$ and $p \perp m$, prove that $p \perp n$.

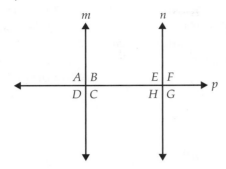

11. **MP 2, 3** Prove that the angle bisectors of adjacent supplementary angles are perpendicular to each other.

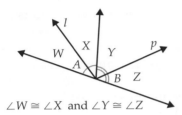

$\angle W \cong \angle X$ and $\angle Y \cong \angle Z$

12. On a plane, a is perpendicular to b, b is parallel to c, and n is perpendicular to a. Is line n perpendicular to c? Explain your answer.

Exercises 13–17: In the diagram, the measure of angle GDK is 35°, $c \perp a$, $d \perp e$, $a \parallel b$, and $e \parallel f$.

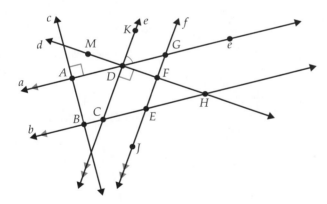

13. List all pairs of perpendicular lines.

14. What is the measure of $\angle GDM$?

15. Find the measure of $\angle BCD$.

16. Find the measure of $\angle EHF$.

17. What is the measure of $\angle CEJ$?

18. When two parallel lines are intersected by a transversal, the alternate exterior angles add up to 180°. What could be said about the angle between the lines and the transversal? Why?

19. Find the distance between the point $(-5, -3)$ and the x-axis.

20. Find the distance between the point $(-7, -5)$ and the x-axis.

21. Find the distance between the point $(-0.57, -21)$ and the y-axis.

22. Find the distance between the point $(-0.54, -7)$ and the y-axis.

23. Find the distance between the point A and the line a.

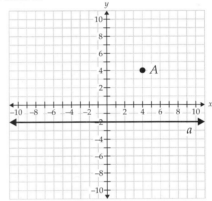

24. Cori says that the distance from a point (x, y) to the y-axis is the point's x-coordinate. Using the point $(-4, -3)$, explain whether Cori's statement is correct.

25. The coordinates of point M are $(x, -3)$. If the distance from point M to the y-axis is 9 units, list all values of x.

26. The coordinates of point N are $(5, y)$. If the distance from point N to the x-axis is 3 units, list all values of y.

Exercises 27–30: The line going through point M and perpendicular to line a intersects line a at point C. The coordinates of the points are given. Find the distance from point M to line a.

27. $M(8, -3), C(1, -11)$

28. $M(7, -3), C(-3, -10)$

29. $M(7, -4), C(-4, -10)$

30. $M(10, -3), C(4, -10)$

Practice Problems continue . . .

31. Using information from the diagram, find the angle between the rays *a* and *b*.

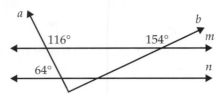

32. **MP 3, 5** Line *m* passes through point *M*. Explain how to construct a line *p* through point *M* and perpendicular to line *m* using a compass and a straightedge. Perform the constructions.

33. Describe the set of all points that are the same distance *d* from a given line *a*, and which are in a single plane passing through line *a*.

34. Describe the set of all points that are the same distance from parallel lines *a* and *b* and line in the plane containing the lines.

35. **MP 4** Two mirrors are placed so they form a right angle. A light ray is directed into one mirror so it forms a 45° angle with it. Using the fact that the incoming and outgoing angles are congruent, prove that the ray reflected from the second mirror is parallel to the ray striking the first mirror.

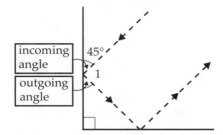

36. **MP 4, 5** Using geometric construction tools, construct a map of Commercial Avenue, 2nd Street, and 3rd Street with the following constraints: 2nd and 3rd Streets are parallel to each other; Commercial Avenue intersects both 2nd and 3rd Streets, but not at right angles.

LESSON 4.4

4.4 Parallel Lines, Perpendicular Lines, and Slope

Determining When Lines Are Parallel or Perpendicular

Parallel Lines

We recall from Algebra how to determine if two lines are parallel.
(1) If both lines are vertical, then they are parallel.
Any two horizontal lines are also parallel.

- Two vertical lines, such as $x = 4$ and $x = 5$, are parallel.
- Two horizontal lines, such as $y = 2$ and $y = -1$, are parallel.

(2) If both the lines are not conveniently vertical or horizontal, then you have to consider their slopes to determine if they are parallel. If their slopes are the same, the lines are parallel.

- Lines with the same slope, such as $y = 3x + 2$ and $y = 3x - 1$, are parallel.

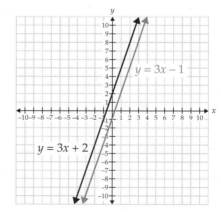

<u>Perpendicular Lines</u>

As with parallel lines, the slopes of perpendicular lines have a specific mathematical relationship.

(1) If one line is vertical and another horizontal, they are perpendicular.

(2) If the lines are not vertical and horizontal, you have to consider their slopes to determine whether they are perpendicular. The slopes of perpendicular lines are negative reciprocals.

- The two lines in the diagram are perpendicular because their slopes, -2 and $\frac{1}{2}$, are negative reciprocals. To put it another way, the product of the slopes is -1.

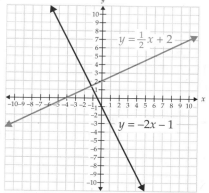

Rotations and Perpendicular Lines

Perpendicular lines have slopes that are negative reciprocals. We show how this is true with a 90° clockwise rotation in the graph to the right. We call the perpendicular lines a and p. The equations for the lines will be $y = m_a x$, and $y = m_p x$.

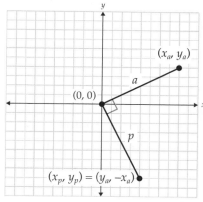

Slope of line a

$$m_a = \text{Slope}_a = \frac{y_2 - y_1}{x_2 - x_1}$$

This is the equation for the slope of a line.

$$\text{Slope}_a = \frac{y_2 - y_1}{x_2 - x_1}$$

We use $(0, 0)$ for (x_1, y_1), (x_a, y_a) for (x_2, y_2), and calculate the slope.

$$\text{Slope}_a = \frac{y_a - 0}{x_a - 0} = \frac{y_a}{x_a}$$

Rotate the line 90° clockwise

$$(x_a, y_a) \rightarrow (x_p, y_p) = (y_a, -x_a)$$

Now rotate the line using the coordinate relationship for a 90° clockwise rotation. The point remains on the line as it rotates.

Slopes of line a and p are negative reciprocals

$$m_p = \frac{y_p}{x_p} = \frac{-x_a}{y_a}$$

Use the equation for the slope again, substituting the coordinates of the point on the rotated line. Comparing it to our original slope, we see that the slopes are negative reciprocals.

MODEL PROBLEMS

1. A line is rotated 90°. The slope of the original line and slope of the line created by the rotation, are

    A. Equal.   C. Negative reciprocals.

    B. Opposite.   D. None of the above.

SOLUTION

The answer is C. Rotating a line 90° will create a perpendicular line. Perpendicular lines have negative reciprocal slopes.

2. Using the graph on the right, write the equations for b and c.

The equation for a is $y = \frac{1}{2}x + 2$.

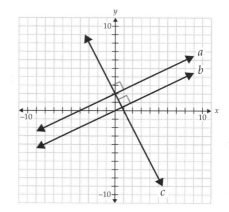

SOLUTION

Equation for b Same slope, passes through origin $y = \frac{1}{2}x$ Line b is parallel to a, because both lines are perpendicular to c. Thus, a and b have the same slope, $\frac{1}{2}$. The y-intercept of b is zero since it passes through the origin.

Equation for c Slope is the negative reciprocal; y-intercept at $y = 2$; $y = -2x + 1$ Line c is perpendicular to a. Thus, the slope of c is the negative reciprocal of $\frac{1}{2}$, the slope of a. The y-intercept of c is 2, since c passes through the point $(0, 2)$.

3.   **MP 1, 2, 3** A teacher says: "Triangle ABC has vertex A at $(2, 3)$, vertex B at $(1, 10)$, and vertex C at $(5, 7)$. ABC is a right triangle, with C its right angle." Is he correct?

SOLUTION

Calculate slope AC $\text{Slope } AC = \dfrac{\text{rise}}{\text{run}} = \dfrac{7 - 3}{5 - 2} = \dfrac{4}{3}$ If the legs are at right angles, they are perpendicular and will have slopes that are negative reciprocals. Calculate the slope of AC.

> We can use the slopes of two line segments to determine if a triangle is a right triangle.

Calculate slope CB $\text{Slope } CB = \dfrac{\text{rise}}{\text{run}} = \dfrac{7 - 10}{5 - 1} = -\dfrac{3}{4}$ Calculate the slope of the other leg.

Slopes are negative reciprocals $\dfrac{4}{3} \cdot \left(-\dfrac{3}{4}\right) = -1$

C is right angle

The slopes are negative reciprocals: their product is -1. This means the lines are perpendicular and it is a right triangle.

Distance Between a Point and a Line

Earlier, we calculated the distance between a point and a horizontal or vertical line, or the shortest path between the two. Now we do the more difficult task of computing the distance between a point and a line that is neither horizontal nor vertical.

To calculate the distance, we need to determine the perpendicular distance between the point and the line, since that will be the shortest path. This means we must first determine a line perpendicular to the line and passing through the point.

MODEL PROBLEM

Find the distance between the point and the line.

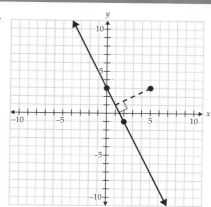

SOLUTION

Calculate slope of line	$\text{slope} = \dfrac{y_2 - y_1}{x_2 - x_1} = \dfrac{-1 - 3}{2 - 0} = \dfrac{-4}{2} = -2$	Calculate the slope of the line.
Write equation	$y = -2x + 3$	Write in slope-intercept form. The line crosses the y-axis at 3, so $b = 3$.
Write equation for perpendicular line	$y = \dfrac{1}{2}x + b$	The distance will be along the perpendicular line. Its slope is the negative reciprocal of the slope of the given line.
Substitute point into line equation	$(3) = \dfrac{1}{2}(5) + b$ $b = \dfrac{1}{2}$ $y = \dfrac{1}{2}x + \dfrac{1}{2}$	Calculate b by substituting the x- and y-values of the point we want to find the distance to into the equation.
Calculate x of intersection point	$\dfrac{1}{2}x + \dfrac{1}{2} = -2x + 3$ $x = 1$	Set the two equations for the lines equal to each other. Where the lines intersect, their y- and x-values will be the same.
Substitute	$y = -2x + 3 = -2(1) + 3 = 1$	Solve for y.
Identify the intersection point	$(1, 1)$	
Use distance formula	$\text{distance} = \sqrt{(x_2 - x_1)^2 + (y_2 - y_1)^2}$ $\text{distance} = \sqrt{(3 - 1)^2 + (5 - 1)^2}$	Use the distance formula to calculate the distance between the point $(5, 3)$, and the point of intersection $(1, 1)$.
Evaluate	$\text{distance} = \sqrt{(2)^2 + (4)^2} = \sqrt{20}$ $\text{distance} = 2\sqrt{5} \approx 4.47$	Square the terms and add. The distance is about 4.47.

PRACTICE

1. Which of the following equations represents a line parallel to the graph of the equation $y = 9x + 0.4$?

   A. $y = 0.4x + 9$
   B. $y = -9x$
   C. $y = 9x - 3.6$

2. Which of the following equations represents a line parallel to the graph of the equation $y = 3x + 0.4$?

   A. $y = 0.4x + 3$
   B. $y = -3x$
   C. $y = 3x + 2.4$

3. The graph of the equation $y = 1$ is parallel to the graph of which of the following equations? Choose all that apply.

   A. $y = 1x$
   B. $y = -1$
   C. $y = x + 1$
   D. $y = 5$
   E. $x = 0$
   F. $y = 0$
   G. $x = 5$

4. The graph of the equation $y = 4$ is parallel to the graph of which of the following equations? Select all that apply.

   A. $y = 4x$ E. $x = 0$
   B. $y = -4$ F. $y = 0$
   C. $y = x + 4$ G. $x = 5$
   D. $y = 5$

5. Which of the following equations represents a line perpendicular to the graph of the equation $y = 9x + 4$?

   A. $y = -\dfrac{1}{9}x + (-2)$

   B. $y = \dfrac{1}{9}x + 4$

   C. $y = -9x$

6. The graph of the equation $y = 5.3$ is perpendicular to which of the following graphs? Select all that apply.

   A. $y = -\dfrac{1}{5.3}$ D. $x = 0$

   B. $x = 5.3$ E. $y = 0$
   C. $y = -5.3$ F. $x = 0.3$

7. A beetle sits at the origin on a coordinate plane. If he crawls along the shortest distance to the line $y = -x + 4$, how far, in units, does he need to crawl?

   A. $2\sqrt{2}$ C. $\sqrt{2}$
   B. 3 D. 4

8. Which of the following equations represents the line that passes through the points $(-2, 24)$ and $(3, -31)$?

   A. $y = -12x + 4$
   B. $y = -9x - 3$

   C. $y = -11x + 2$
   D. $y = -10x - 6$

Exercises 9–11: Given three points, determine if they define a right triangle, a non-right triangle, or do not define a triangle.

9. $(-6, -5)$, $(5, -2)$, and $(-2, 2)$
   A. Not a right triangle
   B. Right triangle
   C. The points do not define a triangle

10. $(-4, -2)$, $(6, 3)$, and $(3, 9)$
    A. Not a right triangle
    B. Right triangle
    C. The points do not define a triangle

11. $(-4, -2)$, $(7, -2)$, and $(-3, -2)$
    A. Not a right triangle
    B. Right triangle
    C. The points do not define a triangle

Practice Problems continue . . .

12. Are the lines described by the equations $y = 5x + 7$ and $y = 2x + 3$ parallel? Justify your answer.

13. What is the slope of a line perpendicular to $y = -x$?

14. What is the slope of a line perpendicular to $y = 0.5x + 4$?

15. What is the slope of a line perpendicular to $y = -4x + 1$?

16. Find the equation of the line that passes through $(0, -5)$ and is perpendicular to $y = -\dfrac{1}{3}x + \dfrac{1}{4}$.

17. What is the slope of a line that passes through the origin and is parallel to $y = \dfrac{1}{5}x + 8$?

18. What is the slope of a line that passes through the origin and is parallel to $y = \dfrac{1}{6}x + 8$?

19. Give an equation of a line that is parallel to the line $x = -2.8$ and passes through the point $(-7.2, 0)$.

20. The line a goes through the points $(6, -4)$ and $(-5, 0)$. The line b passes through the points $(2, -7)$ and $(-9, -3)$. Are these lines parallel? Why or why not?

21. Find the shortest distance between the point $(5, 2)$ and the line $y = 3x + 6$.

22. Use the diagram to answer the questions.

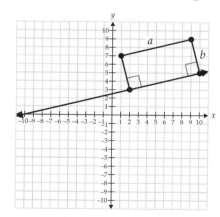

  a What is the slope of line segment a?
  b What is the slope of line segment b?

23. On the diagram, the triangles ABC and DBK are similar, that is, their corresponding angles are congruent. Prove that the lines have the same slope.

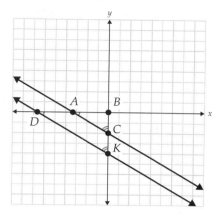

24. Triangle DEF has vertices located at $D(2, 0)$, $E(6, 1)$, and $F(4, 5)$. Is $\triangle DEF$ a right triangle? How do you know?

25. Is the triangle in the graph below a right triangle? Justify your answer.

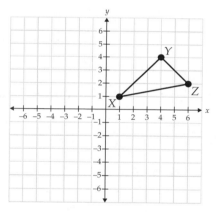

26. Find the coordinates of 3 points in the coordinate plane that form a right triangle. Do not use problems or examples shown in the text. State how you know the triangle is a right triangle.

27. Suppose you have a positively sloped line. If you rotate that line 90° counterclockwise about the origin, will the rotation form a line that is perpendicular to the first? Explain your answer.

Practice Problems continue . . .

28. The sides of a triangle are given by the equations $y = 0.4x - 34.5$, $y = -4x + 1.9$, and $y = -2.5x + 8$. Determine if it is a right triangle.

29. MP 3 Two vertices of a triangle are $(0, 5)$ and $(0, -5)$. Define the third vertex in such a way that the resulting triangle has a right angle. (Note that there are many possible correct answers.)

30. Graph the lines $y = x + 2$ and $y = x - 4$. On your graph, mark a segment showing the shortest distance between the lines. Find the distance between the lines to the nearest tenth of a unit.

31. State and graph the equation of a line that goes through the point $(4, 3)$ and is parallel to the line that connects the points $(1, 2)$ and $(-1, -5)$.

32. State and graph the equation of a line that goes through the point $(1, 2)$ and is perpendicular to the line that connects the points $(4, 3)$ and $(-2, 1)$.

33. Two robots, Daisy and Chaise, are standing on the adjacent vertices of a playing field shaped as a quadrilateral. Coordinates of the four vertices are $(2, 2)$, $(5, 1)$, $(3, 6)$, and $(0, 3)$. On a signal, each robot sends a laser beam toward the opposite vertex. Find the coordinates of the point where these beams meet.

34. MP 3 A teacher says: "Triangle ABC has vertex A at $(-5, -2)$, vertex B at $(2, -10)$, and vertex C at $(0, 0)$. ABC is a right triangle, with C its right angle." Is he correct? Justify your answer.

• Multi-Part PROBLEM Practice •

MP 3, 7 Points A $(-4, 6)$, B $(2, 10)$, C $(11, 3)$, and D $(2, -3)$ form a quadrilateral.

a Graph the quadrilateral on a coordinate plane.

b What type of quadrilateral is $ABCD$? Explain.

c Move point C or D to make $ABCD$ a parallelogram but not a rectangle. Justify your action.

d Move point C or D to make $ABCD$ a rectangle. Justify your action.

e Is your rectangle from part **d** a square? Explain.

LESSON 4.5

4.5 Parallel Lines and Triangles

Interior and Exterior Angles

Interior angles of a polygon are the angles inside a polygon. **Exterior angles** of a polygon are angles formed by a side of a polygon and the extension of its adjacent side.

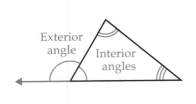

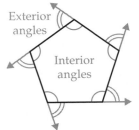

> An interior angle and its exterior angle form a linear pair, so that the measures of the angles sum to 180°.

You may already be familiar with the following theorem—that the measures of the angles in a triangle sum to 180°.

Triangle sum theorem

The sum of the interior angle measures in a triangle is 180 degrees.

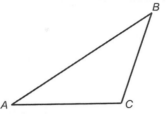

In a triangle, $m\angle A + m\angle B + m\angle C = 180°$.

We will prove that the measures of a triangle's angles sum to 180°. To prove this theorem, we do a little planning first, adding a line not present in the diagram. An **auxiliary line** is a line added to help in a proof.

> We can add a point or segment as an auxiliary in a proof.

Prove: $m\angle 4 + m\angle 2 + m\angle 5 = 180°$

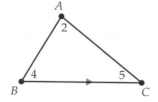

Draw a line parallel to segment BC:

We want to prove the measures of the angles in a triangle sum to 180°. To do this, we start by drawing the line AD. We know that the measures of angles 1, 2, and 3 sum to 180°, since the angles form a line.

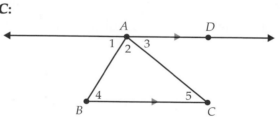

> If we can show that $\angle 1$ and $\angle 3$ are congruent to $\angle 4$ and $\angle 5$, the triangle's interior angles, we will have proven that the sum of interior angles of a triangle is 180°.

Statement	Reason	
$\overleftrightarrow{AD} \parallel \overline{BC}$	Diagram	The auxiliary line is parallel to $\overline{BC}$.
$m\angle 1 + m\angle 2 + m\angle 3 = 180°$	Definition of a straight angle	Since angles 1, 2, and 3 form a line, we know that their measures sum to 180°.
$\angle 1 \cong \angle 4$	Alternate interior angles theorem	$\overline{AB}$ is a transversal of the parallel line and line segment, so these alternate interior angles are congruent.
$\angle 3 \cong \angle 5$	Alternate interior angles theorem	$\overline{AC}$ is also a transversal of the parallel line and line segment, so these alternate interior angles are congruent too.
$m\angle 4 + m\angle 2 + m\angle 5 = 180°$	Substitution	Replace angles 1 and 3 from the previous steps with 4 and 5 to prove that the interior angle measures of a triangle sum to 180°.

We state the exterior angle theorem.

Exterior angle theorem

The measure of a triangle's exterior angle equals the sum of the measures of the two non-adjacent interior angles.

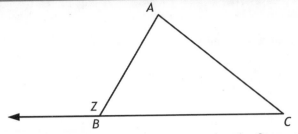

If $\angle A$ and $\angle C$ are not adjacent to $\angle Z$, then $m\angle A + m\angle C = m\angle Z$.

MODEL PROBLEMS

1. What is $m\angle Z$?

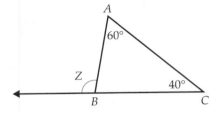

SOLUTION

Exterior angle theorem $m\angle Z = m\angle A + m\angle C$ The exterior angle theorem states that the measure of the angle equals the sum of the measures of the two remote interior angles.

Evaluate $m\angle Z = 60° + 40° = 100°$ Substitute and add.

2. What is $m\angle N$, given $m\angle N = (2x + 10°)$?

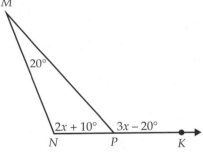

SOLUTION

Exterior angle theorem
$$m\angle KPM = m\angle N + m\angle M$$
$$3x - 20° = (2x + 10°) + 20°$$
The exterior angle theorem states that the measure of the exterior angle equals the sum of the measures of the two remote interior angles. Substitute the expressions and values shown in the diagram.

Solve equation
$$3x - 20° = 2x + 30°$$
$$3x = 2x + 50°$$
$$x = 50°$$
Combine the constants, then isolate the variable.

Substitute
$$m\angle N = 2x + 10°$$
$$m\angle N = 2(50°) + 10° = 110°$$
Substitute the value of x into the expression for $m\angle N$.

Angles in a Right Triangle

The **corollary** below follows from the theorem that a triangle's angles sum to 180°.
A corollary is a statement that follows from an already proven theorem or postulate.

Triangle sum corollary

If a triangle is a right triangle, then the measures of its two other angles sum to 90 degrees.

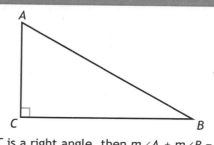

To put it another way, the other two angles in a right triangle are complementary.

If $\angle C$ is a right angle, then $m\angle A + m\angle B = 90°$.

MODEL PROBLEM

What is the value of z?

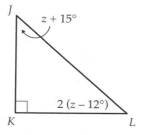

SOLUTION

Use triangle sum corollary
$$2(z - 12°) + z + 15° = 90°$$

Distribute, combine
$$2z - 24° + z + 15° = 90°$$
$$3z - 9 = 90°$$

Solve equation
$$3z = 99°$$
$$z = 33°$$

Substitute
We substitute our value for z into the expressions $2(z - 12°)$ and $z + 15°$. The angles equal 42° and 48°. They sum to 90°, as expected.

PRACTICE

1. In a triangle *ABC*, *A* is a right angle. If the sum of angles *A* and *B* is less than 150°, which of the following best describes the measure of angle *C*?

   A.   Greater than 150°

   B.   Equal to 30°

   C.   Greater than 30°

   D.   Greater than 45°

2. In a right triangle *XYZ*, $\angle Y$ is a right angle and $\overline{YW}$ is perpendicular to $\overline{XZ}$ where *W* is a point on $\overline{XZ}$. If $\angle X = 34°$, then $m\angle ZYW$ is:

   A.   34°

   B.   56°

   C.   90°

   D.   146°

Practice Problems continue . . .

3. Which angles are interior angles? Choose all that apply.

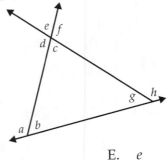

A. *a*   E. *e*
B. *b*   F. *f*
C. *c*   G. *g*
D. *d*   H. *h*

4. Which angles are exterior angles? Choose all that apply.

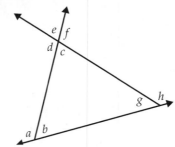

A. *a*   E. *e*
B. *b*   F. *f*
C. *c*   G. *g*
D. *d*   H. *h*

5. In a triangle, the measure of the first angle is 12° less than the measure of the second one, and the measure of the third angle is twice as great as the measure of the first one. What are the measures of the angles of the triangle?

A. 48°, 96°, 36°
B. 54°, 108°, 42°
C. 54°, 108°, 94°
D. 54°, 84°, 42°

Exercises 6–10: Given the measures of two interior angles *A* and *B* of a triangle *ABC*, find the measure of the third interior angle, *C*.

6. $\angle A = 50°$, $\angle B = 30°$

7. $\angle A = 75°$, $\angle B = 40°$

8. $\angle A = 55°$, $\angle B = 80°$

9. $\angle A = 35°$, $\angle B = 120°$

10. $\angle A = 60°$, $\angle B = 60°$

Exercises 11–12: Find the measures of all interior angles of a triangle, using the given ratio between them.

11. Angles' ratio: $5 : 6 : 7$

12. Angles' ratio: $1 : 2 : 3$

13. In a triangle, the measure of the second angle is twice as big as the measure of the first angle. The measure of the third angle is 6 times as big as the measure of the second one. Find the angles of the triangle.

14. Dorothy says two angles in a triangle she drew have the measures 94° and 98°. Can Dorothy be right about her triangle? Why or why not?

15. **MP 2** The measure of one of the exterior angles of a triangle is 40°, and the measure of one of the interior angles is 30°. Make a sketch, marking these angles, and find the measures of all interior angles of the triangle.

16. **MP 3, 6** Can there be both an obtuse and a right angle in a triangle? If so, give an example. If not, explain why.

17. Using the diagram, find the measures of the angles of the triangle.

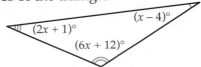

18. In triangle *ABC*, $m\angle A = 40°$ and $m\angle B = 84°$. Find the measure of the exterior angle adjacent to $\angle C$.

19. One acute angle of a right triangle is 20° smaller than the other. Find the measure of the larger acute angle of the triangle.

20. One acute angle of a right triangle is 5 times larger than the other acute angle. Find the measures of the acute angles.

21. One acute angle of a right triangle is 2 times as great as the other. Find the measures of the acute angles of the triangle.

22. Two exterior angles of a triangle are equal to 116° and 144°. Find the measures of all three interior angles of the triangle.

Practice Problems continue . . .

23. Two exterior angles of a triangle are equal to 101° and 141°. Find all three interior angles of the triangle.

24. The sum of the exterior angles adjacent to angles *A* and *B* of the triangle *ABC* is equal to 240°. Find the interior angle *C* of the triangle.

25. One of the angles of a triangle is 50°, and the difference of the other two angles is 20°. Find the angles of the triangle.

26. Two exterior angles of a triangle are equal to 120° and 135°. Find the third exterior angle of the triangle.

27. Two exterior angles of a triangle are equal to 100° and 145°. Find the third exterior angle of the triangle.

28. An exterior angle of a right triangle is equal to 135°. Find the acute angles of the triangle.

29. One acute angle of a right triangle is 10° smaller than the other. Find the larger acute angle of the triangle.

30. In the diagram, *ABC* is a right triangle and $\overline{CD} \perp \overline{AB}$. Prove that $m\angle A = m\angle BCD$.

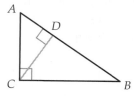

31. Find the angles of a right triangle with two congruent acute angles.

32. The sum of the exterior angles adjacent to angles *A* and *B* of the triangle *ABC* is equal to 230°. Find the interior angle *C* of the triangle.

33. **MP 3** Identify one exterior angle for each vertex of a triangle. What is the sum of these angles? Justify your response.

34. **MP 3** The sum of the measures of any two interior angles of a particular triangle is greater than 90°. Determine the type of triangle: obtuse, right, or acute. In acute triangles, the measures of all angles are less than 90°, and obtuse triangles have an angle whose measure is greater than 90°. Explain your answer.

35. **MP 3, 6** Prove the sum of the measures of the exterior angles of a triangle is 360°.

CHAPTER 4 REVIEW

1. The two lines shown are parallel. Which expression must be true?

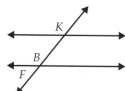

 A. *K = F*
 B. *K + B* = 180°
 C. *K + F* = 180°
 D. *K + F = B*

2. Angle *Z* forms a vertical pair with angle *B*, and angle *Z* is also a corresponding angle with *Y*. *Z* and *Y* are angles formed by a transversal and two parallel lines. Angles *B* and *Y* could be

 A. Consecutive interior
 B. Alternate interior
 C. Alternate exterior
 D. Corresponding

3. Point *A* is not on line *j*. How many lines pass through *A* and are parallel to *j*?

 A. 0   C. 2
 B. 1   D. An infinite number

4. The angles *A* and *E* are

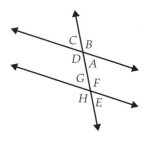

 A. Consecutive interior.
 B. Alternate interior.
 C. Alternate exterior.
 D. Corresponding.

Chapter Review continues . . .

5. Point *b* is not on line *z*. You can correctly say:

   A. No line can pass through *b* and be parallel to *z*.

   B. Only one line passes through *b* and is perpendicular to *z*.

   C. *b* and *z* cannot be coplanar.

   D. None of the above.

6. Two lines never intersect. This means:

   A. They must be coplanar.

   B. They must be parallel lines.

   C. They must be skew lines.

   D. None of the above.

7. If $m \parallel n$, how do we know that $p \perp n$?

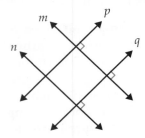

   A. *p* is perpendicular to *m*, and *m* is parallel to *n*.

   B. *p* is perpendicular to *m*, and *m* is perpendicular to *n*.

   C. *q* is perpendicular to *n*.

8. Do the points $(-5, 4)$, $(8, 3)$, and $(-2, -2)$ define a right triangle?

   A. No.

   B. Yes.

   C. The points do not define a triangle at all.

   D. It is not possible to tell.

9. Using the diagram, prove the consecutive interior angles theorem converse.

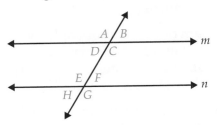

Prove: $m \parallel n$ Given: $m\angle D + m\angle E = 180°$

10. When two parallel lines are intersected by a transversal, the difference of two consecutive interior angles formed is 50°. Find the measures of these angles.

11. In the diagram, assume the measure of angle *A* is twice the measure of angle *B*. What is the measure of angle *G*?

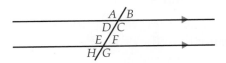

12. Given $m\angle 1 = (2y - 1)$, $m\angle 2 = (3x - 52)$, $m\angle 5 = (2x + 34)$, and $m\angle 7 = (3y - 10)$, what is $m\angle 8$?

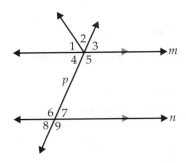

13. Prove that the opposite angles of the quadrilateral *ABCD* are congruent. That is, prove that $\angle 1 \cong \angle 2$ and $\angle 3 \cong \angle 4$.

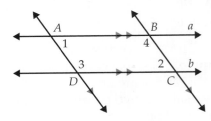

Chapter Review continues . . .

14. Two parallel lines are intersected by a transversal. Two consecutive interior angles have measures of $2(x - 1)$ and $3x - 3$. What is the measure of the smaller angle?

15. When two parallel lines p and q are intersected by a transversal n, the interior consecutive angles A and B are congruent. Prove that the transversal is perpendicular to both parallel lines.

16. Find the distance between the point M and the line t.

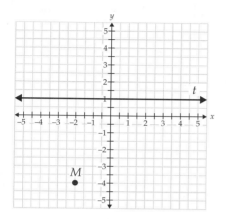

17. Find the distance between the point P and the line l.

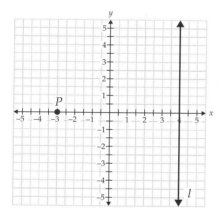

18. A snail moves along a straight line with a constant speed, changing direction by a right angle every 3 minutes. It follows this pattern for 2 hours and 45 minutes. During the last minute of its trip, will the snail be parallel to the line it started along or perpendicular to it?

19. In the diagram, $AB \parallel DE$ and $m\angle CDE = 21°$. Find the measure of $\angle ABC$.

20. Lines b and d are perpendicular to each other. Line a is parallel to line b. Line c intersects line b, forming an angle of $142°$. All lines are coplanar. Find the smaller of the angles that line c forms with line a. Then find the smaller of the angles that line c forms with line d. Provide a sketch with your answer.

21. **MP 5** Point M does not lie on line m. Explain how to construct a line p through point M and perpendicular to line m using a compass and a straightedge. Perform the constructions.

22. Using the diagram, prove the perpendicular lines and right angles theorem.

Prove: Angles A, B, C, and D are right angles.

Given: $m \perp n$

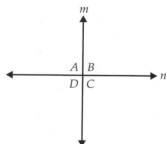

23. Explain how to determine if three given points could be the vertices of a right triangle.

24. Kathy found the slopes of two lines that she thought might be perpendicular. Both slopes were negative. What should Kathy conclude about the angle between these lines?

25. Explain why a triangle cannot have two right angles.

26. What is the measure of angle *B*?

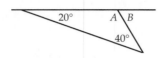

27. Find the measure of the exterior angle adjacent to interior angle *C* of the triangle *ABC*, if $\angle A = 45°$ and $\angle B = 110°$.

28. The measure of the exterior angle adjacent to the interior angle *M* of the triangle *KLM* is 110°. The two non-adjacent interior angles of the triangle are congruent. Find all interior angles of the triangle.

29. Using the diagram, prove the triangle sum corollary.
Prove: $m\angle A + m\angle B = 90°$
Given: $m\angle C = 90°$

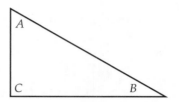

Cumulative Review
for Chapters 1–4

1. Two lines are described by the equations $y = -zx + 5$ and $y = zx - 3$. The lines are

  A. Parallel.

  B. Perpendicular.

  C. Overlapping.

  D. None of the above.

2. How could the angle below be named? Choose all that apply.

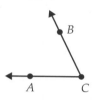

  A. $\angle ABC$ D. $\angle A$

  B. $\angle CBA$ E. $\angle C$

  C. $\angle ACB$

3. Choose all that apply. $\overleftrightarrow{AB}$ and $\overleftrightarrow{AC}$ are

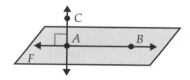

  A. Coplanar in plane F.

  B. Parallel.

  C. Perpendicular.

  D. None of the above.

4. Two of the lines shown are parallel. This means that angles V and W

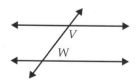

  A. Are congruent.

  B. Are supplementary.

  C. Are complementary.

  D. Have no defined mathematical relationship.

5. How would the congruent triangles be described?

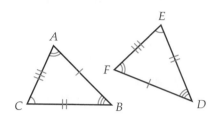

  A. $\triangle ABC \cong \triangle DEF$

  B. $\triangle ABC \cong \triangle FDE$

  C. $\triangle ABC \cong \triangle FED$

6. Consider the true statement: "If it is an even number, then it is divisible by 2." Which of the following is also a true statement? Choose all that apply.

  A. Converse

  B. Inverse

  C. Contrapositive

7. Dr. Watson said: "If the patient has the boola-boola disease, he sneezes 4 times a minute. If a patient mumbles 'Eli, Eli' twice an hour, the patient has the boola-boola disease." Dr. Watson should conclude

  A. If a patient sneezes 4 times a minute, he mumbles 'Eli, Eli' twice an hour.

  B. If a patient sneezes 4 times a minute, the patient has the boola-boola disease.

  C. A person who does not have the boola-boola disease never sneezes.

  D. If a patient mumbles 'Eli, Eli' twice an hour, he sneezes 4 times a minute.

8. Select the statement(s) that are true.

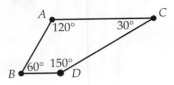

  A. Angles A and B are complementary.
  B. Angles A and B are supplementary.
  C. Angles B and C are complementary.
  D. Angles B and D are supplementary.

9. What is $m\angle C$?

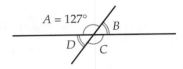

10. Point P lies on $\overline{YZ}$. If $\overline{YZ}$ has length 28 and $\overline{YP}$ has length 21, what is the length of $\overline{PZ}$?

11. J is on $\overline{HI}$, and $HI = 33$. If $\dfrac{HJ}{JI} = \dfrac{8}{3}$, how far is J from H?

12. You want to translate a figure 8 units horizontally and 6 units vertically. What constants do you add to the x- and y-coordinates for this translation?

13. **MP 3** Suppose 3 straight lines, a, b, and c, all lie in the same plane. If lines a and b are parallel and lines b and c are parallel, what can you conclude about the relationship between lines a and c? How do you know?

14. In the diagram below, line a is parallel to line b, $\angle 1 \cong \angle 3$, and the measure of $\angle 9 = 120°$. Prove the shaded triangle is equilateral.

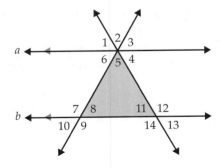

15. The measure of angle D is twice the measure of angle E. What is the measure of angle B?

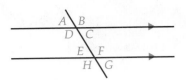

16. Two parallel lines are intersected by a transversal. Prove that the angle bisectors of two consecutive interior angles are perpendicular. Make a sketch, label the angles, and refer to them in your proof.

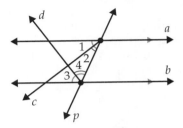

17. A teacher says: "Triangle ABC has vertex A at $(-4, -1)$, vertex B at $(2, -8)$, and vertex C at $(0, 0)$. ABC is a right triangle, with C its right angle." Is she correct? Justify your answer.

18. What is the measure of angle $2x$?

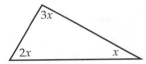

19. $\triangle ABC$ is translated as shown. What is the translation?

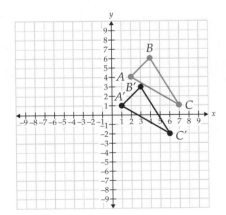

20. Figure *A* is dilated by a scale factor of 5 to form figure *B*, which is then dilated by a scale factor of $\frac{7}{4}$ to form figure *C*. What is the scale factor that dilates figure *A* to figure *C*?

21. Two triangles are similar. Triangle *ABC* has 36 times the area of triangle *DEF*. How many times longer would a side of triangle *ABC* be than the corresponding side in triangle *DEF*?

22. Using the point (a, b), show algebraically that four 90° counterclockwise rotations about the origin return you to the original point (a, b).

23. What are the coordinates of the upper right vertex of a figure if it is dilated by a factor of 7? The original figure's coordinates are $(1, 3)$, $(1, 5)$, $(-7, 3)$, and $(-7, 5)$, and the center of dilation is the origin.

Exercises 24–27: Write the biconditional for each definition.

24. The real numbers are composed of the rational and irrational numbers.

25. An integer prime is a number with exactly two positive distinct factors.

26. Two angles that sum to 180° are called supplementary angles.

27. Parallel lines are lines on a plane that do not intersect.

28. **MP 5** Draw and label the sides and angles of two similar quadrilaterals.

29. Two rectangles are similar. Their widths are corresponding sides: the width of rectangle *A* is 5, and the width of rectangle *B* is 3. If the larger rectangle has a height of 15, what is the height of the smaller rectangle?

30. The corresponding sides of two similar octagons (8-sided figures) have a scale factor of 2.4. If the smaller octagon has a perimeter of 20, what is the perimeter of the larger octagon?

31. Kim's office is 14 feet by 20 feet. She wishes to lengthen the walls of her office by a scale factor of 1.5. What will be the dimensions of the expanded office?

Exercises 32–33: Determine whether the following statement is always true, sometimes true, or never true. Justify your answer.

32. Inductive reasoning leads to a correct conclusion.

33. Deductive reasoning based on true statements leads to a correct conclusion.

34. **MP 2, 3 ,4** There were 437 homes in the county of Piranha Lake in 1995. Ten years later, the number of homes had increased to 761. Therefore, the number of homes in Piranha Lake in 2010 was exactly 923. Is this an example of inductive or deductive reasoning using a graph? Justify your answer.

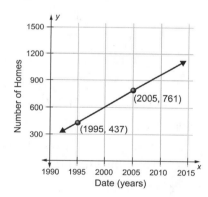

Chapter Content

Chapter Vocabulary

acute triangle	coordinate proof	scalene triangle
angle-angle-side (AAS) theorem	equilateral triangle	side-angle-side (SAS) postulate
angle-side-angle (ASA) postulate	flow proof	side-side-side (SSS) postulate
base	isosceles triangle	triangle
base angle	obtuse triangle	vertex angle

LESSON 5.1

5.1 Isosceles and Equilateral Triangles

Determining Types of Triangles

A **triangle** is a closed plane figure with three straight sides and three angles. One way a triangle can be described is by the measure of its largest angle.

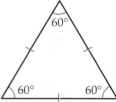

Acute
Largest angle less than 90°

Right
Largest angle is 90°

Obtuse
Largest angle is greater than 90°

Another property of a triangle is the number of congruent sides or congruent angles it has.

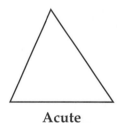

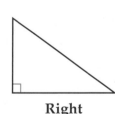

Equilateral triangles have:

• all sides congruent
• three congruent angles

Isosceles triangles have:

• at least two congruent sides
• at least two congruent angles

Scalene triangles have:

• no congruent sides
• no congruent angles

Some triangles can be described with two of the terms. For instance, an equilateral triangle is also an acute triangle, since it has only 60° angles. Some combinations are impossible—for example, a triangle cannot be a right triangle and an equilateral triangle. Why? A right triangle has a 90° angle, but all the angles in an equilateral triangle are 60°.

MODEL PROBLEMS

1. $m\angle B$ is 4 times $m\angle A$, and $m\angle A = 20°$. What type of triangle is $\triangle ABC$? Sketch the triangle.

SOLUTION

Calculate $m\angle B$	$m\angle B = 4 \cdot 20° = 80°$	The problem states that $m\angle B$ is 4 times $m\angle A$, which is 20°.
Calculate $m\angle C$	$m\angle A + m\angle B + m\angle C = 180°$	The angles in the triangle sum to 180°. We know two of the angles, and subtract them from 180° to compute $m\angle C$.
	$m\angle C = 180° - m\angle A - m\angle B$	
	$m\angle C = 180° - 20° - 80° = 80°$	
Triangle is isosceles and acute	$m\angle B = m\angle C = 80°$	Two of the angles equal 80°, so the triangle is an isosceles triangle. Isosceles triangles have two congruent angles. The triangle is also acute since no angle is greater than or equal to 90°.

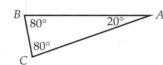

2. **MP 1** **a** Based on the lengths of its sides, classify $\triangle ABC$.

b Suppose $\angle C$ was moved so it was located at $(3, 2)$. How does this change the classification of the triangle?

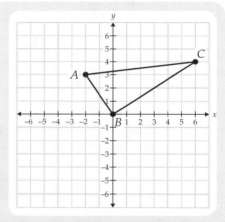

SOLUTION

a Calculate AB

$d = \sqrt{(x_2 - x_1)^2 + (y_2 - y_1)^2}$

$d = \sqrt{(-2 - 0)^2 + (3 - 0)^2}$

$= \sqrt{13} \approx 3.6$

First, calculate the lengths of the sides. This will enable us to determine if the triangle is scalene, isosceles, or equilateral. Using the distance formula, we calculate AB.

> We can use the distance formula and the slope of segments to determine what type of triangle *ABC* is. We start with the distance formula to find the relationship of the lengths of its sides.

Calculate BC

$d = \sqrt{(0 - 6)^2 + (0 - 4)^2}$

$= \sqrt{52} = 2\sqrt{13} \approx 7.2$

Use the distance formula again, this time to calculate BC.

Calculate AC

$d = \sqrt{(-2 - 6)^2 + (3 - 4)^2}$

$= \sqrt{65} \approx 8.1$

Calculate AC.

Model Problems continue . . .

Triangle type	No congruent sides: Scalene	Since no two sides of the triangle are equal in length, the triangle is scalene.
Calculate slopes	Slope $\overline{AB} = \dfrac{3-0}{-2-0} = -\dfrac{3}{2}$ Slope $\overline{BC} = \dfrac{0-4}{0-6} = \dfrac{2}{3}$	Since $\overline{AB}$ and $\overline{BC}$ look like they might form a right angle, we calculate their slopes.
Slopes are negative reciprocals	$-\dfrac{3}{2} \cdot \dfrac{2}{3} = -1$	Perpendicular lines have slopes that are negative reciprocals, which means the product of their slopes equals -1. Since the segments are perpendicular, this is a right triangle.

The triangle is a scalene, right triangle.

b The points $(-2, 3)$ and $(3, 2)$ are the same distance from the origin, so the triangle would have two sides the same length and be isosceles. We could calculate the slope of $\overline{BC}$ again, but it is easier to note that $(3, 2)$ is on the same line as before, so it has the same slope as before. This means it is still perpendicular to $\overline{AB}$, and the triangle remains a right triangle.

PRACTICE

1. In $\triangle XYZ$, $m\angle X = 60°$ and $m\angle Y = 30°$. Which descriptions match this triangle? Choose all that apply.

   A. Right triangle
   B. Obtuse triangle
   C. Scalene triangle
   D. Isosceles triangle

2. In $\triangle BDE$, $m\angle B = 120°$ and $m\angle D = 14.2°$. Which descriptions match this triangle? Choose all that apply.

   A. Right triangle
   B. Obtuse triangle
   C. Acute triangle
   D. Isosceles triangle

3. In $\triangle ABC$, $m\angle A = 50°$, as does $m\angle B$. Which descriptions match this triangle? Choose all that apply.

   A. Right triangle
   B. Obtuse triangle
   C. Acute triangle
   D. Isosceles triangle

4. In $\triangle WUT$, $\angle W$ and $\angle U$ are complementary but not equal. Which type of triangle is $\triangle WUT$? Check all that apply.

   A. Right
   B. Acute
   C. Scalene
   D. Obtuse
   E. Isosceles

5. If the perimeter of the triangle below is 35, what is the value of x?

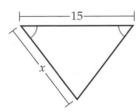

   A. 10
   B. 15
   C. 17.5
   D. 20

Practice Problems continue . . .

Practice Problems continued . . .

6. In △CAT, m∠C = 80° and m∠A = 20°. △CAT is best described as

   A. Scalene and obtuse.

   B. Isosceles and obtuse.

   C. Isosceles and acute.

   D. Scalene and right.

7. Triangle XYZ is scalene, and the m∠X is 50°. Which of the following statements cannot be true? Select all that apply.

   A. The m∠X and m∠Z are equal.

   B. The m∠Z is twice the m∠X.

   C. The m∠Y is four times the m∠X.

   D. The m∠Y is 1.6 times the m∠X.

8. Sketch an obtuse scalene triangle. Label each angle with its measure.

9. The length of $\overline{GH}$ is 11 inches. How long is $\overline{FH}$?

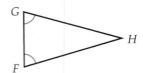

10. **MP 5** Triangle DEF has two vertices located at D(1, 1) and E(5, 3). Plot these two points, and then plot point F so that triangle DEF is both scalene and acute.

11. **MP 4** A building inspector needs to make sure a roof was constructed properly. The roof is in the shape of an isosceles triangle, and each of the bottom angles should measure 35°. The inspector has verified that the left angle is the correct measurement, but he is having trouble getting into a good position to determine the size of the right angle. How else could he verify that the roof has the correct dimensions?

12. The triangle ABC is a right isosceles triangle in the first quadrant. Point A is at (3, 3), and point B is at (13, 3). The right angle is ∠BAC. What is the location of point C?

13. When triangle BUG is graphed in the coordinate plane, the slope of $\overline{BU} = -18$, the slope of $\overline{GU} = \dfrac{1}{2}$, and the slope of $\overline{BG} = -2$. Is triangle BUG a right triangle? Explain your reasoning.

14. In an isosceles right triangle, the length of one leg can be represented by the expression $2x - 3$, and the length of the other leg can be represented by the expression $5x - 21$. What is the length of the triangle's hypotenuse, in simplest radical form?

Isosceles Triangles and Theorems

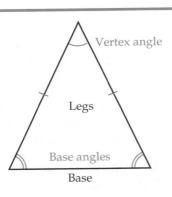

The **base angles** in an isosceles triangle are congruent. The **vertex angle** is the third angle in an isosceles triangle. If it is congruent to another angle, then the triangle is equilateral as well as isosceles. The legs are the sides opposite the base angles and are congruent. The **base** is the third side, opposite the vertex.

The following theorems apply to and define isosceles triangles:

Isosceles triangle theorems

If two sides of a triangle are congruent, then the angles opposite them are congruent.

If two angles of a triangle are congruent, then the sides opposite them are congruent.

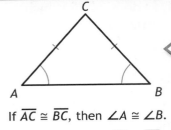

If $\overline{AC} \cong \overline{BC}$, then ∠A ≅ ∠B.

If ∠A ≅ ∠B, then $\overline{AC} \cong \overline{BC}$.

The first statement is the base angles theorem. The second statement is the converse of the base angles theorem. We will prove the base angles theorem later.

198   Chapter 5: Congruent Triangles

Isosceles bisector theorem

If a line bisects an isosceles triangle's vertex angle, then it is a perpendicular bisector of the base.

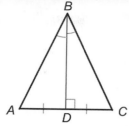

If $\overline{BD}$ bisects $\angle B$, then $\overline{BD}$ is a $\perp$ bisector of $\overline{AC}$.

Isosceles bisector theorem converse

If a line is the perpendicular bisector of an isosceles triangle's base, then it is also the angle bisector of the vertex angle.

If $\overline{BD}$ is a $\perp$ bisector of $\overline{AC}$, then $\overline{BD}$ bisects $\angle B$.

MODEL PROBLEM

What is $m\angle A$?

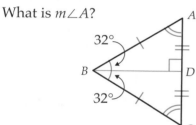

One way to calculate $m\angle A$ would be to realize that $\triangle ABD$ is a right triangle (since it is formed by a perpendicular bisector), so two angles are known—the angle shown in the diagram and the right angle. You could subtract these two angles from 180° to find $m\angle A$.

SOLUTION

Calculate $m\angle ABC$	$m\angle ABC = 2 \cdot 32° = 64°$	$m\angle ABC$ equals two times 32°.
$\triangle ABC$ is isosceles	$\overline{AB} \cong \overline{BC}$ $$m\angle A = m\angle C$$	The triangle is isosceles since it has a pair of congruent sides. The angles opposite congruent sides are congruent.
Angles sum to 180°	$m\angle A + m\angle ABC + m\angle C = 180°$	The angles in a triangle sum to 180°.
Substitute	$m\angle A = m\angle C$, and $m\angle ABC = 64°$ $$m\angle A + 64° + m\angle A = 180°$$	Since $m\angle A = m\angle C$, substitute $m\angle A$ for $m\angle C$. Substitute for $m\angle ABC$.
Solve for $m\angle A$	$2(m\angle A) + 64° = 180°$ $$2(m\angle A) = 116°$$ $$m\angle A = 58°$$	Solve for $m\angle A$ by combining like terms and isolating $m\angle A$.

Equilateral Triangle Theorems

Equilateral triangle theorems

If three sides of a triangle are congruent, then the angles opposite them are congruent.

If three angles of a triangle are congruent, then the sides opposite them are congruent.

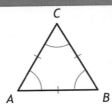

If $\overline{AB} \cong \overline{BC} \cong \overline{AC}$, then $\angle A \cong \angle B \cong \angle C$.

If $\angle A \cong \angle B \cong \angle C$, then $\overline{AB} \cong \overline{BC} \cong \overline{AC}$.

> The second statement is the converse of the first. Since there are three congruent angles, the measure of each angle in an equilateral triangle equals 60°, because 180° ÷ 3 = 60°.

MODEL PROBLEM

The figure is a rhombus (all sides congruent and opposite sides parallel). What are $m\angle A$ and $m\angle ABC$?

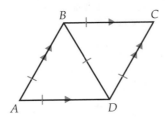

SOLUTION

Triangles are equilateral

$$m\angle A = 60°$$

The triangles are equilateral, which means the measures of each of their angles equals 60°.

Sum angles

$$m\angle ABC = m\angle ABD + m\angle CBD$$
$$m\angle ABC = 60° + 60°$$
$$m\angle ABC = 120°$$

This angle is formed by the two others. We know these two angles' measures since they are part of equilateral triangles, so substitute them and sum.

Construction: Equilateral Triangle

Construction Method 1

We construct an equilateral triangle in the traditional manner with a compass and straightedge:

1. Begin with line segment AB.

2. Extend compass to length AB. Place compass point at A and draw arc.

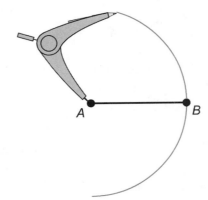

3. Keeping the compass at length AB, make an arc from point B.

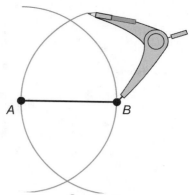

4. Connect an intersection to A and B.

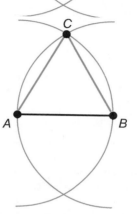

Construction Method 2

You can construct an equilateral triangle with a compass and straightedge, or one can use lines of symmetry with a semi-transparent plastic object. It has the reflective quality of a mirror, as well as a transparent quality so that you can see through it. For simplicity's sake, we will refer to it as the "device," short for *reflective device*.

To construct an equilateral triangle with a "device":

1. Construct a perpendicular bisector.

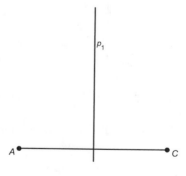

2. Place device on $\overline{CA}$ and rotate about A.

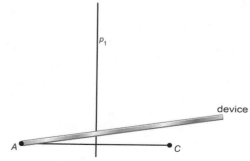

3. Rotate it until C is reflected onto p_1. Mark C' (reflected image of C) and draw line along device and label p_2.

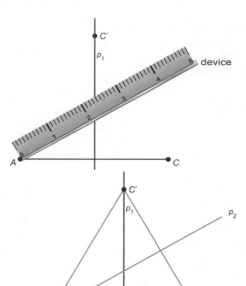

4. Draw $\overline{CC'}$ and $\overline{AC'}$ with a straightedge to construct the other two sides of the triangle.

We prove that our construction above is, in fact, an equilateral triangle by using our construction techniques and the perpendicular bisector theorem.

Statement	Reason	
p_1 is a perpendicular bisector of $\overline{AC}$	Construction	We constructed p_1 as a perpendicular bisector of $\overline{AC}$ with a compass and straightedge.
$\overline{AC'} \cong \overline{CC'}$	Perpendicular bisector theorem	Use the perpendicular bisector theorem to prove that the two segments are congruent.
p_2 is a perpendicular bisector of $\overline{CC'}$	Construction Definition of axis of symmetry	p_2 was constructed along the "device," which acts as an axis of reflection symmetry. By definition, an axis of reflection symmetry is equidistant from both C and C' and creates a right angle with $\overline{CC'}$. These are the properties of a perpendicular bisector.
$\overline{AC'} \cong \overline{AC}$	Perpendicular bisector theorem	A point on a perpendicular bisector is equidistant from the original segment's endpoints, so these two segments are also congruent.
$\overline{CC'} \cong \overline{AC}$	Transitive property of congruence	The three sides of the triangle are congruent by the transitive property of congruence, proving that the triangle is equilateral.

Try it! For another way to show that perpendicular bisectors of an equilateral triangle are axes of reflection symmetry, first cut out the triangle after you have constructed it. Fold one vertex to the opposite side, folding the paper across a perpendicular bisector, to see that the perpendicular bisectors are axes of reflection symmetry. They are examples of reflection symmetry since the two sides form a perfect overlap—each point on one side has a matching point on the other side. You can do this for all three vertices.

MODEL PROBLEM

Prove the first equilateral triangle theorem: If three sides of a triangle are congruent, then the angles opposite them are congruent.

Prove: $\angle A \cong \angle B \cong \angle C$
Given: $\overline{AB} \cong \overline{BC} \cong \overline{AC}$

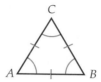

SOLUTION

Statement	Reason
$\overline{AB} \cong \overline{BC} \cong \overline{AC}$	Given
$\overline{AB} \cong \overline{BC}$ so $\angle A \cong \angle C$	Isosceles Triangle Theorem
$\overline{BC} \cong \overline{AC}$ so $\angle A \cong \angle B$	Isosceles Triangle Theorem
$\angle A \cong \angle C$ and $\angle A \cong \angle B$ so $\angle B \cong \angle A \cong \angle C$	Both angle B and angle C are congruent to angle A, so they are congruent to each other.

PRACTICE

1. One base angle of an isosceles triangle measures 50°. What is the measure of the vertex angle?

   A. 50°
   B. 80°
   C. 100°
   D. 130°

2. In isosceles $\triangle JKL$, $m\angle J = 100°$ and $m\angle K = 40°$. This means

   A. The side opposite $\angle J$ is congruent to the side opposite $\angle K$.
   B. The side opposite $\angle J$ is congruent to the side opposite $\angle L$.
   C. The side opposite $\angle K$ is congruent to the side opposite $\angle L$.

3. In isosceles $\triangle ABC$, the side opposite $\angle A$ has a length of 6, and the side opposite $\angle B$ has a length of 9. $m\angle A = 39°$. This means

   A. $m\angle B = 39°$
   B. $m\angle B \neq 39°$
   C. There is not enough information to draw a conclusion.

4. If the measure of angle A is 57°, what is the measure of angle B?

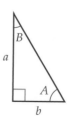

Practice Problems continue . . .

5. $x = 24°$. What is the value of y?

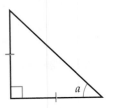

6. What is the value of a?

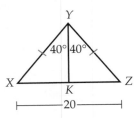

7. What is the measure of $\angle YKZ$?

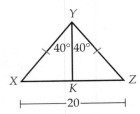

8. What is the measure of $\angle Z$?

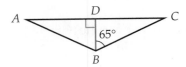

9. **MP 2** Triangle XYZ is a right triangle where $\angle Z$ is the right angle. Write an expression for the value of the measure of $\angle Y$ in terms of the measure of $\angle X$.

10. In $\triangle ABC$, $m\angle B$ is 30° greater than $m\angle A$, and $m\angle C$ is 3 times $m\angle B$. What is $m\angle A$?

11. $\triangle ABC$ is isosceles, with the vertex angle at B. $\overline{BD}$ is a perpendicular bisector. What is the measure of angle A?

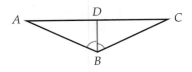

12. $\triangle ABC$ is isosceles, with the vertex angle at B. $\overline{BD}$ is an angle bisector of $\angle B$. If $AD = 13$, what is AC?

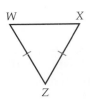

13. A builder is constructing a roof truss, which will be in the shape of an isosceles triangle. If the vertex angle of the truss measures 20° more than twice the measure of one base angle, what is the measure of each base angle of the truss?

14. **MP 5** Construct equilateral triangle $\triangle JKL$. Leave all marks made while using the compass and straightedge.

15. Peter says the triangle below is not an equilateral triangle, because neither all the sides nor all the angles are marked as congruent. Do you agree with Peter? Explain your reasoning.

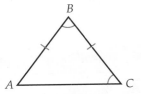

16. Paul has three boards of equal length that he will connect at their ends to form a triangle. What is the measure of each angle in this triangle, and why?

17. The perimeter of the triangle pictured is 32 meters. What is the length of $\overline{DF}$?

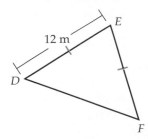

18. **MP 3, 6** $m\angle WZX = 60°$. Prove that $\triangle WZX$ is equilateral.

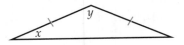

19. The height of an equilateral triangle is $6\sqrt{3}$. What is the length of one side of the triangle?

Practice Problems continue . . .

20. Prove the second equilateral triangle theorem.

Equilateral triangle theorems

If three angles of a triangle are congruent, then the sides opposite them are congruent.

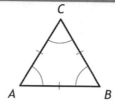

If ∠A ≅ ∠B ≅ ∠C, then $\overline{AB}$ ≅ $\overline{BC}$ ≅ $\overline{AC}$.

• Multi-Part PROBLEM Practice •

MP 4, 6

a Ron is ordering lumber for the trusses (which are triangular support frameworks) he needs for the roof of the second-story addition to his house. The peak of the roof will make a right angle and is supported, as pictured. In addition to the truss frames, there will be supporting pieces that meet the roof line at right angles, also as pictured. If the length of each truss is 12 feet and the height is 6 feet, how much lumber is needed for each truss? Round your answer up to the next foot.

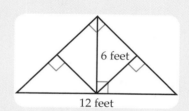

b City inspectors have told Ron that his new roof must be 3 feet lower than his plans indicate. But they have also granted him permission to widen the addition by the 4 feet he had previously requested. Ron has already ordered all of the wood for his trusses. Does he have enough? Explain.

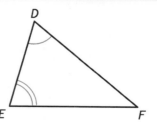

LESSON 5.2

5.2 Congruent Figures

The Third Angles Theorem

Third angles theorem

If two angles in a triangle are congruent to those of another triangle, then the triangles' third angles are congruent.

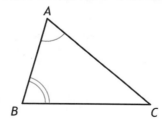

If ∠A ≅ ∠D and ∠B ≅ ∠E, then ∠C ≅ ∠F.

Using the paragraph proof style, we prove the third angles theorem:

Paragraph Proof

To prove the third angles theorem, we start with the given information, which is that two angles in one triangle are congruent with those in another triangle. Also, we are given the information that $\angle A \cong \angle D$ and $\angle B \cong \angle E$ in $\triangle ABC$ and $\triangle DEF$.

Since the angles in a triangle sum to 180°, we know that $m\angle C = 180° - m\angle A - m\angle B$, and $m\angle F = 180° - m\angle D - m\angle E$. Since $m\angle A = m\angle D$ and $m\angle B = m\angle E$, then we can substitute to show that $m\angle C = 180° - m\angle D - m\angle E$, the same as $m\angle F$. We have shown that the third angles are congruent.

MODEL PROBLEMS

1. What is $m\angle BCD$?

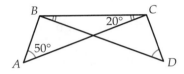

SOLUTION

Statement	Reason	
$m\angle ABC = 180° - 50° - 20°$ $m\angle ABC = 110°$	Triangle sum theorem	Calculate $\angle ABC$ as our first step. The angles in a triangle sum to 180°.
$\angle DBC \cong \angle ACB$ $\angle BAC \cong \angle BDC$	Diagram	The diagram shows these two pairs of angles are congruent.
$m\angle BCD = m\angle ABC = 110°$	Third angles theorem $\angle ABC \cong \angle BCD$	Since two of the angles are congruent, the third angles theorem lets us conclude the third angles of the triangles $\triangle ABC$ and $\triangle DCB$ are congruent.

2. Three pairs of corresponding angles are congruent in two triangles. One can conclude

    A. The triangles are similar.
    B. The figures are congruent.
    C. Neither answer A nor B is true.
    D. Both A and B are true.

SOLUTION

The answer is A. The triangles are similar since they have the same shape. But they are only congruent if their sides are congruent, and that is not stated. This makes B false, as is D. Since A is true, that means C is false.

Model Problems continue . . .

3. Prove: △FAT ≅ △CAT

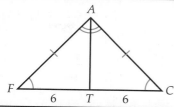

SOLUTION

Statement	Reason	
$\overline{FA} \cong \overline{CA}$, $\overline{FT} \cong \overline{CT}$	Diagram	Using hash marks and a length, the diagram shows these two sides are congruent.
$\overline{AT} \cong \overline{AT}$	Reflexive property of congruence	The reflexive property says that a segment is congruent with itself.
$\angle AFT \cong \angle ACT$, $\angle FAT \cong \angle CAT$	Diagram	The diagram shows these angles as congruent.
$\angle FTA \cong \angle CTA$	Third angles theorem	Two pairs of angles in the triangles are congruent. The third angles theorem says the third angles must be congruent too.
△FAT ≅ △CAT	Corresponding angles, sides all congruent	We have shown the corresponding angles and sides are congruent. This means the triangles are congruent.

4. Prove: △XZY ≅ △BZA

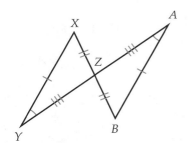

SOLUTION

Statement	Reason	
$\angle XZY \cong \angle BZA$	Vertical angles	Vertical angles are congruent by the vertical angles theorem.
$\angle Y \cong \angle A$	Diagram	The diagram shows these angles are congruent.
$\angle X \cong \angle B$	Third angles theorem	Two pairs of corresponding angles in the triangles are congruent. The third angles theorem says the third angles must be congruent too.
$\overline{XY} \cong \overline{BA}$, $\overline{XZ} \cong \overline{BZ}$, $\overline{YZ} \cong \overline{AZ}$	Diagram	The diagram shows these pairs of sides as congruent.
△XZY ≅ △BZA	Corresponding angles, sides all congruent	We have shown the corresponding angles and sides are congruent. This means the triangles are congruent.

PRACTICE

1. $BC = EF$ and $AC = DF$. Are the triangles congruent?

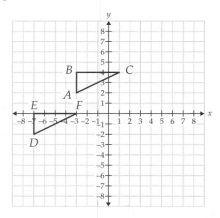

  A. Yes

  B. No

2. Two isosceles triangles are congruent. If the vertex angle of the first triangle measures 130°, what is the measure of one base angle on the second triangle?

  A. 25°   C. 80°

  B. 50°   D. 130°

3. Which of the following could be used in a proof to justify the statement $\angle AEB \cong \angle CED$? Select all that apply.

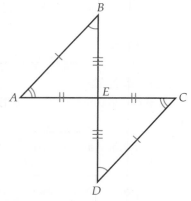

  A. Third angles theorem

  B. Reflexive property

  C. Adjacency theorem

  D. Vertical angles theorem

4. Calculate $m\angle GHE$.

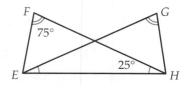

Exercises 5–8: Triangle PQR is congruent to triangle FGH.

5. If $m\angle P = 75°$ and $m\angle R = 40°$, what is the measure of $\angle G$?

6. If $m\angle Q = 37°$ and $m\angle R = 20°$, what is the measure of $\angle F$?

7. If $m\angle H = 42°$ and $m\angle F = 104°$, what is the measure of $\angle Q$?

8. If $m\angle F = 87°$ and $m\angle R = 13°$, what is the measure of $\angle G$?

9. Given two triangles $\triangle BET$ and $\triangle RAG$ where $\angle B \cong \angle R$ and $\angle T \cong \angle G$, what can you conclude about $\angle E$ and $\angle A$?

10. List all pairs of congruent angles.

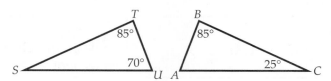

11. A thief stole a triangle from a geometer. The geometer reported to the police that the stolen triangle was scalene and right. The police found a triangle in the possession of the thief. They measured two of the angles and found their measures to be 37° and 55°. Is this the stolen triangle? Why or why not?

12. When enough congruent isosceles triangles are placed with their vertex angles at the same point and their sides adjacent, they may form a regular polygon. If a regular polygon is formed using congruent isosceles triangles whose base angles each measure 70°, what shape is formed?

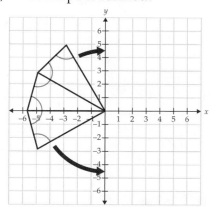

Practice Problems continue . . .

13. Given $\overline{CF} \cong \overline{GE}$, prove $\triangle BCG \cong \triangle DEF$ by showing that all pairs of corresponding sides and angles are congruent. Be sure to justify each step in your proof.

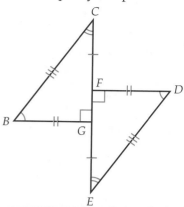

14. In isosceles triangle ABC, $\overline{BD}$ bisects $\angle B$ and intersects base $\overline{AC}$ at point D, as shown in the diagram. Prove $\triangle ABD \cong \triangle CBD$.

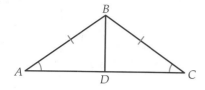

• Multi-Part PROBLEM Practice •

MP 2, 4 A glass artist wants to know if two pieces of glass are the same size and shape. He has already measured the lengths AB and EF, which are both 10 inches. Also, he has noticed that the two pieces of glass form a rectangle when placed next to each other.

a Are the angles congruent?

b Are the sides congruent?

c If $m\angle ABE = 72°$, what is $m\angle BEF$?

d Identify the angle relationship between $\angle ABE$ and $\angle BEF$.

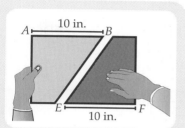

LESSON 5.3

5.3 Proving Triangles Congruent with SSS and SAS

Side-Side-Side (SSS) Postulate

We discussed previously how rigid motion transformations create congruent figures. Another way in geometry to prove that triangles are congruent is a series of postulates and theorems. We start with the **side-side-side (SSS) postulate**.

Side-side-side (SSS) postulate

If three sides of one triangle are congruent to those of another triangle, then the triangles are congruent.

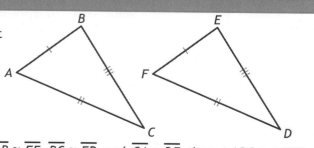

If $\overline{AB} \cong \overline{FE}$, $\overline{BC} \cong \overline{ED}$, and $\overline{CA} \cong \overline{DF}$, then $\triangle ABC \cong \triangle FED$.

Earlier, we showed how to copy any angle using a compass and a straightedge. Here, we use the SSS postulate to justify this approach.

Statement	Reason
$\overline{AD} \cong \overline{YU}$ and $\overline{AE} \cong \overline{YW}$ and $\overline{DE} \cong \overline{UW}$	All segment pairs made with compass at same setting
$\triangle DAE \cong \triangle UYW$	SSS postulate
$\angle DAE \cong \angle UYW$	Corresponding angles in congruent triangles

MODEL PROBLEMS

1. Are the triangles congruent? Apply the SSS postulate to prove that they are.

Prove: $\triangle BAC \cong \triangle BDC$

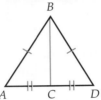

SOLUTION

Statement	Reason
$\overline{AB} \cong \overline{DB}, \overline{AC} \cong \overline{DC}$	Diagram
$\overline{BC} \cong \overline{BC}$	Reflexive property of congruence
$\triangle BAC \cong \triangle BDC$	SSS postulate

2. Use SSS to prove the base angles theorem.

Prove: $\angle B \cong \angle C$

SOLUTION

Statement	Reason
Construct $\overline{AD}$ so D is midpoint of $\overline{BC}$	Construction of auxiliary line segment (not shown)
$\overline{AB} \cong \overline{AC}$	Given
$\overline{BD} \cong \overline{CD}$	Definition of midpoint
$\overline{AD} \cong \overline{AD}$	Reflexive property of congruence
$\triangle ABD \cong \triangle ACD$	SSS congruence postulate
$\angle B \cong \angle C$	Definition of congruent triangles

Model Problems continue . . .

3. Prove: $\triangle ABC \cong \triangle DEF$

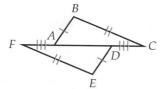

SOLUTION

Statement	Reason
$\overline{FE} \cong \overline{CB}$, $\overline{AB} \cong \overline{DE}$, and $\overline{DC} \cong \overline{AF}$	Diagram
$FD = AF + AD$	Segment addition postulate
$FD = DC + AD$	Substitution property
$CA = AD + DC$	Segment addition postulate
$\overline{FD} \cong \overline{CA}$	Transitive property of equality
$\triangle ABC \cong \triangle DEF$	SSS congruence postulate

> To do this, we have to show first that $\overline{FD} \cong \overline{CA}$. If we can do that, we can use the SSS postulate, since the diagram shows other pairs of congruent sides.

4. In the previous model problem, why do we substitute *DC* for *AF* in the third step?

SOLUTION

We substitute segment *DC* for segment *AF* in the third step, so we can use the transitive property of equality to show $FD = CA$. This is the third corresponding pair of sides for our two triangles, and once we show the sides are congruent, we know the triangles are congruent by SSS.

5. There are SSS criteria for both similarity and congruence. Which statements are true?

    A. The criteria are identical.
    B. A triangle can be both similar and congruent.
    C. SSS requires proportional lengths for similarity, identical lengths for congruence.
    D. B and C

SOLUTION

The answer is D. The criteria are not identical, so A is false. A congruent triangle is also similar, so B is true. The statement C is correct, so D, which includes both, is the correct option.

Hypotenuse-Leg Theorem

The hypotenuse-leg theorem applies *only* to right triangles. (Remember: only right triangles have hypotenuses).

Hypotenuse-leg congruence theorem

If the hypotenuse and a leg of a right triangle are congruent to those of another right triangle, then the triangles are congruent.

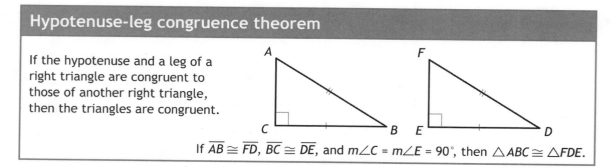

If $\overline{AB} \cong \overline{FD}$, $\overline{BC} \cong \overline{DE}$, and $m\angle C = m\angle E = 90°$, then $\triangle ABC \cong \triangle FDE$.

The Pythagorean theorem and SSS postulate can be used to prove the hypotenuse-leg theorem. If one leg and the hypotenuse are congruent to those of another triangle, then the other legs must be congruent as well due to the Pythagorean theorem, and then the triangles are congruent according to the SSS postulate.

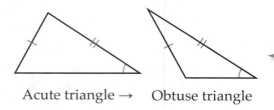

Acute triangle →   Obtuse triangle

There is not a side-side-angle (SSA) postulate. This is an example of how two sides and an angle not between those sides can create two different triangles. Because of this, SSA does not guarantee that two triangles are congruent—one could be obtuse and one could be acute.

MODEL PROBLEMS

1. Prove the gray and orange triangles are congruent, given that the dividing line is perpendicular to the base so the triangles are right triangles. The hypotenuses of both triangles are congruent.

SOLUTION

Statement	Reason	
Hypotenuses are congruent	Given	The text says the hypotenuses have the same length.
Vertical leg congruent	Reflexive property of congruence	The vertical leg is common to both triangles. A segment is always congruent with itself.
Triangles are congruent	Hypotenuse-leg theorem	We have shown a hypotenuse and leg are congruent, so the triangles are congruent. Flipping one over shows it is the same shape and size as the other.

2. $\overline{AJ}$ is a perpendicular bisector of $\overline{KM}$.
   a Show that the triangles $\triangle KJR$ and $\triangle MAR$ are congruent.
   b In the proof, why must we state that we have to calculate AM?

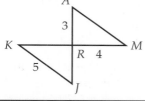

SOLUTION

a

Statement	Reason
$\overline{AJ}$ is a perpendicular bisector of $\overline{KM}$	Given
$m\angle ARM = m\angle JRK = 90°$	Definition of a perpendicular bisector
$AM = 5$	Pythagorean theorem: $c^2 = a^2 + b^2$ $c^2 = 3^2 + 4^2$, so $c = 5$
$KJ = 5$	Diagram
$\overline{AM} \cong \overline{KJ}$	Transitive property of equality
$\overline{KR} \cong \overline{MR}$	Definition of perpendicular bisector
$\triangle KJR \cong \triangle MAR$	Hypotenuse-leg theorem

Model Problems continue . . .

b To use the hypotenuse-leg theorem, we need to show that the hypotenuses of both triangles are congruent. One way to do this is to calculate the lengths of both hypotenuses and compare them.

Side-Angle-Side (SAS) Postulate

Another way to prove that triangles are congruent is the **side-angle-side (SAS) postulate**. The angle is the angle included (formed) by the two sides.

Side-angle-side (SAS) postulate

If two sides and the included angle of a triangle are congruent to those of another triangle, then the triangles are congruent.

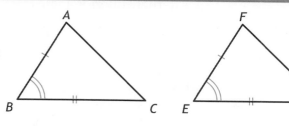

If $\overline{AB} \cong \overline{FE}$, $\overline{BC} \cong \overline{ED}$, and $\angle B \cong \angle E$, then $\triangle ABC \cong \triangle FED$.

We apply the postulate to prove two triangles in a figure are congruent. The proof takes advantage of the fact that the distance from the center of a circle to a point on the circle is always the same.

Prove: $\triangle ACB \cong \triangle DCE$

Given: C is the center of the circle

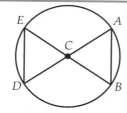

Statement	Reason
Point C is at the center of the circle	Given
$\overline{AC} \cong \overline{DC}$, $\overline{BC} \cong \overline{EC}$	All radii of a circle have the same length
$\angle ACB \cong \angle DCE$	Vertical angles theorem
$\triangle ACB \cong \triangle DCE$	SAS postulate

MODEL PROBLEMS

1. a Prove: △SEA ≅ △TAE
Given: $\overline{SA} \cong \overline{TE}$

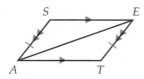

b In the proof, why do we need to show that $\overline{AE} \cong \overline{AE}$?

SOLUTION

a

Statement	Reason
$\overline{SE} \parallel \overline{AT}$	Diagram
$\angle SAE \cong \angle TEA$	Alternate interior angles
$\overline{AE} \cong \overline{AE}$	Reflexive property of congruence
$\overline{SA} \cong \overline{TE}$	Given
△SEA ≅ △TAE	SAS congruence postulate

> We can prove that a pair of triangles is congruent by using SAS and the fact that the triangles form a parallelogram when placed together. The figure is a parallelogram. Opposite sides of a parallelogram are parallel and congruent.

b To prove that △SEA ≅ △TAE using SAS, we need to show that two pairs of corresponding sides, and the angles in between them, are congruent. $\overline{AE}$ is one of our "pairs" of corresponding sides, even though it is singular, because it is a side of both triangles. Therefore, by showing that it is congruent to itself, we are proving one of our S's of SAS.

2. $\overline{RO}$ is a perpendicular bisector of $\overline{FL}$ in the diagram. Using SAS, prove that △FRO ≅ △LRO.

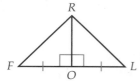

SOLUTION

Statement	Reason
$\angle FOR \cong \angle LOR$	Definition of perpendicular bisector
$\overline{RO} \cong \overline{RO}$	Reflexive property of congruence
$\overline{FO} \cong \overline{LO}$	Definition of perpendicular bisector
△FRO ≅ △LRO	SAS congruence postulate

Model Problems continue . . .

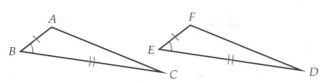

3. *AB* is one-fourth *BC*, and
FE is 15 less than *ED*.
What is *BC*?

SOLUTION

$\triangle ABC \cong \triangle FED$ SAS congruence postulate

Lengths of corresponding sides are equal $BC = ED$ and $AB = FE$

Derive equations from problem statement $AB = \dfrac{1}{4} BC$, and $FE = ED - 15$

                                      $FE = ED - 15$, so then $AB = BC - 15$

Substitute $\dfrac{1}{4} BC = BC - 15$

Solve $BC = 4BC - 60$

                                       $BC = 20$

PRACTICE

1. Are the triangles congruent?

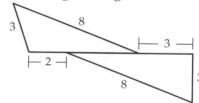

  A.   Yes
  B.   No
  C.   There's no way to tell for sure

2. Are the triangles congruent?

  A.   Yes
  B.   No
  C.   There's no way to tell for sure

3. Triangle *ABC* is described by the points
(0, 0), (12, 0), and (5, 7). Triangle *JKL* is
described by the points (0, 0), (0, 12), and
(−7, 5). Are the triangles congruent?

  A.   Yes
  B.   No
  C.   There's no way to tell for sure

4. Based on the diagram, by which of the
following methods can the triangles be
proved congruent?

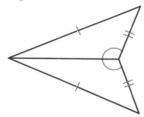

  A.   SSS only
  B.   SAS only
  C.   Both SSS and SAS
  D.   Neither method

5. Based on the diagram, which reason justifies
the statement $\angle CLA \cong \angle LCK$?

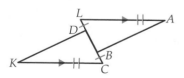

  A.   SAS postulate
  B.   Reflexive property
  C.   Alternate interior angles theorem
  D.   Alternate exterior angles theorem

Practice Problems continue . . .

6. Triangle *DEF* is described by the points (0, 0), (−11, 0), and (−6, 3). Triangle *MNP* is described by the points (0, 0), (0, −6), and (3, −11). Are the triangles congruent?

   A. Yes

   B. No

   C. There's no way to tell for sure

7. $\triangle ABC \cong \triangle YZX$ and *A* and *Y* are right angles. $\overline{AB} \cong \overline{YZ}$ and $\overline{BC} \cong \overline{ZX}$. Can we use the hypotenuse-leg theorem to prove that these two triangles are congruent?

   A. Yes

   B. No

8. $\triangle ABC$ and $\triangle DEF$ have hypotenuses of length 13. $\triangle ABC$ has a leg of length 5, and $\triangle DEF$ has a leg of length 11. Are these congruent triangles?

   A. Yes

   B. No

9. Triangle *A*'s vertices are at (0, 0), (5, 0), and (5, 12), and triangle *B*'s vertices are at (3, −3), (3, −8), and (15, −8). Are the triangles congruent? Hint: Sketch the triangles.

   A. Yes

   B. No

10. a Are these triangles congruent?

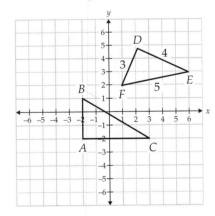

   A. Yes

   B. No

   b Would the triangles be congruent if $\angle C$ were located at (2, −2)?

   A. Yes

   B. No

Exercises 11–12: $\overline{AB}$ and $\overline{DE}$ are corresponding sides in two congruent triangles, $\triangle ABC$ and $\triangle DEF$.

11. If *BC* is 2.5 times longer than *AB* and 6 centimeters longer than *DE*, calculate *DE*.

12. If *BC* is 3 times longer than *AB* and 4 centimeters longer than *DE*, calculate *DE*.

13. Suppose two triangles, *FED* and *FAD*, share side $\overline{FD}$. If $\overline{ED} \cong \overline{AD}$ and $\overline{FD}$ bisects $\angle D$, sketch the two triangles.

14. **MP 2, 4, 6** A builder is making two identical triangular frames to support a staircase. He makes the first frame using pieces of lumber which are 3 feet, 4 feet, and 5 feet long. He then finds pieces of lumber for the second frame that are 3 feet long and 4 feet long in his lumber pile. Remaining in the lumber pile are two pieces which are 4 feet long, three pieces which are 5 feet long, and one piece which is 6 feet long. What is the chance that if the builder selects one piece at random from the pile, it will be the correct length for the third side of the second frame? Write your answer as a percentage.

15. Two sides of one triangle measure 13 inches and 19 inches. In a second triangle, two of the sides measure 19 inches and 24 inches. If the triangles are congruent, what is the perimeter of the first triangle, in inches?

Exercises 16–22: Using the diagram, provide a justification for each statement. The statements are part of a proof that triangle *BAT* is congruent to triangle *ENR*.

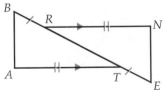

16. $\overline{AT} \cong \overline{RN}$

17. $\angle BTA \cong \angle ERN$

18. $\overline{BR} \cong \overline{ET}$

19. $\overline{RT} \cong \overline{RT}$

20. $BR + RT = ET + RT$

21. $\overline{BT} \cong \overline{ER}$

22. $\triangle BAT \cong \triangle ENR$

   Practice Problems continue . . .

Practice Problems continued . . .

23. Given $\triangle AXE \cong \triangle TRY$ by the side-side-side postulate, if $AX = 2x + y$, $AE = 3y - 4$, $TR = x + 9$, and $TY = 5x + 7$, find the length of $\overline{TY}$.

24. What additional piece of information is needed to prove $\triangle PUE \cong \triangle REU$ by the hypotenuse-leg theorem?

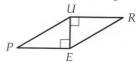

25. What additional piece of information is needed to prove $\triangle SYR \cong \triangle BUF$ by the hypotenuse-leg theorem?

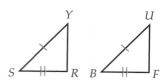

26. **MP 7** Prove $\triangle ABC \cong \triangle DEF$ by SSS.

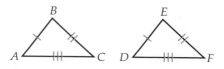

27. **MP 7** Prove $\triangle JKL \cong \triangle RST$ using the side-side-side postulate.

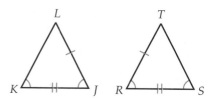

28. Tricia needs to prove the two right triangles below are congruent, but she says she can't do it because she doesn't know the length of each triangle's hypotenuse. Is Tricia correct in saying there is no way to prove the triangles congruent? Explain your reasoning.

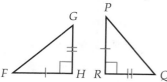

29. What value of x would make the triangles congruent?

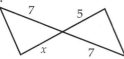

30. Luis says $\triangle SET \cong \triangle BAR$ by the side-angle-side postulate. Do you agree? Explain your reasoning.

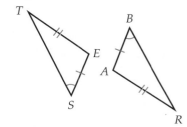

31. Given $\overleftrightarrow{JE} \parallel \overleftrightarrow{AP}$, prove $\triangle JET \cong \triangle PAL$.

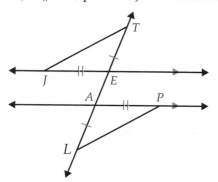

32. **MP 3** Using the diagram, prove the isosceles bisector theorem converse.

Isosceles bisector theorem converse

If a line through the vertex of an isosceles triangle is the perpendicular bisector of the base, then it is also the angle bisector of the vertex angle.

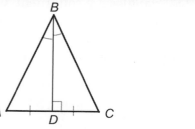

If $\overline{BD}$ is a $\perp$ bisector of $\overline{AC}$, then $\overline{BD}$ bisects $\angle B$.

LESSON 5.4

5.4 Proving Triangles Congruent with ASA and AAS

Angle-Side-Angle (ASA) Postulate

We add to your congruency tools: The **angle-side-angle (ASA) postulate**.

Angle-side-angle (ASA) postulate	
If two angles of a triangle and the side between them are congruent to those of another triangle, then the triangles are congruent.	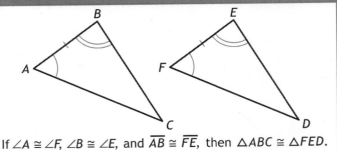

If $\angle A \cong \angle F$, $\angle B \cong \angle E$, and $\overline{AB} \cong \overline{FE}$, then $\triangle ABC \cong \triangle FED$.

MODEL PROBLEMS

1. Which triangles are congruent?

> You need to determine when you can (and cannot) apply the ASA postulate.

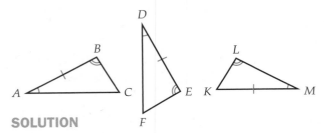

SOLUTION

$\triangle ABC \cong \triangle DEF$ ASA postulate

$\triangle KLM$ Unknown: Congruent side not between congruent angles

2. Prove: $\triangle ABD \cong \triangle CBD$

Given: $\overline{BD}$ is the perpendicular bisector of $\overline{AC}$

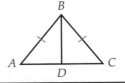

SOLUTION

Paragraph Proof
To prove that the two triangles are congruent, we will use the ASA postulate. We start with $\angle BAD \cong \angle BCD$ since the triangle is isosceles, with $\overline{AB} \cong \overline{BC}$. $\overline{AD} \cong \overline{CD}$ since $\overline{BD}$ is a bisector, so we now have an angle and a side. We still need to prove that the other two angles adjacent to $\overline{AD}$ and $\overline{CD}$ are congruent. Since $\overline{BD}$ is a perpendicular bisector, both $\angle ADB$ and $\angle CDB$ are right angles, so they are congruent. We have used the ASA postulate to prove the triangles congruent.

There is another way to do the proof using SAS. The two bottom segments AD and CD are congruent as shown above, as are the right angles. Since $\overline{BD} \cong \overline{BD}$ due to the reflexive congruence property, we have SAS.

Rigid Motion and Congruent Triangles

We do rigid motion transformation to have one triangle carry onto another, to show they are congruent triangles. The criteria for triangle congruence (ASA, SAS, and SSS) follow from the definition of congruence in terms of rigid motions.

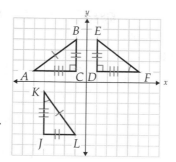

A transformation that creates a congruent figure is called an *isometry*.

SSS is one way to test if triangles are congruent. If we take $\triangle KLJ$, we can do two rigid motions (a translation and a rotation) so that $\triangle ABC$ and $\triangle KLJ$ will overlap. They overlap since all their sides are congruent.

$\triangle ABC$ and $\triangle FED$ have two congruent corresponding sides and a congruent angle in between them. Do a rigid motion, such as a reflection, and you will see that they are congruent.

Finally, we use all three rigid motions (a translation, rotation, then reflection) to see how $\triangle KLJ$ is congruent to $\triangle FED$. Since we already know $\triangle KLJ \cong \triangle ABC$, $\angle K \cong \angle A$. We then use ASA to show $\triangle KLJ \cong \triangle FED$.

The method above shows how transformational geometry relates to three methods for showing triangle congruence. Since translation does not change the measure of an angle or the length of a segment, then translation creates congruent figures. Corresponding angles and sides remain the same.

Introduction to Coordinate Proofs

Positioning one vertex at the origin simplifies coordinate proofs.

A **coordinate proof** is one that uses the coordinate system. Before we begin doing coordinate proofs, we practice substituting variables for coordinate points to show how the area of a rectangle can be calculated.

Represent points with variables	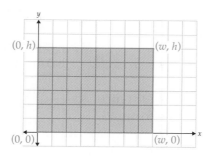	We place a figure on the coordinate plane and represent the coordinates of the vertices with variables. In this example, we put the base of the rectangle on the x-axis, and the height of the rectangle on the y-axis.
Calculate dimensions	height $= h - 0 = h$ width $= w - 0 = w$	The height of the rectangle is the distance from the x-axis to the line $y = h$, which is $h - 0$, equal to h. Similarly, the width is w.
Area	$A = h \cdot w$	The area equals the product of the height and the width (also referred to as the base).

Now we begin doing coordinate proofs. We prove that a translation creates a congruent figure and is an example of rigid motion.

Prove: $\triangle ABC \cong A'B'C'$
Given: $\triangle A'B'C'$ is a translation of $\triangle ABC$

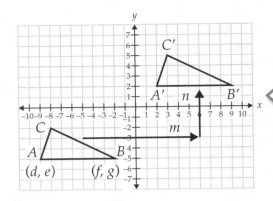

For our proof, use two points, *A* and *B*, on a triangle. They have the coordinates (*d*, *e*) and (*f*, *g*), as you see in the diagram. They are translated by *m* along the *x*-axis and *n* along the *y*-axis.

Statement	Reason	
$A' = (d + m, e + n)$ $B' = (f + m, g + n)$	Definition of translation	Translations are defined as adding the same constant to *x*- and *y*- values.
$AB = \sqrt{(f - d)^2 + (g - e)^2}$	Distance formula	Use the distance formula to calculate *AB*.
$A'B' = \sqrt{[(f + m) - (d + m)]^2 + [(g + n) - (e + n)]^2}$	Addition and distance formula	Calculate it for *A'B'*. Add the translated distance to the original coordinates.
$A'B' = \sqrt{(f + m - m - d)^2 + (g + n - n - e)^2}$ $A'B' = \sqrt{(f - d)^2 + (g - e)^2}$ $A'B' = AB$	Simplify	Simplify the expression in the radical, and we end up with the same distance that we calculated for *AB*. We have shown that $AB = A'B'$, so the translation has created a congruent line segment.
$A'C' = AC$, and $B'C' = BC$	Distance formula	Prove that the other corresponding legs of the triangles are congruent.
$\overline{A'B'} \cong \overline{AB}$, $\overline{A'C'} \cong \overline{AC}$, and $\overline{B'C'} \cong \overline{BC}$	Definition of congruent segments	Because the segments have the same length, they are congruent.
$\triangle ABC \cong A'B'C'$	SSS congruence postulate	By SSS for congruent triangles, the original triangle is congruent to its translated image.

Rigid motion provides a definition of congruent figures, including triangles. In a rigid motion transformation, all corresponding angles and all corresponding sides remain congruent. In other words, a rigid motion transformation does not change the measure of an angle or the length of a triangle side. This means that two triangles are congruent if and only if one can be transformed into the other by rigid motion transformations.

MODEL PROBLEM

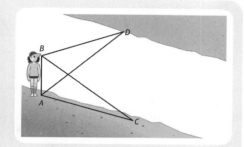

MP 2 Sheila is using her visor to estimate a distance. She cannot cross the chasm, but she can use her hat to measure the distance. Sheila looks straight across the chasm, lining up her visor's tip with a point across the chasm. She then rotates her head, keeping the visor at the same angle to the ground, and lines the visor's tip with a point at the same height on her side. She then paces off the distance to that point. If you look at the illustration to the right, you will see the two different triangles she is using.

a Why does the method work?

b If C is at ground level but D is higher than ground level, the proof fails. Why?

SOLUTION

a Use ASA congruence postulate

$\angle BAD \cong \angle BAC$

Why does the method work? It works because Sheila has created two congruent triangles. We can show this with the ASA congruence postulate. These two angles are congruent since both are right angles.

$\overline{AB} \cong \overline{AB}$

The side is Sheila's height. It is common to both triangles.

$\angle ABD \cong \angle ABC$

The last pair of angles is congruent since Sheila keeps her visor at the same angle as she rotates. The triangles are congruent due to the ASA congruence postulate.

Since the triangles are congruent, if Sheila can locate point C on her side of the canyon (perhaps a cactus marks the spot), she can walk to that point, and that is approximately the same distance as the chasm's width. In other words, $AC = AD$.

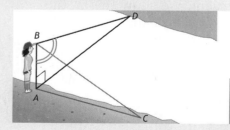

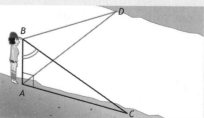

b $\angle BAD$ would be acute and would not be the same measure as right angle BAC if D was higher than ground level. One of the "A's" in ASA would be invalid.

Angle-Angle-Side (AAS) Theorem

The **angle-angle-side (AAS) theorem** follows from the ASA congruence postulate.

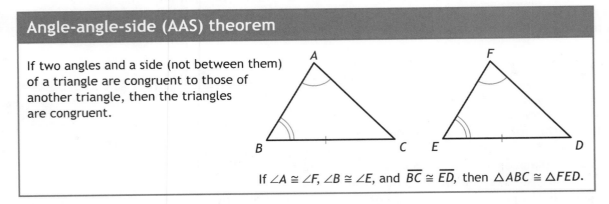

Angle-angle-side (AAS) theorem

If two angles and a side (not between them) of a triangle are congruent to those of another triangle, then the triangles are congruent.

If $\angle A \cong \angle F$, $\angle B \cong \angle E$, and $\overline{BC} \cong \overline{ED}$, then $\triangle ABC \cong \triangle FED$.

Instead of a two-column proof, we do a **flow proof**. These proofs are intended to let you see the various "paths" of a proof—the sets of steps that could be done in parallel. For instance, showing that we have congruent angles and sides occurs at the same level in the proof.

Prove: $\triangle SAN \cong \triangle AST$

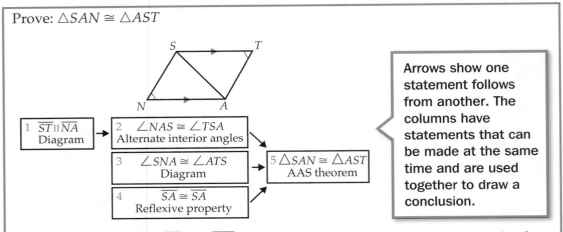

> Arrows show one statement follows from another. The columns have statements that can be made at the same time and are used together to draw a conclusion.

1. The diagram shows $\overline{ST}$ and $\overline{NA}$ as parallel. We show this as the first step (with its reason) in the flow diagram.

2. Since the lines are parallel, the alternate interior angles $\angle NAS$ and $\angle TSA$ are congruent. We use the arrow to indicate the sequence of our proof.

3. The diagram shows $\angle SNA$ and $\angle ATS$ are congruent. We show this in the same column—it does not matter whether we wrote this or the other angle congruence statement first.

4. $\overline{SA}$ is congruent with itself. Again, we put this in the same column. There is no arrow to it from step 1, since it does not follow from the parallel sides statement.

5. We have shown a congruent angle, angle, and side, so we have shown that the triangles are congruent. We needed all three statements in column 2 to make this conclusion. The arrows indicate that all three statements are required for our conclusion.

PRACTICE

1. Which of these are valid postulates to prove that two triangles are congruent? Select all that apply.

   A. SSS
   B. ASA
   C. SSA
   D. AAA
   E. SAS

2. Which congruence postulate or theorem is demonstrated by the rigid motion shown below?

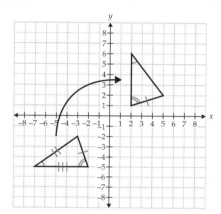

   A. SSS
   B. SAS
   C. ASA
   D. AAS

3. Sam uses a paragraph proof to show $\triangle ABD \cong \triangle CBD$. She says: "$\overline{AD} \cong \overline{DC}$ since $\overline{BD}$ is a bisector. $\overline{BD} \cong \overline{BD}$ due to the reflexive congruence property. Since $\angle ADB$ and $\angle CDB$ are right angles, use the Pythagorean theorem to show the congruence of the two hypotenuses, $\overline{AB} \cong \overline{BC}$." What postulate or theorem is she using?

   A. SSS
   B. ASA
   C. SSA
   D. AAA
   E. SAS

4. Two triangles have one pair of corresponding congruent sides. Which additional information would be needed to prove that the triangles are congruent?

   A. A second pair of corresponding congruent sides
   B. A second pair of corresponding congruent sides and a pair of non-included corresponding congruent angles
   C. One pair of corresponding congruent angles
   D. Two pairs of corresponding congruent angles

5. Which of the following justifications cannot be used to prove two triangles are congruent?

   A. SSS
   B. AAS
   C. SSA
   D. ASA

6. Which set of statements can be used to prove $\triangle MAN \cong \triangle DOG$?

   A. $\angle M \cong \angle D$; $\angle A \cong \angle O$; $\angle N \cong \angle G$
   B. $\angle N \cong \angle G$; $\overline{MA} \cong \overline{DO}$; $\overline{AN} \cong \overline{OG}$
   C. $\angle N \cong \angle G$; $\overline{MA} \cong \overline{DO}$; $\angle A \cong \angle O$

7. How could you prove $\triangle DEG \cong \triangle FEG$? Select all postulates that apply.

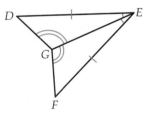

   A. SSS
   B. SAS
   C. ASA
   D. Hypotenuse-Leg
   E. SSA

Practice Problems continue . . .

8. The hypotenuse of right triangle *KJR* is congruent to the hypotenuse of right triangle *MAR*. Are the two triangles necessarily congruent? Explain.

9. $\angle B \cong \angle D$ and $\angle C \cong \angle E$. Are the triangles congruent? Explain.

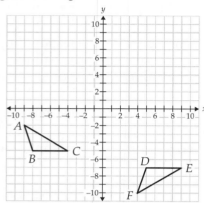

10. $\angle G \cong \angle K$ and $\angle H \cong \angle L$. Are the triangles congruent? Explain.

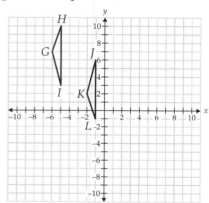

11. $\angle M \cong \angle R$ and $\angle O \cong \angle Q$. Are the triangles congruent? Explain.

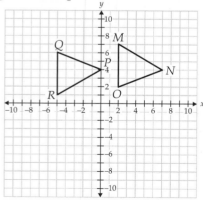

12. Two triangles, $\triangle ABC$ and $\triangle DEF$, are constructed as follows: *B* is at (3, 7), *C* is at (3, 1), *E* is at (−2, 10), and *F* is at (−2, 5). $\angle A \cong \angle D$, and $\angle B \cong \angle E$. Is $\triangle ABC \cong \triangle DEF$? Explain.

13. Two triangles, $\triangle GHI$ and $\triangle KLJ$, are constructed as follows: *G* is at (−4, 1), *H* is at (−1, 1), *K* is at (4, 0), and *L* is at (8, 0). $\angle G \cong \angle K$, and $\angle H \cong \angle L$. Is $\triangle GHI \cong \triangle KLJ$? Explain.

14. Two triangles, $\triangle MON$ and $\triangle RQP$, are constructed as follows: *M* is at (3, −3), *O* is at (−2, −3), *Q* is at (−2, 8), and *R* is at (3, 8). $\angle M \cong \angle R$, and $\angle O \cong \angle Q$. Is $\triangle MON \cong \triangle RQP$? Explain.

15. What additional piece of information is needed to prove $\triangle HIK \cong \triangle JIK$ by the ASA postulate?

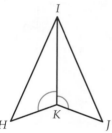

16. If $\triangle LAB \cong \triangle GEO$ by the ASA postulate, what is the value of *x*?

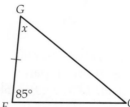

17. If the two triangles below are congruent, what is the value of *y*?

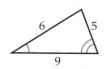
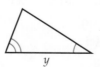

Practice Problems continue . . .

18. Prove △DEG ≅ △FEG using the ASA postulate.

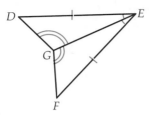

19. Prove that △ABC is congruent to △EDC using the ASA postulate.

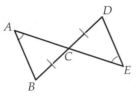

20. Prove △SRK ≅ △PRA using the ASA postulate.

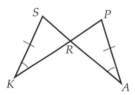

21. From the top of an air traffic control tower, a worker looks down toward the end of one runway and sees a plane, which he knows is 800 feet from the tower. Looking down at the exact same angle, but in a different direction, the worker sees another plane that is waiting to take off. How far is the second plane from the control tower?

22. Taylor proved △BWI ≅ △LGA by the AAS theorem using three given pieces of information about corresponding congruent parts of the two triangles. Two of the given pieces of information were that ∠W ≅ ∠G and $\overline{WI} ≅ \overline{GA}$.

  a Sketch the two triangles and indicate the known congruent parts based on the given information.

  b What is the third piece of information Taylor must have been given in order to complete her proof?

23. Prove △PAS ≅ △APL using the angle-angle-side theorem.

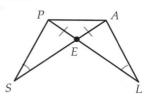

24. Two triangles each contain two angles which both measure 50° and a non-included side which measures 10 centimeters. What is the most efficient method for proving the triangles congruent?

25. What method(s) can be used to prove the two triangles are congruent?

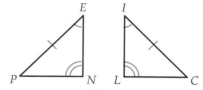

Exercises 26–27: State which method could be used to prove △ABC ≅ △DEF, based on the given information. If it is not possible to prove the triangles congruent, state "Not possible."

26. ∠A ≅ ∠D; ∠C ≅ ∠F; $\overline{AB} ≅ \overline{DE}$

27. ∠A ≅ ∠D; ∠B ≅ ∠E; $\overline{AB} ≅ \overline{DE}$

28. The three angles of triangle KJR are congruent to the three angles of triangle MAR. It is also known that $\overline{KR} ≅ \overline{MR}$. Are the two triangles necessarily congruent? Explain.

29. △TRA is equilateral. What method could be used to prove △GRT ≅ △ERA?

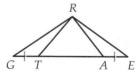

30. Regular pentagon PQRST has one diagonal connecting vertex T and vertex Q, and another diagonal connecting vertex T and vertex R. By what method can △TPQ be proved congruent to △TSR?

31. Quadrilateral WXYZ is not a parallelogram. When the quadrilateral is cut by diagonal WY, two congruent, scalene, non-right triangles are formed. What shape is WXYZ?

Practice Problems continue . . .

32. Quadrilateral *BEAR* is congruent to quadrilateral *LYNX*.

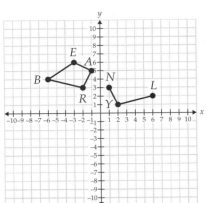

   a What are the coordinates of point *X*?

   b If point *B* is moved to $(-7, 3)$, where must point *L* be moved to keep the figures congruent?

   c Which two rigid motion transformations are required to move *BEAR* to *LYNX*?

   d Do *BEAR* and *LYNX* have the same area? Why or why not?

33. Prove the isosceles bisector theorem.

Isosceles bisector theorem

If a line bisects an isosceles triangle's vertex angle, then it is a perpendicular bisector of the base.

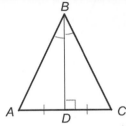

If $\overline{BD}$ bisects $\angle B$, then $\overline{BD}$ is a $\perp$ bisector of $\overline{AC}$.

CHAPTER 5 REVIEW

1. Angle *M* in triangle *LMN* has a measure of $120°$, and angle *N* has a measure that is 25% of angle *M*. Which descriptions match this triangle? Select all that apply.

   A. Right   C. Scalene

   B. Equilateral   D. Isosceles

2. In $\triangle ABC$, $m\angle A = 10°$, and $m\angle B$ is 5 times $m\angle A$. What type of triangle is this? Choose all descriptions that apply.

   A. Equilateral   D. Scalene

   B. Isosceles   E. Obtuse

   C. Acute   F. Cannot tell

3. In a triangle, $m\angle A = 40°$, and angle *B* has twice the measure of *A*. Which descriptions match this triangle? Choose all that apply.

   A. Acute   C. Scalene

   B. Equilateral   D. Isosceles

4. If *C* in the diagram were at $(3, 2)$ instead of $(6, 4)$, what description would match the triangle?

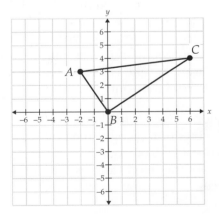

   A. Right scalene

   B. Right isosceles

   C. Equilateral

Chapter Review continues . . .

5. In isosceles △*XYZ*, *m*∠*X* = 35°, *m*∠*Y* = 110°. This means

   A. The side opposite ∠*X* is congruent to the side opposite ∠*Y*.

   B. The side opposite ∠*X* is congruent to the side opposite ∠*Z*.

   C. The side opposite ∠*Y* is congruent to the side opposite ∠*Z*.

6. In isosceles △*ABC*, the side opposite ∠*B* has a length of 7, and the side opposite ∠*C* has a length of $7\sqrt{2}$. *m*∠*B* = 45°. This means

   A. *m*∠*C* = 45°

   B. *m*∠*C* ≠ 45°

   C. There is not enough information to draw a conclusion.

7. One angle in a triangle has a measure of 80°, and another angle has a measure 30° less than that. Which descriptions match this triangle? Choose all that apply.

   A. Right   C. Scalene

   B. Equilateral   D. Isosceles

8. In △*PEG*, the slope of $\overline{PE}$ is $\frac{2}{3}$ and the slope of $\overline{PG}$ is $-\frac{1}{4}$. In order for △*PEG* to be a right triangle, the slope of $\overline{EG}$ can be

   A. $-\frac{2}{3}$ C. $\frac{3}{2}$

   B. $\frac{1}{4}$ D. 4

9. In △*GHI*, the *m*∠*G* = 60°, and *m*∠*H* = *m*∠*I*. What type of triangle is this? Choose all descriptions that apply.

   A. Scalene   D. Acute

   B. Isosceles   E. Right

   C. Equilateral F. Obtuse

10. Based on the diagram, one can conclude that these two triangles are

   A. Similar.

   B. Congruent.

   C. Similar and congruent.

   D. One can draw no conclusion.

11. Select the true statement.

   A. All similar figures are also congruent.

   B. All congruent figures are similar.

   C. A figure cannot be both congruent and similar.

   D. Some but not all congruent figures are similar.

12. Are the triangles congruent?

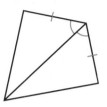

   A. Yes

   B. No

   C. There's no way to tell for sure

13. What value of *n* will make the triangles congruent?

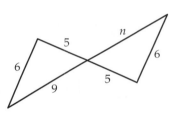

14. Two triangles, △*HIP* and △*RAT*, are graphed in the coordinate plane. If point *T* is found in quadrant IV, where must it be located to make the statement △*HIP* ≅ △*RAT* true?

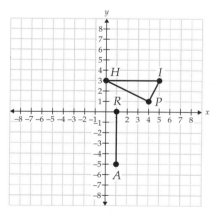

15. In an obtuse isosceles triangle, what is the largest possible integer degree measure of one base angle? Explain your reasoning.

16. **MP 3** Prove: $\triangle SAR \cong \triangle TRA$

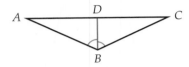

17. $\triangle ABC$ is isosceles, with the vertex angle at B. $\overline{BD}$ is an angle bisector of $\angle B$. If the length of $\overline{AC} = 34$, what is the length of $\overline{AD}$?

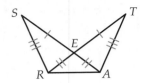

18. **MP 1, 2** The area of a right isosceles triangle is 32 square centimeters. Another triangle is formed inside the original triangle by connecting the midpoints of each of its sides. What is the area of the smaller triangle, in square centimeters?

19. Triangle *BCE* is isosceles. Prove that $\triangle ACF$ is congruent to $\triangle DBG$.

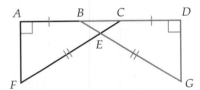

20. In $\triangle XYZ$, $m\angle Z = 15°$ and $\angle Y$ is a right angle. If $a \cdot m\angle Z = m\angle X$, what is the value of a?

21. Is the triangle below an isosceles triangle? Explain your reasoning.

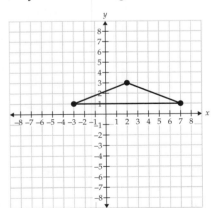

22. **MP 6, 7** Triangle *ABC* has vertices $A(3, -2)$, $B(5, 1)$, and $C(-3, 2)$.

  a Classify the triangle by its angles and side lengths.

  b Designate a vertex that can be changed to make the triangle both a right triangle and an isosceles triangle and describe the change.

  c What rigid transformation would put the right angle of the triangle at the origin, while keeping the triangle the same shape, size, and orientation?

Exercises 23–26: Refer to the diagram.

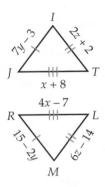

23. What is the length of $\overline{JI}$?

24. What is the length of $\overline{RM}$?

25. What is the length of $\overline{RL}$?

26. What is the perimeter of $\triangle LMR$?

27. **MP 2** In congruent triangles $\triangle STU$ and $\triangle GLN$, *SU* is eleven less than three times *ST*, and *GN* is three more than *ST*. What is the length of $\overline{ST}$?

28. In right triangle $\triangle RGT$, $RG = 6$, $GT = 8$, and $RT = 10$. Graph $\triangle LEF$ in the coordinate plane such that $\triangle RGT \cong \triangle LEF$.

29. Sketch two right triangles that each have two sides measuring 3 and 5 but are not congruent.

30. **MP 3** Parallelogram *PEAT* contains diagonal $\overline{PA}$. Prove $\triangle APE \cong \triangle PAT$.

1. In isosceles △ABC, the side opposite ∠B has a length of 4, and the side opposite ∠C has a length of 4. m∠C = 52°. This means

  A.   m∠B = 52°

  B.   m∠B ≠ 52°

  C.   There is not enough information to draw a conclusion.

2. The lengths of the sides of a triangle are $3\sqrt{2}$, 4, and $3\sqrt{2}$. The triangle is

  A.   Scalene.

  B.   Isosceles.

  C.   Equilateral.

3. In the coordinate plane below, AB = DF and AC = DE. Are the triangles congruent?

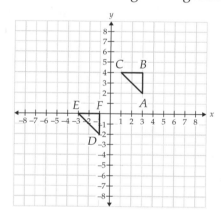

  A.   Yes

  B.   No

4. Select all sides and angles that are congruent.

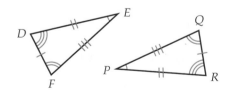

  A.   ∠E ≅ ∠P

  B.   ∠D ≅ ∠Q

  C.   ∠F ≅ ∠Q

  D. $\overline{DF} ≅ \overline{RP}$

5. How would the congruent triangles below be described?

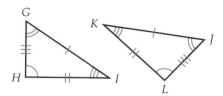

  A.   △GHI ≅ △JKL

  B.   △GHI ≅ △JLK

  C.   △GHI ≅ △LJK

6. Which is the inverse of "A triangle is a polygon"?

  A.   If it is a polygon, then it is a triangle.

  B.   If it is not a triangle, then it is not a polygon.

  C.   If it is not a polygon, then it is not a triangle.

  D.   It is not a polygon, and it is a triangle.

7. Consider the true statement "If it is a lion, it is a mammal." Which of the following is also a true statement? Choose all that apply.

  A.   Converse

  B.   Inverse

  C.   Contrapositive

8. The lines a, b, c, d, and p are coplanar. If a is parallel to b, c is parallel to d, b is perpendicular to p, and d is perpendicular to p, then which of the following are true? Choose all that apply.

  A.   c is parallel to b

  B.   c is perpendicular to p

  C.   a is parallel to p

  D.   c is perpendicular to a

9. Two similar triangles have a pair of congruent sides. One can conclude

   A. The triangles are congruent.
   B. The triangles may be congruent, but more information is required.
   C. This situation is not possible.
   D. None of the above.

10. The concepts of similarity and congruence apply only to triangles.

   A. True
   B. False

11. You are told "Kaitlyn will eat the fruit if it is an apple." What else must you be told to conclude "Kaitlyn will eat the fruit if and only if it is an apple?"

   A. If it is not an apple, then Kaitlyn will not eat the fruit.
   B. If Kaitlyn will eat the fruit, then it is an apple.

MP 7 Exercises 12–15: Determine the coordinates of the checker piece after the translations.

12. Position of checker piece: (3, 2);
Translation 1: 4 units right and 4 units up;
Translation 2: 2 units left and 2 units up

13. Position of checker piece: (8, 1);
Translation 1: 2 units left and 2 units up;
Translation 2: 2 units right and 2 units up

14. Position of checker piece: (6, 1);
Translation 1: 5 units left and 5 units up;
Translation 2: 2 units right and 2 units up

15. Position of checker piece: (5, 2);
Translation 1: 2 units left and 2 units up;
Translation 2: 4 units right and 4 units up

16. What is the result of rotating the point (a, b) about the point (a, b)?

17. Find the exact coordinates of the point resulting from rotating the point (6, 0) 45° clockwise about the origin.

18. **MP 7** In the diagram, which line is a transversal of the other two?

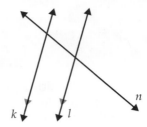

19. Martin buys a laptop that has a screen size of 16 inches by 12 inches. He wishes to buy another laptop that is related to this one by a scale factor of $\frac{3}{4}$. What would the dimensions of the new laptop be?

20. Two rectangles are similar. The length and width of the first rectangle are 9 inches and 4 inches, respectively. If the second rectangle is related to the first rectangle by a scale factor of 1.5, what are the length and width of the second rectangle?

21. A carpenter must create a right triangular brace for a cabinet. Given the included right angle, what must be the sum of the other two angle measures?

22. In a triangle, two angles are congruent, and the third one is 30° greater than each of the smaller ones. Find the angles of the triangle.

23. Point B lies on line segment $\overline{AC}$. The length of $\overline{AC}$ is 56 and the length of $\overline{AB}$ is 11. What is the length of $\overline{BC}$?

24. **MP 6** What is the difference between postulates and theorems?

25. An angle, with a measure of $4a$, is adjacent to two angles. It is supplementary to one, and complementary to the other. Write an expression which represents the sum, in degrees, of the measures of the two angles which adjoin the given angle.

26. A triangle's three angle measures are $x - 9$, $2x$, and $6x$. What is the measure of the triangle's smallest angle?

27. Using the coordinate plane below, translate the given image 3 units left and then sketch the translated image.

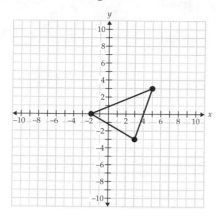

Exercises 28–30: In each of the exercises below, the given rectangles are similar. If diagonals were drawn in rectangle *EFGH*, what would be their lengths?

28.

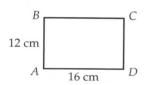

29.

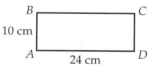

30.

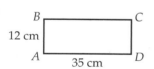

31. Parallel lines *l*, *k*, and *n* are in the same plane. Line *k* is 5 inches away from line *l* and is 7 inches from line *n*. What is the distance between the lines *l* and *n*? Give all possible answers.

32. In the triangle *ABC*, $m\angle A = a$ and $m\angle B = b$. $b > a$. Using *a* and *b*, give an expression for the measure of the angle between the height and the angle bisector drawn from the third vertex *C*.

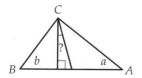

33. If $\angle A$ is supplementary to a 120° angle and $m\angle B = 60°$, are $\angle A$ and $\angle B$ supplementary angles? Explain.

34. Let *A* and *B* be vertical angles formed by two intersecting lines. Give a range for the measure of $\angle A$. That is, how small and how large can angle *A* be?

35. Any angle of a particular triangle is smaller than the sum of the two other angles. Determine the type of the triangle: obtuse, right, or acute. Explain your answer.

36. [MP 3] A teacher says: "Triangle *ABC* has vertex *A* at $(5, -4)$, vertex *B* at $(8, 15)$, and vertex *C* at $(0, 0)$. *ABC* is a right triangle, with *C* its right angle." Is she correct? Justify your answer.

37. The vertices of a triangle are at the points $(8, 5)$, $(2, -7)$, and $(0, 0)$. Find the equation of the line that passes through the vertex at the origin and the midpoint of the opposite side, which is known as a median of this triangle.

38. What is the distance between the point and the line?

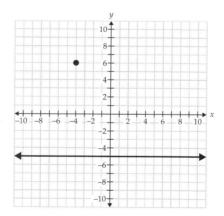

Chapter Content

Chapter Vocabulary

altitude	concurrent lines	median
angle bisector	concurrent rays	midsegment
centroid	concurrent segments	orthocenter
circumcenter	incenter	point of concurrency
circumscribe	indirect reasoning	

LESSON 6.1

6.1 Midsegments

A **midsegment** is a segment that connects the midpoints of two sides of a triangle. A triangle has three midsegments, which we show in gray. The hash marks show how a midsegment bisects each side of the triangle.

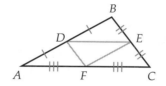

> $\overline{DE}$ is one of the triangle's three midsegments.

Triangle midsegments have various properties, including the ones that we state here.

Midsegment theorem: Parallel to third side

If a segment joins the midpoints of two triangle sides, then the segment is parallel to the third triangle side.

If $\overline{AD} \cong \overline{BD}$ and $\overline{BE} \cong \overline{CE}$, then $\overline{AC} \| \overline{DE}$.

Midsegment theorem: Length is half of third side

> This theorem provides a way to calculate the length of a midsegment.

If a segment joins the midpoints of two triangle sides, then the segment's length is one-half the third side's length.

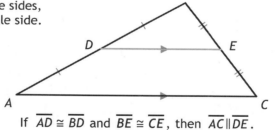

If $\overline{AD} \cong \overline{BD}$ and $\overline{BE} \cong \overline{CE}$, then $\frac{1}{2}AC = DE$, or $AC = 2DE$.

We prove the midsegment theorem: parallel to third side.

Prove: $\overline{DE} \parallel \overline{AC}$
Given: $\overline{AD} \cong \overline{DB}$ and $\overline{BE} \cong \overline{EC}$

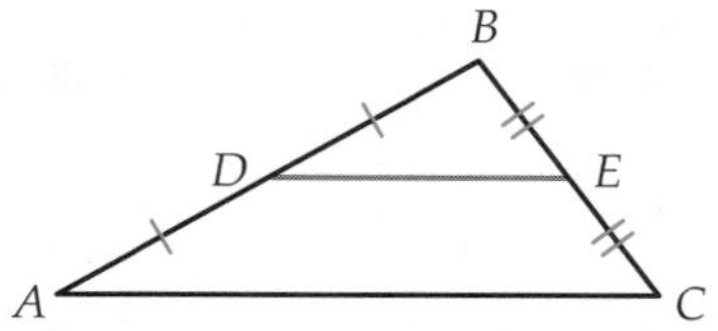

Statement	Reason	
$\overline{AD} \cong \overline{DB}$ and $\overline{BE} \cong \overline{EC}$	Given	The hypothesis of the theorem states that these segments are congruent.
$\dfrac{AB}{DB} = \dfrac{BC}{BE} = 2$	Diagram	$\overline{AB}$ is twice the length of $\overline{DB}$, because it is made up of $\overline{DB}$ plus another segment equal in length to $\overline{DB}$. The same applies to $\overline{BC}$ and $\overline{BE}$.
$\angle B \cong \angle B$	Reflexive property of congruence	An angle is congruent to itself.
$\triangle ABC \sim \triangle DBE$	SAS similarity theorem	Because two corresponding sides of the triangles are proportional, and the angle between them is congruent, the triangles are similar by SAS for similar triangles. We discuss the similarity theorem in depth in the next chapter.
$\angle D \cong \angle A$	Definition of similar triangles	Corresponding angles of similar triangles are congruent, so these angles are congruent as well.
$\overline{DE} \parallel \overline{AC}$	Corresponding angles theorem converse	$\overline{AB}$ acts as a transversal for corresponding angles A and D. Because the two angles are congruent, the two segments that define them (that are not the transversal) must be parallel.

We use a coordinate proof below to prove a midsegment theorem.

Prove: $DE = \frac{1}{2}AC$

Given: $\overline{DE}$ is the midsegment of $\triangle ABC$

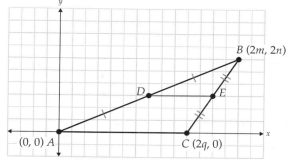

Statement	Reason	
$\overline{DE}$ is midsegment of $\triangle ABC$	Given	We are told that $\overline{DE}$ is a midsegment of the triangle. We want to prove that DE is one-half AC. Locate the vertices using coordinates. It is convenient to identify B as being at $(2m, 2n)$ as opposed to simply (m, n). These expressions represent any possible coordinates of these vertices.
Calculate midpoint of $\overline{AB} = (m, n)$	$D = \left(\dfrac{x_1 + x_2}{2}, \dfrac{y_1 + y_2}{2} \right)$ $D = \left(\dfrac{0 + 2m}{2}, \dfrac{0 + 2n}{2} \right) = (m, n)$	D is an endpoint of a midsegment, which means it is a midpoint on $\overline{AB}$. Use the midpoint formula to calculate its location. Substitute the x- and y-coordinates of the vertices A and B. A is at $(0, 0)$ and B is at $(2m, 2n)$. Simplify. This is why we located the points at locations like $2m$ instead of m—it makes the next steps easier since we don't have fractions.
Calculate midpoint of $\overline{BC} = (m + q, n)$	$E = \left(\dfrac{2m + 2q}{2}, \dfrac{2n + 0}{2} \right) = (m + q, n)$	Do the same for E since it is also a midpoint.
Calculate $DE = q$	$DE = |x_2 - x_1|$ $DE = |(m + q) - m|$ $DE = q$	Now calculate DE. It is horizontal, so we subtract the x-coordinates.
Calculate $AC = 2q$	$AC = |(2q - 0)|$ $AC = 2q$	Calculate AC in a similar fashion, subtracting x-coordinates also.
DE is equal to half of AC	$DE = \frac{1}{2}AC$	$AC = 2q$ and $DE = q$, so we have proven that $DE = \frac{1}{2}AC$.

1. $\overline{AD}$ is a midsegment of a triangle, and parallel to the side $\overline{FE}$, which has endpoints $(4, 3)$ and $(4, -5)$. What pair of coordinates are possible endpoints of $\overline{AD}$?

    A. $(0, 3)$ and $(4, -5)$
    B. $(2, 1)$ and $(2, -3)$
    C. $(-2, 3)$ and $(-2, -5)$
    D. $(-2, 0)$ and $(-2, -2)$

SOLUTION

The answer is B. As mentioned, the midsegment is parallel to the side $\overline{FE}$, and $\overline{FE}$ is a vertical segment, since its x-coordinates are the same. A midsegment also has half the length of the side it is parallel to. $FE = 8$, the absolute value of the difference of its y-coordinates. Choice A describes a segment that is not parallel since it is not vertical, so we can eliminate that. Choices B through D are parallel, but only B describes a segment with a length of 4, since only that segment has a difference of 4 between its y-coordinates.

2. Identify the parallel segments.

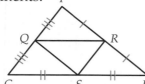

SOLUTION

$\overline{QR}, \overline{RS}, \overline{QS}$ are midsegments   Segments bisect sides   The diagram shows these as midsegments, since they divide the sides of the triangle into equal lengths.

$\overline{QR} \parallel \overline{GH}, \overline{RS} \parallel \overline{FG}, \overline{QS} \parallel \overline{FH}$ Triangle midsegment theorem   A midsegment is parallel to the side it does not intersect.

3. $\overline{QR}, \overline{QS}$, and $\overline{RS}$ are midsegments. $RH = 4$, $RS = 3.5$, and $QR = 5$. What are the lengths of $\overline{GH}, \overline{GI}$, and $\overline{HI}$?

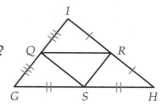

SOLUTION

Calculate GH $GH = 2QR$ Use the theorem to calculate GH, since we know QR.
$GH = 2 \cdot 5 = 10$

Calculate GI $GI = 2RS$ Again, we a midsegment theorem to calculate GI, since we
$GI = 2 \cdot 3.5 = 7$ know RS.

Calculate HI $RI = RH = 4$ Since $\overline{QR}$ is a midsegment, R bisects $\overline{HI}$, and $\overline{RH}$ and $\overline{RI}$ have
$RI + RH = 4 + 4$ equal lengths. We already know that RH is 4, because it is in
$HI = 8$ the problem statement. Add RH and RI to get the length of $\overline{HI}$.

Model Problems continue . . .

MODEL PROBLEMS *continued*

4. **MP 4** A student makes the rabbit shadow you see in the diagram. The part of his hand making the shadow is 4.5 inches tall, and it is halfway between the flashlight and the wall. The top of his fingers are halfway between the flashlight and the top of the shadow.

a How tall is the rabbit?

b Now assume that the boy's hand is 3.7 inches and the shadow 7.6 inches. Is the part of the boy that creates the shadow a midsegment?

SOLUTION

a *DE* is a midsegment

Diagram the situation. *DE* is a midsegment, since the problem describes its endpoints as halfway between *A* and *B*, and *A* and *C*.

Midsegment theorem

$$DE = \frac{1}{2}BC$$

$$BC = 2 \cdot DE$$
$$BC = 2 \cdot 4.5 = 9 \text{ inches}$$

The midsegment theorem about length says that *DE* equals one-half *BC*. Since we want to know *BC*, solve for it.

b No, *DE* is not a midsegment. If it were a midsegment, $\frac{3.7}{7.6}$ would equal $\frac{1}{2}$, and it does not.

PRACTICE

1. In a right triangle, the triangle's midsegments form a triangle that is

A. Acute.

B. Right.

C. Cannot be determined.

2. The sides of a triangle have lengths of 22, 26, and 30. Which of the following could be the length of a midsegment of this triangle?

A. 10

B. 12

C. 14

D. 15

Practice Problems continue . . .

Exercises 3–4: Use the diagram to answer the following questions.

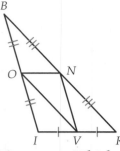

3. $\overline{NV}$ is a midsegment. Which of the following are true statements? Select all that apply.

A. The length of $\overline{IB}$ is twice that of $\overline{NV}$
B. $BO = OI$
C. $RV = RN$
D. $\overline{NV}$ and $\overline{BI}$ are parallel
E. $BN = NR$

4. $\overline{OV}$ is a midsegment. Which of the following are true statements? Select all that apply.

A. The length of $\overline{BR}$ is twice that of $\overline{OV}$
B. $BO = BN$
C. $RV = RN$
D. $\overline{BR}$ and $\overline{OV}$ are parallel
E. $\overline{NV}$ and $\overline{ON}$ are parallel

5. What is the value of x?

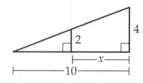

A. 2   C. 5
B. 4   D. 6

6. In a scalene triangle, how many of the midsegments will be congruent to one another?

A. None   C. 3
B. 2   D. Cannot be determined

7. If $BC = 24$, what is MN?

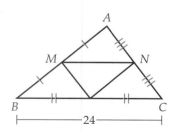

Exercises 8–10: Use the diagram to answer the questions. Line segment AT is a midsegment of triangle PSE.

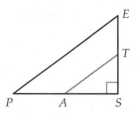

8. If $PS = 12$, what is PA?

9. Which line segment is congruent to $\overline{PA}$?

10. Which line segment is parallel to $\overline{PE}$?

11. Sketch triangle KMP, with midsegment $\overline{NL}$, where N is the midpoint of $\overline{KM}$ and L is the midpoint of $\overline{MP}$. Mark all congruent and parallel line segments.

12. **MP 2, 8** Line segment DE is a midsegment of triangle ABC.

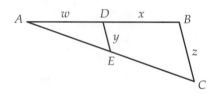

a If the perimeter of $\triangle ABC$ is 26 inches, what is the perimeter of $\triangle ADE$, in inches?
b If y is 11 inches, how long is z?
c If z is 20 inches, how long is y?
d If w is 8 inches, how long is x?

13. **MP 2, 4** Bridges are often designed with triangles to make them stronger. For this bridge, the triangles AHJ, CJL, and ELN are congruent and equilateral. $\overline{FI}$ is a midsegment of the triangle AHJ, and $\overline{GM}$ is a midsegment of the triangle ELN. $\overline{AI}$, $\overline{BJ}$, $\overline{CK}$, $\overline{DL}$, and $\overline{EM}$ are all congruent and vertical. $\overline{AH}$ is 20 feet long, and $\overline{BJ}$ is 17.3 feet long. What is the total length of steel required to construct this side of the bridge?

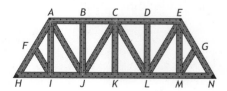

Practice Problems continue . . .

14. Prove: $\angle ORC \cong \angle OES$

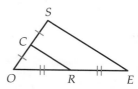

15. MP 2, 6 X, Y, and Z are midpoints of the sides of triangle ABC. We can express XY as $3k - 1$ and AC as $5k + 7$. What is the value of XY?

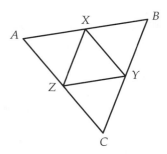

16. Triangle RST is equilateral. If side $\overline{RS}$ is extended from point S to a new point, P, the length $RP = 2RS$. If side $\overline{RT}$ is extended from point T to a new point, Q, $RQ = 2RT$. $\overline{PQ}$ is then constructed.

   a Sketch the situation, and mark all congruent line segments and angles.

   b If the perimeter of $\triangle RST$ is 48 feet, how long is $\overline{PQ}$, in feet?

MP 5, 6 Exercises 17–19: Triangle KEY has vertices $K(4a, 6b)$, $E(0, 0)$, and $Y(8a, 2b)$. Both a and b are real positive numbers.

17. Sketch triangle KEY in the coordinate plane. Note that there is more than one correct answer since a and b are variables.

18. Midsegment $\overline{TH}$ is drawn parallel to side $\overline{EY}$, with point T located on side $\overline{EK}$. Find the coordinates of T and H in terms of a and b.

19. Verify that $\overline{TH}$ is parallel to $\overline{EY}$ using the slope formula.

20. A triangle is graphed on the coordinate plane. One midsegment of the triangle has a slope of $\frac{1}{3}$. Sketch a triangle which meets these conditions.

21. Triangle SAY contains midsegment $\overline{CR}$, which is parallel to side $\overline{SY}$. If $CR = 2x + 7$ and $SY = 6x - 2$, how long is side $\overline{SY}$?

22. MP 3, 6 Refer to the diagram of $\triangle ATR$. Without using the slope formula, prove $\overline{TR}$ is parallel to $\overline{LI}$.

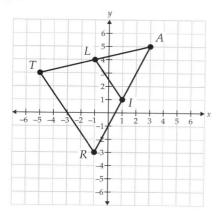

23. Triangle ATK contains midsegment RC. Point R is the midpoint of $\overline{TA}$ and point C is the midpoint of $\overline{AK}$. Given $A(-3, 7)$, $R(1, -3)$, and $C(2, 9)$, find the coordinates of point T and point K.

MP 2, 3, 7 Exercises 24–27: Triangle ABC includes point E located on line segment AB and point F located on line segment AC.

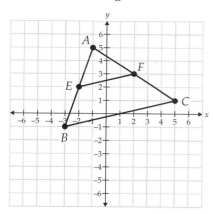

24. Verify that E is the midpoint of $\overline{AB}$ using the midpoint formula.

25. Verify that F is the midpoint of $\overline{AC}$ using the distance formula.

26. Is $\overline{EF}$ a midsegment of $\triangle ABC$? Explain your reasoning.

27. Derrick says that all he needs to do to prove $\overline{EF}$ is a midsegment of $\triangle ABC$ is to show that $\overline{EF}$ is parallel to $\overline{BC}$. Do you agree with Derrick? Why or why not?

MP 4, 8 An artist is painting a mural on the side of a building. Everything in the mural will be twice as big as it is in real life. In order to sketch the outline of a dancer in the mural, the artist is having an actual dancer stand between a projector and the side of the building so he can trace the dancer's shadow on the wall.

a If the distance along the ground from the projector to the dancer is 10 feet, how far from the wall should the dancer stand so his shadow is exactly twice as tall as he is?

b If the dancer is 1.7 meters tall and his shadow is 3.8 meters tall, is the dancer's height a midsegment of triangle *MRA*? Why or why not?

c Assume that the dancer is 1.85 meters tall and he is standing exactly halfway between the wall and the projector. How tall is his shadow, in meters?

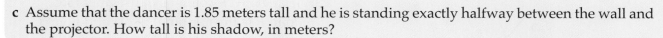

LESSON 6.2

6.2 Perpendicular and Angle Bisectors

Perpendicular Bisectors

A perpendicular bisector of a line segment is a line that is perpendicular to the line segment and divides it in half. Every point on the bisector is equidistant from the endpoints of the line segment.

Perpendicular bisector theorem

If a point is on a line segment's perpendicular bisector, then it is the same distance from each of the line segment's endpoints.

> Point *P* can be any point along the bisector.

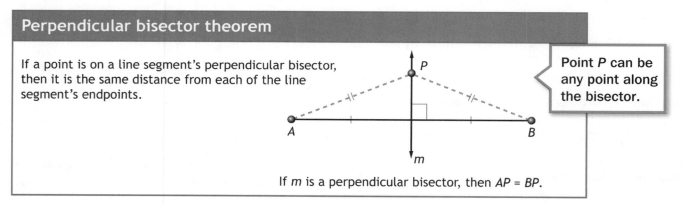

If *m* is a perpendicular bisector, then $AP = BP$.

We prove the theorem:

Prove: $PA = PB$
Given: $\overline{PM}$ is a $\perp$ bisector of $\overline{AB}$

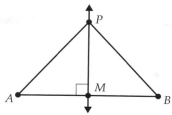

Statement	Reason	
$m\angle PMA = m\angle PMB = 90°$	Given; Definition of a perpendicular bisector	The hypothesis of the theorem is that P is on the perpendicular bisector of $\overline{AB}$. By definition, perpendicular lines (or segments) create four right angles, and all right angles are congruent.
$AM = MB$	Given; Definition of a midpoint	Also by definition, a perpendicular bisector intersects its segment at the segment's midpoint, M. A midpoint is equidistant from both of its endpoints.
$PM = PM$	Reflexive property of congruence	A segment is congruent to itself.
$\triangle AMP \cong \triangle BMP$	SAS postulate	The two triangles are congruent, because two pairs of corresponding sides and their included angles are equal in measure. This means that they are congruent.
$PA = PB$	Definition of congruent triangles	Corresponding parts of congruent triangles are congruent.

Perpendicular bisector theorem converse

If a point is the same distance from a segment's endpoints, then it is on the segment's perpendicular bisector.

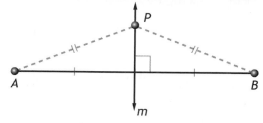

If $AP = BP$, then P is on the $\perp$ bisector of $\overline{AB}$.

1. What is the length of $\overline{IB}$?

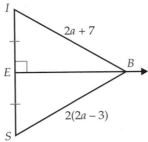

SOLUTION

$IB = SB$	Points on perpendicular bisector are equidistant from endpoints	Any point on a perpendicular bisector is the same distance from the endpoints of the segment it bisects. This means these two lengths are the same.
Solve equation	$2a + 7 = 2(2a - 3)$ $2a + 7 = 4a - 6$ $-2a = -13$ $a = 6.5$	Set the expressions for the two lengths equal to each other and solve the equation.
Substitute	$IB = 2a + 7$ $IB = 2(6.5) + 7 = 20$	To find IB, substitute the value of a we just calculated and evaluate.

> To double-check the answer, we substitute 6.5 into the expression for *SB* and find that it, too, equals 20.

2. Prove: $\triangle XYZ$ is isosceles

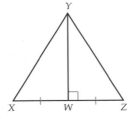

SOLUTION

Statement	Reason	
$\overline{WY}$ is a perpendicular bisector of $\overline{XZ}$	Diagram	$\overline{WY}$ bisects $\overline{XZ}$ at a right angle, and $\overline{XW} \cong \overline{WZ}$.
$XY = YZ$	Perpendicular bisector theorem	Since Y is on the perpendicular bisector, these two lengths from the bisected segment must be equal.
$\triangle XYZ$ is isosceles	Definition of isosceles triangle	Since $XY = YZ$, at least two sides of our triangle are congruent, making it an isosceles triangle by definition.

Model Problems continue . . .

MODEL PROBLEMS *continued*

3. An acrobat is secured by two 7-meter ropes which are attached to the ends of a 4-meter bar. What is his vertical distance from the bar, to the nearest tenth?

SOLUTION

Acrobat on perpendicular bisector $\overline{AC}$	Equidistant from endpoints of $\overline{BD}$	The acrobat is the same distance from two endpoints of a segment. This means the perpendicular segment from the acrobat to the bar is a bisector of the bar's segment.
$\triangle ABC$ is right triangle	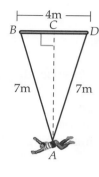	Since he is on the perpendicular bisector, the acrobat is part of a right triangle. $\angle BCA$ is a right angle.
Use Pythagorean theorem	$AC^2 + BC^2 = AB^2$	Apply the Pythagorean theorem to calculate how far the acrobat is from the bar.
Solve	$AC = \sqrt{AB^2 - BC^2}$ $AC = \sqrt{7^2 - 2^2}$ $AC = 6.7$ meters	Solve for AC and substitute the lengths. $BC = 2$ m since $\overline{AC}$ bisects $\overline{BD}$. Evaluate the expression and round to the nearest tenth. The acrobat is about 6.7 meters from the horizontal bar.

Angle Bisectors

Similar to a perpendicular bisector, an **angle bisector** is a ray that divides an angle into two equal halves. There are several important concepts associated with angle bisectors.

Angle bisector theorem

If a point is on the bisector of an angle, then that point is the same distance from the sides that form that angle.

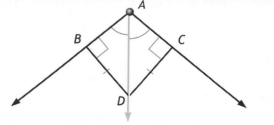

If $\overrightarrow{AD}$ bisects $\angle BAC$ and $\overline{DB} \perp \overrightarrow{AB}$ and $\overline{DC} \perp \overrightarrow{AC}$, then $\overline{DB} \cong \overline{DC}$.

Angle bisector theorem converse

If a point in the interior of an angle is the same distance from that angle's sides, then it is on the bisector.

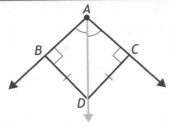

If $\overrightarrow{DB} \perp \overrightarrow{AB}$ and $\overrightarrow{DC} \perp \overrightarrow{AC}$ and $\overline{DB} \cong \overline{DC}$, then $\overrightarrow{AD}$ bisects $\angle BAC$.

MODEL PROBLEMS

1. What is $m\angle MNP$?
Explain how you know.

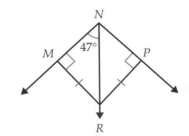

> We apply the converse of the angle bisector theorem in the following proof.

SOLUTION

$m\angle MNP$ is 94 degrees. We know this because NR is the angle bisector of $m\angle MNP$ by the converse of the angle bisector theorem. Thus $m\angle MNP = 2 \cdot m\angle MNR$ and $2 \cdot 47 = 94$ degrees.

2. Point Q is on the angle bisector of $\angle RST$. If $\overline{QT} \perp \overline{ST}$ and $\overline{QR} \perp \overline{SR}$, which statement must be true?

A. $\overline{QS} \cong \overline{QT}$
B. $\overline{QT} \parallel \overline{QR}$
C. $\overline{QT} \perp \overline{QR}$
D. $\overline{QT} \cong \overline{QR}$

SOLUTION

A. $\overline{QS}$ is the hypotenuse of a right triangle formed by the side of the angle, the angle bisector, and segment $\overline{QT}$. Since $\overline{QS}$ is the hypotenuse and $\overline{QT}$ is a leg, these two segments cannot be congruent.

B. Since each segment is perpendicular to one of the rays that forms angle RST, and since angle RST does not have a measure of 0 degrees, QT cannot be parallel to QR, so choice B is invalid.

C. These segments could be perpendicular, but it depends on the measure of the angle and the location of point Q along the angle bisector. There is not enough information to tell if these segments are perpendicular.

D. **Correct answer.** The angle bisector theorem states that if a point is on the angle bisector then it is equidistant from the sides of the angle. Since it is stated that $\overline{QT} \perp \overline{ST}$ and $\overline{QR} \perp \overline{SR}$, this gives enough information to say that $\overline{QT} \cong \overline{QR}$, since triangles QRS and QTS are then congruent with $\overline{QT}$ and $\overline{QR}$ as corresponding sides, which makes them congruent.

Construction: Angle Bisector

You can create an angle bisector using a compass and a straightedge:

1. Place compass point on angle's vertex and draw an arc across rays.

2. Move compass point to an intersection of an arc and ray and draw arc from this point.

3. Repeat at the other intersection without changing the width of the compass.

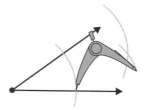

4. Draw a line through the vertex and arcs' intersection. The angle is bisected.

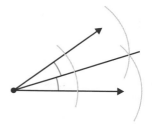

Why does this construction create two congruent angles? The proof is similar to several other constructions we have discussed. We will use the diagram to explain.

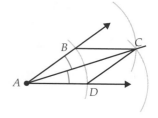

Paragraph Proof

Two congruent triangles, *ABC* and *ADC*, are formed since the segments $\overline{AB}$ and $\overline{AD}$ are created with the compass set at a constant position, segments $\overline{BC}$ and $\overline{DC}$, are created with the compass at the same width, and the triangles share the side $\overline{AC}$. Three pairs of congruent sides means we can apply the SSS congruence postulate and conclude the triangles are congruent. This means angles *BAC* and *DAC* are congruent, since they are corresponding angles in congruent triangles.

PRACTICE

1. Two line segments share the same perpendicular bisector. What can you conclude about the line segments?

  A. They are parallel.
  B. They are perpendicular.
  C. They are neither parallel nor perpendicular.
  D. Not enough information given.

2. Two perpendicular line segments share an endpoint. The perpendicular bisectors of these line segments must be

  A. Parallel.
  B. Perpendicular.
  C. Neither parallel nor perpendicular.
  D. Not enough information to tell.

3. When the angle bisector of an obtuse angle is constructed, it forms

  A. Two congruent obtuse angles.
  B. Two non-congruent obtuse angles.
  C. Two non-congruent acute angles.
  D. Two congruent acute angles.

4. Which points are on the perpendicular bisector of $\overline{BE}$? Select all that apply.

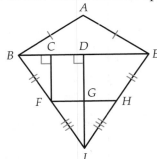

  A. *A*   E. *G*
  B. *C*   F. *H*
  C. *D*   G. *I*
  D. *F*

5. $\angle ABC$ is made up of two rays. The ray BA makes an angle of 10° from the horizontal, and the ray BC makes an angle of 120° from the horizontal. What is the measure of the angle from the horizontal that bisects $\angle ABC$?

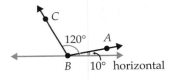

6. $\angle ABC$ is made up of two rays. The ray BA makes an angle of 30° from the horizontal, and the ray BC makes an angle of 60° from the horizontal. What is the measure of the angle from the horizontal that bisects $\angle ABC$?

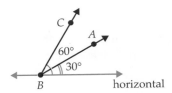

7. $\angle ABC$ is made up of two rays. The ray BA makes an angle of 5° from the horizontal, and the ray BC makes an angle of 55° from the horizontal. What is the measure of the angle from the horizontal that bisects $\angle ABC$?

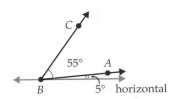

8. $\overrightarrow{AB}$ is the angle bisector of $\angle SAM$. If $m\angle SAB = (2x^2 - 47)°$ and $m\angle MAB = (3x^2 - 14x + 1)°$, find the measure(s) of $\angle SAM$.

Exercises 9–12: Use the diagram to answer the questions. Remember that the interior angles of a quadrilateral sum to 360°.

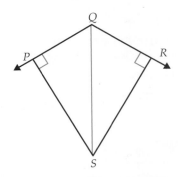

9. If $PS = 21$, $RS = 21$, and $\angle PSR$ measures 84°, what is the measure of $\angle SQR$?

10. Given $\angle PQS \cong \angle RQS$ and $RS = 14$, what is PS?

Practice Problems continue . . .

11. If point S lies on the angle bisector of $\angle PQR$, $PS = 5x - 2$, and $RS = 2x + 7$, how long is $\overline{RS}$?

12. If $\overline{PS}$ is not congruent to $\overline{RS}$, and $\angle RQS$ measures 33°, what value cannot be the degree measure of $\angle PQR$?

Exercises 13–14: Use the diagram below for the following problems.

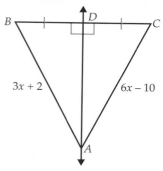

13. Determine the value of x.

14. Explain why we solve the previous problem for x by setting $AB = AC$.

15. Write an equation of the line which is the angle bisector of the angle formed by the y-axis above the origin and the x-axis to the right of the origin.

16. For which type of triangle is each angle bisector also a perpendicular bisector of a side? Include a sketch to illustrate your response.

17. An angle is cut by its angle bisector, forming two angles. Each of these angles is then cut by its own angle bisector, forming four smaller angles. If the measure of a smaller angle is increased by twelve, it is one-third of the measure of the original angle. Find the measure of the original angle.

MP 1, 2 Exercises 18–19: Use the diagram to answer the following questions.

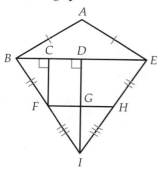

18. If $\overline{BC} \cong \overline{CD}$, is $\overline{CF}$ a perpendicular bisector of $\overline{BD}$? Explain your reasoning.

19. If the extension of line segment $\overline{ID}$ passes through point A, $BD = x + 5$, and $BE = 8x - 14$, find the length of $\overline{BE}$.

20. **MP 3, 4** Two neighboring towns are building a new community center. The community center must be located the same distance from each of the towns, which are exactly 10 miles apart. Trey says the only place to locate the community center is at the halfway point between the towns, so it is exactly five miles from each town. Do you agree with Trey? Why or why not?

21. In a circus act, a performer is suspended by two ropes of the same length that are attached to the ends of a 12-foot-long horizontal bar. If the performer hangs 8 feet below the center of the bar, how long is one of the ropes, in feet?

22. **MP 4, 6** For a scene in a movie, a stuntman is being fired from a giant slingshot. The slingshot consists of two anchor points connected by a giant rubber band. The stuntman is placed in the center of the rubber band and pulled backward along the perpendicular bisector of an imaginary line segment connecting the two anchor points. The anchor points are 16 feet apart, and the stuntman is fired from a point 15 feet behind the midpoint of the anchor points.

a Sketch the situation.

b What is the total length of the stretched rubber band at the moment the stuntman is released?

23. ∠KLM is bisected by $\overrightarrow{LP}$. If
$m∠KLP = (3x + 5y - 6z)°$, write an
expression that represents the measure of
∠KLM.

24. Will the angle bisectors of the interior angles
of a regular polygon all intersect at the same
point? Explain your reasoning.

25. Prove the angle bisector theorem.

Angle bisector theorem

If a point is on the bisector of an angle,
then that point is the same distance
from the sides that form that angle.

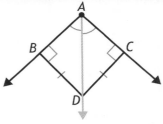

If $\overrightarrow{AD}$ bisects ∠BAC and $\overline{DB} \perp \overline{AB}$ and $\overline{DC} \perp \overline{AC}$, then $\overline{DB} \cong \overline{DC}$.

• Multi-Part PROBLEM Practice •

MP 2, 3 Use the diagram to answer the following questions.

a ∠XWY ≅ ∠YWZ, XY = 8 inches, and WX = 7 inches. What is YZ?

b $\overline{XY} \cong \overline{YZ}$, and $m∠YWZ = 51°$. What is $m∠XWZ$?

c $\overline{XY} \cong \overline{YZ}$, and $m∠YWZ = 53°$. What is $m∠XWZ$?

d If $\overline{XY}$ is not congruent to $\overline{YZ}$, is it possible for $\overline{WY}$ to be the angle
bisector of ∠XWZ? Why or why not?

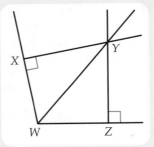

LESSON 6.3

6.3 Circumcenters

Concurrency

In lesson 6.2 we learned that we can create a perpendicular bisector to any line or
line segment. Similarly, we can create the perpendicular bisectors to each side of a
polygon, such as a triangle. When we do so, those bisectors meet at a single point,
which is called a **point of concurrency**, and the bisectors are known as **concurrent
segments**, **concurrent rays**, or **concurrent lines**.

> *Concurrent
> means
> intersecting
> at the same
> point.*

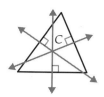 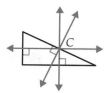 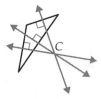

Acute triangle   Right triangle   Obtuse triangle

The point of concurrency, *C*, can be inside, on, or outside of a triangle.

As shown, the point of concurrency does not have to exist inside the polygon (triangle). Wherever it is located, it is perfectly equidistant from each of the polygon's (triangle's) vertices.

Concurrency and perpendicular bisectors theorem

A triangle's perpendicular bisectors intersect at a point of concurrency that is equidistant from the triangle's vertices.

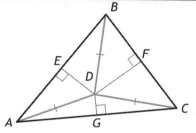

If $\overline{DE}$, $\overline{DF}$, and $\overline{DG}$ are $\perp$ bisectors, then $\overline{DA} \cong \overline{DB} \cong \overline{DC}$.

MODEL PROBLEM

MP 1, 2 Examine the diagram to the right. The triangle's three perpendicular bisectors intersect at the point of concurrency (7, 4), which is exactly 13 units from each vertex. If point *R* is in the first quadrant and has an *x*-coordinate of 12, what is its *y*-coordinate?

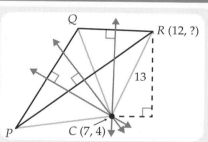

SOLUTION

Use the Pythagorean theorem	$\text{distance} = \sqrt{(y_2 - y_1)^2 + (x_2 - x_1)^2}$ $13 = \sqrt{(y - 4)^2 + (12 - 7)^2}$	We want to find a point's *y*-coordinate. We know the *x*-coordinate of the point, and its distance to the point of concurrency. Use the Pythagorean theorem and substitute the known values.
Square both sides	$13^2 = \left(\sqrt{(y - 4)^2 + (5)^2}\right)^2$ $169 = y^2 - 8y + 16 + 25$ $169 = y^2 - 8y + 41$	Square both sides of the equation and combine like terms.
Set terms equal to zero	$y^2 - 8y - 128 = 0$	Write the equation with the zero on the right side.
Factor	$(y - 16)(y + 8) = 0$	Factor the equation.
Use the zero-factor property	$y - 16 = 0, y + 8 = 0$	Set the factors equal to zero.
Solve the equations	$y = 16, y = -8$	Solve the two equations.
Pick the coordinates in the first quadrant	$(12, 16)$	The problem said the vertex was in the first quadrant.

Circumcenters

In the previous section, we learned that a polygon's point of concurrency is equidistant from each of its vertices. A point of concurrency is also known as a **circumcenter**. This is because we can **circumscribe** a circle around the polygon, and the circumcenter (or point of concurrency) is the center of the circle. Note that the circle just touches each of the polygon's vertices. In this illustration, each perpendicular bisector contains a diameter of the circle and each of the triangle sides is a chord.

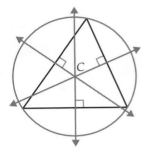

MODEL PROBLEMS

1. **MP 1, 7** Calculate and graph the circumcenter of the given triangle.

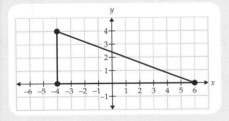

> We can use two perpendicular bisectors to locate the circumcenter of the triangle. A bisector passes through the midpoint.

SOLUTION

Midpoint of vertical segment	$y_{\text{midpoint}} = \dfrac{y_1 + y_2}{2} = \dfrac{0 + 4}{2} = 2$ $(-4, 2)$	Find two perpendicular bisectors, since they will intersect at the circumcenter of the triangle. x-coordinates on the segment are -4.
Horizontal line	$y = 2$	The side is vertical, so its perpendicular bisector will be a horizontal line that passes through the midpoint we just calculated.
Midpoint of horizontal segment	$x_{\text{midpoint}} = \dfrac{x_1 + x_2}{2} = \dfrac{-4 + 6}{2} = 1$ $(1, 0)$	Repeat the exercise for another side. y-coordinates on the segment are 0.

Model Problems continue . . .

Vertical line $x = 1$ This is the equation for a vertical line that passes through the midpoint.

Circumcenter

The lines $x = 1$ and $y = 2$ intersect at $(1, 2)$. This is the triangle's circumcenter. This circumcenter is located on a side of the triangle.

 2. MP 2 The mayor of Sportston wants the town hall to be the same distance from the football, baseball, and soccer stadiums.

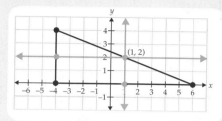

a How might he locate its exact position?

b On the map of Sportston, the football stadium is at the coordinate point $(-2, 1)$, the baseball stadium at $(6, -3)$, and the soccer stadium at $(-4, -3)$. Find the coordinate point where the mayor wants the town hall.

SOLUTION

a

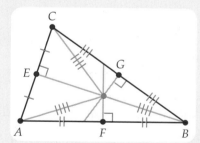

To find a point that is the same distance from the mayor's three favorite locations, connect the three locations with a triangle.

Draw perpendicular bisectors.

We only need two perpendicular bisectors to find the circumcenter, but we draw the third one for you to see. The circumcenter is the same distance from the three vertices.

Model Problems continue . . .

b To find the coordinates of the point where the town hall will be located, find the equations of the perpendicular bisectors of the triangle, and then find where they intersect. Again, we only need to find equations for two of the bisectors, so start with the easy one, the bisector of the horizontal line. We will refer to the diagram that we drew in part **a**.

Midpoint of horizontal segment	$x = \left(\dfrac{6 + (-4)}{2}\right) = \dfrac{2}{2} = 1$ y-coordinate will be -3	Since the segment is horizontal, its y-coordinate will not change.
Equation of bisector through F	$x = 1$	Since the segment is horizontal, the bisector will be a vertical line through the midpoint.
Midpoint of $\overline{AC}$	$x = \left(\dfrac{(-4) + (-2)}{2}\right) = \dfrac{-6}{2} = -3$ $y = \left(\dfrac{1 + (-3)}{2}\right) = \dfrac{-2}{2} = -1$ $(-3, -1)$	We could choose either of the other 2 segments.
Slope of $\overline{AC}$	$m = \dfrac{1 - (-3)}{(-2) - (-4)} = \dfrac{4}{2} = 2$	In order to find the equation of the perpendicular bisector, we must first know the slope of the original line.
Slope of the perpendicular bisector	$m = -\dfrac{1}{2}$	Slopes of perpendicular lines are negative reciprocals.
Equation of the perpendicular bisector	$y = -\dfrac{1}{2}x + b$ $-1 = -\dfrac{1}{2}(-3) + b$ $-\dfrac{5}{2} = b$ $y = -\dfrac{1}{2}x - \dfrac{5}{2}$	Substitute the slope and a known point into the equation and solve for b.
Find where the two bisectors intersect	$x = 1$ $y = -\left(\dfrac{1}{2}\right)(1) - \dfrac{5}{2} = -\dfrac{6}{2} = -3$	The equation for one line is $x = 1$, so we know the x-coordinate. Substitute that into the other equation to find y.
Identify the point	$(1, -3)$	This is where the town hall should be located.

PRACTICE

1. For a triangle, the circumcenter is the point

   A. That is equidistant from the triangle's vertices.
   B. Where the medians of the triangle cross.
   C. Where the midsegments of the triangle cross.
   D. That is equidistant from the sides of the triangle.

2. Two vertices of a triangle are located at $(-1, 5)$ and $(3, 1)$. Which of the following points could not be the circumcenter of the triangle?

   A. $(-3, -1)$
   B. $(-1, 1)$
   C. $(2, 4)$
   D. $(3, 7)$

Exercises 3–4: Use the diagram to answer the following questions. D is the same distance from the three vertices of the triangle.

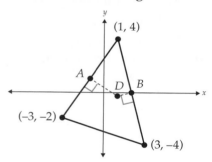

3. What are the coordinates of A?

4. What are the coordinates of B?

5. A triangle has vertices at $(0, 0)$, $(-6, 0)$, and $(0, 4)$. What is the location of its circumcenter?

6. A triangle has vertices at $(-2, -3)$, $(-2, -16)$, and $(-6, -3)$. What is the location of its circumcenter?

7. The circumcenter of a triangle is $(3, 1)$. Its distance from each vertex is 5. One vertex in the second quadrant has a y-coordinate of 4. Find the x-coordinate of the vertex.

8. The circumcenter of a triangle is $(1, 6)$. Its distance from each vertex is $\sqrt{20}$. One vertex in the first quadrant has a y-coordinate of 8. Find the x-coordinate of the vertex.

9. The circumcenter of a triangle is $(-2, 6)$. Its distance from each vertex is $\sqrt{41}$. One vertex in the first quadrant has a y-coordinate of 10. Find the x-coordinate of the vertex.

10. Based on the diagram, name the point of concurrency.

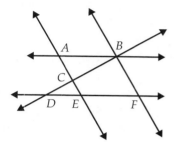

11. For what type of triangle is the point of concurrency of the perpendicular bisectors of the sides located outside the triangle?

12. For what type of triangle is the point of concurrency of the perpendicular bisectors of the sides located inside the triangle?

13. The point of concurrency for the perpendicular bisectors of a triangle is located on one side, which measures 15 feet. If another side of the triangle measures 9 feet, what is the length of the third side, in feet?

MP 1, 8 Exercises 14–16: Use the diagram to answer the questions. Line segments $\overline{RB}$, $\overline{SB}$, and $\overline{TB}$ are the perpendicular bisectors of the sides of triangle JKL.

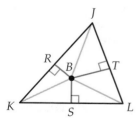

14. Given $JR = 8$ and $RB = 6$, what is LB?

15. Given $KB = 26$ and $TB = 10$, what is JT?

16. Given $KL = 30$ and $SB = 8$, what is JB?

17. A triangle's point of concurrency is at $(2, 1)$, and it is a distance of 5 from the vertices. If the x-coordinate of a vertex is 5, what must its y-coordinate be? The vertex is in quadrant IV.

Practice Problems continue . . .

18. The point (5, 2) is equidistant from the vertices of a triangle, and it is 5 units from one vertex. If the *x*-coordinate of one of the triangle's vertices is 1 and the vertex is located in quadrant IV, find its *y*-coordinate.

19. The point of concurrency of the perpendicular bisectors of a triangle is located at (4, 1). If the vertices are all 3 units from the point of concurrency, name all the quadrant(s) in which the vertices could be located.

20. MP 4 A utility company wants to place a new switching station in such a way that it will be equidistant from three existing power plants. If the existing plants could be plotted on a map at (0, 0), (0, 10), and (4, 0), where should the new switching station be located?

21. MP 3, 4 Tom plans to open a new restaurant. He will buy all his ingredients from a butcher, farmer's market, and bakery. He wants his restaurant to be the same distance from each of his suppliers. Explain to Tom how he could use a map and geometry skills to determine the best location for his restaurant.

22. MP 3 Explain why connecting any three distinct points on the circumference of a circle will result in a triangle whose circumcenter is located at the center of the circle.

23. The distance from the circumcenter of a triangle to one vertex is $2x^2 + 3x$. The distance from the circumcenter to another vertex is $x^2 + 70$. Find the distance from the circumcenter to the third vertex of the triangle.

24. MP 3, 4 A triangular park, which is in the shape of an obtuse triangle, needs a new building to house the bathrooms. The entrances to the park are at the vertices of the triangle. The park superintendent wants to place the new bathrooms so they are within the park and are equidistant from each entrance. Make a sketch showing why this is not possible. Explain your reasoning.

25. William says that the way to find the point which is equidistant from the vertices of a triangle is by locating the place where the angle bisectors of the triangle intersect. Is William correct? Why or why not?

26. MP 2, 4 Three friends all live the exact same distance from the school they attend. Kim lives nine miles east and three miles north of Jackie. Leon lives seven miles north and one mile east of Jackie. How far does each of the friends live from the school?

27. Draw a triangle *ABC*. Then, using a protractor and a straightedge, construct the circumcenter of *ABC*.

28. MP 3 Why are only two perpendicular bisectors needed to find the circumcenter? How do you know the third will intersect? Explain your answer.

LESSON 6.4

6.4 Centroids and Orthocenters

Medians

A **median** in a triangle starts at a triangle's vertex and goes to the midpoint of the opposite side. The three medians' point of concurrency, called the **centroid**, is inside the triangle.

Medians intersection theorem

The medians of a triangle meet at a single point.

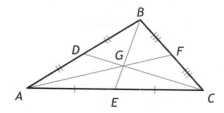

The medians for △ABC meet at point G.

Concurrency and medians theorem

The distance from a vertex to the centroid is two-thirds the length of the median.

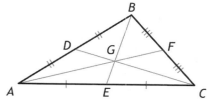

> We state a theorem about the relationship of the centroid and the length of a median.

If $\overline{AF}$, $\overline{BE}$, and $\overline{CD}$ are medians, then $AG = \frac{2}{3}AF$, $BG = \frac{2}{3}BE$, and $CG = \frac{2}{3}CD$.

We want to prove the theorem that states the distance from a vertex to the centroid is two-thirds the length of the median. Before we can prove the theorem, we need to show how three medians divide a triangle into six smaller triangles of equal area.

Prove: △AGE, △ADG, △CGE, △CFG, △BDG, △BFG have equal areas

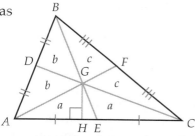

Statement	Reason	
△AGE and △CGE have equal areas	$AE = EC$; $\overline{GH}$ is their height	Median $\overline{BE}$ divides $\overline{AC}$ into equal lengths, AE and EC, so the triangles have bases of equal length. Since the triangles have the same height and equal bases, their areas are equal.
Same for △ADG and △BDG, △BFG and △CFG	Same logic	The same logic can be applied to triangles ADG and BDG, as well as BFG and CFG. We represent areas with lowercase letters a, b, and c.
Areas b and c are equal	$a + 2b = a + 2c$ $2b = 2c$ $b = c$	By the same logic, $\overline{BE}$ divides △ABC into equal areas: $a + 2b$ and $a + 2c$. We use algebra to show how areas with values b and c are equal.
All areas are equal	$a = b = c$	Use similar reasoning to show that areas a and c are equal, as well as areas a and b, proving that the triangle is split into six equal areas.

We can now prove the concurrency and medians theorem:

Prove: $\frac{2}{3}CD = CG$

Given: $\overline{BH}$ is a height of $\triangle BDG$ and $\triangle BGC$

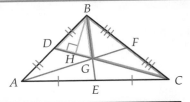

Statement	Reason	
Areas of $\triangle BDG$, $\triangle BGF$, and $\triangle FGC$ are equal	3 medians divide triangle into equal areas	We showed how 3 medians of a triangle divide the triangle into 6 smaller triangles of equal area.
Area of $\triangle BGC$ is twice that of $\triangle BDG$	Substitution	$\triangle BGC$ is made up of $\triangle BGF$ and $\triangle FGC$, so it has twice the area of $\triangle BDG$.
$\frac{1}{2} \cdot CG \cdot BH = 2 \cdot \frac{1}{2} \cdot DG \cdot BH$	Triangle area formula	Set the area of one triangle equal to twice the area of the other, using the formula for the area of a triangle and the variables that represent the lengths.
$CG = 2 \cdot DG$	Algebraic simplification	Simplify the equation.
$CG + DG = 2 \cdot DG + DG$	Addition property of equality	Add DG to both sides of the equation.
$CD = 3 \cdot DG$	Segment addition postulate	Combine like terms and use the segment addition postulate to replace $CG + DG$ with CD.
$\frac{1}{3}CD = DG$	Multiplication property of equality	Multiply each side by $\frac{1}{3}$, which is the same as dividing both sides by 3.
$\frac{2}{3}CD = CG$	Substitution	Since CG is twice the length of DG, substitute CG for DG, and multiply the other side of the equation by 2. We have proved the concurrency of medians theorem.

1. What is the length of $\overline{XC}$?

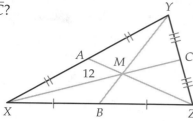

SOLUTION

M is centroid	At intersection of three medians	M is the centroid, the medians' point of concurrency.
Centroid theorem	$XM = \dfrac{2}{3}XC$	The centroid theorem says that the distance from the vertex to the centroid is $\dfrac{2}{3}$ the length of the median. XC is a median, and M is the concurrent point.
Substitute and solve	$12 = \dfrac{2}{3}XC$ $XC = 18$	We substitute the value of XM given in the problem. We multiply both sides by $\dfrac{3}{2}$ to isolate the variable. The median $\overline{XC}$ is 18 units long.

2. Prove: $\overline{AF}$, $\overline{BE}$, and $\overline{CD}$ intersect at G

Given: $\overline{AF}$, $\overline{BE}$, and $\overline{CD}$ are medians

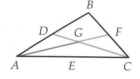 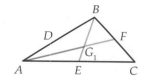

SOLUTION

Statement	Reason	
$\overline{AF}$, $\overline{BE}$, and $\overline{CD}$ are medians	Given	The hypothesis of the theorem assumes that the three segments are medians. We will prove that they intersect at the same point, G.
$\overline{AF}$ and $\overline{CD}$ intersect at G	Point, line, and plane postulate (p. 38)	The two medians intersect inside the triangle at G.
$\overline{AF}$ and $\overline{BE}$ intersect at G_1	Point, line, and plane postulate (p. 38)	These two medians also intersect inside the triangle at a point we will call G_1. If we can show that $G = G_1$, then our proof will be complete.
$AG = \dfrac{2}{3}AF$ and $AG_1 = \dfrac{2}{3}AF$	Concurrency and medians theorem	$\overline{AG}$ and $\overline{AG_1}$ are both two-thirds the length of $\overline{AF}$. We could do similar analyses for other pairs of medians.

Altitudes

An **altitude** is a line segment from a vertex that is perpendicular to the line containing the opposite side. An altitude can be inside or outside the triangle.

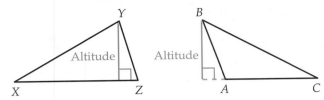

The altitudes of a triangle intersect at a point called the **orthocenter**. The location of the orthocenter depends on the type of triangle. We label the orthocenter with the letter O. With an acute triangle, it is inside the triangle. With a right triangle, it is on the triangle, at the right-angle vertex (the two legs are altitudes of that triangle). With an obtuse triangle, the orthocenter is outside the triangle.

Acute triangle
O is inside
the triangle

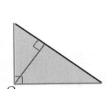

Right triangle
O is on
triangle

Obtuse triangle
O is outside
triangle

MODEL PROBLEMS

1. For $\triangle ABC$, is $\overline{BD}$ an altitude, median, or neither? What about $\overline{AE}$?

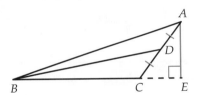

SOLUTION

$\overline{BD}$ is median

$\overline{BD}$ is a median since it extends from a vertex to an opposite side, and bisects that side; $\overline{AD} \cong \overline{DC}$.

$\overline{AE}$ is altitude

$\overline{AE}$ extends from a vertex to the continuation of the opposite side (which is shown with a dashed line). It is perpendicular to that continuation. This means it is an altitude.

2. $\overline{CA}$ is both a median and altitude of $\triangle AMK$. This means $\overline{CA}$ is

   A. A perpendicular bisector of $\overline{MK}$.

   B. Parallel to $\overline{MK}$.

   C. At the midpoint of $\overline{MK}$ but not necessarily perpendicular to it.

   D. Perpendicular to $\overline{MK}$ but not necessarily at its midpoint.

SOLUTION

The answer is A. By definition, a median is a bisector of both a vertex angle and a segment. Therefore, we know it intersects the midpoint of $\overline{MK}$. This eliminates B and D. Then, because $\overline{CA}$ is also an altitude, we know it must be perpendicular.

Model Problems continue . . .

3. What are the coordinates of this triangle's orthocenter?

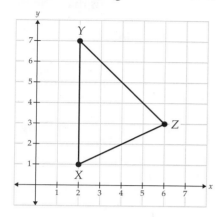

SOLUTION

Draw horizontal line from Z	$y = 3$	The orthocenter of a triangle is where its altitudes intersect. By determining the equations for two altitudes, we can find that point. One altitude is easy: It's a horizontal line.
Calculate slope of XZ	slope $= \dfrac{1-3}{2-6} = \dfrac{-2}{-4} = \dfrac{1}{2}$	The second altitude is harder, since no sides are conveniently horizontal or vertical. To calculate the equation of a line perpendicular to $\overline{XZ}$, we first find that segment's slope.
Perpendicular slope is negative reciprocal	$\dfrac{1}{2} \rightarrow -2$	A line perpendicular to the segment will have a slope that is the negative reciprocal.
Substitute values to find b	$y = mx + b$ $7 = -2(2) + b$ $b = 11$	We want to calculate b, the y-intercept. Substitute in the vertex Y, since that point is on the altitude line. We also use the slope we just calculated. Solve for b.
State equation in standard form	$y = -2x + 11$	We know m and b, so we can write the equation for a line that contains a second altitude.
Solve system of equations based on equations of lines	$y = 3$ $y = -2x + 11$	We have equations for two lines. The intersection of the altitudes is the solution to these two equations.
Substitute $y = 3$ into equation	$3 = -2x + 11$ $-8 = -2x$ $x = 4$	Substitute 3 for y, and solve.
Orthocenter is at shared solution to equations	$(4, 3)$	We have located the orthocenter, since we know that $(4, 3)$ is a solution to the system of equations.

PRACTICE

1. In a right triangle, how many altitudes coincide with sides of the triangle?

   A. 0   C. 2
   B. 1   D. 3

2. The median of a triangle connects vertex $B(2, -5)$ to midpoint $M(2, 4)$. The distance from vertex B to the centroid of the triangle is

   A. 2 units.   C. 6 units.
   B. 3 units.   D. 9 units.

3. The orthocenter is
   A. The altitudes' point of concurrency.
   B. Equidistant from each of the triangle's sides.
   C. Equidistant from each of the triangle's vertices.

4. The circumcenter is
   A. The median's point of concurrency.
   B. Equidistant from each of the triangle's sides.
   C. Equidistant from each of the triangle's vertices.

5. Which line segments are altitudes of triangle ABC? Select all that apply.

   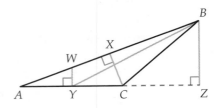

   A. $\overline{WY}$ D. $\overline{BZ}$
   B. $\overline{YB}$ E. $\overline{CZ}$
   C. $\overline{XC}$

6. In a triangle, a median's endpoints are $(1, 6)$ and $(1, 18)$. How far is it from the vertex at the end of this median to the centroid of the triangle?

7. **MP 2, 5** The median of a triangle has endpoints at $(2, -11)$ and $(2, 4)$.
   a State the coordinates of all possible locations of the centroid of the triangle.
   b What additional information is needed to determine which of the points is actually the centroid?

8. The centroid of triangle ABC is at point X. The length of the median from vertex B is 33 inches. What is the distance between the midpoint of $\overline{AC}$ and point X?

9. Sketch a triangle. Then, construct the medians of the triangle and locate and label the centroid.

10. In an obtuse triangle, how many of the altitudes are located outside the triangle? Include a sketch illustrating your response.

11. Sketch an acute triangle. Then, sketch all the altitudes and locate the orthocenter of the triangle.

12. Sketch an obtuse triangle. Then, sketch all the altitudes and locate the orthocenter of the triangle.

13. Use the diagram to answer the questions.

    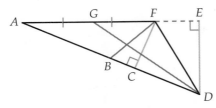

    a Name the median which originates at vertex D.
    b Name the altitude which has one endpoint at point F.
    c What additional information is needed to prove that $\overline{FB}$ is a median of $\triangle ADF$?
    d If an altitude was constructed from vertex A, would it fall inside or outside of the triangle?

14. Find the orthocenter of $\triangle ABC$, a triangle with vertices at $A(-2, -2)$, $B(2, -5)$, and $C(1, 2)$.

15. Find the orthocenter of $\triangle JKL$, a triangle with vertices at $J(3, 4)$, $K(-5, -4)$, and $L(7, -4)$.

16. Find the orthocenter of $\triangle DEF$, a triangle with vertices at $D(3, 8)$, $E(1, 2)$, and $F(9, 2)$.

17. The centroid of a triangle is located at $(7, -12)$, and a vertex is at $(-14, 8)$. What is the length of the median from that same vertex?

Practice Problems continue . . .

18. The centroid of a triangle is located at $(-20, 20)$, and a vertex is at $(15, 8)$. What is the length of the median from that same vertex?

19. A triangle's vertices are $(1, 1)$, $(3, 5)$, and $(7, 1)$. What are the coordinates of the triangle's orthocenter?

20. A triangle's vertices are $(0, 6)$, $(4, 8)$, and $(4, 2)$. What are the coordinates of the triangle's orthocenter?

21. A triangle's vertices are $(1, 3)$, $(1, 12)$, and $(8, 10)$. What are the coordinates of the triangle's orthocenter?

22. A triangle's vertices are $(0, 2)$, $(4, 2)$, and $(2, 6)$. What are the coordinates of the triangle's orthocenter?

23. Knowledge of the location of the midpoints of the sides of a triangle is needed to locate which point(s) of concurrency?

24. **MP 3** Jared needs to find the centroid of a triangle. He locates the midpoint of each side and constructs a perpendicular bisector through each midpoint, then locates the point where the perpendicular bisectors intersect. Did Jared locate the centroid correctly? Why or why not?

25. In a triangle, one median has endpoints at $(1, -1)$ and $(4, -4)$, and a second median has endpoints at $(4, 2)$ and $(1, -4)$. Find the coordinates of the centroid of the triangle.

26. The centroid of triangle DEF is located at point C, and point M is the midpoint of $\overline{EF}$. The length of the median from vertex D to point M is an integer number between 40 and 44, and both DC and CM are integer numbers. How long is $\overline{DC}$?

27. The length of a triangle's median is expressed as $12x - 9$. The distance from the centroid of the triangle to the midpoint of one side along this median is $5 + 2x$. How long is the median?

28. In a triangle, a median connects vertex $A(4, 7)$ to the midpoint, $M(-2, 10)$, of the opposite side. What are the coordinates of the centroid of this triangle?

29. The area of a triangle is 66 square units, and the triangle has sides of 11, 13, and 20. List the lengths of the three altitudes of the triangle. Round your answers to the nearest tenth.

30. An altitude and a median are constructed from the top vertex of an acute triangle to the opposite base. The median divides the triangle into two smaller triangles. If the area of one of the smaller triangles is 30 cm², and the length of the base of the original triangle is 10 cm, what is the length of the altitude?

31. If $KT = 9$, $AC = 36$, $AP = 33$, and $AT = 22$, prove $\triangle ARK \cong \triangle ATK$.

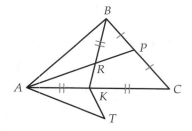

6.5 Incenters

Like the perpendicular bisectors, the angle bisectors of a triangle also have a point of concurrency. This point of concurrency of angle bisectors is called the **incenter**. A triangle's incenter is equidistant from each <u>side</u> of the triangle. Remember that the point of concurrency of perpendicular bisectors is the same distance from the <u>vertices</u> of the triangle.

> The incenter is the same distance from the sides of the triangle.

Concurrency and angle bisectors theorem

The angle bisectors of a triangle intersect at a point that is the same distance from each side of the triangle.

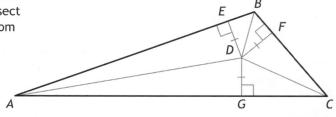

If $\overline{AD}$, $\overline{BD}$, and $\overline{CD}$ are $\angle$ bisectors, then $\overline{DE} \cong \overline{DF} \cong \overline{DG}$.

The angle bisectors' point of concurrency is called the *incenter* for a specific reason. Examine the triangle to the right of this paragraph. You'll note that the triangle has been inscribed with a circle. The circle's center is the triangle's incenter.

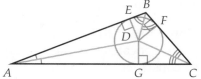

MODEL PROBLEMS

1. If $AD = 12$ and $AP = 13$, what is the length of $\overline{FP}$? $\overline{AP}$, $\overline{BP}$, and $\overline{CP}$ are angle bisectors.

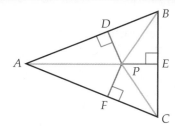

SOLUTION

P is equidistant from sides	$FP = DP$	P is located at the intersection of three angle bisectors, which means it is the same distance from each side of the triangle. We cannot directly calculate FP from the diagram, but since $FP = DP$, we can calculate DP to find FP.
Calculate DP with Pythagorean theorem	$a^2 + b^2 = c^2$ $b = \sqrt{c^2 - a^2}$ $b = \sqrt{169 - 144} = 5,$ $DP = 5$	Use the Pythagorean theorem to calculate DP, since it is a leg in a right triangle. Solve for b, substitute, and evaluate.
$FP = DP$	$FP = DP = 5$	Since we've calculated DP, we know FP.

Model Problems continue . . .

2. Point I is an incenter. $EI = 17$ and $EC = 15$.
   What is the length of $\overline{AI}$?

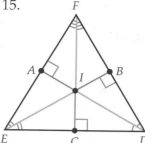

SOLUTION

I is same distance to each side	Concurrency of angle bisectors theorem	We are told I is an incenter, which means by the concurrency of angle bisectors theorem, it is the same distance to each side.
$AI = IC$	Two distances from incenter	Both of these are distances to a side, since they are perpendicular to the side.
Use Pythagorean theorem	$EC^2 + IC^2 = EI^2$ $IC^2 = EI^2 - EC^2$	These 3 sides form a right triangle. It means this relationship must be true. Solve for the length we do not know by subtracting EC^2 from both sides.
Evaluate	$IC = \sqrt{EI^2 - EC^2} = \sqrt{17^2 - 15^2}$ $IC = 8$, so $AI = 8$	Take the square root of both sides and substitute, then evaluate. $IC = 8$. Since AI is also a distance to a side, and I is an incenter, $AI = IC = 8$.

Summary of Circumcenters, Incenters, Centroids, and Orthocenters

We summarize the features of the terms circumcenter, incenter, centroid, and orthocenter.

Circumcenter

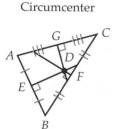

Perpendicular bisectors

Incenter

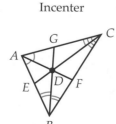

Angle bisectors

Centroid

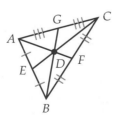

Medians

Orthocenter

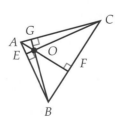

Altitudes

PRACTICE

1. The incenter of a triangle is located

   A. Inside the triangle.

   B. On a side of the triangle.

   C. Outside the triangle.

   D. Any of the above.

2. For an acute triangle, how many of the points of concurrency (circumcenter, incenter, centroid, and orthocenter) are located inside the triangle?

   A. 1

   B. 2

   C. 3

   D. 4

Exercises 3–6: Use the diagram to answer the questions. Line segments MH, LH, and NH are the angle bisectors of the vertex angles of the triangle.

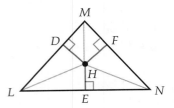

3. If $DL = 12$ and $FH = 5$, what is LH?

4. If $NH = 41$ and $NF = 40$, what is DH?

5. If $EH = 3$, $MH = 5$, and $MN = 11$, what is FN?

6. If a circle were inscribed in $\triangle MLN$, which point(s) would be on its circumference?

MP 2, 7 Exercises 7–12: Point C is the incenter of triangle AEG.

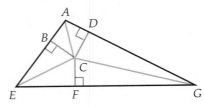

7. If $AC = 5$, $BC = 4$, and $EC = 7$, what is CD?

8. If $AC = 3$, $BC = 2$, and $EC = 5$, what is CD?

9. If $AC = 4$, $BC = 3$, and $EC = 6$, what is CD?

10. If $AC = 2$, $BC = 1$, and $EC = 4$, what is CD?

11. If $AC = 7$, $BC = 6$, and $EC = 10$, what is EF?

12. If a circle were inscribed in $\triangle AEG$, what point(s) would be on the circumference of the circle?

13. The shortest distance from the incenter of a triangle to one of its sides is 11 centimeters. If a circle is inscribed in the triangle, what is its diameter?

14. The shortest distance from the incenter of a triangle to one of its sides is 8 centimeters. If a circle is inscribed in the triangle, what is its radius?

15. For an obtuse triangle, which points of concurrency are located outside the triangle?

16. Sketch a triangle. Then construct the angle bisectors of each angle, and locate the incenter of the triangle. For construction of angle bisectors, see p. 244.

17. **MP 4** An oil driller has a lease to drill a new well. They want to locate the well so it is equally distant from three existing oil pipelines. The three existing pipelines form the sides of a triangle. Where should the new oil well be located, and why?

18. When two angle bisector segments are constructed to stop at the incenter of a triangle, is it possible for the angle formed between them to measure less than 90°? Explain your reasoning.

19. Using the diagram below as a reference, prove that the incenter, D, is equidistant from each side of the triangle. Hint: Use the angle bisector theorem.

Prove: $DE = DF = DG$

Given: D is the incenter of $\triangle ABC$

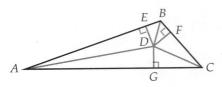

Practice Problems continue . . .

20. The orange lines are angle bisectors. The diagram is not drawn to scale. If $PC = 10$ and $EC = 6$, what is the length of $\overline{PD}$?

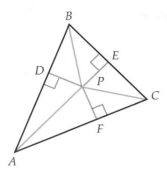

21. **MP 1, 2** For any triangle which is not equilateral, three of the four points of concurrency are located on the same line, which is called the Euler line because it was discovered by the Swiss mathematician Leonhard Euler.

a Research which three points of concurrency are located on the Euler line. Name the points of concurrency.

b Must all three points of concurrency be found in order to locate the Euler line? Explain your reasoning.

c Sketch a triangle. Then, using points of concurrency, locate and draw its Euler line.

d Why is it impossible for an equilateral triangle to have an Euler line?

LESSON 6.6

6.6 Optional: Inequalities in One Triangle

We define triangles as being three-sided polygons. The following theorems flow from this definition.

Triangle inequality theorem

Each side of a triangle is shorter than the sum of its other two sides.

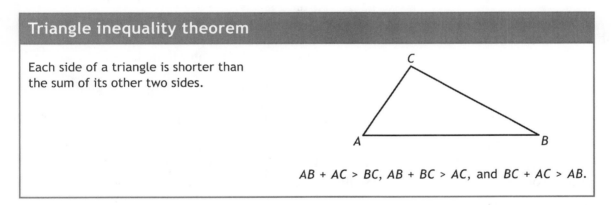

$AB + AC > BC$, $AB + BC > AC$, and $BC + AC > AB$.

Unequal sides theorem

If, in a triangle, two sides are unequal in length, then the angle opposite the longer side is greater than the angle opposite the shorter side.

> Longer sides in a triangle are across from greater angles.

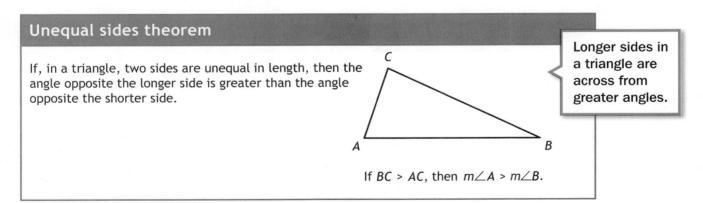

If $BC > AC$, then $m\angle A > m\angle B$.

Unequal sides theorem converse

If, in a triangle, two angles are unequal in measure, then the side opposite the greater angle is longer than the side opposite the smaller angle.

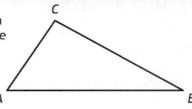

If $m\angle A > m\angle B$, then $BC > AC$.

MODEL PROBLEMS

1. A triangle has sides of length 5 and 9. Write an inequality to describe the possible lengths of the third side.

> We can use the triangle inequality theorem to determine the potential lengths of the sides of a triangle. We use a compound inequality—one that describes two possibilities—to answer the question.

SOLUTION

Determine minimum value	$z + 5 > 9$	The triangle inequality theorem says that two sides of a triangle must be longer than the third side. Let z represent the unknown third side. z plus 5 must be greater than 9.
Solve inequality	$z + 5 - 5 > 9 - 5$ $z > 4$	To solve the inequality, subtract 5 from both sides. The third side must be greater than 4.
Determine maximum value	$5 + 9 > z$ $z < 14$	The length of the two other sides must be greater than the third. Add the constants, and write the inequality with the variable on the left.
Write compound inequality	$z > 4$ and $z < 14$	There are two statements which must be true: $z > 4$ and $z < 14$. Since they are both true, use the conjunction "and."

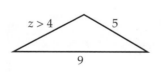

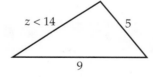

2. Place the sides of length 10, 13.5, and 15.3 based on the angles.

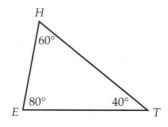

Model Problems continue . . .

SOLUTION

Longest versus greatest angle	15.3 across from *E*	Applying the unequal sides theorem, the longest side of a triangle will be across from its greatest angle.
Shortest across from smallest angle	10 across from *T*	And the shortest side is across from the smallest angle.
Middle length across from middle angle	13.5 across from *H*	The middle length is across from the middle angle—or you could just use the process of elimination for this one.

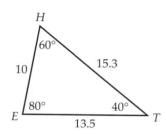

3. In △*ABC*, $m\angle B$ is half of $m\angle A$, and $m\angle C$ is 30° less than $m\angle A$. Place the angles correctly.

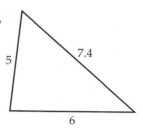

SOLUTION

To place the angles, we need to know the measures of the angles. Then the smallest angle will be opposite the shortest side and the greatest angle opposite the longest side.

Expressions for angles	$m\angle B = 0.5(m\angle A)$ $m\angle C = m\angle A - 30°$	Write expressions for the angles based on the problem. $m\angle B$ is half of $m\angle A$, and $m\angle C$ is 30 less than $m\angle A$.
Write equation	$m\angle A + m\angle B + m\angle C = 180°$	The angles must sum to 180°.
Substitute expressions	$m\angle A + 0.5(m\angle A) + (m\angle A - 30°) = 180°$	Substitute using the expressions we wrote earlier so that there is only one unknown in the equation.
Solve	$m\angle A = 84°$	Combine like terms and divide to calculate $m\angle A$.
Evaluate	$m\angle B = 0.5(m\angle A) = 0.5(84) = 42°$ $m\angle C = m\angle A - 30° = 84° - 30° = 54°$	Substitute the value of *A* into the other expressions, and evaluate.
Angles follow side lengths	*A* across from longest side, *B* across from shortest side, *C* across from middle side	Since $\angle A$ is the largest angle, it is across from the longest side, of length 7.4. Since $\angle B$ is the smallest angle, it is across from the shortest side, of length 5. This leaves $\angle C$ across from the side of length 6.

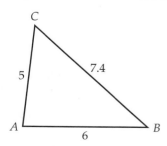

The Hinge Theorem and Its Converse

Before, we discussed the relationship of angles and lengths within <u>one</u> triangle. In this section, we discuss the relationship of angles and lengths between <u>two</u> triangles.

Hinge theorem

If two sides of a triangle are congruent to those of another triangle, and the included angle of the first is larger than the included angle of the second, then the third side of the first triangle is longer than the third side of the second triangle.

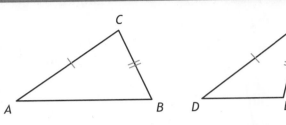

If $\overline{AC} \cong \overline{DF}$, $\overline{BC} \cong \overline{EF}$, and $m\angle C > m\angle F$, then $AB > DE$.

> The converse of the hinge theorem is sometimes called the *side-side-side (SSS) inequality.*

Converse of the hinge theorem

If the two sides of one triangle are congruent to two sides of another triangle, and the third side of the first triangle is longer than the third side of the second triangle, then the included angle of the first triangle is larger than the included angle of the second triangle.

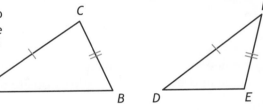

If $\overline{AC} \cong \overline{DF}$, $\overline{BC} \cong \overline{EF}$, and $AB > DE$, then $m\angle C > m\angle F$.

MODEL PROBLEM

What are the possible values for x? $m\angle G = x + 10°$ and $m\angle T = 2x - 30°$.

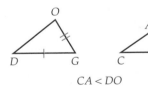

$CA < DO$

> Using the converse of the hinge theorem as the basis of our reasoning, we solve inequalities to determine the possible values of x.

Model Problem continues . . .

SOLUTION

Apply converse of hinge theorem	$m\angle T < m\angle G$	The diagram shows the two pairs of sides as congruent. The converse of the hinge theorem tells us that $m\angle T < m\angle G$, since $CA < DO$.
Solve $m\angle T < m\angle G$	$2x - 30° < x + 10°$	Substitute the expressions for the angles in the diagram.
	$x - 30° < 10°$ $x < 40°$	Solve the inequality. First, subtract x from both sides. Then add 30° to both sides. x must be less than 40°.
Solve $m\angle T > 0°$	$2x - 30° > 0°$ $2x > 30°$ $x > 15°$	The $m\angle T$ must be greater than 0°. When the $m\angle G$ is greater than $m\angle T$, and $m\angle T$ is positive, the $m\angle G$ is also positive. Solve for x. x must be greater than 15°.
Combine inequalities	$15° < x < 40°$	Combine the two inequalities to form a compound inequality.

PRACTICE

1. A triangle has lengths 5, 12, and 13; it has angles that measure about 23°, 67°, and 90°. Which angle is opposite the side with the length of 12?

  A. 23°

  B. 67°

  C. 90°

2. If $HI > RS$, then this means

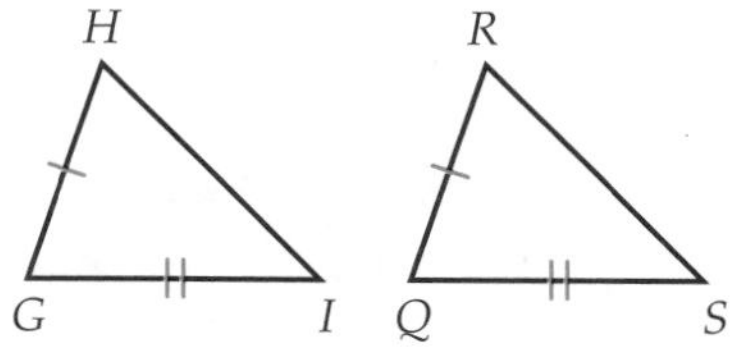

  A. $m\angle Q = m\angle G$

  B. $m\angle Q > m\angle G$

  C. $m\angle Q < m\angle G$

  D. These are isosceles triangles.

3. The lengths of $\triangle ABC$ are 7, 4, and 5. One of its angles measures about 44° and the other 55°. What is the length of the side across from the 55° angle?

  A. 4

  B. 5

  C. 7

4. Triangle *RAW* is an equilateral triangle. If the lengths of $\overline{RA}$ and $\overline{AW}$ are kept the same, and the measure of $\angle A$ is increased, what will happen to the length of $\overline{RW}$?

  A. It will increase.

  B. It will remain the same.

  C. It will decrease.

  D. It is impossible to determine.

5. Based on the diagram and the knowledge that $m\angle D > m\angle J$, which of the following statements must be true?

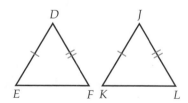

  A. $m\angle E > m\angle K$

  B. $EF = KL$

  C. $EF < KL$

  D. $EF > KL$

Practice Problems continue . . .

6. For any given triangle, if the length of one side is decreased while the lengths of the other two sides are held constant, what will happen to the measure of the angle opposite the side which is decreased?

    A. It will increase.

    B. It will stay the same.

    C. It will decrease.

    D. It is impossible to determine.

7. A triangle has a side of length 5.3, and another side of length 6.2. What is the maximum possible length for the third side?

8. A triangle has a side of length 6.5, and another side of length 7.3. What is the minimum possible length for the third side?

9. A triangle has a side of length 6.5, and another side of length 7.3. What is the maximum possible length for the third side?

10. A triangle has a side of length 4.3, and another side of length 9.1. What is the maximum possible length for the third side?

11. A triangle has a side of length 4.9, and another side of length 8.2. What is the minimum possible length for the third side?

12. Two of the angles in this triangle are 60° and 70°, and the approximate lengths of the sides are shown. What is $m\angle C$?

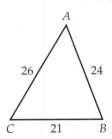

13. Winifred says: "My favorite triangle has sides of lengths 3, 3, and 3." Is this possible? Explain.

14. Tanya says: "The lengths of the three sides of the triangle are 3, 6, and 12." Is this possible? Explain.

15. **MP 5** In $\triangle JKL$, $JK = x^2 - 2x$, $KL = 3x - 3$, and $JL = 2x + 1$. The perimeter of $\triangle JKL$ is 38. Determine which angle in the triangle is the largest.

16. **MP 3, 5** Triangle QUA has vertices located at $Q(-2, 2)$, $U(3, -3)$, and $A(2, 5)$. Graph the triangle, and then prove $\angle Q$ is the largest angle. Hint: Consider using the distance formula.

17. **MP 2, 3** Use the hinge theorem to explain why it is impossible to prove two non-right triangles congruent using SSA. You may wish to include an illustration to support your answer.

18. Given point D is the centroid of $\triangle ABC$, $\overline{BM} \cong \overline{BC}$, and $m\angle MBC = 40°$, prove $AB > BC$.

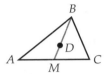

19. Given triangle FAC with vertices at $F(4, 6)$, $A(5, 4)$, and $C(1, 2)$ and triangle TOR with vertices at $T(5, 1)$, $O(7, 0)$, and $R(1, -2)$, use the hinge theorem to show that $m\angle T > m\angle F$.

20. Use the diagram below to prove the hinge theorem for triangles ABC and DEF. Hint: First find ways to prove that $\overline{AP} \cong \overline{DF}$ and $\overline{PQ} \cong \overline{CQ}$. Then prove that $AQ + QC > AP$ and $AC > AP$.

Given: $m\angle ABC > m\angle DEF$
Prove: $AC > DF$

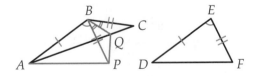

6.7 Optional: Indirect Reasoning

So far the reasoning in this book has been direct reasoning. We use a series of true statements to make a conclusion. This method of proof is called *proof by contradiction*.

For example:

- *The restaurant is open all day on weekends.*
  For instance, a student knows a restaurant is open all day on weekends.
- *It is closed (not open).*
  It is closed, so it is not true that it is open.
- *Today is a weekday.*
  This enables you to conclude it is a weekday.

> We use indirect reasoning because some ideas are difficult to prove with direct reasoning.

We use indirect reasoning in an indirect proof. We take the conclusion that we want to prove, assume for a bit that its opposite is true, and then show there must be a logical contradiction—a situation that cannot occur. Hence the name *proof by contradiction*.

How to write an indirect proof:

1. **State what you want to prove.** The first step in doing an indirect proof is to state what you want to prove.

2. **Assume it is not true.** Now, assume (for the moment) that it is not true.

3. **Reason until you reach contradiction.** Reason, using your assumption, until you reach a contradiction.

MODEL PROBLEMS

1. Prove that an odd perfect square has an odd square root. Use indirect reasoning.

SOLUTION

What we want to prove	If n^2 is odd, n is odd.	We want to show that if a whole number squared is odd, then the number is odd. In other words, if n^2 is odd, then n is odd.
Assume the opposite conclusion	n is even.	We assume for a bit the opposite conclusion: that n is even.
A contradiction!	An even number times an even number cannot equal an odd number.	If n is even, then the product of two even numbers must be an odd number. But that is impossible—the product of two even numbers is always even.
	The contradiction shows that the number must be odd.	Since the number cannot be even, it must be odd. We have proved that if a number squared is odd, then the number itself is odd.

Model Problems continue . . .

2. In the triangles below, X and A are angles that are included (formed) by pairs of congruent sides, and $YZ > BC$. Prove the converse of the hinge theorem.

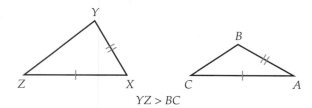

$YZ > BC$

> We prove the converse of the hinge theorem using the hinge theorem and indirect reasoning. Using the theorem, we would conclude that $m\angle X > m\angle A$. However, as you can see, we assume the opposite of this to prove the theorem, and see if a contradiction occurs.

SOLUTION

Assume the opposite	Opposite of $m\angle X > m\angle A$ is $m\angle X \leq m\angle A$	To prove the converse of the hinge theorem, we assume the opposite conclusion. Instead of $m\angle X$ being greater than $m\angle A$, as the theorem concludes, we assume it is less than or equal to $m\angle A$.
$m\angle X = m\angle A$	SAS, but SAS not possible	If $m\angle X = m\angle A$, then the two triangles are congruent because of the side-angle-side congruency postulate. But we know this is not possible because the third side of one triangle is greater than that of the other.
$m\angle X < m\angle A$	Opposite of what the problem states	If $m\angle X < m\angle A$, then by the hinge theorem, $YZ < BC$. However, that is not possible since we were told that the opposite of this is true.
$m\angle X > m\angle A$	Because it is impossible for $m\angle X \leq m\angle A$	We have shown that it is impossible for $m\angle X \leq m\angle A$, so that proves the converse: The greater angle is opposite the longer side.

PRACTICE

1. When you assume a statement to be true in a proof and then show that it leads to a logical contradiction, you are using

   A. Anecdotal reasoning.
   B. Direct reasoning.
   C. Indirect reasoning.
   D. Inductive reasoning.

2. Which statement is a negation of the statement "The triangle is right"?

   A. The triangle is scalene.
   B. The triangle is isosceles.
   C. The triangle has one right angle.
   D. The triangle is not right.

3. Jon wants to prove that he is not guilty of taking a cookie from the cookie jar at 4 P.M., so he tells his mom to assume he is guilty. If he is guilty, then he had to be home to take the cookie. He then shows that he was not home at 4 P.M. What conclusion should his mom draw from his logic?

   A. Jon took the cookie at 4 P.M.
   B. Jon did not take the cookie at 4 P.M.
   C. There is not enough information to tell.
   D. Jon hired someone else to take the cookie.

Practice Problems continue . . .

4. In an indirect proof, a student finds that the two acute angles in a right triangle sum to 92°. Which of the following statements logically contradicts this finding?

    A. The two acute angles in a right triangle are congruent.

    B. The two acute angles in a right triangle are complementary.

    C. The two right angles in an acute triangle are supplementary.

    D. A right triangle has all right angles.

5. Given the true statements, "If water freezes, then the temperature is below 0° C" and "The lake is frozen over," Lyle concludes that the temperature is below zero degrees Celsius. This is an example of

    A. Direct reasoning.

    B. Indirect reasoning.

    C. Too little information to tell.

6. William is asked to prove that two triangles are not congruent. He decides to use a strategy of initially assuming the triangles are congruent while writing his proof. This is an example of

    A. Direct reasoning.

    B. Indirect reasoning.

    C. Too little information to tell.

7. Which series of statements uses indirect reasoning? Select all that apply.

    A. Hilary likes cheese; The pizza has cheese; Hilary likes the pizza.

    B. Ian watches every Lions football game; Today Ian is not watching any games; the Lions are not playing today.

    C. Tim said he would stop driving his old car when he got his new car; Tim is driving his new car; Tim sold his old car.

    D. Patty only cooks vegetarian dishes; The dish isn't vegetarian; Patty didn't cook the dish.

8. Suppose the statement we want to prove is "$\triangle ABC$ is an equilateral triangle." Select the statements that could come next in an indirect proof for proving this. Select all that apply.

    A. $\triangle ABC$ is not an equilateral triangle.

    B. The opposite of $\triangle ABC$ is an equilateral triangle.

    C. $\triangle ABC$ is scalene or isosceles.

9. We have already stated what we want to prove: "$l \parallel m$." Select the statements that could come next in an indirect proof. Select all that apply.

    A. l and m are perpendicular.

    B. l is not parallel to m.

    C. l and m intersect at P.

10. We have already stated what we want to prove: "$l \perp m$." Select the statements that could come next in an indirect proof. Select all that apply.

    A. l and m are not perpendicular.

    B. The angle formed by l and m is a right angle.

    C. The angle formed by l and m is acute.

11. We have already stated what we want to prove: "$\angle l$ and $\angle m$ are complementary." Select the statements that could come next in an indirect proof.

    A. $\angle l$ and $\angle m$ do not sum to 180°.

    B. $\angle l$ and $\angle m$ sum to 90°.

    C. $\angle l$ and $\angle m$ do not sum to 90°.

12. There exist two scalene triangles, $\triangle ABC$ and $\triangle DEF$, with corresponding sides and angles as indicated. Which two statements contradict each other?

    A. $\angle C \cong \angle F$

    B. $\overline{AC} \cong \overline{EF}$

    C. Scalene $\triangle ABC$ can be proven congruent to $\triangle DEF$ using SAS.

    D. Scalene $\triangle ABC$ cannot be proven congruent to $\triangle DEF$ using AAS.

Practice Problems continue . . .

13. Which two statements contradict each other?

    A. $\triangle ABC$ is acute.

    B. $\triangle ABC$ is isosceles.

    C. $\triangle ABC$ has a perpendicular bisector that is also an angle bisector.

    D. $\triangle ABC$ has a right angle.

14. A triangle has vertices located at $C(0, 5)$, $A(-2, 1)$, and $T(4, 3)$. Prove $\triangle CAT$ is not equilateral using indirect reasoning.

15. While using indirect reasoning in a proof, a student determines that the three interior angles of a given triangle sum to 185°. What known piece of information logically contradicts this statement?

16. What true statement logically contradicts the following statement? Two angles of an equilateral triangle measure 65° each, so the third angle measures 50°.

17. A philosopher wishes to prove the statement "Two wrongs do not make a right." If she is using indirect reasoning, what assumption should she make when setting up her proof?

18. In an indirect proof, a student determines that "Two angles of a triangle can be obtuse." Make a sketch which logically contradicts this statement.

19. **MP 4** Ryan just got his driver's license, and his mother agreed to let him drive to a nearby town to visit his cousin. The speed limit between his house and the nearby town is 50 mph, and it is a total distance of 50 miles between his house and his cousin's house. Ryan left his house at 4:30 P.M. and arrived at his cousin's house at 5:15 P.M. His mother says he must have been speeding on the way to his cousin's house.

    a If Ryan's mother wants to prove that Ryan was speeding using indirect reasoning, what assumption should she make?

    b If Ryan was not speeding, what is the shortest time it should have taken him to reach his cousin's house? Explain your reasoning.

    c How long did it take Ryan to arrive at his cousin's house?

    d Is Ryan's mother correct that he was speeding? Explain your reasoning.

20. **MP 3, 7** Given triangle JKL and triangle ABC where JK is congruent to AB, KL is congruent to BC, and JL is not congruent to AC.

    a Sketch triangles $\triangle JKL$ and $\triangle ABC$. Be sure to indicate congruent sides with hash marks.

    b You need to prove $\triangle JKL$ is not congruent to $\triangle ABC$ using indirect reasoning. What statement should you assume to be true to begin your proof?

    c Based on the given information and an assumption of the opposite conclusion, what theorem or postulate could you use to attempt to prove the triangles congruent?

    d Use the information and your answers to parts **a–c** to write a proof that $\triangle JKL$ is not congruent to $\triangle ABC$.

21. Given the sides of a triangle measure 5 units, 11 units, and 14 units, answer the following questions.

    a If you wanted to use the converse of the Pythagorean theorem to test if the sides could make a right triangle, which side length should you use as the hypotenuse?

    b You are asked to prove the triangle is not right by indirect reasoning. What initial assumption should you make to begin your proof?

    c Use the given information and your answers to parts **a** and **b** to prove that the triangle is not right using indirect reasoning.

22. Triangle LGA has vertices at $L(3, 5)$, $G(0, 3)$, and $A(6, 1)$.

    a Graph $\triangle LGA$.

    b Find the slope of $\overline{LG}$.

    c Find the slope of $\overline{GA}$.

    d Find the slope of $\overline{LA}$.

    e Use your graph and information from parts **a–d** to prove that $\triangle LGA$ is a not a right triangle by indirect reasoning.

Practice Problems continue . . .

23. Shayla was asked to prove the statement "If it is an altitude, then it is not an angle bisector" for any scalene triangle. Shayla started her proof by assuming that the segment she was working with was not an altitude. Do you agree with Shayla's assumption? Why or why not?

24. Use indirect reasoning to show that $(-3, 11)$ is not the midpoint of the line segment with endpoints at $(-5, 13)$ and $(-1, 15)$.

25. **MP 2, 3** Quentin wanted to prove that the sum of two consecutive odd integers is not an odd integer. He did so in the proof shown. Refer to his proof to answer the questions.

Prove: The sum of two consecutive odd integers is not an odd integer.

Given: n = first odd integer and $n + 2$ = second odd integer

	Statement	Reason
1	The sum of two consecutive odd integers is an odd integer	
2	$n + n + 2 = 2n + 2$	Addition property of equality
3	$2n + 2 = 2(n + 1)$	Distributive property
4	If n is an integer, then $n + 1$ is an integer	Definition of an integer
5	$2(n + 1)$ is an even integer	Multiplying an integer by two produces an even integer
6	$n + n + 2$ is an even integer	Transitive property
7	The sum of two consecutive odd integers is not an odd integer	

a What reason justifies the statement made in line 1 of the proof?

b A contradiction between which two lines of the proof can be used to justify line 7?

c Because he wanted to be able to generalize his proof to any two consecutive odd integers, Quentin used variables to stand for the integers. However, he could also have used specific numbers in the proof. Provide a counterexample, using numbers, that contradicts line 1 of the proof.

CHAPTER 6 REVIEW

1. Which line segments are parallel in the figure? Choose all that apply.

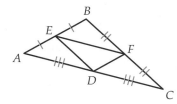

A. $\overline{AC}$ and $\overline{EF}$
B. $\overline{AE}$ and $\overline{AD}$
C. $\overline{AD}$ and $\overline{FC}$
D. $\overline{BC}$ and $\overline{ED}$

2. Which statement is true for $\triangle ABC$?

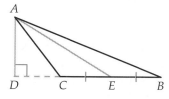

A. $\overline{AB}$ is an altitude and $\overline{AD}$ is a median.
B. $\overline{AD}$ is an altitude and $\overline{AE}$ is a median.
C. $\overline{AE}$ is an altitude and $\overline{AD}$ is a median.
D. $\overline{AD}$ is an altitude and $\overline{AB}$ is a median.

Chapter Review continues . . .

3. The segment connecting a triangle's vertex and centroid is

   A. Congruent to the other two segments. connecting the vertices and centroid.

   B. Two-thirds the length of the vertex's median.

   C. Perpendicular to the side opposite the vertex.

4. Two sides of a triangle measure 15 and 19. Which of the following could be the length of the third side? Choose all that apply.

   A. 3

   B. 12

   C. 34

   D. 37

5. Which of the following sets of side lengths could make a triangle? Choose all that apply.

   A. 3, 3, 6

   B. 3, 7, 1

   C. 12, 4, 8

   D. 6, 7, 8

6. Choose the answer to fill in the blank correctly. A midsegment is at the midpoint of _____ side(s) of a triangle.

   A. Zero

   B. One

   C. Two

   D. Three

7. In $\triangle PQR$, $m\angle P = 75°$ and $m\angle Q = 55°$. What is the shortest side of the triangle?

   A. $\overline{PQ}$

   B. $\overline{QR}$

   C. $\overline{PR}$

   D. Cannot be determined from the given information

8. The lengths of $\triangle ABC$ are 3, 4, and 5. One of its angles measures about 37° and the other 90°. What is the length of the side opposite the 37° angle?

   A. 3

   B. 4

   C. 5

9. The lengths of $\triangle ABC$ are 3, 7, and 5. One of its angles measures about 65° and the other 71°. What is the length of the side across from the 71° angle?

   A. 3

   B. 5

   C. 7

Exercises 10–12: Use the diagram to answer the questions.

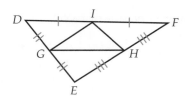

10. Name the three midsegments of $\triangle DEF$.

11. Which line segment is parallel to $\overline{EF}$?

12. Which line segment is parallel to $\overline{DE}$?

Exercises 13–17: Use the diagram to answer the questions. Ray AR is the angle bisector of angle CAT.

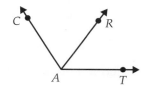

13. If $m\angle CAT$ is 112°, what is the measure of $\angle CAR$?

14. If $m\angle RAT$ is 51°, what is the measure of $\angle CAT$?

15. If $m\angle RAT = (5x + 9)°$ and $m\angle CAR = (8x - 15)°$, what is the measure of $\angle RAT$?

16. If $m\angle CAR = (7 + 2x)°$ and $m\angle CAT = (5x - 16)°$, what is $m\angle CAR$?

17. If the measure of $\angle CAT$ is given by the expression $(4a + 6b)°$, write an expression for the measure of $\angle RAT$.

18. A triangle's point of concurrency created by its perpendicular bisectors is at (2, 2), and it is a distance of 5 from the vertices. If the y-coordinate of a vertex is 5, what must its x-coordinate be? The vertex is in quadrant I.

Chapter Review continues . . .

19. The centroid of triangle *ABC* is at point *X*. The length of the median from vertex *A* is 15 inches. What is the length of $\overline{AX}$?

20. The centroid of a triangle is located at $(-6, 4)$, and a vertex is at $(2, 19)$. What is the length of the median from that same vertex?

21. A triangle's vertices are $(2, 5)$, $(6, 7)$, and $(8, 5)$. What are the coordinates of the triangle's orthocenter?

22. Point *D* is the same distance from each of the three vertices of the triangle. What are the coordinates of *C*?

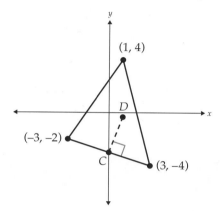

23. **MP 5** Draw an acute triangle. Then, draw the perpendicular bisector of each side and locate the circumcenter of the triangle.

24. A triangle has vertices at $(1, 8)$, $(9, 8)$, and $(3, 2)$. Where is its orthocenter?

25. A cell phone company is expanding its network capacity. They want to build a new cellular tower which is equally distant from three existing towers. Tower B is located 18 miles directly north of Tower A, and Tower C is located 12 miles directly west of Tower A. Relative to Tower A, where should the new tower be located?

26. **MP 2, 3, 6** The measures of the interior angles of a triangle can be represented by $(2x + 7)°$, $(3x - 9)°$, and $(5x - 18)°$. Prove that the triangle is not isosceles using indirect reasoning.

27. The citizens of Abbottsville buried a time capsule in the town park 50 years ago, but they lost the map showing exactly where the capsule was buried. However, a newspaper article written at the time describes the location as "…100 feet inside the park from the point where Main Street and Oak Street meet, and equally distant from the two streets." If Main Street and Oak Street meet at a right angle, make a sketch of the situation and indicate with an "X" where the time capsule is buried.

28. Use the diagram to prove $\overrightarrow{BD}$ is the angle bisector of $\angle ABC$.

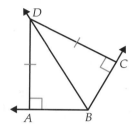

29. **MP 2, 4** An engineer is designing a tool in the shape of a triangle. The tool has a piece which must be attached to the triangle and located in such a way that, regardless of which side of the triangle is treated as the base, the piece will be positioned on the line which is the shortest distance between the top vertex of the triangle and the base. Where should the engineer attach the piece?

30. The vertices of a triangle are located at $(0, 0)$, $(0, a)$, and $(b, 0)$. What are the coordinates of the centroid of this triangle?

31. The centroid of a triangle is located at $(5, 1)$. Graph a triangle which meets this condition, and state the coordinates of the vertices of the triangle you have graphed.

32. Using the diagram below, if the length of $\overline{PC} = 15$ and the length of $\overline{EC} = 9$, what is the length of $\overline{PD}$?

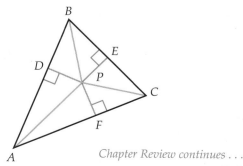

Chapter Review continues . . .

33. In the diagram, the length of $\overline{LS} = 13$ and the length of $\overline{DL} = 12$. What is the length of $\overline{AS}$?

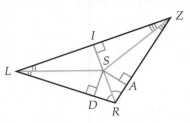

34. In trapezoid *JKLM*, for which $\overline{JM} \cong \overline{KL}$ and $JK > ML$, diagonal $\overline{MK}$ is constructed. Write a statement relating the measures of $\angle LKM$ and $\angle JMK$.

35. **MP 3, 4** Two fishing trawlers left an island at the same time. One headed east for 8 miles, then turned southeast and went an additional 7 miles, and then returned to the island. The other boat headed north for seven miles, then turned northwest and went another 8 miles, and then returned to the island. Based on the diagram, prove that the two boats did not travel the same total distance. Use indirect reasoning in your proof.

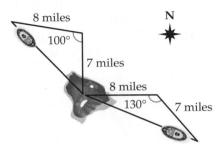

36. Prove the triangle sides and their sum theorem.

Triangle inequality theorem

Each side of a triangle is shorter than the sum of its other two sides.

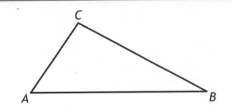

$AB + AC > BC$, $AB + BC > AC$, and $BC + AC > AB$.

1. Choose all that apply: $\overleftrightarrow{JK}$ and $\overleftrightarrow{HM}$ are

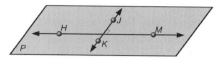

A. Coplanar.
B. Parallel.
C. Perpendicular.
D. None of the above.

2. Angles C and E are

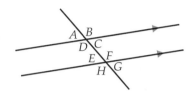

A. Consecutive interior angles.
B. Alternate interior angles.
C. Alternate exterior angles.
D. Corresponding angles.

3. The midsegment of a triangle is part of a line. It intersects two sides of a triangle. The third side of the triangle is along a line defined by the equation $y = 2x - 3$. Which equation could describe the line that the midsegment is part of?

A. $y = 2x - 3$
B. $y = x - 3$
C. $y = 2x + 4$
D. $y = -\dfrac{1}{2}x - 3$

4. You are told, "If two lines are perpendicular, their intersection creates right angles." What else must you be told to conclude, "Two lines are perpendicular if and only if their intersection creates right angles"?

A. If two lines are not perpendicular, then their intersection does not create right angles.
B. If an intersection creates right angles, then the two lines are perpendicular.
C. If two lines are parallel, then they cannot be perpendicular.
D. If two lines create right angles, then they cannot be parallel.

5. Choose all true statements that apply to the diagram.

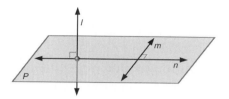

A. Lines l, m, and n are skew lines.
B. Lines l and n are perpendicular.
C. Lines m and n are parallel.
D. Lines l and n are both in plane P.

6. A student using a computer takes the image of a trapezoid, increases the length of all its sides by 140%, and then moves it 47 pixels to the left. The resulting image is

A. Similar to the original trapezoid.
B. Congruent with the original trapezoid.
C. Both similar and congruent with the original trapezoid.
D. None of the above.

7. Collinear points lie on the same line. Which two conditional statements, when taken together as true, are equivalent to that definition? Select the two.

A. If points are collinear, then they lie on the same line.
B. If points are not collinear, then they may lie on the same line.
C. If points lie on the same line, then they are collinear.
D. If points lie on different lines, then they are not collinear.

8. The statement: "All dishes in Maria's kitchen are clean" is equivalent to

A. If Maria cleans all her dishes, then her kitchen is clean.
B. If a person is Maria, then all the dishes in her kitchen are clean.
C. If it's a dish in Maria's kitchen, then it is clean.

9. The phrase "All triangles are polygons" can be written as which conditional statement?

   A. If a figure is a polygon, then it is a triangle.

   B. All polygons are triangles.

   C. If a figure is a triangle, then it is a polygon.

10. $2(3x + 9) = 24$ is equivalent to $6x + 18 = 24$. Which property is being applied to help solve the equation?

   A. Distributive property

   B. Addition property of equality

   C. Multiplication property of equality

   D. None of the above

11. How do we know that $p \parallel q$? Choose all answers that apply.

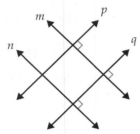

   A. m and n are both perpendicular to p

   B. p and q are both perpendicular to m

   C. p and q are both perpendicular to n

12. The corresponding sides of two similar rectangular gardens are 50 ft and 56 ft. The perimeter of the larger garden is 175 ft. What is the perimeter of the smaller garden?

13. MP 7, 8 A triangle contains two segments parallel to one side. Find each indicated segment length.

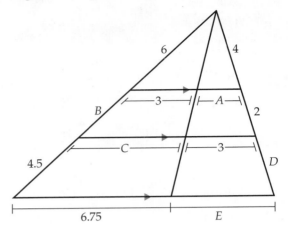

   a Find A.

   b Find B.

   c Find C.

   d Find D.

   e Find E.

14. Prove: $\triangle ACB \cong \triangle ECF$

Given: The midpoint of $\overline{AE}$ is C; $BC = CF$.

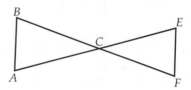

15. Prove the concurrency and perpendicular bisectors theorem.

Prove: $\overline{DA} \cong \overline{DB} \cong \overline{DC}$

Given: $\overline{DE}, \overline{DF},$ and $\overline{DG}$ are $\perp$ bisectors

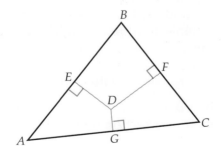

16. Two non-congruent line segments JK and LM bisect each other at point N. Connecting points J and L with line segment JL, and points K and M with line segment KM, forms triangles JNL and KNM.

    a Complete a sketch of the situation.
    b Prove that $\triangle JNL \cong \triangle KNM$.

17. Prove that the median of a triangle cannot form two obtuse angles with the side that it bisects.

18. Sketch an isosceles triangle in the coordinate plane. Then, prove that your triangle is not scalene using indirect reasoning.

19. Quadrilateral $GOAT$ has vertices located at $G(-3, 3)$, $O(4, 4)$, $A(6, -1)$, and $T(-2, -2)$. Use indirect reasoning to prove that $GOAT$ is not a parallelogram.

20. Given: $\triangle FED$ and $\triangle FAD$, which share side $\overline{FD}$; $\overline{ED} \cong \overline{AD}$, and $\overline{FD}$ bisects $\angle D$
Prove: $\triangle FED \cong \triangle FAD$

21. What is the slope of a line perpendicular to $y = \dfrac{1}{9}x + 8$?

22. In $\triangle NYC$, $m\angle N = 35°$ and $m\angle C$ is ten more than twice the measure of $\angle N$. Find the measure of $\angle Y$ and describe $\triangle NYC$ using all relevant words from the following list: acute, right, obtuse, equilateral, isosceles, and scalene.

23. Create a diagram with vertical and supplementary angles. Label all angle measures.

24. What additional piece of information is needed to prove $\triangle TUV \cong \triangle WXY$ by SSS?

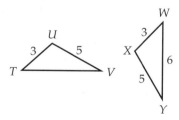

Exercises 25–27: Find all interior angles of a triangle, using the given the ratios among them.

25. Angles' ratio: $2 : 3 : 4$

26. Angles' ratio: $3 : 4 : 5$

27. Angles' ratio: $4 : 5 : 6$

28. Is it possible for a triangle to have two obtuse angles? Justify your answer.

29. **MP 2, 3, 4** Jonestown is planning to build a new performing arts center for its three schools, Washington High School, Lincoln Middle School, and Jefferson Elementary. The schools are located on the grid below and joined by roads, as shown. The superintendent has proposed that the performing arts center be built equidistant from all three schools.

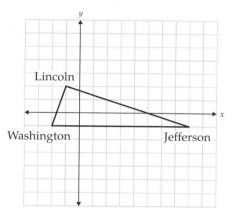

    a Find the coordinates of this location algebraically.

    b Describe how you found this position and tell what this point is called.

    c The city manager suggests that the performing arts center be built in a location equidistant from the three roads connecting the schools, reducing the cost of building new roads to the center. How would you locate this point on the map? What is it called?

    d Which two schools' principals are happy with the city manager's suggestion, and which one is not? Explain why.

    e What argument could this third principal make to convince the city manager that the first option is better?

Chapter Content

Chapter Vocabulary

adjacent leg	law of cosines	side-side-side (SSS) similarity theorem
angle-angle (AA) similarity postulate	law of sines	sine
angle of depression	oblique triangles	tangent
angle of elevation	opposite leg	trigonometric ratio
cosine	Pythagorean triple	trigonometry
inverse function	side-angle-side (SAS) similarity theorem	

LESSON 7.1

7.1 Similarity: Angle-Angle and Side-Side-Side

Angle-Angle (AA) Similarity Postulate

We have discussed several ways to determine if triangles are similar, including the side-angle-side (SAS) theorem and the side-side-side (SSS) theorem. A third way to determine if triangles are similar is to use the **angle-angle (AA) similarity postulate**, which is defined below. Remember that it is important to name triangles so their vertices are in the correct order according to their congruent angles.

> *A* is first for the vertex of one triangle and *Z* for the other, since those angles are congruent.

Angle-angle (AA) similarity postulate

If two angles of one triangle are congruent to two angles of another triangle, then the triangles are similar.

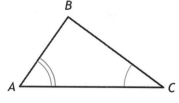 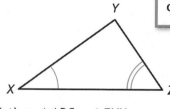

If $\angle A \cong \angle Z$ and $\angle C \cong \angle X$, then $\triangle ABC \sim \triangle ZYX$.

Note that if two pairs of corresponding angles in two triangles are congruent, we can use the triangle sum theorem to show that the third angles of both triangles are also congruent.

Earlier in this book, we stated that if a triangle's line segments increase or decrease by a scale factor, each side will change length proportionally. But what happens to an angle when the side lengths change by a scale factor? We use the diagram on the next page to answer this question.

In the diagram to the right, we dilate the line segments forming angle ABC. The length of $\overline{AB} = 5$ and the length of $\overline{BC} = 3$. We use the diagram to determine what happens to angles when the line segments composing it are dilated:

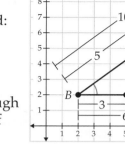

1. **Dilate points that define angle.** Use the angle's vertex as the center of dilation, although the result of dilation is the same regardless of where the center of dilation is placed.

2. **Center of dilation is the vertex, B.** Since B is the vertex, BA is multiplied by the scale factor 2, a scale factor we chose for this example, to get BA'. Similarly, BC is multiplied by 2 to get BC'.

$$BA \cdot 2 = BA'$$
$$BC \cdot 2 = BC'$$

3. **Angle's measure stays the same.** The original angle is congruent to the angle resulting from the dilation, since only the distances from the vertex were multiplied with the scale factor.

$$\angle ABC \cong \angle A'BC'$$

Another way to confirm that dilation creates congruent angles is to consider what happens to an angle when a dilation is performed (with an arbitrary center of dilation):

Paragraph Proof

Dilation creates parallel lines. When we perform a dilation, the rays AB and $A'B'$ are parallel, as are rays AC and $A'C'$. Given that these rays are part of parallel lines, both AE and $A'B'$ are transversals to two parallel lines. Now we can use a theorem discussed earlier: Angles BAC and $B'DE$ are corresponding angles, which means they are congruent. Similarly, angles $B'DE$ and $B'A'C'$ are congruent. By transitivity, angles BAC and $B'A'C'$ are congruent, and we have shown that dilation changes an angle into a congruent angle. Since angle measures are preserved in dilation, this means that we have established that dilations produce similar triangles, according to the AA criterion for similarity.

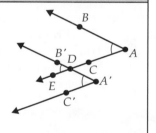

In the figure to the right, we use rigid motion to transform $\triangle XYZ$ to $\triangle X'Y'Z'$. We can see that $\angle X \cong \angle X'$ and that $\angle Y \cong \angle Y'$; thus, by the AA similarity postulate, we know that $\triangle XYZ \sim \triangle X'Y'Z'$. Thus two congruent figures are also similar figures.

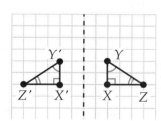

To sum it up:

Rigid motion creates congruent figures

- Angles continue to have same measure

Dilation creates similar figures

- Angles keep same measure
- Side lengths do **not** change

AA postulate

- Any two angles are congruent

1. Are the two triangles similar?

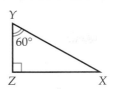

SOLUTION

Calculate third angle	$m\angle M = 180° - 90° - 30°$ $= 60°$	Calculate $m\angle M$ using the fact that the angles sum to 180° in a triangle and noting that N is a right angle.
Two pairs of congruent angles	$m\angle M = 60°, m\angle N = 90°$ $m\angle Y = 60°, m\angle Z = 90°$	The triangles have two pairs of congruent angles. Both have 60° angles and both have right angles.
$\triangle MNP \sim \triangle YZX$	AA similarity postulate	The angle-angle similarity postulate lets us say the two triangles are similar.

2. Are the triangles similar? If so, write a similarity statement.

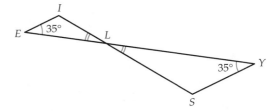

SOLUTION

Congruent angles based on diagram	$\angle IEL \cong \angle SYL$	The diagram shows these two angles as both measuring 35°, so they are congruent.
Congruent angles since they are vertical angles	$\angle ELI \cong \angle YLS$	These angles form a vertical pair. This means they are congruent.
Similar due to AA similarity postulate	$\triangle IEL \sim \triangle SYL$	Since the triangles have two pairs of congruent angles, they are similar triangles. We are careful to write them so that the corresponding angles and sides come in the same order.

3. **MP 3** Prove: $\triangle CAB \sim \triangle ZXY$

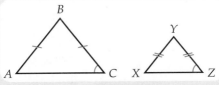

SOLUTION

Statement	Reason	
$\angle C \cong \angle Z$	Diagram	The diagram shows these angles as congruent.
$\overline{AB} \cong \overline{BC}, \overline{XY} \cong \overline{YZ}$	Diagram	The hash marks show that the triangles are isosceles.
$\angle C \cong \angle A, \angle Z \cong \angle X$	Isosceles triangle theorem	Angles opposite congruent sides of an isosceles triangle are congruent.
$\angle A \cong \angle X$	Transitive property of congruence	Since $\angle C \cong \angle Z$ and $\angle Z \cong \angle X$ and $\angle C \cong \angle A$, then $\angle A \cong \angle X$.
$\triangle CAB \sim \triangle ZXY$	Angle-angle similarity postulate	We have shown two pairs of angles are congruent, so the two triangles are similar.

Model Problems continue . . .

4. MP 1

a In the diagram to the right, $m_1 \parallel m_2$. Prove the slope of m_1 is equal to the slope of m_2 by using equations involving segment lengths.

b Prove the slope of m_1 is equal to the slope of m_2 by showing that $\triangle ABC \sim \triangle YXC$.

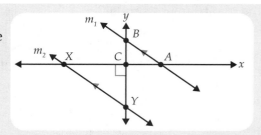

SOLUTION

a

$$\text{slope}_1 = \frac{BC}{AC}$$

The slope of the first line, m_1, is the rise over the run, which is the ratio of these two legs.

$$\text{slope}_2 = \frac{YC}{XC}$$

Calculate the slope of m_2 in the same fashion.

if $\dfrac{BC}{AC} = \dfrac{YC}{XC}$

If the ratios are equal, then the slopes are equal.

then $\text{slope}_1 = \text{slope}_2$

> We show that slopes of parallel lines are equal by comparing the ratios of the two lines.

b We need to show the ratio equality above is true. To do so, we will show the two triangles we drew are similar using the AA similarity postulate and the fact that the ratios of corresponding sides of similar triangles are equal.

$\angle BAC \cong \angle YXC$	Alternate interior angles	$\overleftrightarrow{XA}$ is a transversal to the two parallel lines, so these two angles are alternate interior angles, which means they are congruent.
$\angle BCA \cong \angle YCX$	Both right angles	These are both right angles according to the diagram and the vertical angle congruence theorem, so they are congruent.
$\triangle ABC \sim \triangle XYC$	Angle-angle similarity postulate	We have shown two angles are congruent, so the angle-angle similarity postulate says these triangles are similar.
Ratios of corresponding sides are equal	$\dfrac{BC}{YC} = \dfrac{AC}{XC}$	The ratios of corresponding sides of similar triangles are equal.
Multiplication property of equality	$\dfrac{YC}{AC}\left(\dfrac{BC}{YC}\right) = \dfrac{YC}{AC}\left(\dfrac{AC}{XC}\right)$ $\dfrac{BC}{AC} = \dfrac{YC}{XC}$	Multiply both sides by the fraction $\dfrac{YC}{AC}$. The result is the ratio that shows the slopes of these parallel lines are equal.

Model Problems continue . . .

5. What is the length of $\overline{AB}$?

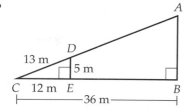

> Diagrams are often not drawn to scale, so use the numbers given.

SOLUTION

Find two similar triangles

To calculate AB, use two triangles. One is $\triangle CDE$. The other is $\triangle CAB$. They are similar triangles.

Similar due to AA similarity postulate

Why are the triangles similar? Both share $\angle C$, so that is one pair of congruent angles. Both triangles have right angles, so that is another pair of congruent angles. This means they have two congruent angles and are similar by the AA similarity postulate.

Write and solve proportion

$$\frac{AB}{DE} = \frac{BC}{EC}$$

$$\frac{AB}{5} = \frac{36}{12}$$

$$5 \cdot \frac{AB}{5} = 5 \cdot \frac{36}{12}$$

$$AB = \frac{180}{12} = 15 \text{ meters}$$

Write the proportion with corresponding sides. Substitute the known values. Solve the proportion.

Side-Side-Side (SSS) Similarity Theorem

The **side-side-side (SSS) similarity theorem** provides another tool for showing that two triangles are similar.

Side-side-side (SSS) similarity theorem

If the corresponding sides of two triangles are proportional, then the triangles are similar.

 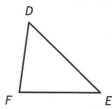

If $\frac{AB}{DE} = \frac{BC}{EF} = \frac{AC}{DF}$, then $\triangle ABC \sim \triangle DEF$.

> This theorem confirms that dilation creates similar triangles.

1. Only two of the triangles in the diagram are similar. Determine which two.

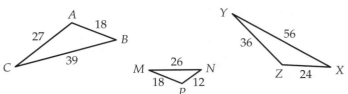

SOLUTION

Determine if
$\triangle NPM \sim \triangle BAC$

$$\text{Shortest} = \frac{AB}{NP} = \frac{18}{12} = \frac{3}{2}$$

$$\text{Longest} = \frac{BC}{NM} = \frac{39}{26} = \frac{3}{2}$$

$$\text{Medium} = \frac{CA}{MP} = \frac{27}{18} = \frac{3}{2}$$

$$\triangle NPM \sim \triangle BAC$$

We start with $\triangle NPM$ and $\triangle BAC$. Note that we write the triangles in this fashion so the sides of the triangles correspond, from shortest to longest. Calculate the ratio of the shortest sides, then the ratio of the longest sides, and the other pair of sides. All have the same ratio. The two triangles are similar.

Determine if
$\triangle NPM \sim \triangle XZY$

$$\text{Shortest} = \frac{ZX}{PN} = \frac{24}{12} = 2$$

$$\text{Longest} = \frac{XY}{NM} = \frac{56}{26} = \frac{28}{13}$$

$$\text{Medium} = \frac{YZ}{MP} = \frac{36}{18} = 2$$

$\triangle NPM$ and $\triangle XZY$ are not similar!

Try another pair of triangles, calculating the ratios of the corresponding sides. The ratios are not the same. The triangles are not similar.

We could continue to show that triangles $\triangle BAC$ and $\triangle XZY$ are not similar, or use transitivity to argue that $\triangle BAC$ and $\triangle XZY$ cannot be similar since $\triangle NPM$ is similar to $\triangle BAC$, but not to $\triangle XZY$.

2. **MP 7** Show $\triangle FED \sim \triangle GIH \sim \triangle ABC$.

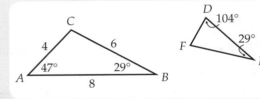

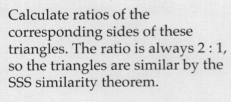

SOLUTION

Determine if
$\triangle ABC \sim \triangle GIH$

$$\text{Shortest} = \frac{CA}{HG} = \frac{4}{2} = \frac{2}{1}$$

$$\text{Medium} = \frac{BC}{IH} = \frac{6}{3} = \frac{2}{1}$$

$$\text{Longest} = \frac{AB}{GI} = \frac{8}{4} = \frac{2}{1}$$

Calculate ratios of the corresponding sides of these triangles. The ratio is always $2:1$, so the triangles are similar by the SSS similarity theorem.

Calculate third angle in $\triangle FED$

$$m\angle DEF + m\angle EFD + m\angle FDE = 180°$$
$$m\angle EFD = 180° - 104° - 29°$$
$$m\angle EFD = 47°$$

Calculate the third angle in the middle triangle. Do this by using the fact that the angles sum to 180° in a triangle.

$\triangle FED \sim \triangle GIH$ AA similarity postulate

We can show the triangles are similar due to the angle-angle similarity.

$\triangle FED \sim \triangle GIH \sim \triangle ABC$ Transitive similarity

Both triangles are similar to $\triangle GIH$, so all three triangles are similar.

PRACTICE

1. $\triangle XYZ$ has angles with measures of 60° and 80°. $\triangle UVW$ has angles with measures of 80° and 50°. Are they similar triangles?

   A. Yes
   B. No
   C. It's impossible to tell

2. Given the two similar triangles shown, what is the length of $\overline{BC}$?

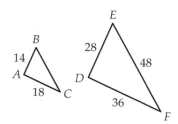

   A. 16   C. 24
   B. 20   D. 26

3. $\triangle ABC$ has angle measures of 85° and 30°. $\triangle DEF$ has angle measures of 30° and 65°. If the two triangles are similar, what is the remaining angle measure in $\triangle ABC$?

   A. 70°   C. 55°
   B. 65°   D. 75°

4. Which of the following side lengths represent two similar triangles?

   A. $\triangle ABC$: 12 in, 8 in, 6 in
       $\triangle XYZ$: 24 in, 16 in, 10 in

   B. $\triangle ABC$: 9 in, 4 in, 8 in
       $\triangle XYZ$: 13.5 in, 6 in, 12 in

   C. $\triangle ABC$: 5 in, 7 in, 11 in
       $\triangle XYZ$: 12.5 in, 14 in, 27.5 in

   D. $\triangle ABC$: 7 in, 12 in, 9 in
       $\triangle XYZ$: 5.25 in, 9 in, 4.5 in

5. One triangle has sides of length 5, 10, and 9. Another triangle has sides of length 20, 40, and 36. Are the triangles similar?

   A. Yes
   B. No
   C. There's no way to tell

6. Given the two triangles, which of the following statements is true?

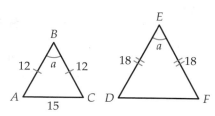

   A. The two triangles are not similar, so the length of $\overline{DF}$ cannot be determined.
   B. The two triangles are similar and $DF = 21$.
   C. The two triangles are similar and $DF = 22.5$.
   D. The two triangles are not similar and $DF = 21$.

7. In $\triangle ABC$ and $\triangle DEF$, $\angle A \cong \angle F$, $\angle B \cong \angle D$, $AC = 20$, $DE = 5$, and $DF = 10$. What is AB?

   A. 2
   B. 10
   C. 40
   D. There is not enough information to calculate AB

8. $\triangle GHJ$ has angles with measures of 75° and 25°. $\triangle KLM$ has angles with measures of 80° and 25°. Are they similar triangles? Explain.

9. $\triangle YNO$ and $\triangle YUP$ have two pairs of sides with a scale factor of 3. The third sides have lengths of 64 and 16. Are the triangles similar? Explain.

10. $\triangle ABC$ has angle measures of 25° and 65°. $\triangle DEF$ is a right triangle with one angle measuring 65°. Are the two triangles similar? Explain.

11. The triangles below are similar. What is $m\angle E$?

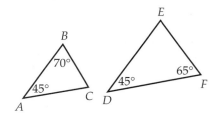

Practice Problems continue . . .

12. **MP 3** State whether the two right triangles below are similar or not. Justify your answer.

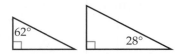

13. Name two statements that can be made about two pairs of congruent corresponding angles.

14. Given the similar triangles below, what is the length of $\overline{AB}$?

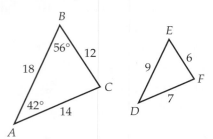

15. Given the triangles below, what is $m\angle DFE$?

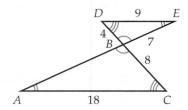

16. Given the triangles below, what is $m\angle EDF$?

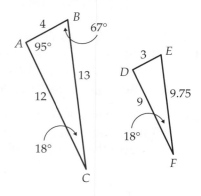

17. Given $\triangle ABC \sim \triangle DEF$, what is the length of $\overline{BC}$?

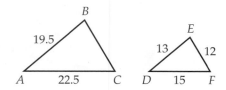

18. What is the value of b?

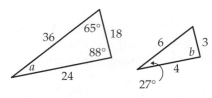

19. Given the similar triangles below, represent the corresponding sides as a proportion.

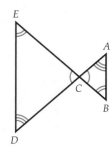

20. How do we know the two triangles shown below are similar?

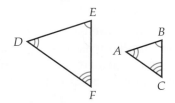

21. State whether the two triangles below are similar or not. Justify your answer.

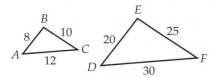

22. Right triangle #1 contains an additional angle measure of 38°. Right triangle #2 contains an additional angle measure of 54°. Are the two right triangles similar? Explain.

23. **MP 2** $\triangle ABC$ has side lengths of 14, 12, and 22. $\triangle DEF$ has side lengths of 35, 30, and 55. $\triangle GHI$ has side lengths of 21, 16, and 33. Which two triangles are similar? Justify your answer.

24. Provide a diagram that shows two similar triangles created when two parallel lines are cut by two transversals. Mark congruent corresponding angles.

Practice Problems continue . . .

25. A carpenter builds a triangular brace that will support a desk. The brace has one right angle and an angle measuring 60°. The brace is too small. The carpenter must enlarge the brace by a scale factor, k. What will be the angle measures of the enlarged triangular brace?

26. An artist creates a tessellation of triangles. Each triangle has side lengths of 2 inches, 3 inches, and 4 inches. He wishes to enlarge the size of each triangle when creating a new tessellation. He plans to use lengths of 5 inches and 7.5 inches for two of the sides. What will be the length of the third side of each triangle, in the new tessellation?

27. Given: $m\angle A = m\angle E$
Prove: $\triangle ABC \sim \triangle EBD$

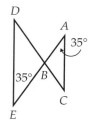

28. An artist creates a triangular painting. She takes a picture of her painting, cuts out the triangular shape, and identifies the dimensions. If the sides of the cut-out shape are 3.5 inches, 2.5 inches, and 3 inches, and the cut-out is related to the original painting by a scale factor of 0.25, what are the corresponding lengths of the sides of the original painting?

29. Aaron states, "All right triangles are similar." Is he correct? Why or why not?

30. Create a set of two similar triangles and 1 non-similar triangle. Label the sides and angles of each triangle and identify the similar triangles.

31. Given the diagram below and the statement that $\overline{BD}$ is not parallel to $\overline{AE}$, prove $\triangle CBD$ is not similar to $\triangle CAE$.

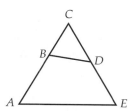

32. In a given triangle, the altitude is constructed, creating two smaller, similar triangles. An altitude is constructed in each of these triangles, creating four even smaller, but also similar, triangles. This process is continued as many times as desired. Of what type was the original triangle?

33. **MP 3, 6** In the diagram below, $AB = 10$, $BE = 8$, $AE = 7$, $DC = 15$, $DE = 12$, and $CE = 10.5$. Prove $\overline{AB} \parallel \overline{DC}$.

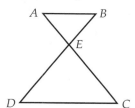

LESSON 7.2

7.2 Similar Triangles: Side-Angle-Side Theorem

The **side-angle-side (SAS) similarity theorem** provides another way to show that triangles are similar.

Side-angle-side (SAS) similarity theorem

If the lengths of two pairs of corresponding sides of two triangles are proportional and the angles the sides form are congruent, then the triangles are similar.

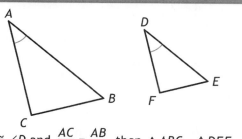

If $\angle A \cong \angle D$ and $\dfrac{AC}{DF} = \dfrac{AB}{DE}$, then $\triangle ABC \sim \triangle DEF$.

1. Prove: $\triangle ABC \sim \triangle ADE$

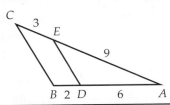

SOLUTION

Statement	Reason	
$AB = AD + BD$ $AB = 6 + 2 = 8$	Segment addition postulate	Use the segment addition postulate to calculate AB.
$AC = AE + CE$ $AC = 9 + 3 = 12$	Segment addition postulate	Do the same for AC.
$\dfrac{AD}{AB} = \dfrac{AE}{AC}$	$\dfrac{AD}{AB} = \dfrac{6}{8} = \dfrac{3}{4}$ $\dfrac{AE}{AC} = \dfrac{9}{12} = \dfrac{3}{4}$	Calculate the other ratio and simplify it. The two ratios are equal, so the sides are proportional.
$\angle CAB \cong \angle CAB$	Reflexive property of congruence	An angle is congruent with itself.
$\triangle ABC \sim \triangle ADE$	SAS similarity theorem	We have shown two pairs of sides are proportional and the angles they form are congruent. This means the two triangles are similar.

2. The orange part of the surveyor's staff, shown to the right, is 5 feet tall, and the surveyor is 8 feet from the other surveyor. If the other surveyor is 300 feet from the tower, how tall is the tower? The base of the tower is at the height shown.

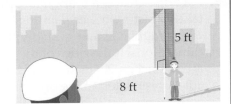

SOLUTION

Draw diagram

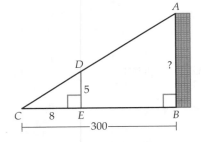

$\triangle CDE \sim \triangle CAB$ Similar due to AA similarity postulate

Two angles are congruent, so they are similar by the AA similarity postulate. Both triangles share $\angle C$ and have right angles.

Write and solve proportion

$$\dfrac{AB}{DE} = \dfrac{BC}{EC}$$
$$\dfrac{AB}{5} = \dfrac{300}{8}$$
$$5 \cdot \dfrac{AB}{5} = 5 \cdot \dfrac{300}{8}$$
$$AB = \dfrac{1500}{8} = 187.5 \text{ feet}$$

Write the proportion. The ratio of the two heights is equal to the ratio of the two distances along the ground. Substitute the values into the proportion and evaluate. The height of the tower is 187.5 feet.

Model Problems continue . . .

MODEL PROBLEMS *continued*

3. **MP 7** A person who is 2 meters tall looks into a mirror that has been placed on the ground 3 meters away and sees the reflection of the top of a telephone pole. If the distance between the telephone pole and the mirror is 21 meters, how tall is the telephone pole?

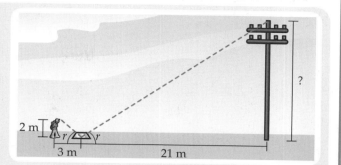

SOLUTION

Draw diagram

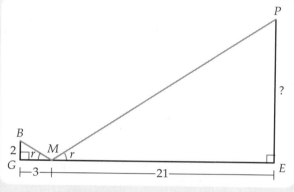

Triangles formed by the person and mirror, and the telephone pole and mirror, are similar. Both the pole and the person are standing vertically, so they form right angles with the ground. When an object is reflected, the two angles, labeled r, will be congruent. With two congruent angles, we can use the AA similarity postulate to conclude the triangles are similar.

Write proportion

$$\frac{PE}{BG} = \frac{ME}{MG}$$

The triangles formed by the person and the mirror, and the pole and the mirror, are similar. That means this proportion must hold true, that corresponding sides form the same ratio.

Substitute and solve equation

$$\frac{PE}{2} = \frac{21}{3}$$

$$2\left(\frac{PE}{2}\right) = 2\left(\frac{21}{3}\right)$$

$$PE = \frac{2 \cdot 21}{3} = 14 \text{ m}$$

Substitute the lengths shown in the diagram. Multiply both sides by 2 to isolate PE. The height of the pole is 14 meters.

PRACTICE

1. $\triangle ABC \sim \triangle DEF$ and $AB = 26$ inches, $AC = 18$ inches, and $DF = 12$ inches. What is the length of $\overline{DE}$?

   A. 8.3 in

   B. $16\frac{1}{2}$ in

   C. $17\frac{1}{3}$ in

   D. 39 in

2. Henry casts a shadow, 3 feet in length. His son, who is 3.5 feet tall, casts a shadow that is 1.8 feet in length. Which of the following best represents Henry's height?

   A. 5 ft 6 in

   B. 5 ft 8 in

   C. 5 ft 10 in

   D. 6 ft

Practice Problems continue . . .

3. Which of the following triangles is similar to the orange triangle shown below? Figures are not drawn to scale.

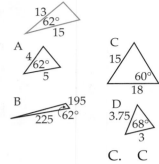

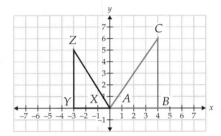

A. A

B. B

C. C

D. D

4. Are the two triangles below similar? Explain.

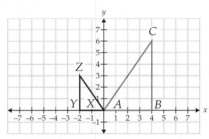

5. Are the two triangles below similar? Explain.

6. With △ICE and △TEA, ∠I and ∠T are congruent. IC = 4, IE = 6, TE = 24, and TA = 30. Are the triangles similar?

7. With △ABC and △XYZ, ∠A and ∠X are congruent. AB = 5, AC = 7, XY = 50, and XZ = 70. Are the triangles similar?

8. With △FAT and △NOT, ∠F and ∠N are congruent. FA = 12, FT = 9, NO = 4, and NT = 3. Are the triangles similar?

9. In the picture below, the orange staff is 4 feet tall. If all the other distances shown are also measured in feet, how tall is the building?

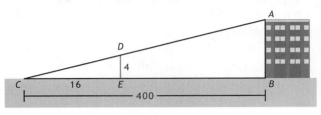

10. AB is 9 feet and AC is 36 feet. If the surveyor's staff is 5 feet tall, how tall is the flagpole?

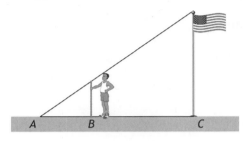

11. **MP 7** Show that the two triangles are similar.

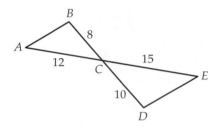

12. In the diagram below, △ABC ~ △DEF. What is the length of BC and m∠E?

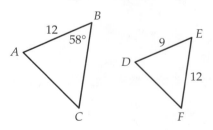

13. In the diagram below, △ABC ~ △DEF. What is the length of CA and m∠F?

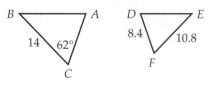

Practice Problems continue . . .

14. In the diagram below, △ABC ~ △DEF. What is the length of *DE* and *m∠D*?

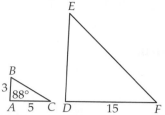

15. In the diagram below, △ABC ~ △DEF. What is the length of *AB* and *m∠D*?

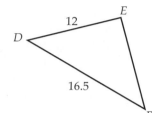

16. In the diagram below, △ABC ~ △DEF. What is the length of *DE* and *m∠A*?

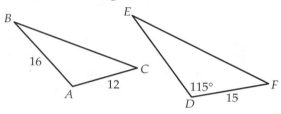

17. In the diagram below, △ABC ~ △DEF. What is the length of *DF* and *m∠D*?

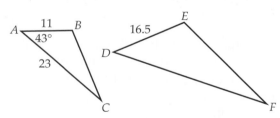

18. What must be the length of $\overline{EF}$ if △ABC and △DEF, shown below, are to be similar?

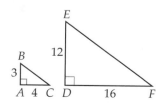

19. Determine if the right triangles below are similar. Justify your answer.

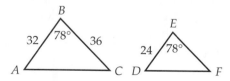

20. Determine if the right triangles below are similar. Justify your answer.

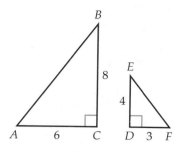

21. Determine if the right triangles below are similar. Justify your answer.

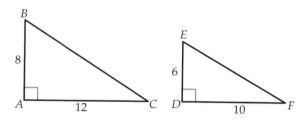

22. Given that $\overline{AB} \parallel \overline{ED}$, determine if the triangles in the diagram below are similar. If the triangles are similar, write a short proof. If the triangles are not similar, write a short explanation.

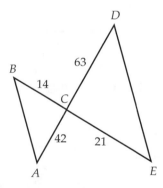

23. Given that $\overline{AB} \parallel \overline{ED}$, determine if the triangles in the diagram below are similar. If the triangles are similar, write a short proof. If the triangles are not similar, write a short explanation.

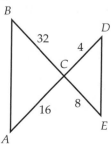

Practice Problems continue . . .

24. $\triangle RST \sim \triangle UVW$. $RT = 9$ cm, $ST = 15$ cm, and $UW = 13.5$ cm. The angle formed by $\overline{RT}$ and $\overline{ST}$ measures $62°$.

   a What is the length of $\overline{VW}$?

   b What is the measure of the angle formed by $\overline{UW}$ and $\overline{VW}$?

25. **MP 2** Explain the side-angle-side similarity theorem in your own words.

26. Draw two triangles that are formed when a pair of parallel lines is intersected by two transversals. Measure and label the non-parallel side lengths. State whether the triangles are similar or not and explain how you know.

27. Given the triangles shown below, identify the similar triangles using a similarity statement.

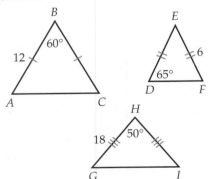

28. Given the triangles shown below, identify the similar triangles using a similarity statement.

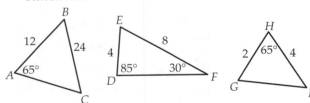

29. Given the triangles shown below, identify the similar triangles using a similarity statement. Figures are not drawn to scale.

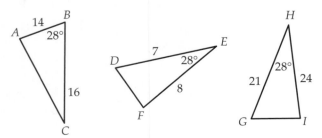

30. Aaron draws a sketch of a triangular brace. The sketch of the triangle is similar to the actual brace. If the sides of the triangular sketch measure 2 inches, 3 inches, and 4 inches, and the scale factor from the sketch to the actual brace is 12, what are the measures of the sides of the actual brace?

31. An 18-foot pole casts a 5-foot shadow. Jacob, who is 6 feet tall, stands next to the pole. How long is his shadow?

32. A board rests on a box, forming a ramp. The box is 3 feet in height. The board rests at a point on the ground 4 feet from the base of the box. Suppose a box measuring 2 feet in height is used instead. How long will the board need to be to make a ramp with the same angle with the ground that the first ramp has?

33. **MP 2, 4** Kevin ties a string to the trunk of a tree, 18 feet above the ground, and secures the string to a location on the ground that is 14 feet from the base of the tree. He then ties another string to the trunk of the tree, at a location 22 feet above the ground, and secures the string to a location on the ground that is 18 feet from the base of the tree. Considering the two triangles formed by the tree, the string, and the ground, determine if they are similar. Explain.

34. **MP 4** In physics, the Law of Reflection says that when light hits a mirror, it reflects off the mirror at the same angle that it hit the mirror. Derek and Eric are playing laser tag. There is a barrier between them, but a mirror off to the side. Derek is 10 feet from the mirror, and Eric is 6 feet from the mirror. The distance along the mirror is 12 feet, as shown in the diagram. At what distance along the mirror, x, must Derek aim his laser if he wishes to hit Eric?

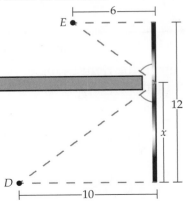

Practice Problems continue . . .

35. Two right triangles are similar. One has a base of 30 centimeters and a hypotenuse of 40 centimeters. If the second triangle has a base which measures 18 centimeters, how long is its hypotenuse, in centimeters? Make a sketch of the situation to help you find your answer.

36. Given: $\dfrac{AB}{XY} = \dfrac{BC}{YZ}$

Prove: $\triangle ZCP$ is isosceles

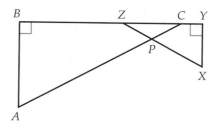

37. Given: $\angle HGI \cong \angle GFJ$

Prove: $\triangle ABC \sim \triangle FED$

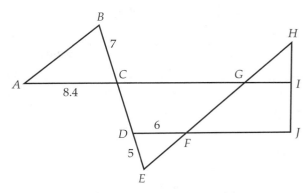

---

38. **MP 3, 6** Prove the side-angle-side similarity theorem. Hint: Place a point, X, on $\overline{AC}$ so that $\overline{AX} \cong \overline{DF}$. Then draw a line segment $\overline{XY}$ where point Y is on $\overline{AB}$ and $\overline{XY} \parallel \overline{BC}$.

Side-angle-side (SAS) similarity theorem

If the lengths of two pairs of corresponding sides of two triangles are proportional and the angles the sides form are congruent, then the triangles are similar.

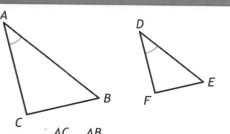

If $\angle A \cong \angle D$ and $\dfrac{AC}{DF} = \dfrac{AB}{DE}$, then $\triangle ABC \sim \triangle DEF$.

Use the diagram below to begin your proof.

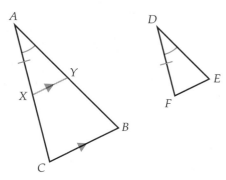

7.3 Pythagorean Theorem

From your previous studies of mathematics, you are familiar with the Pythagorean equation, which is the algebraic expression of the Pythagorean theorem. It is one of geometry's most famous theorems, and there are over 100 proofs of it. There are numerous applications of the Pythagorean theorem. Below, we show a proof and some problems that can be solved using the equation.

Prove: $a^2 + b^2 = c^2$

Proof Strategy To prove the Pythagorean theorem, we start with a square within a square. Label the triangles so that the hypotenuse of each is c, a side of the larger square. Their legs are a and b. We place four congruent right triangles inside a larger square, which creates a smaller square. We then compute the area of the larger square as the sum of the areas of the triangles and smaller square.

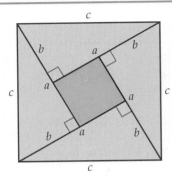

$a^2 + b^2 = c^2$, with a and b the legs of a right triangle with a hypotenuse of c.

Compute area of larger square	$\text{area}_{\text{larger square}} = \text{area}_{\text{4 triangles}} + \text{area}_{\text{smaller square}}$	The area of the larger square equals the sum of the shapes that make it up.
Write equation	$c^2 = \ldots$	The area of a square equals the square of the length of a side. The length of a side is c.
	$c^2 = 4\left(\dfrac{1}{2}ab\right) + \ldots$	Part of the area of the larger square is the area of the four triangles. This part of the area equals one-half the product of the base and height of an individual triangle, times 4 since there are 4 triangles.
	$c^2 = 4\left(\dfrac{1}{2}ab\right) + (a-b)^2$	The rest of the area of the larger square is the area of the smaller square, which has a side length of $a - b$. Square the side length to encompass the smaller square in the equation.
Simplify	$c^2 = 2ab + a^2 - 2ab + b^2$ $c^2 = a^2 + b^2$	Multiply, and expand the squared expression on the right. The expression $2ab$ cancels out, leaving the Pythagorean relationship for the sides of a right triangle.

MODEL PROBLEMS

1. **MP 2** How high is the top of the antenna from the ground, to the nearest meter? The antenna is on top of the tower, with an orange light at its peak.

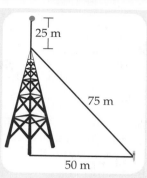

SOLUTION

Draw diagram

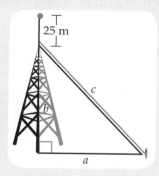

Use the Pythagorean theorem to solve the problem. Label the two legs and the hypotenuse.

Solve for leg
$$c^2 = a^2 + b^2$$
$$b = \sqrt{c^2 - a^2}$$

Write the Pythagorean theorem and solve for b.

Substitute and evaluate
$$b = \sqrt{75^2 - 50^2}$$
$$b = \sqrt{3125} \approx 56 \text{ meters}$$

Substitute and evaluate. At about 56 meters the wire attaches to the tower.

Add
$$56 + 25 \approx 81 \text{ meters}$$

Take the height that was just calculated and add it to the 25 extra meters.

2. What is the area of the larger triangle?

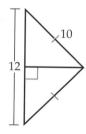

SOLUTION

Apply Pythagorean theorem
$$c^2 = a^2 + b^2$$
$$b = \sqrt{c^2 - a^2}$$

We need to find the height of the isosceles triangle, which is the length of the leg shared by the two right triangles.

Substitute and evaluate
$$b = \sqrt{10^2 - 6^2} = 8$$

Since the altitude (or height) of an isosceles triangle bisects its base, divide 12 by 2 to get the length of the other leg of one of the right triangles. Solve for the shared length, b. Substitute and evaluate.

Area of two triangles
$$A = 2\left(\frac{1}{2}b \cdot h\right) = b \cdot h$$
$$A = 6 \cdot 8 = 48$$

Use the formula for the area of a triangle, but multiply by 2, since two right triangles make up the area of the isosceles triangle. Substitute and evaluate.

PRACTICE

1. The legs of a right triangle measure 6 inches and 8 inches. What is the length of the hypotenuse of the triangle in inches?

   A.   14 inches
   C.   14 inches
   B.   10 inches
   D.   24 inches

2. A brace is used to support a balcony, as shown in the diagram. The brace attaches to the building 4 feet below the balcony and measures 10 feet long. The balcony extends an additional 2 feet away from the building past where the brace attaches. What is the length of the balcony, from the building to its edge, to the nearest whole number?

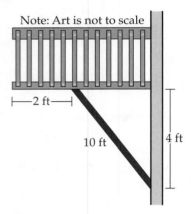

   A.   8 feet
   C.   11 feet
   B.   9 feet
   D.   12 feet

3. The area of an isosceles triangle is 12 square units and its height, as measured from the base, is 3 units. How long is one of the congruent sides of this triangle?

   A.   2 units
   C.   5 units
   B.   4 units
   D.   8 units

4. A right triangle has two legs, one with length 5 and the other with length 6. What is the length of the hypotenuse?

5. A right triangle has two legs, one with length 6 and the other with length 3. What is the length of the hypotenuse?

6. A right triangle has legs of 12 and 3. What is the length of the hypotenuse? Round your answer to the nearest tenth.

7. A right triangle has legs with lengths of 4 cm and 8 cm. What is the length of the hypotenuse to the nearest tenth?

8. Find the length of the missing side. Round to the nearest tenth.

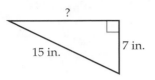

9. Consider the two right triangles below. Can x and y be the same length? Why or why not?

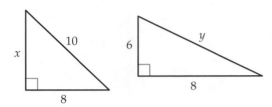

10. Find the area of a right triangle with legs of lengths 16 cm and 20 cm.

11. Find the area of a right triangle with a hypotenuse of length 9 in and one leg with length 5 in. Round your answer to the nearest tenth.

12. What is the area of the right triangle?

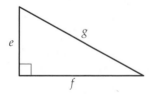

13. What is the area of the isosceles triangle? Round your answer to the nearest tenth.

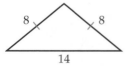

14. An isosceles triangle has a base measuring 24 meters, and its two congruent sides each measure 15 meters.

   a Make a sketch of the situation. Make sure to indicate the location of the altitude in your sketch.

   b Find the area of the triangle, to the nearest square meter.

Practice Problems continue . . .

15. **MP 2, 4** A diagonal brace is used to support a wall. The brace is 8.5 feet long, and its base is placed 3 feet from the wall. The upper end of the brace is located 4 feet below the top of the wall.

   a Make a sketch of the situation.

   b How high is the wall, to the nearest tenth of a foot?

   c If the bottom of the brace is moved so it is located 4.75 feet from the base of the wall, how far will the upper end of the brace be from the top of the wall, to the nearest foot?

16. A 15-foot ladder leans against a wall. If the base of the ladder is 8 feet from the wall, how far up the wall is the top of the ladder? State your answer to the nearest tenth of a foot.

17. **MP 2, 3** Rory was asked to find the area of an isosceles triangle. The triangle's base measures 30 inches, and the length of each of its congruent sides is 17 inches. Rory says the area of the triangle is 240 square inches. Do you agree? Why or why not?

18. **MP 5** Square *ABCD* has sides of length 17. Point *E* is constructed on side *AB* such that it is 12 units from vertex *A* and 5 units from vertex *B*. Point *F* is located on side *BC* such that it is 12 units from vertex *B* and 5 units from vertex *C*. This process is repeated twice more, locating point *G* 12 units from point *C* on *CD*, and point *H* 12 units from point *D* on *DA*.

   a Make a sketch of the situation. Then, on your sketch, construct line segments $\overline{EF}$, $\overline{FG}$, $\overline{GH}$, and $\overline{HE}$.

   b Are line segments $\overline{EF}$, $\overline{FG}$, $\overline{GH}$, and $\overline{HE}$ congruent? Explain your reasoning.

   c Find the area of square *EFGH* in square units.

19. An airplane takes off from an airport and climbs upward until it is 1 mile directly above your house. Your house is 1 mile from the airport. What distance did the airplane fly through the air?

20. George and Mark are driving from Mark's home to a warehouse to pick up new furniture. George will drive the van along routes *A* and *B*, while Mark will drive the truck along route *C*, as shown in the diagram. How much farther will George drive than Mark? Round your answer to the nearest tenth of a mile.

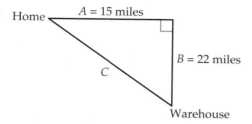

21. A cell phone tower is 2 kilometers from a long, straight stretch of highway. The signal of the tower can reach a cell phone at most 6 kilometers away. What is the length of the part of the highway the tower can provide a signal to, to the nearest tenth of a kilometer?

22. **MP 2, 4** A 7-foot-tall basketball player is designing an unusual attic whose floor, wall, and roof form a right triangle. He wants its peak to be one foot taller than he is. If he lies down along the floor, he wants his toes to be 4 feet from the wall. What should the length of the roof be, to the nearest tenth of a foot?

23. It takes 4 wires to help hold up a radio tower that is 200 meters tall. The wires are anchored 130 meters from the base of the tower. Two wires go to the top of the tower, and the other two are attached exactly halfway up the tower. How much wire is required, to the nearest meter?

24. In the diagram below, each vertex of the small square is the midpoint of a side of the larger square. What is the perimeter of the smaller square if the larger square has a perimeter of 20 inches?

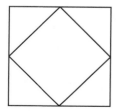

Practice Problems continue . . .

25. The area of an isosceles triangle is 360 square centimeters. If the height of the triangle, as measured from the base, is 9 centimeters, what is its perimeter, to the nearest centimeter?

26. **MP 3, 6** Prove: $\angle EHG$ is a right angle

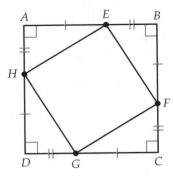

Pythagorean Triples

A **Pythagorean triple** is a set of three integers that satisfy the Pythagorean relationship. For example, 3, 4, and 5 make a Pythagorean triple, because $3^2 + 4^2 = 5^2$. There are an infinite number of Pythagorean triples.

Examples include:

3, 4, 5	6, 8, 10	9, 12, 15
5, 12, 13	10, 24, 26	15, 36, 39
7, 24, 25	14, 48, 50	21, 72, 75
8, 15, 17	16, 30, 34	24, 45, 51

MODEL PROBLEMS

1. **MP 7** Two members of a Pythagorean triple are 9 and 40. What is the third member?

SOLUTION

There are only two possibilities: either the square of 9 plus the square of a third number equals the square of 40, or the square of 9 plus the square of 40 equals a perfect square. Some trial and error shows that the square of 9 plus the square of 40 equals the square of 41.

2. **MP 7** Show that multiplying the members of a Pythagorean triple by the same integer results in another Pythagorean triple.

SOLUTION

Multiplying the Pythagorean triple (11, 60, 61) by 3 results in the Pythagorean triple (33, 180, 183).

Optional: A Formula for Pythagorean Triples

A formula known as Euclid's formula allows you to generate Pythagorean triples from a pair of positive integers, m and n. It is closely related to the proof of the Pythagorean theorem, as you will note if you consider the terms.

When $m < n$...

$a = n^2 - m^2$

$b = 2mn$

$c = n^2 + m^2$

These formulas let you calculate two legs and the hypotenuse. Keep in mind that m needs to be less than n.

Example:

$m = 8, n = 11$

$a = 11^2 - 8^2 = 57$

$b = 2 \cdot 8 \cdot 11 = 176$

$c = 11^2 + 8^2 = 185$

Use the formula to calculate two legs and the hypotenuse.

MODEL PROBLEM

What Pythagorean triple is generated by Euclid's formula with $m = 5, n = 7$?

SOLUTION

Use Euclid's formula to find a

$a = n^2 - m^2$

$a = 7^2 - 5^2$

Evaluate

$a = 24$

Find b

$b = 2mn$

$b = 2(5)(7)$

$b = 70$

Find c

$c = n^2 + m^2$

$c = 7^2 + 5^2$

$c = 74$

Express as a triple

$(a, b, c) = (24, 70, 74)$

PRACTICE

1. Which of the following is *not* a Pythagorean triple?

A. 5, 12, 13
B. 7, 18, 19
C. 12, 35, 37
D. 10, 24, 26

2. Two members of a Pythagorean triple are 9 and 40. What is the third member?

3. Two members of a Pythagorean triple are 15 and 17. What is the third member?

4. A new Pythagorean triple can be formed by multiplying each member of a known triple by the same integer. What number was used to produce the triple (18, 24, 30) from the original triple (3, 4, 5)?

Practice Problems continue . . .

5. Why is it impossible for the values m and n to be equal when using Euclid's formula to generate Pythagorean triples?

6. What Pythagorean triple is generated with Euclid's formula if $m = 3$ and $n = 5$?

7. Is it possible to generate a Pythagorean triple whose members are all odd using Euclid's formula? Explain your reasoning.

8. **MP 1, 7** Find the value of x given the area of the larger square is 8836 square units, the area of the smaller square is 5476 square units, $y = 3x - 2$, and x, y, and z form a Pythagorean triple.

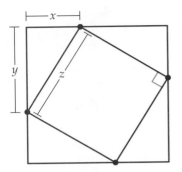

9. Is it possible to have a right triangle such that both legs have irrational lengths, yet the hypotenuse has a rational length? If yes, provide an example.

LESSON 7.4

7.4 Similar Right Triangles

An altitude in a right triangle creates similar triangles, as the theorem describes:

Altitude-hypotenuse theorem

If a triangle is a right triangle, then the altitude from the right angle to the hypotenuse creates two triangles that are similar to the original right triangle and to each other.

If $\triangle ABC$ is a right triangle, then $\triangle ABC \sim \triangle ACX \sim \triangle CBX$.

We prove the altitude-hypotenuse theorem:

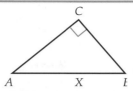

Prove: $\triangle ABC \sim \triangle ACX \sim \triangle CBX$

Given: $\triangle ABC$ is right triangle and $\overline{CX}$ is an altitude

Statement	Reason	
$\triangle ABC$ is right triangle	Given	This is given in the problem statement.
$\overline{CX} \perp \overline{AB}$	Definition of an altitude	By definition of an altitude, the two segments are perpendicular.
$\angle A \cong \angle A$ and $\angle B \cong \angle B$	Reflexive property of congruence	An angle is congruent to itself.
$\triangle ABC \sim \triangle ACX$ and $\triangle ABC \sim \triangle CBX$	AA similarity postulate	Because both pairs of triangles possess a right angle and either $\angle A$ or $\angle B$, they are similar.
$\triangle ABC \sim \triangle ACX \sim \triangle CBX$	Transitive property of similarity	Since two of the triangles are similar to $\triangle ABC$, they are similar to each other.

We use the altitude-hypotenuse theorem for another proof of the Pythagorean theorem:

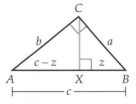

Prove: $a^2 + b^2 = c^2$

Given: $\triangle ABC$ is right triangle and $\overline{CX}$ is an altitude

Statement	Reason	
$\triangle ABC \sim \triangle ACX \sim \triangle CBX$	Altitude-hypotenuse theorem	We know that the altitude of $\triangle ABC$ divides the triangle into two triangles that are similar to the large triangle and to each other.
$\dfrac{a}{z} = \dfrac{c}{a}$	Definition of similar triangles	We know $\triangle ABC \sim \triangle CBX$, so we know that the hypotenuses and shorter legs are proportional.
$a^2 = cz$	Multiplication property of equality	Cross multiply to get rid of the fractions.
$\dfrac{b}{c - z} = \dfrac{c}{b}$	Definition of similar triangles	We know $\triangle ABC \sim \triangle ACX$, so we know that the hypotenuses and longer legs are proportional.
$c^2 = cz + b^2$	Multiplication property of equality	Cross multiply to get rid of the fractions, and isolate c^2.
$c^2 = a^2 + b^2$	Substitution	Substitute a^2 for cz to finish the proof.

MODEL PROBLEMS

1. Given the diagram, answer the following questions.

   a Identify the similar triangles given that $\overline{WY}$ is an altitude.
   b What is the length of $\overline{WY}$? Round to the nearest tenth.

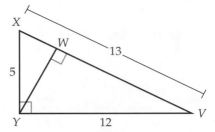

SOLUTION

a $\triangle YXW \sim \triangle VYW \sim \triangle VXY$. It is important to list the triangles with their corresponding sides in the same order. List them hypotenuse first, shorter leg second.

b Identify similar triangles $\quad \triangle VXY \sim \triangle YXW$

We only need one pair of similar triangles to calculate WY, the length of the drawn altitude. We use $\triangle VXY$ and $\triangle YXW$.

Write proportion using corresponding sides
$$\frac{WY}{XY} = \frac{VY}{VX}$$

State a proportion, using the ratio of the longer legs to the hypotenuses.

Solve proportion
$$WY = XY\left(\frac{VY}{VX}\right)$$
$$WY = 5\left(\frac{12}{13}\right)$$
$$WY = 4.6$$

Solve the equation for WY by multiplying both sides by XY. Then substitute and evaluate.

2. $\triangle ABC$ is a right triangle with sides of $AB = 104$, $BC = 153$, and $AC = 185$. What is the length of altitude $\overline{BD}$? Round to the nearest tenth.

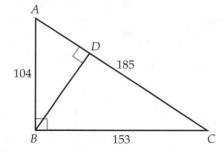

SOLUTION

Identify the similar right triangles $\qquad \triangle ABC \sim \triangle ADB$

Write proportion using corresponding sides and solve
$$\frac{BD}{AB} = \frac{BC}{AC}$$
$$BD = AB\left(\frac{BC}{AC}\right)$$
$$BD = 104\left(\frac{153}{185}\right) \approx 86.0$$

Converse of Pythagorean Theorem

The converse of the Pythagorean theorem is also true:

Converse of Pythagorean theorem

If the sides of a triangle have lengths a, b, c that satisfy $a^2 + b^2 = c^2$, then the triangle is a right triangle.

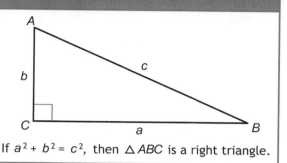

If $a^2 + b^2 = c^2$, then $\triangle ABC$ is a right triangle.

MODEL PROBLEMS

1. A triangle has sides of lengths 21, 72, and 75 meters. Is it a right triangle?

SOLUTION

Test with Pythagorean theorem

$$a^2 + b^2 = c^2$$
$$21^2 + 72^2 \stackrel{?}{=} 75^2$$

The longest side must be the hypotenuse, since its square is the sum of the squares of the legs. Substitute.

Yes: the triangle is a right triangle

$$441 + 5184 \stackrel{?}{=} 5625$$
$$5625 = 5625$$

Square the numbers and add. The two sides of the equation are equal: The triangle is a right triangle.

2. A triangle has sides 5, 7, and 9. Is it a right triangle?

SOLUTION

Test with Pythagorean theorem

$$a^2 + b^2 = c^2$$
$$5^2 + 7^2 \stackrel{?}{=} 9^2$$

Test the triangle by seeing if the sides satisfy the Pythagorean theorem. Since 9 is the longest side, it must be the hypotenuse.

No: the triangle is not a right triangle

$$25 + 49 \stackrel{?}{=} 81$$
$$74 \neq 81$$

Do the calculations for the squares. Square 5, 7, and 9.

Add 25 and 49 on the left side. The triangle does not satisfy the Pythagorean relationship, so it is not a right triangle

3. A triangle has sides 2, 3, and $\sqrt{13}$. Is it a right triangle?

SOLUTION

Test with Pythagorean theorem

$$a^2 + b^2 = c^2$$
$$2^2 + 3^2 \stackrel{?}{=} \sqrt{13}^2$$

Test the triangle by seeing if the sides satisfy the Pythagorean theorem. Since $\sqrt{13}$ is the longest side, it must be the hypotenuse.

Yes: the triangle is a right triangle

$$4 + 9 \stackrel{?}{=} 13$$
$$13 = 13$$

Do the calculations for the squares. Square 2, 3, and $\sqrt{13}$.

Add 4 and 9 on the left side. The triangle satisfies the Pythagorean relationship, so it is a right triangle.

Classifying Triangles Using the Pythagorean Theorem

We can combine inequalities and the Pythagorean theorem to describe types of triangles. We write two related theorems:

Pythagorean acute inequality theorem

If the square of the triangle's longest side is less than the sum of the squares of the other two sides, then the triangle is acute.

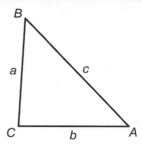

If $c^2 < a^2 + b^2$, then $\triangle ABC$ is acute.

There is a similar theorem for obtuse triangles:

> The converses of both of these theorems are also true.

Pythagorean obtuse inequality theorem

If the square of the triangle's longest side is greater than the sum of the squares of the other two sides, then the triangle is obtuse.

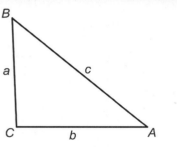

If $c^2 > a^2 + b^2$, then $\triangle ABC$ is obtuse.

MODEL PROBLEMS

1. Is this triangle obtuse, acute, or right?

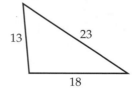

> Remember, we cannot simply rely on how a diagram looks. It may not be drawn to scale.

SOLUTION

Calculate values	$a^2 = 13^2$, $b^2 = 18^2$, $c^2 = 23^2$	Calculate the squares of the values.
	$a^2 = 169$, $b^2 = 324$, $c^2 = 529$	
Calculate $a^2 + b^2$, compare to c^2	$169 + 324 = 493$	Since the sum of the squares of the shorter sides is less than the square of the longest side, the triangle is obtuse.
	$a^2 + b^2 \, ? \, c^2$	
	$493 < 529$	
	Obtuse!	

Model Problems continue . . .

MODEL PROBLEMS *continued*

2. **MP 4** Yarrr! Some pirates be takin' some measurements of their ship.

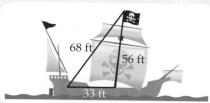

a According to the measurements given in the diagram, is the mast perpendicular to the deck?

b The pirates think that they have fixed their ship. The line is now only 65 feet in length and hits the deck 33 feet from the mast. It is now only 55 feet from the deck up to where the line connects with the mast. Have the pirates fixed their ship so that the mast is perpendicular to the deck?

SOLUTION

a Is it a Pythagorean triple?

$$a^2 + b^2 = c^2$$

$$33^2 + 56^2 \overset{?}{=} 68^2$$

$$4225 \neq 4624$$

If the mast is perpendicular to the deck, then it must form a right triangle. If it is a right triangle, then this equation must be true when we substitute.

The mast is not perpendicular since the two sides of the equation are not equal. The pirates have some work to do.

b Is it a Pythagorean triple?

$$a^2 + b^2 = c^2$$

$$33^2 + 55^2 \overset{?}{=} 65^2$$

$$4114 \neq 4225$$

The mast is still not perpendicular to the deck, since the two sides of the equation are still not equal.

PRACTICE

1. A triangle has sides of 28, 45, and 53. What kind of triangle is it?

A. Acute
B. Obtuse
C. Right
D. Cannot tell

2. A triangle has sides of 12, 4, and 10. What type of triangle is it?

A. Obtuse
B. Acute
C. Right
D. Cannot tell

3. Which of the following sets of side lengths could not form a right triangle?

A. 3, 4, 5
B. 5, 12, 13
C. 8, 15, 17
D. 9, 12, 14

4. Which of the following sets of side lengths will form an acute triangle?

A. 6, 7, 8
B. 10, 11, 17
C. 3, 5, 7
D. 9, 11, 18

5. A triangle has sides that measure $\sqrt{37}$, $\sqrt{44}$, and 9. Is the triangle a right triangle?

A. Yes
B. No
C. Not enough information to tell

Practice Problems continue . . .

Practice Problems continued . . .

6. Based on the triangle below, write an inequality showing possible angle measures for angle *P*.

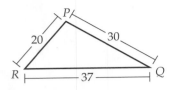

A. $0 < x < 90$ C. $90 < x < 180$
B. $x = 90$ D. Cannot tell

7. Which set of values could form the sides of a right triangle?

A. 4, 5, 6   C. 7, 9, 12
B. 8, 12, 13   D. 10, 24, 26

8. A triangle has sides that measure 20, 35, and 50. Is the triangle a right triangle?

A. Yes
B. No
C. Not enough information to tell

Exercises 9–13: Determine if a triangle with the given side lengths is acute, right, or obtuse.

9. 8, 9, 10

10. 20, 20, 30

11. 15, $\sqrt{99}$, 17

12. 6, 6, $6\sqrt{2}$

13. 4, $4\sqrt{3}$, 8

14. A triangle has sides 3, 5, and 7. Is it a right triangle? Explain.

15. The legs of a right triangle have lengths of 5 and 12. If the length of the triangle's hypotenuse is 13, what is the measure of the largest interior angle of the triangle?

16. $\triangle ABC$ is a right triangle with sides of $AB = 104$, $BC = 153$, $AC = 185$. What is the length of altitude $\overline{BD}$? Round to the nearest tenth.

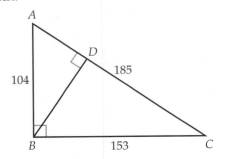

Exercises 17–20: In $\triangle JKL$, $JK = x$, $KL = 2x - 1$, and $JL = 3x - 7$.

17. Sketch $\triangle JKL$ and label each side with the expression for its length.

18. If the perimeter of $\triangle JKL$ is equal to 40, find the measure of each side.

19. Which of the 3 angles in $\triangle JKL$ is the largest? How do you know?

20. Determine if $\triangle JKL$ is a right triangle. Justify your response.

21. Sketch an acute scalene triangle. Label the length of each side of the triangle.

22. Sketch an obtuse triangle. Label the length of each side of the triangle.

23. Use the triangle to answer the questions. Line segment *AR* is an altitude of right triangle *MAT*.

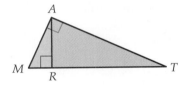

a Write a similarity statement for $\triangle MAT$ and the triangle shaded gray.

b Write a similarity statement for $\triangle MAT$ and the triangle shaded orange.

c If the measure of $\angle M = 55°$, what is $m\angle RAT$?

d If the measure of $\angle T = 25°$, what is $m\angle MAR$?

e Name the line segment length that should replace *y* in the proportion:
$$\frac{MR}{AR} = \frac{MA}{y}$$

f If $MA = 40$, $AT = 42$, and $MT = 58$, what is AR, to the nearest tenth?

g If $MR = 12$ and $AR = 16$, what is RT, to the nearest tenth?

Practice Problems continue . . .

24. Line segment *CE* is an altitude of right triangle *BCD*.

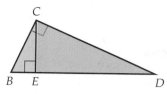

  a Write a similarity statement for △*BCD* and the triangle shaded in gray.
  b Write a similarity statement for △*BCD* and the triangle shaded in orange.

25. **MP 3** Show that △*WXY* and △*WYZ* are similar.

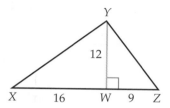

26. Use the converse of the Pythagorean theorem to show that a triangle with side lengths of 9, 12, and 15 is a right triangle.

27. Use the contrapositive of the Pythagorean theorem to show that a triangle with side lengths of $\sqrt{13}$, 9, and 11 is not a right triangle.

28. Trey says the triangle below is a right triangle. Do you agree with Trey? Explain your reasoning.

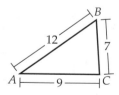

29. The towns of Carthage, Utica, and Marcellus are connected by straight roads. Mr. Nelson drove 10 miles from Carthage to Utica, then turned and drove 12 miles from Utica to Marcellus. The direct distance from Carthage to Marcellus is 15 miles.

  a Make a sketch of the situation.
  b Did Mr. Nelson make a 90° turn in Utica? Justify your answer.

30. **MP 3, 6** Use the diagram below to prove the converse of the Pythagorean theorem. Hint: You are allowed to use the Pythagorean theorem to prove its converse.

Given: $a^2 + b^2 = c^2$

Prove: $m\angle C = 90°$

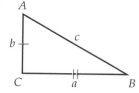
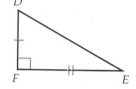

31. **MP 2, 3** The altitude of a non-right scalene triangle is constructed. The altitude is contained inside the triangle and forms two smaller triangles within the original triangle.

  a Make a sketch of the situation.
  b Will the sides of either of the two smaller triangles satisfy the Pythagorean theorem? Why or why not?

32. △*DEF* has sides that measure x, x, and $\sqrt{3x}$. Assuming x is a positive integer, what type of triangle is △*DEF*? Be as specific as possible.

33. **MP 6** Show that the triangle with vertices located at (3, 4), (6, 5), and (2, −1) is an obtuse triangle.

34. **MP 1** A rhombus is a quadrilateral with four congruent sides. When the two diagonals of a rhombus are constructed, they form four congruent triangles. Will these triangles satisfy the Pythagorean theorem? Explain your reasoning.

7.5 Special Right Triangles

In mathematics, we can calculate the length of a missing side of a right triangle by using the Pythagorean theorem. This method will always work when computations are carried out correctly, but there are certain right triangles, called *special right triangles*, that have regular features that make solving easier because simple formulas exist. We describe two of those triangles below.

45-45-90 Triangles

Recall that in an isosceles triangle, the acute angles are equal in measure. So, the angles of an isosceles right triangle measure 45°, 45°, and 90°; hence the name, 45-45-90 triangles. In the figure to the right, we define the legs to be of length 1, and we use the Pythagorean theorem to find the length of the hypotenuse, $\sqrt{1+1} = \sqrt{2}$. It turns out, for any 45-45-90 triangle, if we know the length of one of the legs, then we can find the length of the hypotenuse using this relation, and, conversely, if we know the length of the hypotenuse, we can find the length of a leg. Let h = the length of the hypotenuse and l = the length of each leg. Then the length of the hypotenuse of any 45-45-90 triangle is

$l\sqrt{2}$, and the length of each leg is $\dfrac{h\sqrt{2}}{2}$.

> All 45-45-90 triangles are similar, so their pairs of corresponding sides are proportional. The ratio of the hypotenuse to a leg is $\sqrt{2}$: 1 in an isosceles right triangle.

30-60-90 Triangles

Similar to 45-45-90 triangles, 30-60-90 triangles also share a known proportionality relationship among the lengths of their sides. We use the diagram shown to the right to explain how we derive the lengths of the sides. We construct an equilateral triangle (all angles equal to 60°) with side lengths equal to 2 and drop in an altitude that is both the angle bisector of the vertex angle and the perpendicular bisector of the base. This creates 90° angles and splits the vertex angle into two 30° angles and the equilateral triangle into two right triangles. Since the altitude is a perpendicular bisector, the length of each right-triangle base is 1 and the altitude has a length of $\sqrt{2^2 - 1} = \sqrt{3}$. To summarize these relationships for each right triangle, let h = the length of the hypotenuse, SL = the length of the short leg, which is opposite the 30° angle, and LL = the length of the long leg. Then the length of the short

leg is $\dfrac{h}{2}$, and the length of the long leg is $SL \cdot \sqrt{3}$.

> In a 30-60-90 triangle, the ratio of the shorter leg to the hypotenuse is 1 : 2. The ratio of the longer leg to the hypotenuse is $\dfrac{\sqrt{3}}{2}$.

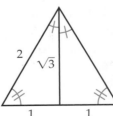

1. What are the lengths of the legs of this triangle?

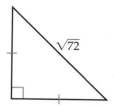

SOLUTION

We see by the markings on the diagram that this is a 45-45-90 triangle, so the length of each leg is $\dfrac{h\sqrt{2}}{2}$.
Note that the length of the hypotenuse is not expressed in these terms, but we can rewrite it with a little algebraic manipulation.

Rewrite $\qquad\qquad\qquad \sqrt{72} = \sqrt{9} \cdot \sqrt{8} = 3\sqrt{4}\sqrt{2} = 6\sqrt{2}$

Solve for the leg $\qquad\quad \dfrac{(6\sqrt{2})\sqrt{2}}{2} = \dfrac{12}{2} = 6$

2. What are the angles in this triangle?

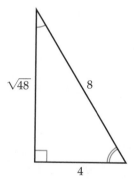

SOLUTION

Simplify	$\sqrt{48} = \sqrt{16 \cdot 3} = 4\sqrt{3}$	In the triangle, the longer leg is $\sqrt{48}$. Simplify this to $4\sqrt{3}$.
Divide all sides by 4	$\dfrac{4}{4} = 1$	Divide each side by 4.
	$\dfrac{4\sqrt{3}}{4} = \sqrt{3}$	
	$\dfrac{8}{4} = 2$	
30-60-90 triangle	$1, \sqrt{3}, 2$	This is the ratio of the sides of a 30-60-90 triangle.

Model Problems continue . . .

3. Jolene has a ramp that she wants to make into a jump. She is curious how high off the ground it will be if it makes a 30° angle compared to a 60° angle from the ground. She would like to know the answer to the nearest tenth of a foot.

SOLUTION

Draw triangles

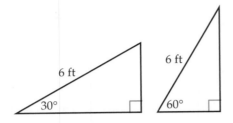

Draw two cases of a 30° and 60° triangle.

Use 30° ratio

30° opposite leg to hypotenuse = 1 : 2

$\dfrac{x}{6} = \dfrac{1}{2}$

This is the ratio of the leg opposite the 30° angle to the hypotenuse in a 30-60-90 triangle.

Evaluate

$x = 6 \cdot \dfrac{1}{2} = 3$ feet

The 30° leg is one-half the length of the hypotenuse. Multiply, and calculate that the end of the ramp would be 3 feet high.

Calculate the height with the 60° angle

60° opposite leg to hypotenuse = $\sqrt{3}$: 2

$\dfrac{x}{6} = \dfrac{\sqrt{3}}{2}$

$x = 6 \cdot \dfrac{\sqrt{3}}{2} \approx 5.2$ feet

Rounded to the nearest tenth of a foot, the end of the ramp is about 5.2 feet high when it makes a 60° angle with the ground.

We can check the answers for being reasonable. The 60° jump is higher than the 30° jump, which makes sense. Also, both lengths are less than the hypotenuse, which also makes sense.

4. **MP 2, 4** It is 90 feet from home plate to first base, and the same distance between any two consecutive bases. How far does a catcher have to throw from home plate to second base, to the nearest foot?

SOLUTION

Draw isosceles right triangle

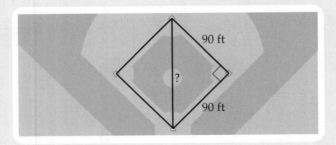

Start by recognizing that the indicated base paths form two legs of an isosceles right triangle. Both are 90 feet.

Use the relationship

$h = l\sqrt{2}$

Substitute

$h = 90\sqrt{2} \approx 127$ feet

1. If the sides of a right triangle measure 8, $8\sqrt{3}$, and 16, what is the measure of the smallest interior angle of the triangle?

   A. 30° C. 60°
   B. 45° D. 90°

2. The area of a 30-60-90 triangle is $18\sqrt{3}$. How long is the shortest side of the triangle?

   A. 6 C. 12
   B. $6\sqrt{3}$ D. $9\sqrt{3}$

3. A triangle has sides that measure 2, $2\sqrt{3}$, and 4. This triangle is best described as a(n)

   A. 30-60-90 triangle.
   B. Scalene obtuse triangle.
   C. Scalene acute triangle.
   D. Isosceles right triangle.

4. The hypotenuse of an isosceles right triangle has a length of $3\sqrt{2}$. What is the length of a leg?

5. The leg opposite the 30° angle of a 30-60-90 triangle has a length of 5. What is the length of the hypotenuse?

6. The leg opposite the 30° angle of a 30-60-90 triangle has a length of 4. What is the length of the hypotenuse?

7. The leg opposite the 60° angle of a 30-60-90 triangle has a length of $7\sqrt{3}$. What is the length of the hypotenuse?

8. The leg opposite the 60° angle of a 30-60-90 triangle has a length of $11\sqrt{3}$. What is the length of the hypotenuse?

9. The leg opposite the 60° angle of a 30-60-90 triangle has a length of $3\sqrt{3}$. What is the length of the hypotenuse?

10. One leg of an isosceles right triangle measures 1 unit. What is the exact length of the hypotenuse of this triangle?

11. The hypotenuse of an isosceles right triangle has a length of $5\sqrt{2}$. What is the length of a leg?

12. The hypotenuse of an isosceles right triangle has a length of $\sqrt{18}$. What is the length of a leg?

13. The hypotenuse of an isosceles right triangle has a length of 8. What is the length of a leg?

14. The hypotenuse of an isosceles right triangle has a length of $12\sqrt{2}$. What is the length of a leg?

15. A right triangle has a hypotenuse that measures 2 cm and a base that measures 1 cm. What is the exact length of its height?

16. In a 30-60-90 triangle, the hypotenuse measures 12 inches. What is the length of the shorter leg?

17. In a 45-45-90 triangle, the hypotenuse measures $7\sqrt{2}$ centimeters. What is the length of one leg?

18. The longer leg of a 30-60-90 triangle measures $\sqrt{75}$ units. How long is the shorter leg?

19. The hypotenuse of a 30-60-90 triangle measures 22 units. How long is the leg opposite the 60° angle?

20. An isosceles right triangle has a hypotenuse of $3\sqrt{2}$. Sketch the triangle and label the measures of all three angles. Then state the length of each of the legs.

21. Sketch a 30-60-90 triangle with a hypotenuse of 6. Label the measures of all three angles, as well as the lengths of both legs.

22. A square courtyard is crossed by two diagonal footpaths that connect its corners. One side of the courtyard measures 120 feet.
   a Make a sketch of the situation.
   b Find the length of one diagonal footpath, to the nearest tenth of a foot.

Practice Problems continue . . .

23. On a fast-pitch softball field, it is 60 feet from home plate to first base, and the same distance between any two consecutive bases. How far does a catcher have to throw from home plate to second base, to the nearest foot?

24. Joel has an 8-foot-long ramp that he wants to make into a jump. He wants the jump to be as high as possible, as long as it's not higher than 7 feet. Should he use a 30° or 60° angle between the ground and board?

25. Mr. Nichols built a ramp over his front steps so he could move a piano into his house. The ramp makes a 30° angle with the ground and reaches a height of 4.25 feet at the top of the steps. How long is the ramp?

26. The perimeter of an equilateral triangle is 42 feet. What is the exact length of its altitude?

27. An obtuse isosceles triangle has a vertex angle that measures 120°, and its two congruent sides each measure 8 centimeters. How long is the altitude of the triangle, in centimeters?

28. **MP 1, 3** Is it possible for the lengths of all three sides in a 45-45-90 triangle to be integers? Why or why not?

29. **MP 2** The diagonal of a rectangle is equal to twice the length of the base of the rectangle. What is the measure of the smallest angle of a triangle formed by the base, height, and diagonal of the rectangle?

30. What type(s) of triangles are formed within a 30-60-90 triangle when the altitude connecting the right angle to the hypotenuse is constructed? Explain your reasoning.

31. Write a word problem based on a 30-60-90 triangle. Make sure to include a solution to the problem you have written.

32. **MP 2, 3** Assuming that the legs of an isosceles right triangle each measure x, show that the length of the hypotenuse will be $x\sqrt{2}$.

33. An artist is designing a window. The window will be a square within a square, with the interior square formed by connecting the midpoints of the sides of the outer square. If the outer square has a perimeter of 80 inches, what is the area of the interior square?

34. The legs of an isosceles right triangle each measure 6 feet. An altitude of the triangle is constructed connecting the triangle's right angle and its hypotenuse. What is the exact length of the altitude, in feet?

35. **MP 2** The interior of a regular hexagon can be divided into 6 congruent equilateral triangles. If the perimeter of the hexagon is 60 units, what is its exact area, in square units?

MP 2, 4 Four tent poles stand perpendicular to the ground. The top of each tent pole is attached to an anchor on the ground with a rope, forming a 60-degree angle with the ground at the anchor point. The anchor is 5 feet from the base of the pole.

a Make a sketch of the situation. Label all degree measures in the triangle formed by each pole, its rope, and the ground.

b How high is each tent pole, to the nearest tenth of a foot?

c How long is the rope connecting the top of the pole to the anchor, to the nearest foot?

d It's a very windy day, so the campers decide that the ropes should be staked farther away from the poles for greater stability. They want the distance from the stake to the pole to be the same as the height of the pole. How much more rope do they need for each pole, to the nearest tenth of a foot?

LESSON 7.6

7.6 Trigonometric Ratios

Trigonometry is the study of the relationships of the sides and angles of triangles. Ratios of the sides of triangles play a crucial role in trigonometry.

Trigonometric ratios are the ratios of two sides of a right triangle and are related to the triangle's acute angles. For the rest of this explanation, we will use $\angle A$ to denote the related angle for defining the ratios, but the ratios are defined for either acute angle in the right triangle. We will call that acute angle, $\angle A$. The **adjacent leg** is next to angle A. The hypotenuse and the adjacent leg form $\angle A$. The **opposite leg** is the other leg, which lies across from $\angle A$.

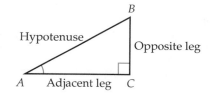

The **sine**, **cosine**, and **tangent** are the most commonly used trigonometric ratios.

Sine of A	$\sin A = \dfrac{\text{length of opposite leg}}{\text{length of hypotenuse}}$	The sine of $\angle A$ is the ratio of the lengths of the leg opposite to $\angle A$ and the hypotenuse. The abbreviation for the sine is "sin."	The classic way to remember the ratios is: SOH CAH TOA. It is **Sine Opposite Hypotenuse, Cosine Adjacent Hypotenuse, and Tangent Opposite Adjacent.** If you say it aloud, it helps you to remember the relationships.
Cosine of A	$\cos A = \dfrac{\text{length of adjacent leg}}{\text{length of hypotenuse}}$	The cosine of $\angle A$ is the ratio of the lengths of the leg adjacent to $\angle A$ and the hypotenuse. The abbreviation for the cosine is "cos."	
Tangent of A	$\tan A = \dfrac{\text{length of opposite leg}}{\text{length of adjacent leg}}$	The tangent of $\angle A$ is the ratio of the lengths of the leg opposite to $\angle A$ and the leg adjacent to $\angle A$. The abbreviation for the tangent is "tan."	

Trigonometric ratios are an outcome of similar right triangles. We examine the side ratios for two similar triangles, and show that the ratios depend only on the angles of the triangles.

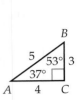
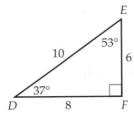

> If two right triangles are similar, then the values of their trigonometric ratios will be equal, since the ratios only depend on the acute angle measures.

$\triangle ABC$ and $\triangle DEF$ are similar

By definition of similar triangles, all corresponding angles are congruent and corresponding sides are proportional.

The corresponding side ratios are equal

$$\frac{BC}{AB} = \frac{EF}{DE} = \frac{3}{5},$$

$$\frac{BC}{AC} = \frac{EF}{DF} = \frac{3}{4},$$

$$\frac{AC}{AB} = \frac{DF}{DE} = \frac{4}{5}$$

Calculate the ratio of the sides in one triangle and compare it to the ratio of the corresponding sides in the other triangle. The ratios are equal. This is true for any pair of side ratios between the two triangles.

Trigonometric function

$$\frac{AC}{AB} = \frac{DF}{DE} = \sin 53°$$

Trigonometric ratios are side ratios that reference specific sides related to one of the acute angles. For example, $\frac{AC}{AB}$ and $\frac{DF}{DE}$ are the ratios of the opposite leg to the hypotenuse with respect to the 53° angle. This is the sine of 53°.

The values of many trigonometric functions are irrational numbers. This means their digits continue forever with no pattern. We use the "approximately equals" symbol, $\approx$, to indicate we are rounding their values to the nearest thousandth.

 In this activity, experiment with right triangles and the sine, cosine, and tangent functions. You can drag vertices A or B to change the triangle.

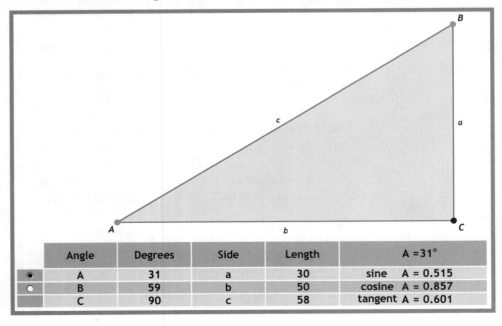

> You can use a calculator to evaluate the sine, cosine, and tangent of angles. Press the SIN, COS, or TAN button, enter the angle, and press the equals key to calculate the function. Make sure your calculator is in degree (DEG) mode.

Angle	Degrees	Side	Length	A =31°
A	31	a	30	sine A = 0.515
B	59	b	50	cosine A = 0.857
C	90	c	58	tangent A = 0.601

1. What are the sine, cosine, and tangent of *A*?

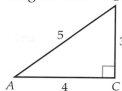

SOLUTION

Sine of *A*
$$\sin A = \frac{\text{length of opposite leg}}{\text{length of hypotenuse}} = \frac{3}{5}$$
The sine of $\angle A$ is the ratio of the lengths of the opposite leg and the hypotenuse.

Cosine of *A*
$$\cos A = \frac{\text{length of adjacent leg}}{\text{length of hypotenuse}} = \frac{4}{5}$$
The cosine of $\angle A$ is the ratio of the lengths of the adjacent leg and the hypotenuse.

Tangent of *A*
$$\tan A = \frac{\text{length of opposite leg}}{\text{length of adjacent leg}} = \frac{3}{4}$$
The tangent of $\angle A$ is the ratio of the lengths of the opposite leg and the adjacent leg.

2. What are the sine, cosine, and tangent of *B*?

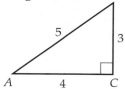

SOLUTION

Sine of *B*
$$\sin B = \frac{\text{length of opposite leg}}{\text{length of hypotenuse}} = \frac{4}{5}$$
The sine of $\angle B$ is the ratio of the lengths of the leg opposite to $\angle B$ and the hypotenuse.

Cosine of *B*
$$\cos B = \frac{\text{length of adjacent leg}}{\text{length of hypotenuse}} = \frac{3}{5}$$
The cosine of $\angle B$ is the ratio of the lengths of the leg adjacent to $\angle B$ and the hypotenuse.

Tangent of *B*
$$\tan B = \frac{\text{length of opposite leg}}{\text{length of adjacent leg}} = \frac{4}{3}$$
The tangent of $\angle B$ is the ratio of the lengths of the opposite leg and the adjacent leg.

Model Problems continue . . .

3. Calculate the sine, cosine, and tangent of 40°.

SOLUTION

sin 40° ≈ 0.643   Use a calculator to determine the value of sin 40°. It is approximately 0.643. The value of the sine of this angle is irrational, so the digits continue forever.

> The values of some trigonometric functions are rational. For instance, the tangent of 45° is 1, since it is the ratio of two equal sides in an isosceles triangle.

cos 40° ≈ 0.766   The cos 40° is approximately 0.766.

tan 40° ≈ 0.839   The tan 40° is approximately 0.839.

Sine, Cosine, and Complementary Angles

In right triangles, the two acute angles are always complementary. Because of this, the sine and cosine ratios have a special relationship. See if you can figure it out by looking at the table without reading ahead. All numbers are rounded to the nearest thousandth.

m∠A	m∠B	sin A	cos A	sin B	cos B
10°	80°	0.174	0.985	0.985	0.174
20°	70°	0.342	0.940	0.940	0.342
30°	60°	0.500	0.866	0.866	0.500
40°	50°	0.643	0.766	0.766	0.643
50°	40°	0.766	0.643	0.643	0.766
60°	30°	0.866	0.500	0.500	0.866
70°	20°	0.940	0.342	0.342	0.940
80°	10°	0.985	0.174	0.174	0.985

As you may have noticed, the sine of one angle is the cosine of its complementary angle, and vice versa. For instance, look at the cosine of 20° and the sine of 70°.

We discuss this relationship further by examining a general right triangle.

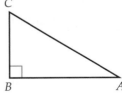

Find sin A $\sin A = \dfrac{\text{opposite}}{\text{hypotenuse}}$ Find the sine of ∠A, using the appropriate trigonometric ratio.

$\sin A = \dfrac{BC}{AC}$

Find cos C $\cos C = \dfrac{\text{adjacent}}{\text{hypotenuse}}$ Find the cosine of ∠C using the appropriate trigonometric ratio.

$\cos C = \dfrac{BC}{AC}$

$\sin A = \cos C$ ∠A's opposite side is the same as ∠C's adjacent side.   Because the *opposite side* from ∠A is the same side as the *adjacent side* to ∠C, the trigonometric ratios are equal.

MODEL PROBLEMS

1. a What is the length of *a*, to the nearest tenth?

  b What is the length of *b*, to the nearest tenth?

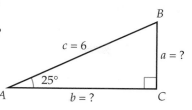

SOLUTION

a Use definition of sine

$$\frac{\text{opposite}}{\text{hypotenuse}} = \sin A$$

The sine equals the opposite leg divided by the hypotenuse.

Substitute

$$\frac{a}{6} = \sin 25°$$

$$\frac{a}{6} \approx 0.423$$

The angle is 25°. Substitute and calculate the sine of the angle.

Solve

$$6 \cdot \frac{a}{6} = 6 \cdot \sin 25°$$

$$a \approx 2.5$$

Solve for *a* by multiplying both sides of the equation by 6. Round the answer to the nearest tenth.

> With *a* calculated, there are a variety of ways to calculate *b*. We could use the Pythagorean theorem since we know the length of a leg and the hypotenuse, or we could use the cosine of 25°.

b Calculate $m\angle B$

$$m\angle A + m\angle B + m\angle C = 180°$$
$$m\angle B = 180° - 90° - 25°$$
$$m\angle B = 65°$$

One way to calculate the length of the leg *b* is to calculate $m\angle B$. Since the measure of the angles sum to 180°, $m\angle B = 65°$.

Use definition of sine to calculate *b*

$$\frac{\text{opposite}}{\text{hypotenuse}} = \sin B$$

$$\text{opposite} = \sin B \cdot \text{hypotenuse}$$

Use the definition of the sine. Solve the equation for the opposite leg by multiplying both sides of the equation by the hypotenuse.

$$b = (\sin 65°)(6)$$
$$b \approx (0.906)(6) \approx 5.4$$

Substitute in the values we know from the diagram. The measure of $\angle B$ is 65°, and the hypotenuse is 6. The leg opposite $\angle B$ is *b*. Multiply and calculate. *b* to the nearest tenth is 5.4.

> We can check the answer using the Pythagorean theorem. Since $2.5^2 + 5.4^2 \approx 6^2$, the answer is correct.

2. The sine of an angle in a triangle equals 0.3. The triangle is then dilated by a scale factor of 3. The same angle's sine is now:

A. 0.1   C. 0.9

B. 0.3   D. 3.3

SOLUTION

The answer is B. The dilation produces a similar triangle, so the ratio of sides does not change and neither do the measures of the angles. That means the trigonometric functions do not change either.

Model Problems continue . . .

3. What is the length of the hypotenuse, to the nearest tenth?

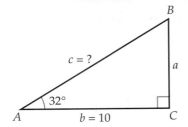

SOLUTION

Use definition of cosine

$$\frac{\text{adjacent}}{\text{hypotenuse}} = \cos A$$

Since we know the length of the adjacent leg, use the cosine ratio.

Substitute

$$\frac{10}{c} = \cos 32°$$

$$\frac{10}{c} \approx 0.848$$

The angle is 32°. Substitute and calculate the cosine of the angle.

Solve

$$c \cdot \frac{10}{c} \approx c \cdot 0.848$$

$$10 \approx c \cdot 0.848$$

$$11.8 \approx c$$

Solve the equation. First, remove c as the denominator of a fraction. Multiply both sides by c. Divide both sides by 0.848. Rounded to the nearest tenth, c is approximately 11.8.

 4. **MP 2, 4** Ted is estimating the height of the Space Needle using the angle of 75° between his line of sight and the horizontal. Based on this diagram, how tall is the Space Needle? Note, the angle between a horizontal line and the line of sight to an object above the horizontal line is called the **angle of elevation**. In this problem, that angle is 75°. Surveyors use angles of elevation to estimate the heights of objects that cannot be easily measured directly. We ignore Ted's height in this estimate.

SOLUTION

Use definition of tangent

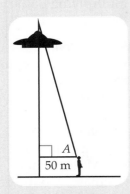

Use the diagram. The tangent of $\angle A$ is the opposite leg divided by the adjacent leg. Solve for the opposite leg.

$$\tan A = \frac{\text{opposite}}{\text{adjacent}}$$

$$\text{opposite} = (\tan A)(\text{adjacent})$$

Substitute and evaluate

$$a \approx (3.73)(50)$$

$$a \approx 186.5 \text{ meters}$$

Substitute a for the length of the opposite leg, 75° for the measure of $\angle A$, and 50 for the length of the adjacent leg. The tangent is approximately 3.73. The tower is approximately 186.5 meters tall. The calculation is close to the actual height of the tower, which is about 184 meters.

Model Problems continue . . .

5. A carpenter reads that the steepest angle her 50-foot ladder should make with the horizontal is 80°. If she fully extends her ladder and follows the angle guideline, what is the maximum height she can reach?

SOLUTION

Use definition of sine

Start with a diagram. The ladder is 50 feet, and the maximum angle is 80°. She needs to calculate how high the ladder can be placed against the wall. That is the leg opposite the 80° angle.

$$\sin A = \frac{\text{opposite}}{\text{hypotenuse}}$$

$$\text{opposite} = (\sin A)(\text{hypotenuse})$$

Use the sine ratio since we know the length of the hypotenuse and the measure of $\angle A$. Solve for the opposite leg, since that is the unknown.

Substitute and evaluate

$$a \approx (0.985)(50)$$
$$a \approx 49 \text{ feet}$$

Use a for the length of the opposite leg. Substitute 80° for the measure of angle A and 50 for the length of the hypotenuse, which is the length of the ladder. The sine 80° equals approximately 0.985. The ladder can be raised to about 49 feet.

6. **MP 7** If $\cos A = \frac{15}{17}$, what is $\sin A$?

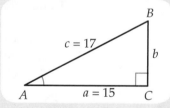

The triangle we draw is one possible triangle given the stated value of the cosine. Any other similar triangle would be possible, such as one with lengths of 16, 30, and 34. Since the sides are proportional, it does not change the value of the sine ratio.

SOLUTION

Use definition of cosine

$$\cos A = \frac{\text{adjacent}}{\text{hypotenuse}} = \frac{15}{17}$$

Start with the definition of the cosine, the length of the adjacent leg divided by the length of the hypotenuse.

Pythagorean theorem
Calculate other leg

$$15^2 + b^2 = 17^2$$
$$b^2 = 289 - 225$$
$$b = 8$$

To calculate the sine, we need the length of the other leg. Use the Pythagorean theorem to calculate that the leg has length 8.

Use definition of sine

$$\sin A = \frac{\text{opposite}}{\text{hypotenuse}} = \frac{8}{17}$$

The sine is the length of the opposite leg divided by the length of the hypotenuse. Enter the values for the opposite leg and the hypotenuse. The sine

of $\angle A = \frac{8}{17}$.

Sine, Cosine, and Tangent for Special Triangles

The values of the sine, cosine, and tangent in 30-60-90 and 45-45-90 triangles are frequently used. We show how to calculate them below.

30-60-90 Triangle: 30° angle

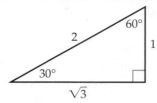

$$\sin 30° = \frac{\text{opposite}}{\text{hypotenuse}} = \frac{1}{2}$$

For a 30° angle, use the 30-60-90 triangle shown here to calculate the trigonometric ratios. The sine equals the length of the opposite leg divided by the length of the hypotenuse, which means the sine of 30° is $\frac{1}{2}$.

$$\cos 30° = \frac{\text{adjacent}}{\text{hypotenuse}} = \frac{\sqrt{3}}{2}$$

The length of the leg adjacent to the 30° angle is $\sqrt{3}$. The cosine equals the length of the adjacent leg divided by the

length of the hypotenuse, which means the cosine of 30° is $\frac{\sqrt{3}}{2}$.

$$\tan 30° = \frac{\text{opposite}}{\text{adjacent}} = \frac{1}{\sqrt{3}} \cdot \frac{\sqrt{3}}{\sqrt{3}} = \frac{\sqrt{3}}{3}$$

The tangent equals the length of the opposite leg divided by the length of the adjacent leg, which means the tangent of 30° equals $\frac{1}{\sqrt{3}}$.

> We rationalize the denominator for some values, which means we state the radicals without a radical sign in the denominator. To do this, multiply by a fraction equal to one that includes the denominator.

30-60-90 Triangle: 60° angle

Rotate the diagram to calculate these ratios for a 60° angle.

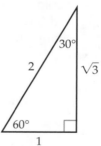

$$\sin 60° = \frac{\text{opposite}}{\text{hypotenuse}} = \frac{\sqrt{3}}{2}$$

For a 60° angle, use the 30-60-90 triangle above to calculate the sine. The sine equals the length of the leg opposite the 60° angle divided by the length of the hypotenuse, which means the sine of 60° is $\frac{\sqrt{3}}{2}$.

$$\cos 60° = \frac{\text{adjacent}}{\text{hypotenuse}} = \frac{1}{2}$$

As always, the cosine equals the length of the leg adjacent to the 60° angle divided by the length of the hypotenuse. The cosine of 60° is $\frac{1}{2}$.

$$\tan 60° = \frac{\text{opposite}}{\text{adjacent}} = \frac{\sqrt{3}}{1} = \sqrt{3}$$

And as always, the tangent is the length of the opposite leg divided by the length of the adjacent leg. The tangent of 60° is $\sqrt{3}$.

45-45-90 Triangles

We now calculate the same ratios for an isosceles right triangle. We calculated the length of the hypotenuse using the Pythagorean theorem.

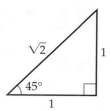

$$\sin 45° = \frac{1}{\sqrt{2}} = \frac{\sqrt{2}}{2}$$

For a 45° angle, use the 45-45-90 triangle shown above to calculate the trigonometric ratios. The length of each leg is 1, and the length of the hypotenuse is $\sqrt{2}$. The sine equals the opposite leg divided by the length of the hypotenuse. For those who like their denominators rationalized, we do so.

$$\cos 45° = \frac{1}{\sqrt{2}} = \frac{\sqrt{2}}{2}$$

The cosine equals the adjacent leg's length over the hypotenuse's length. It has the same value as the sine since both legs have the same length.

$$\tan 45° = \frac{1}{1} = 1$$

The tangent equals the opposite leg's length over the adjacent's. Since the lengths are the same, $\tan 45° = 1$.

You will start to recognize the values for the trigonometric ratios for 30°, 45°, and 60° angles. These are ratios that you may want to refer to frequently, so we summarize them in a table.

	sin A	cos A	tan A
30°	$\frac{1}{2}$	$\frac{\sqrt{3}}{2}$	$\frac{\sqrt{3}}{3}$
45°	$\frac{\sqrt{2}}{2}$	$\frac{\sqrt{2}}{2}$	1
60°	$\frac{\sqrt{3}}{2}$	$\frac{1}{2}$	$\sqrt{3}$

MODEL PROBLEMS

1. Based on the diagram, which statement must be true?

A. $\cos A = \cos B$

B. $\cos A + \sin A = 1$

C. $\cos A = \sin B$

D. $\cos A + \sin A = \tan A$

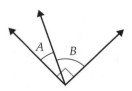

SOLUTION

The answer is C. Angles A and B are complementary, since they form a right angle. The sine of an angle equals the cosine of its complementary angle. The other statements are either false or would only be true for a specific set of values.

Model Problems continue . . .

2. *A* is an acute angle and $\cos A = \dfrac{1}{2}$.

What is the measure of *A* in degrees?

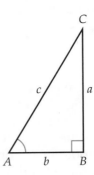

SOLUTION

Use definition of cosine

$\cos A = \dfrac{\text{adjacent}}{\text{hypotenuse}} = \dfrac{1}{2}$

Start with the definition of the cosine, the length of the adjacent leg divided by the length of the hypotenuse. Use the value of the cosine stated in the problem. The adjacent leg has a length of 1 and the hypotenuse has a length of 2.

30-60-90 triangle

$m\angle A = 60°$

In any 30-60-90 triangle, the hypotenuse is twice as long as the short leg, so this is a 30-60-90 triangle. Based on these lengths, angle *A* must be the 60° angle.

3. The leg opposite angle *B* is $\sqrt{2}$ long, and the hypotenuse has a length of 2. What is the measure of $\angle B$?

SOLUTION

Calculate the ratio

$\sin B = \dfrac{\text{opposite}}{\text{hypotenuse}} = \dfrac{\sqrt{2}}{2}$

Calculate the sine of the angle, since you know the opposite leg and the hypotenuse. Use the chart on page 325 to determine the angle measure.

Evaluate

$m\angle B = 45°$

Evaluate.

PRACTICE

1. For an acute angle in a right triangle, the cosine of the angle is equal to:

A. $\dfrac{\text{length of opposite side}}{\text{length of adjacent side}}$

B. $\dfrac{\text{length of hypotenuse}}{\text{length of adjacent side}}$

C. $\dfrac{\text{length of adjacent side}}{\text{length of hypotenuse}}$

D. $\dfrac{\text{length of opposite side}}{\text{length of hypotenuse}}$

2. Which ratio is equal to $\cos 32°$?

A. $\sin 32°$

B. $-\cos 32°$

C. $\sin 58°$

D. $\cos 58°$

3. In a right triangle, $\sin A = \dfrac{7}{11}$, where the two numbers are actual lengths. If you needed to state the value of $\cos A$, for which of the following sides of the triangle, relative to angle *A*, would you need to find the length?

A. Opposite   C. Hypotenuse

B. Adjacent   D. Height

Practice Problems continue . . .

4. The value of cos $B = \frac{4}{5}$. What is the value of sin B?

   A. $\frac{3}{5}$ C. $\frac{5}{4}$

   B. $\frac{3}{4}$ D. $\frac{4}{3}$

5. What is the value of tan A, rounded to the nearest thousandth, when $m\angle A = 16°$?

   A. 0.28   C. 0.287

   B. 0.286   D. 2.868

6. Which of the following is the value of cos A, if angle A measures 60°?

   A. 0.5   C. $\frac{\sqrt{3}}{2}$

   B. $2\sqrt{2}$ D. 1

7. What is cos 42°? Give your answer to the nearest thousandth.

8. What is tan 65°? Give your answer to the nearest hundredth.

9. What is the value of sin 59°, rounded to the nearest thousandth?

10. What is sin 56°? Give your answer to the nearest hundredth.

11. What is sin 8°? Give your answer to the nearest hundredth.

12. What is the value of sin 28°, rounded to the nearest thousandth?

13. What is the value of tan 21°, rounded to the nearest thousandth?

14. What is the value of cos 13°, rounded to the nearest thousandth?

15. What is the value of tan 68°, rounded to the nearest thousandth?

16. What is the value of cos 61°, rounded to the nearest thousandth?

17. What is the length of side a in the triangle below? State your answer to the nearest tenth.

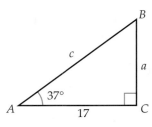

18. What is the length of side c in the triangle below? State your answer to the nearest tenth.

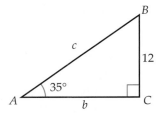

19. What is the length of side c in the triangle below? State your answer to the nearest tenth.

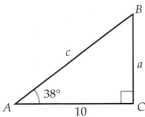

20. If cos $A = \frac{8}{17}$, what is sin A?

21. In a right triangle with acute angles C and D, the value of sin $D = \frac{10}{26}$. Find the value of sin C. Express your answer as a fraction.

Exercises 22–23: Use the diagram below to answer the questions.

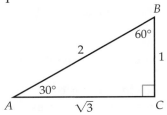

22. What is sin 60°? State the exact value.

23. What is tan 60°? State the exact value.

Practice Problems continue . . .

24. Sketch $\triangle ABC$, where angle B is the right angle, $\sin(A) = \dfrac{4}{5}$, and $\tan(A) = \dfrac{4}{3}$.

25. Gretchen stands 10 meters from the base of a tree. She measures the angle to the top of the tree from the ground to be 60°. What is the height of the tree, to the nearest tenth of a meter?

26. A guy-wire is used to connect the top of a radio antenna to an anchor on the ground. The guy-wire is 120 meters long, and it forms an angle of elevation between the ground and the top of the antenna of 70°. How tall is the radio antenna, to the nearest whole meter?

27. A carpenter uses a 10-foot ladder. When he rests the top of the ladder against the wall, the ladder makes a 65° angle with the floor. How far up the wall does the top of the ladder reach? Round your answer to the nearest tenth of a foot.

28. The leg opposite angle B is $\sqrt{2}$ long, and the hypotenuse has a length of 2. What is the measure of $\angle B$?

Exercises 29–31: Use the diagram to answer the following questions.

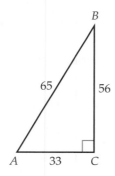

29. What is the cosine of angle A in the triangle? Write your answer as a fraction.

30. What is the tangent of angle A in the triangle above? Write your answer as a fraction.

31. What is the sine of angle A in the triangle above? Write your answer as a fraction.

Exercises 32–33: Use the diagram below to answer the questions.

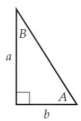

32. What is $\tan(B)$ of the triangle shown if $a = 8$ and $b = 4$? State your answer as an exact expression.

33. What is $\tan(B)$ of the triangle shown if $a = 8$ and $b = 5$? State your answer as an exact expression.

34. **MP 7** For what degree measure are the sine and cosine of an angle equal to each other?

35. **MP 7** As the measure of an angle A increases from 1° to 89°, what happens to the value of the sine of A? Explain your reasoning.

36. Is it possible for the cosine of an angle in a right triangle to be equal to 2? Why or why not?

37. Is it possible for the sine of an acute angle in a right triangle to be equal to one? Explain your reasoning.

38. **MP 3** Using the triangle below, Ivan wrote the following equation to find the height of the triangle: $\sin(40) = \dfrac{x}{15}$. Is Ivan's work correct? Explain your reasoning.

39. A right triangle has a hypotenuse of 12. How long is the leg adjacent to angle A if the angle's measure is 30°? State your answer to the nearest hundredth.

Practice Problems continue . . .

40. Sketch triangle *DEF*, which has a right angle at *E*. Label the length of side *DE* as 10 inches and the length of hypotenuse *DF* as 18 inches. Find and label the length of side *EF* and the measure of angle *F*. Round all answers to the nearest integer.

41. Standing 140 meters from a building, a surveyor measures the angle from the ground to a balcony as 13°. How high is the balcony? Give your answer to the nearest tenth of a meter.

42. Carrie measures the angle from the ground to the top of a tree as 50°. If she is 20 meters from the base of the tree, how tall is it? Give your answer to the nearest tenth of a meter.

43. The angle of elevation from a point on a gym floor to the top of a rope ladder hanging from the ceiling is 40°. The distance from the same point on the floor to the base of the ladder is 30 feet. How long is the ladder, to the nearest tenth of a foot?

44. The pilot of a plane sitting on the tarmac at an airport looks up at the top of the control tower at an angle of 15°. If the pilot is 300 feet horizontally from the tower, how far above his head is the top of the tower? Round your answer to the nearest foot.

45. Clayton is building a bicycle ramp. He wants the angle of the ramp to be 20°. If the length of the board is 8 feet, how high off the ground is the highest part of the ramp, to the nearest hundredth of a foot?

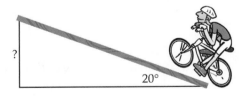

46. A contractor is building a wheelchair ramp to provide access to a building. The ramp must make an angle of 8° with the ground and must rise to a height of three feet at the other end. How long will the slanted part of the ramp be, to the nearest tenth of a foot?

47. **MP 2** A boat is anchored in a part of a lake that has a consistent depth. The rope connecting the boat to its anchor is 60 feet long and makes an angle of 30° with the bottom of the lake. Make a sketch of this situation, and state which trigonometric ratio could be used to find the depth of the lake.

48. In triangle *ABC*, angle *C* is a right angle. If $\sin A = \frac{3}{8}$, find $\cos B$.

49. The leg opposite angle *A* of a right triangle is 15, and the leg adjacent to *A* is 20. What is $\sin A$?

50. What is $\sin(A)$ of the triangle shown if $a = 4$ and $b = \sqrt{65}$?

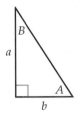

51. An equilateral triangle has sides that measure 4 feet each. What is the exact height of the triangle in feet?

52. Create a word problem that can be solved using the tangent ratio. Show the solution to the problem you have written.

53. Prove that the tangent of an angle is equal to the angle's sine divided by its cosine, or $\tan A = \frac{\sin A}{\cos A}$.

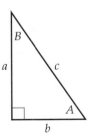

7.7 Optional: Inverses of Trigonometric Functions

An **inverse function** is one that reverses the action of another function, returning the original input value from the original output value. For instance, the sine of 30° is $\frac{1}{2}$. This means that if we know the sine of an angle is $\frac{1}{2}$, then the measure of the angle must be 30°. Although the trigonometric functions are defined for angles of measure greater than 90°, we will limit our discussion in this lesson to the range 0° to 90°.

> The notation $\sin^{-1}$ is an inverse function. If the sine of angle A equals x, then the inverse sine of x = A.

An inverse function can be stated with a −1 raised up, as in $\sin^{-1}$. The notation $\sin^{-1} x$ means the measure of an angle whose sine is x. This is read as "the inverse sine of x" or "the arcsine of x."

$$
\begin{array}{l}
\text{If } \sin A = x, \text{ then } \sin^{-1} x = A. \\
\text{If } \cos A = x, \cos^{-1} x = A. \\
\text{If } \tan A = x, \tan^{-1} x = A.
\end{array}
$$

Example 1 $\quad \sin 30° = \dfrac{1}{2}$

$\sin^{-1}\left(\dfrac{1}{2}\right) = 30°$

The sine of 30° is $\dfrac{1}{2}$. This means that if we know the sine is $\dfrac{1}{2}$, then the measure of the angle must be 30°. The $\sin^{-1}$ of $\dfrac{1}{2}$ is 30°.

Example 2 $\quad \tan 45° = 1$

$\tan^{-1} 1 = 45°$

For example, the tangent of 45° = 1. This means that if the tangent equals 1, the measure of the angle must be 45°. The $\tan^{-1}$ of 1 is 45°.

MODEL PROBLEMS

1. What are the measures of the acute angles in this triangle?

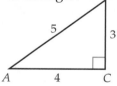

SOLUTION

Calculate sine

$\sin A = \dfrac{\text{opposite}}{\text{hypotenuse}} = \dfrac{3}{5}$

$\sin A = 0.6$

Sin A equals the length opposite of the leg divided by the hypotenuse. Use the values shown on the diagram and state the value as a decimal, 0.6.

Calculate inverse sine

$\sin^{-1} 0.6 \approx 37°$

$m\angle A \approx 37°$

Use a calculator to find $\sin^{-1}$ of 0.6. It is approximately 37°.

Calculate B

$m\angle B = 180° - 37° - 90° = 53°$

Since there are 180° in a triangle, subtract 37° and 90° to calculate the measure of angle B. Subtract 90° since this is a right triangle. Another way to calculate the measure of angle B is to calculate its sine, which is 0.8, and take the inverse sine of that value.

Model Problems continue . . .

MODEL PROBLEMS *continued*

2. **MP 2, 4** A pelican spots a fish in the water. The angle at which the pelican descends is the **angle of depression**. It is a downward angle from the horizontal.

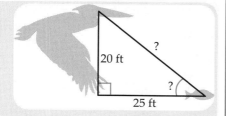

a According to the information in the diagram, at what angle from the horizontal should the pelican descend?

b How far will the pelican travel? Round to the nearest whole number.

SOLUTION

a Locate angle of depression

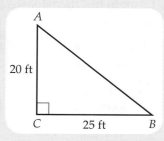

We can locate the angle of depression by starting with the angle between the pelican and the horizontal. Since the horizontals are parallel, use the alternate interior angle theorem to find the measure of $\angle B$.

Use definition of tangent

$$\tan B = \frac{\text{opposite}}{\text{adjacent}} = \frac{20}{25} = 0.8$$

To find $m\angle B$, use the definition of tangent, substituting the length of the opposite leg, 20, and the length of the adjacent leg, 25. Divide to calculate that $\tan B = 0.8$.

Calculate measure of angle of depression

$$\tan B = \frac{\text{opposite}}{\text{adjacent}} = \frac{20}{25} = 0.8$$
$$\tan^{-1}(0.8) \approx 39°$$
$$m\angle B \approx 39°$$

Using the inverse of the tangent function, calculate that $m\angle B \approx 39°$. The pelican will descend at a 39° angle.

b Calculate pelican's distance

$$c^2 = a^2 + b^2$$
$$c^2 = 25^2 + 20^2$$
$$c = 32 \text{ feet}$$

Use the Pythagorean theorem to calculate the distance the bird will travel. After rounding to the nearest whole number, calculate the pelican will travel 32 feet. We can check the angle for being reasonable. The horizontal distance is greater than the vertical distance, so an angle of measure less than 45° makes sense. Also, traveling a distance greater than any of the legs of the triangle makes sense as well since we are calculating the length of the hypotenuse.

PRACTICE

1. What is $\cos^{-1} 0.707$, to the nearest degree?

   A. 40°
   B. 45°
   C. 55°
   D. None of the above

2. What is $\tan^{-1} 0.577$, to the nearest degree?

   A. 20°
   B. 25°
   C. 30°
   D. None of the above

3. What is $\sin^{-1} 0.707$, to the nearest degree?

   A. 20°
   B. 25°
   C. 45°
   D. None of the above

4. You know the lengths of the hypotenuse and one of the legs of a triangle. Which of the following functions could you use to find the measure of an acute angle θ of the triangle?

   A. $\sin \theta$
   B. $\tan \theta$
   C. $\sin^{-1} \theta$
   D. $\tan^{-1} \theta$

5. What is $\cos^{-1} 0.756$, to the nearest degree?

6. If $\tan \theta = \dfrac{20}{21}$, what is $\cos \theta$?

7. An airplane is at an altitude of 3 miles over the city of Daytona. Daytona is 14 miles away from the airport where the plane will land. At what angle from the horizontal should the plane descend, to the nearest degree?

Exercises 8–9: Use the diagram below to answer the questions.

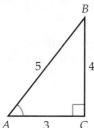

8. What is the measure of angle A, to the nearest degree?

9. What is the measure of angle B, to the nearest degree?

Exercises 10–11: Use the diagram below to answer the questions.

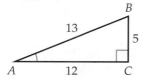

10. What is the measure of angle A, to the nearest degree?

11. What is the measure of angle B, to the nearest degree?

12. **MP 3** Walter was told the sine of angle A was $\dfrac{4}{7}$ and was asked to find the measure of angle A. Walter typed $\sin\left(\dfrac{4}{7}\right)$ into his calculator, but the answer 0.00997 didn't look right to him. What mistake did Walter make, and what is the measure of the angle to the nearest degree?

13. Based on the diagram of a hiker sitting on one side of a canyon, what is the angle of depression, x, to the nearest degree, as the hiker looks down at the bottom of the cliff on the other side of the canyon?

Practice Problems continue . . .

14. A pedestrian bridge connects two high-rise buildings on either side of a busy street. Ryan is standing at one end of the bridge, which is 80 feet long. Ryan knows the bridge is 110 feet above street level.

   a Make a sketch of the situation.

   b What is the measure of the angle of depression, to the nearest degree, from one end of the bridge to the bottom of the building on the other side of the street?

15. If $\tan x = \dfrac{\sqrt{56}}{5}$, what is $\cos x$? Round your answer to the nearest hundredth.

16. If $\tan x = \dfrac{\sqrt{9}}{4}$, what is $\cos x$? Round your answer to the nearest hundredth.

17. If $\cos x = \dfrac{4}{7}$, what is $\sin x$? Round your answer to the nearest hundredth.

18. If $\cos x = \dfrac{5}{8}$, what is $\sin x$? Round your answer to the nearest hundredth.

19. If $\tan x = \dfrac{3}{4}$, what is $\sin x$? Round your answer to the nearest hundredth.

20. If $\cos A = \dfrac{5}{13}$, what is $\sin A$? Round your answer to the nearest hundredth.

21. If $\sin B = \dfrac{\sqrt{39}}{8}$, what is $\cos B$? Round your answer to the nearest hundredth.

22. If $\sin B = \dfrac{3\sqrt{5}}{7}$, what is $\tan B$? Round your answer to the nearest hundredth.

23. The ship heading north is moving at 7 kilometers per hour. The ship heading east is moving at 9 kilometers per hour. They leave from the same point at the same time. What is the measure of angle x, to the nearest tenth of a degree?

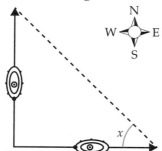

24. To get from Marysville to Georgetown, you must drive 5 miles west and 9 miles south. A new highway is planned that will connect Marysville and Georgetown directly. What is the measure of the angle that the new highway will form with the road that runs west from Marysville? Round your answer to the nearest whole number.

25. **MP 2, 7** Two runners leave from the same location at the same time. One runs due east at 8 mph, while the other runs due north at 5 mph. If you were to draw a line between the two runners at any point in time, the runners and their starting point would form a right triangle. What is the relationship between the runners' speeds and the measure of the eastern angle of the triangle? What is the measure of the eastern angle, to the nearest degree?

26. An adventure course has a zip line that connects two platforms together. The first platform is 90 feet above the ground, and the second platform is 70 feet above the ground. The zip line connecting the two platforms is 164 feet long. Assume the zip line is taut.

   a Make a sketch of the situation.

   b What is the measure of the angle of depression from the first platform to the second platform, to the nearest degree?

   c How far apart are the two platforms, horizontally? Round your answer to the nearest foot.

27. The triangles shown below are similar. Use the information in the diagram to find the measure of angle A to the nearest degree.

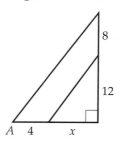

Practice Problems continue . . .

28. The lengths of the legs of a right triangle can be represented by the expressions $x + 2$ and $x - 1$, while the length of its hypotenuse can be represented by the expression $x + 5$. Find the degree measure of the smallest angle of the triangle, rounded to the nearest whole degree.

• Multi-Part PROBLEM Practice •

MP 2, 4 A plane is flying parallel to the ground at an altitude of 4,000 feet and a speed of 120 miles per hour (176 feet per second). The plane is 15,000 feet horizontally from a building on the ground.

a Make a sketch of the situation.

b What is the angle of depression from the plane to the building's ground floor, to the nearest degree?

c How many feet is it, diagonally, from the plane to the building's ground floor? Round your answer to the nearest hundred feet.

d One minute later, what is the angle of depression from the plane to the building's ground floor, to the nearest degree?

e How many feet is it now, diagonally, from the plane to the building's ground floor? Round your answer to the nearest foot.

LESSON 7.8

7.8 Law of Cosines and Law of Sines

The basic trigonometric ratios can be used to solve any right triangle, that is, to find the measures of all the sides and angles. To solve triangles that are not right triangles, which are called **oblique triangles**, other trigonometric relations are used. One of these is the **law of cosines**.

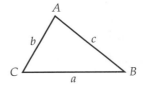

The law of cosines can be stated in any of these three ways shown to the right, depending on the angle that is known or chosen. For instance, if you know or can calculate $m\angle B$, you would use the second equation.

Law of cosines

In <u>any</u> triangle *ABC*:

$$a^2 = b^2 + c^2 - 2bc \cos A$$
$$b^2 = a^2 + c^2 - 2ac \cos B$$
$$c^2 = a^2 + b^2 - 2ab \cos C$$

The law of cosines is an equation that relates the lengths of the three sides of a triangle and one of the angles.

To remember the equations, it may help to note that the side is on the left of the equation and the angle opposite it is on the right.

Prove the law of cosines using $\triangle ABC$:

Prove: $a^2 = b^2 + c^2 - 2bc \cdot \cos(A)$

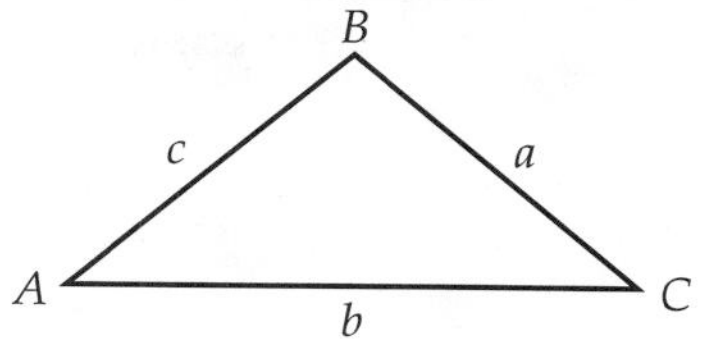

Statement	Reason
	Draw altitude h to point D from point B. This splits the triangle into two right triangles, $\triangle ADB$ and $\triangle CDB$.
	Also, let $AD = x$ and $DC = b - x$ using the segment addition postulate.
For $\triangle ADB \qquad x^2 + h^2 = c^2$ Solving for $x^2 \qquad\qquad x^2 = c^2 - h^2$ For $\triangle CDB \qquad (b - x)^2 + h^2 = a^2$	An equation can be written for each right triangle using the Pythagorean theorem.
For $\triangle ADB \qquad \cos A = \dfrac{x}{c}$ Solving for $x \qquad\quad x = c \cdot \cos A$	Considering triangle ADB, a cosine ratio can be written using x and side c.
$b^2 - 2bx + x^2 + h^2 = a^2$	Expanding the Pythagorean theorem equation for $\triangle CDB$ gives an equation in which substitutions can be made for x and x^2.
$b^2 - 2b(c \cdot \cos A) + (c^2 - h^2) + h^2 = a^2$ $\qquad b^2 - 2bc \cdot \cos A + c^2 = a^2$ $\qquad\qquad a^2 = b^2 + c^2 - 2bc \cdot \cos A$	Substituting $c \cdot \cos A$ for x and $c^2 - h^2$ for x^2 results in this equation. Note that the $-h^2$ and $+h^2$ add up to zero, leaving one form of the law of cosines. The work is similar for the cosine of any angle of the triangle.

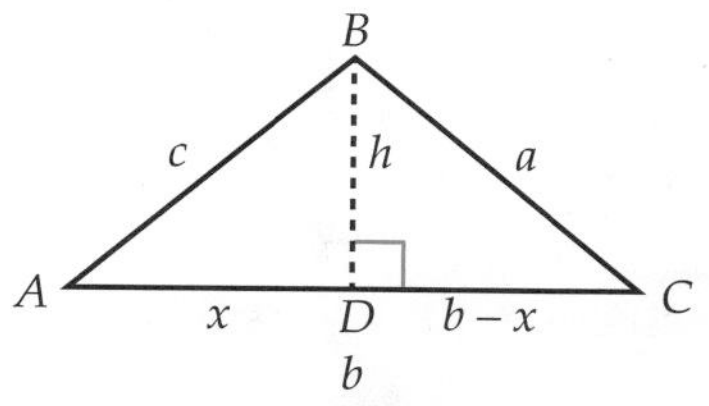

In this activity, you will need to use the law of cosines to calculate the distance the alien spacecraft travels.

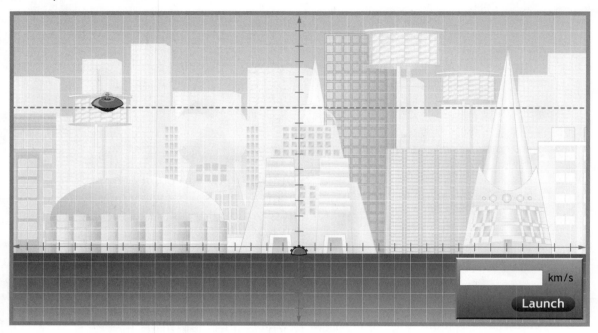

MODEL PROBLEMS

1. Use the law of cosines to determine the length of side *a*. Round to the nearest tenth.

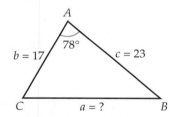

The law of cosines can be used to find the length of the third side of a triangle if you know the lengths of two sides and the measure of the angle between them. You can also use this law to calculate angle measures when all the side lengths are known.

SOLUTION

Law of cosines

$$a^2 = b^2 + c^2 - 2bc \cos A$$
$$a^2 = 17^2 + 23^2 - 2(17)(23)(\cos 78°)$$

Use the law of cosines. Since the measure of angle *A* is given, choose the version of the equation you see in the solution. Substitute the lengths of sides *b* and *c*, and the measure of angle *A*.

Solve equation

$$a^2 \approx 289 + 529 - 2(17)(23)(0.2079)$$
$$a^2 \approx 655.4$$
$$a \approx 25.6$$

Do the calculations. The length of side *a* is 25.6.

Model Problems continue . . .

2. **MP 4** The diagram shows the cross-section of a rock quarry where Jeanette works. It has a constant decline from ground level to the bottom of the quarry. S represents the shallow end of the quarry, D represents the deepest point in the quarry, H represents the steep end of the quarry at ground level, and s represents the distance from the steep end to the bottom, since it is the side opposite vertex S.

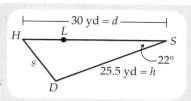

a Jeanette drops her helmet at the steep end and it rolls to the bottom. How far does it roll, to the nearest tenth of a yard?

b If she puts a ladder in at L, and the ratio of SL to LH needs to be 4 : 1, how far is it from end H of the quarry?

SOLUTION

a Use law of cosines

$$s^2 = d^2 + h^2 - 2dh \cdot \cos \angle S$$

We want to calculate s, the distance to the deepest point. Since we know two side lengths and the angle in between them, use the law of cosines to solve for the third side. Rewrite the law of cosines with the variables in the problem.

Substitute

$$s^2 = 30^2 + 25.5^2 - 2(30)(25.5) \cdot \cos 22°$$

Substitute values from the problem into the law of cosines equation.

Calculate s

$$s^2 = 900 + 650.25 - 1530 \cdot 0.927$$

$$s^2 \approx 131.94$$

$$s \approx 11.5 \text{ yards}$$

Use the order of operations to evaluate the equation for s. To the nearest tenth of a yard, the distance is 11.5 yards.

b Solution strategy

Jeanette wants to calculate the distance from the ladder to the steep end at ground level. Use ratios to do this. Given the ratio 4 : 1, find the location of the ladder, L, on line segment $\overline{SH}$. Do this by calculating LH, since the question asks for the distance of the ladder from end H of the quarry.

Draw diagram

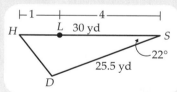

Find the ratio $\dfrac{LH}{SH}$

$$\frac{LH}{SH} = \frac{LH}{SL + LH}$$

$$\frac{LH}{SH} = \frac{1}{4 + 1} = \frac{1}{5}$$

Calculate LH, which we can do by first finding the ratio $\dfrac{LH}{SH}$. Use the ratio $\dfrac{SL}{LH}$ given in the problem.

State as a proportion

$$\frac{LH}{SH} = \frac{x}{30} = \frac{1}{5}$$

Now that we have a ratio for the distance we want to find to the total distance, set up a proportion to calculate the distance we want to find.

Calculate x

$$x = \frac{1}{5} \cdot 30$$

$$x = LH = 6 \text{ yards}$$

Multiply and divide to calculate x, the distance from the ladder to the steep end at ground level.

Trigonometry and Triangle Area

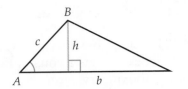

The area of a triangle can be calculated as one-half
of the product of the lengths of the triangle's base and height.
Using trigonometry, we can state another formula for the area.

Represent the height with trigonometry	$h = c \cdot \sin A$	The height of the triangle can be represented with an expression using a trig ratio.
Formula with sides and angle	$\text{Area} = \dfrac{1}{2} \cdot b \cdot c \cdot \sin A$	We state a formula that calculates the area using the lengths of two sides and the measure of the angle between them. The area of a triangle can be calculated as one-half of the product of the lengths of the two sides and the sine of the angle between them.

MODEL PROBLEM

What is the area of the triangle?

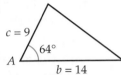

SOLUTION

Formula for area	$\text{Area} = \dfrac{1}{2} \cdot b \cdot c \cdot \sin A$ $\text{Area} = \dfrac{1}{2}(14)(9)(\sin 64°)$	Start with the formula for the area of the triangle, based on two sides and the angle between them. Substitute the values stated in the drawing.
Substitute value for sine and multiply	$\text{Area} \approx \dfrac{1}{2}(14)(9)(0.8988)$ $\text{Area} \approx 56.6$	Substitute the value of the sine of 64°. Multiply to calculate the area, which is 56.6.

The Law of Sines and Solving ASA and AAS Triangles

The **law of sines** states proportions that hold for the sines of the
angles of a triangle and the sides opposite the angles. We show
two equivalent ways to state the law:

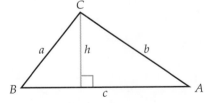

Law of sines

Sides and sines are proportional	$\dfrac{\sin A}{a} = \dfrac{\sin B}{b} = \dfrac{\sin C}{c}$	The law of sines states that the ratios of the sines of the angles and the opposite sides are equal.
	$\dfrac{a}{\sin A} = \dfrac{b}{\sin B} = \dfrac{c}{\sin C}$	This is an equivalent way to state the law of sines, simply taking the reciprocal of each ratio.

> The law of sines states that the ratios of the sides of a triangle and the sines of the opposite angles are equal.

Prove the law of sines using $\triangle ABC$.

Prove: $\dfrac{a}{\sin A} = \dfrac{b}{\sin B} = \dfrac{c}{\sin C}$

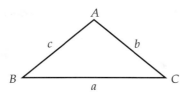

Diagram	Explanation
	Start by inscribing the triangle into a circle with center P, labeling the radius as r. A triangle inscribed in a circle has all vertices on the circle.
	Draw the altitude $\overline{PD}$, which bisects $\angle BPC$ into two congruent angles, $\angle DPC$ and $\angle DPB$, because the triangle is isosceles.
	The inscribed angle $\angle BAC$ and the central angle $\angle BPC$ share the same arc, $\overset{\frown}{BC}$. (We describe central angles on page 363 and inscribed angles on page 370.) The measure of the central angle is equal to the measure of the intercepted arc and the measure of the inscribed angle is equal to half of the measure of the intercepted arc, or $m\angle BAC = \dfrac{1}{2}m\angle BPC = m\angle DPC$.
	Now consider triangle DPC. The altitude $\overline{PD}$ bisects $\overline{BC}$ into two congruent segments because $\triangle BPC$ is isosceles.
	So, since $DC = \dfrac{1}{2}BC$ and $BC = a$, then $DC = \dfrac{a}{2}$.
	Using the sine ratio, $\angle DPC = \dfrac{\frac{a}{2}}{r} = \dfrac{a}{2r}$.
	Since $m\angle DPC = m\angle BAC$, the sine for $\angle BAC$ will have the same ratio: $\sin \angle BAC = \sin A = \dfrac{a}{2r}$.
	This gives $2r = \dfrac{a}{\sin A}$.
	The same rationale follows for $\angle B$ and $\angle C$ so that
	$2r = \dfrac{b}{\sin B} = \dfrac{c}{\sin C}$.
	This gives the law of sines: $\dfrac{a}{\sin A} = \dfrac{b}{\sin B} = \dfrac{c}{\sin C}$.
	The proof is similar if the center of the circle is outside the inscribed triangle.

1. What is the length of side a?

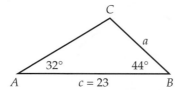

> Because we know the length of only one side, we cannot use the law of cosines here.

SOLUTION

Law of sines	$$\dfrac{a}{\sin A} = \dfrac{c}{\sin C}$$	Write an equation using the law of sines.
Calculate C	$$32° + 44° + m\angle C = 180°$$ $$m\angle C = 104°$$	To calculate C, use the fact that the sum of the angles of any triangle is 180°. Substitute the values of angles A and B and calculate that angle C has measure 104°.
Substitute values in law of sines	$$\dfrac{a}{\sin 32°} = \dfrac{23}{\sin 104°}$$	Substitute the stated values in the law of sines equation.
Solve	$$a = \dfrac{23(\sin 32°)}{\sin 104°} \approx \dfrac{23(0.5299)}{0.9703}$$ $$a \approx 12.6$$	Calculate the values of the sines and solve the equation. The length of side a is 12.6.

2. What is the length of side b?

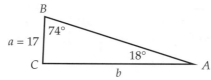

SOLUTION

Law of sines	$$\dfrac{b}{\sin B} = \dfrac{a}{\sin A}$$	Write an equation using the law of sines.
Substitute values	$$\dfrac{b}{\sin 74°} = \dfrac{17}{\sin 18°}$$	Substitute the stated values into the equation.
Solve	$$b = \dfrac{17(\sin 74°)}{\sin 18°} \approx \dfrac{17(0.9613)}{0.3090}$$ $$b \approx 52.9$$	Calculate the values of the sines and solve the equation. The length of side b is 52.9.

Model Problems continue . . .

3. **MP 4** Bear Mountain Lookout and Alpine Lookout are fire lookouts separated by 26 miles, with Alpine Lookout due east of Bear Mountain. Bear Mountain locates the fire at 9° west of north, while Alpine Lookout locates it at 53° west of north. How far is the fire from the Bear Mountain Lookout?

SOLUTION

Draw diagram

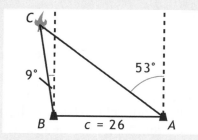

We use a diagram, the law of sines, and a bit of geometry to solve the problem. We represent Bear Mountain with B on the map, Alpine Lookout with A, and the fire with C.

Calculate angles

$m\angle A = 90° - 53° = 37°$

The two stations are separated by 26 miles on an east-west line. Calculate $m\angle A$ of the triangle. A line going north forms a 90° angle with the east-west line, so we calculate that $m\angle A = 37°$.

$m\angle B = 90° + 9° = 99°$

Calculate $m\angle B$ of the triangle. A line going north forms a 90° angle with the east-west line, so we calculate that $m\angle B = 99°$.

$m\angle A + m\angle B + m\angle C = 180°$
$m\angle C = 180° - 37° - 99° = 44°$

We know two angles in the triangle, so subtract them from 180° to calculate the third.

Use law of sines

$$\frac{a}{\sin A} = \frac{c}{\sin C}$$

$$a = \frac{c(\sin A)}{\sin C}$$

We now know two angles and a side, so use the ASA version of the law of sines. State the law and solve for a.

Substitute and evaluate

$$a = \frac{26 \cdot \sin 37°}{\sin 44°} = \frac{26 \cdot 0.602}{0.695}$$

$$a \approx 22.5 \text{ miles}$$

Substitute the angles, evaluate the sines, and divide. The fire is 22.5 miles from the Bear Mountain Lookout. Firefighters use this technique to locate fires in remote areas.

Model Problems continue . . .

4. Courtney wants to figure out the distance from her house to Bill's house. She knows the distance to Amy's house, and she knows the angles that are shown in the diagram. How far is it from Courtney's house to Bill's house, to the nearest foot? In the diagram, Amy is represented by *A*, Bill is represented by *B*, and Courtney is represented by *C*.

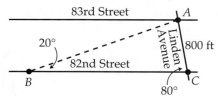

SOLUTION

Calculate angles

$m\angle B = 20°$
$m\angle C = 80°$
$m\angle A = 80°$

The problem states that $m\angle B = 20°$, and $m\angle C = 80°$. Connect the friends' houses to make a triangle. Using the triangle sum theorem, the remaining angle at Amy's house is 80°.

Use the law of sines

$$\frac{a}{\sin A} = \frac{b}{\sin B}$$

$$\frac{a}{\sin 80°} = \frac{800}{\sin 20°}$$

Since we know one side length and the angles in the triangle, use the law of sines to calculate *a*, the distance to Bill's house. Substitute the values into the equation.

Calculate a

$$\frac{a}{0.985} = \frac{800}{0.342}$$

$$a = \frac{800}{0.342} \cdot 0.985$$

$$a \approx 2304 \text{ feet}$$

Multiply and divide to calculate *a*.

PRACTICE

1. A triangle has two sides that measure 12 cm and 18 cm, and the angle between them measures 70°. Approximately how long is the third side?

   A. 6 cm
   B. 18 cm
   C. 22 cm
   D. 25 cm

2. A triangular support in a building has sides that measure 7 feet, 11 feet, and 9 feet. What is the approximate measure of the largest angle in the triangle?

   A. 39°
   B. 55°
   C. 80°
   D. 86°

3. Which of the following formulas can be used to find the area of oblique triangle *DEF*, assuming all side lengths and angle measures are known?

   A. $A = \frac{1}{2}b$ C. $A = \frac{1}{2}de \cos D$

   B. $A = \frac{1}{2}ef \sin D$ D. $A = de \cos F$

4. If you know the lengths of all three sides of an oblique triangle, you can solve the triangle using

   A. The Pythagorean theorem.
   B. Only the law of cosines.
   C. Only the law of sines.
   D. Either the law of sines or the law of cosines.

Practice Problems continue . . .

5. The law of cosines can be used to solve which types of oblique triangles?

    A.   SAS only

    B.   SSS only

    C.   ASA and SAS only

    D.   SSS and SAS only

6. A triangle has sides of length $b = 10$ and $a = 32$. If the measure of angle C is $102°$, what is the length of side c? Round your answer to the nearest tenth.

7. A triangle has side length $c = 6.2$ and angles $A = 98°$ and $B = 40°$. What is the length of side a? Round your answer to the nearest tenth.

8. A triangle has side length $b = 9.1$ and angles $C = 63°$ and $A = 62°$. What is the length of side a? Round your answer to the nearest tenth.

9. A triangle has side length $c = 14$ and angles $A = 65°$ and $C = 17°$. What is the length of side a, to the nearest tenth?

10. A triangle has side length $c = 34$ and angles $B = 65°$ and $C = 94°$. What is the length of side b, to the nearest tenth?

11. A triangle has side length $a = 5$ and angles $A = 20°$ and $B = 64°$. What is the length of side b? Express your answer to the nearest tenth.

12. A triangle has side length $b = 5$ and angles $A = 81°$ and $C = 47°$. What is the length of side a, to the nearest tenth?

13. A triangle has side length $b = 4$ and angles $A = 80°$ and $C = 51°$. What is the length of side a, to the nearest tenth?

14. A triangle has side length $c = 4.5$ and angles $A = 80°$ and $B = 34°$. What is the length of side a? Round your answer to the nearest tenth.

15. A triangle has side length $b = 24$ and angles $A = 46°$ and $B = 117°$. What is the length of side a? Round your answer to the nearest tenth.

16. A triangle has sides of length $c = 5$ and $a = 6$. If the measure of angle B is $134°$, what is the area of the triangle, to the nearest tenth?

17. A triangle has sides of length $b = 14$ and $c = 10$. If the measure of angle A is $160°$, what is the length of side a? Round your answer to the nearest tenth.

18. What is the length of side a in the triangle shown? Express your answer to the nearest tenth.

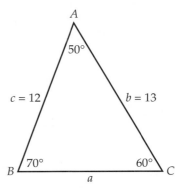

19. What is the area of the triangle below? Give your answer as a decimal to the nearest tenth.

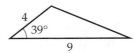

20. Harold's yard is a strange corner lot in the shape of a triangle. One side is 20 feet long and another side is 18 feet. Harold measures the angle between these two sides as $25°$. What is the area of his yard? Express your answer to the nearest square foot.

21. What is the length of side a in the triangle below? Express your answer to the nearest tenth.

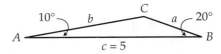

22. A triangle has two sides of length 4 and 4, with an angle of $51°$ between them. What is the length of the remaining side? Express your answer to the nearest tenth.

Practice Problems continue . . .

23. A triangle has two sides of length 5 and 2, with an angle of 42° between them. What is the length of the remaining side? Express your answer to the nearest tenth.

24. A triangle has two sides of length 5 and 7, with an angle of 39° between them. What is the length of the remaining side? Express your answer to the nearest tenth.

25. What is the measure of $\angle R$ to the nearest tenth of a degree?

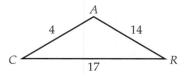

26. In a triangle, $RA = 11$, $AD = 11$, and $RD = 8$. What is the measure of $\angle A$ to the nearest tenth of a degree?

27. A triangle has side lengths 2, 5, and 6 cm. What is the measure of the angle between the sides with lengths 2 cm and 5 cm to the nearest tenth of a degree?

28. A triangle has side length $a = 3$ and angles $A = 20°$ and $B = 59°$. What is the length of side b? Express your answer to the nearest tenth.

29. A triangle has two sides of length 6 and 9, with an angle of 35° between them. What is the length of the remaining side? Express your answer to the nearest tenth.

30. At an amusement park, one of the rides is a slide. Riders enter near the bottom of the slide, pick up a tube, and walk to a staircase at the back of the slide. As shown in the diagram, the walkway between the entrance and the stairs is 60 feet long, the staircase is 20 feet long, and the angle formed between the two is 35°. How long is the slide, to the nearest foot?

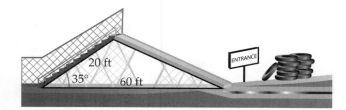

31. Beatrice says the area of the triangle below is 40 square units because it has a base of 10 units and a height of 8 units. Do you agree with Beatrice? Why or why not?

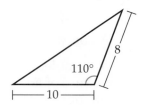

32. Find the measure of side b for the triangle pictured. Round your answer to the nearest tenth of a yard.

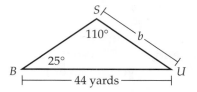

33. **MP 4** Two lighthouses are located along the Atlantic Ocean on a north-south line. The lighthouses are 18 miles apart. Both lighthouses receive a distress call from a ship at the same time. From the northern lighthouse, the ship is at an angle of 10° south of east. From the southern lighthouse, the ship is at an angle of 65° north of east.

   a Make a sketch of the situation. Include all known angles and distances.

   b Which lighthouse is closer to the ship? How do you know?

34. **MP 1, 3, 7** Is it possible to use the law of cosines to solve an oblique triangle in which you know the measures of two angles and the length of the included side? Explain your reasoning.

35. During a game of frisbee, Chloe, Dean, and Edgar form a triangle. Chloe and Dean are 100 feet apart, Dean and Edgar are 130 feet apart, and Chloe and Edgar are 140 feet apart.

   a Which player is located at the largest angle of the triangle? Explain your reasoning.

   b Find the measure of the smallest angle of the triangle, rounded to the nearest degree. Make sure to name the angle in your response.

Practice Problems continue . . .

Practice Problems continued . . .

36. If you start with the measures of two angles of a triangle and the length of one side, is it possible to find the area of the triangle, even though the area formula requires inputs of two sides and their included angle? Explain your reasoning.

37. Find the area of △ABD to the nearest square unit.

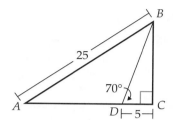

38. Eric is trying to find the area of the triangle below using the law of sines.

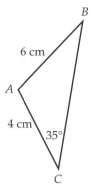

Here is his work:

$$\text{Area} = \frac{1}{2}(6)(4)\sin 35$$

$$\text{Area} = 12 \cdot 0.574$$
$$\text{Area} = 6.9\text{cm}^2$$

Jason says, "That's not right. You can't use the law of sines with those two sides and that angle." Who is right? If Jason is, then show how to find the correct sides and/or angles, and find the correct area.

39. **MP 3, 6** Use the law of cosines to prove the Pythagorean acute inequality theorem. Hint: What are the values of cos C if $m\angle C$ is between 0° and 90°? between 90° and 180°?

Pythagorean acute inequality theorem

If the square of the triangle's longest side is less than the sum of the squares of the other two sides, then the triangle is acute.

If $c^2 < a^2 + b^2$, then △ ABC is acute.

1. Are the triangles similar?

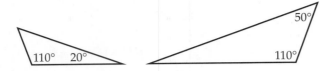

A. Yes

B. No

C. It's impossible to tell

2. Which of these statements is an acceptable way to write that the triangles are similar? Select all that apply.

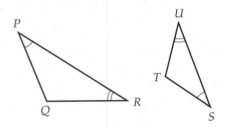

A. $\triangle PQR \sim \triangle STU$ D. $\triangle RQP \sim \triangle UTS$

B. $\triangle PQR \sim \triangle UTS$ E. $\triangle RQP \cong \triangle UTS$

C. $\triangle PQR \cong \triangle STU$ F. $\triangle RQP \cong \triangle STU$

3. Which of the following represents the length of $\overline{DE}$, given that triangles ABC and DEF are similar?

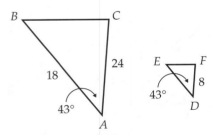

A. 2   C. 6

B. 4   D. 8

4. A triangle has side lengths of 12, 15, and 20. The triangle is

A. Acute.

B. Obtuse.

C. Right.

D. Not enough information to determine.

5. A triangle has side lengths of 9, 12, and 15. The triangle is

A. Acute.

B. Right.

C. Obtuse.

D. Not a triangle.

6. A triangle has sides that measure 5, 5, and $5\sqrt{2}$. This triangle is best described as a(n)

A. 30-60-90 triangle.

B. Scalene obtuse triangle.

C. Isosceles acute triangle.

D. Isosceles right triangle.

7. A triangle has sides that measure 6, $6\sqrt{3}$, and 12. This triangle is best described as a(n)

A. Isosceles right triangle.

B. 45-45-90 triangle.

C. 30-60-90 triangle.

D. Acute triangle.

8. As the measure of an angle increases from 0° to 90°, the value of the sine of the angle increases with it and

A. The value of the cosine and tangent also will increase.

B. The value of the cosine stays constant while the tangent increases.

C. The value of the cosine stays constant while the tangent decreases.

D. The value of the cosine decreases and the value of the tangent increases.

9. A triangle is dilated and then translated. The cosine of one of its angles will

A. Increase if the scale factor is greater than 1.

B. Decrease if the scale factor is greater than 1.

C. Change, but more information is required to predict the change.

D. Stay the same.

10. $\triangle ABC$ has angle measures of 46° and 92°. $\triangle DEF$ has angle measures of 32° and 46°. State whether the triangles are similar or not. Justify your answer.

Chapter Review continues . . .

11. Given the similar triangles shown, what is the value of *a*?

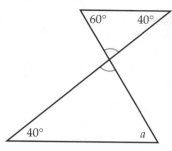

12. $\triangle FAT$ and $\triangle NOT$ have two pairs of sides with a scale factor of $\frac{3}{2}$. The third sides have lengths of 64 and 48. Are the triangles similar? Explain.

13. What must be the length of $\overline{DF}$ if the two triangles *ABC* and *DEF* shown below are to be similar?

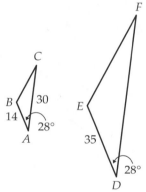

14. Determine if the triangles *ABC* and *DEF* shown below are similar. Justify your answer. If the triangles are similar, state the scale factor applied to $\triangle ABC$ to get $\triangle DEF$.

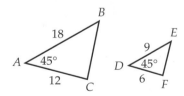

15. Given the triangles below, identify the similar triangles, using a similarity statement.

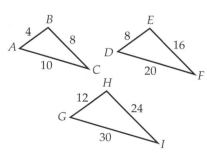

16. Write a word problem involving similar triangles and solve.

17. Right triangle *ABC* sits on the coordinate grid such that the vertex of its right angle is the origin. The triangle is located in quadrant IV, and its horizontal side is 16 units long. The hypotenuse is 20 units long. What are the coordinates of the vertex located on the *y*-axis?

18. When working with the Pythagorean theorem and its converse, which side of a given triangle should always be used as the value of *c* in the formula? Explain your reasoning.

19. **MP 4** A sailboat designer is making a triangular sail for a competition. In order to fit the sponsor's logo onto the sail, the designer needs the angle marked *x* to be greater than 90°. Based on the given dimensions of the sail, what is the shortest possible integer length of the sail's mast?

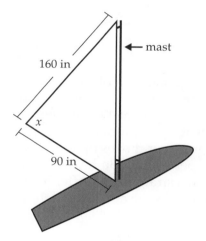

20. Walter is sketching an obtuse triangle. The two shorter sides of the triangle measure 16 centimeters and 30 centimeters. Write an inequality, using *c* for length, showing the range of possible values for the third side of the triangle.

21. Line segment *CE* is an altitude of right triangle *BCD*. If the $m\angle B = 70°$, what is $m\angle ECD$?

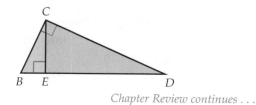

Chapter Review continues . . .

22. In a 45-45-90 triangle, the length of one leg is 10 feet. Laura says the length of the hypotenuse must be 20 feet. Do you agree with Laura? Why or why not?

23. A roof is constructed in the shape of an isosceles right triangle with the 90-degree angle at its peak. Each slanted side of the roof measures 15 feet.

  a Sketch the roof.

  b How long is the base of the roof, to the nearest tenth of a foot?

24. What is sin *A*?

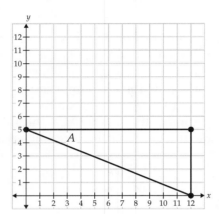

25. In a soccer game, two players both start in front of the goal at the same location. One moves up the field at 4 meters per second to intercept a pass from the other player. The other player moves up the field at 3 meters per second. Both players are moving in a straight line. After 5 seconds, the two players are approximately 12 meters apart.

  a Make a sketch of the situation. Be sure to label the total distance traveled by each player.

  b What angle was formed between the paths of the two players as they headed away from the goal? Round your answer to the nearest tenth of a degree.

  c What type of triangle is formed by the starting and ending locations of the two players? Explain.

26. A right triangle has a hypotenuse of 13. How long is the leg opposite angle *A* if the angle's measure is 41°? State your answer to the nearest tenth.

27. **MP 8** You know the angle of elevation from a point on the ground to the top of a building, as well as the height of the building. Can you use the cosine ratio to find the direct distance from the point on the ground to the top of the building? Explain your reasoning.

28. A 15-foot-long brace is propped against the side of a building. The brace makes an angle of 50° with the ground.

  a Make a sketch of the situation.

  b How far away from the building is the bottom of the brace located, to the nearest tenth of a foot?

  c How far up the building does the brace reach, to the nearest tenth of a foot?

  d The bottom of the brace is moved closer to the building. Explain how this affects the angle the brace makes with the ground, as well as the sine and cosine values for the angle.

29. What is the area of the triangle below, to the nearest square unit?

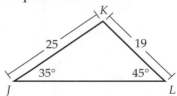

30. Find the area of the triangle below, to the nearest square centimeter.

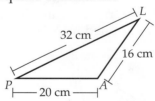

1. The lengths of the sides of a triangle are 3, 4, and 5. The triangle is

   A. Scalene.

   B. Isosceles.

   C. Equilateral.

2. A triangle has sides of length 10, 24, and 26. The triangle

   A. Contains three acute angles.

   B. Contains a right angle.

   C. Is isosceles.

   D. Both A and B are true.

3. Which are correct similarity statements for the triangles shown? Select all that apply.

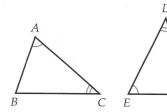

   A. △ABC ~ △DEF

   B. △CBA ~ △DFE

   C. △CBA ~ △FED

   D. △ACB ~ △EDF

4. Which line segments are parallel in the figure shown? Select all that apply.

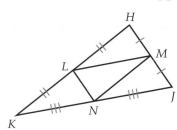

   A. $\overline{LM}$ and $\overline{KJ}$

   B. $\overline{LN}$ and $\overline{KH}$

   C. $\overline{NM}$ and $\overline{JH}$

   D. $\overline{MN}$ and $\overline{HK}$

5. $\overline{AB}$ and $\overline{DE}$ are corresponding sides in two congruent triangles, △ABC and △DEF. BC is 3 times greater than AB and 14 units greater than $\overline{DE}$. What is the length of $\overline{DE}$?

   A. 5

   B. 7

   C. 8

   D. 11

6. If X, then Z. If F, then X. One can conclude:

   A. If F, then Z.

   B. If X, then F.

   C. If Z, then F.

   D. If Z, then X.

7. The sine of an angle of right triangle D equals 0.4. The right triangle X has a hypotenuse of length 20 and one leg of length 8. Triangles D and X must be

   A. Congruent.

   B. Similar.

   C. Similar and congruent.

   D. None of the above.

8. Which statement is *not* true?

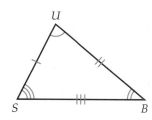
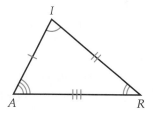

   A. $\overline{SU} \cong \overline{AI}$

   B. $\overline{BU} \cong \overline{RI}$

   C. $\overline{BS} \cong \overline{RA}$

   D. $\overline{BU} \cong \overline{IA}$

9. Clovis uses a paragraph proof to show △EDF ≅ △GFD. He says, "It is given that $\overline{DE} \cong \overline{GF}$. It is also given that $\overline{DE} \| \overline{GF}$, and $\overline{DF}$ is a transversal of these parallel line segments. ∠DFG ≅ ∠EDF, since they are alternate interior angles, and $\overline{DF} \cong \overline{DF}$ due to the reflexive congruence property." What postulate or theorem is he using?

   A. SSS

   B. SAS

   C. SSA

   D. ASA

   E. AAS

10. A triangle has sides of length $c = 5$ and $a = 3$. If the measure of angle B is 42°, what is the length of side b? Round your answer to the nearest tenth.

11. $\overline{AB}$ and $\overline{DE}$ are corresponding sides in two congruent triangles, $\triangle ABC$ and $\triangle DEF$. $\overline{BC}$ is 3 times longer than $\overline{AB}$ and 12 centimeters longer than $\overline{DE}$. What is the length of $\overline{DE}$?

12. $\triangle ABC \sim \triangle DEF$. $AB = 18$ inches and $BC = 14$ inches. The angle formed by $\overline{AB}$ and $\overline{BC}$ measures 65°. $DE = 14.4$ inches. What is the length of $\overline{EF}$? What is the measure of the angle formed by $\overline{DE}$ and $\overline{EF}$?

13. Are the two triangles similar? Explain.

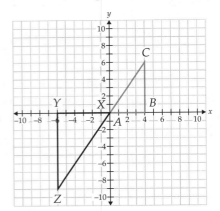

14. Line segment PR is crossed by its perpendicular bisector SU at point T.

   a   Make a sketch of the situation.

   b   When the number 9 and the length of $\overline{PR}$ are added together, the result is equal to eight less than three times the length of $\overline{TR}$. Find the length of $\overline{PR}$.

15. $\triangle PLY$ can be proven to be congruent to $\triangle ART$ by the side-side-side postulate. Sketch the two triangles and provide all necessary information or markings to show that they are congruent by SSS.

16. If $m\angle A = 50°$ and $m\angle B = 75°$ in the diagram, what is $m\angle Z$?

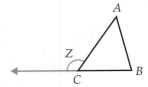

17. Is it possible for a triangle to be both scalene and isosceles? Justify your answer.

18. On a plane, line $a \perp$ line b, line $b \parallel$ line c, and line $m \perp$ line c. Are the lines m and a parallel? Explain your answer.

Exercises 19–20: X, Y, and Z are midpoints of the sides of triangle ABC.

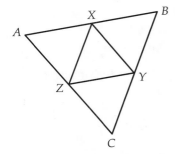

19. If $AB = 17$, what is the length of $\overline{ZY}$?

20. If $XY = 4.9$, what is the length of $\overline{AC}$?

21. $\triangle ABC$ has side lengths of 24, 18, and 10. $\triangle DEF$ has corresponding side lengths of 18, 14, and 8. $\triangle GHI$ has corresponding side lengths of 36, 27, and 15. Which two triangles are similar? Justify your answer.

22. A right triangle is drawn on a coordinate plane, with one vertex at the origin and one leg lying along the x-axis in the positive direction. The right angle is at the point $(7, 0)$ and the hypotenuse has a slope of $\frac{4}{7}$. What is the length of the hypotenuse, to the nearest hundredth?

23. A teacher says: "Triangle ABC has vertex A at $(8, 4)$, vertex B at $(0, 0)$, and vertex C at $(4, -2)$. ABC is a right triangle, with B its right angle." Is he correct? Justify your answer.

24. A builder wants to make sure he has built a door that is "square" before he hangs it. If the door is "square," the angles at its corners will all measure 90°. The builder measures the height of the door, which is 80 inches, and its width, which is 39 inches. He then measures both diagonals of the door and determines they both measure 89 inches. Is the door "square"? Justify your answer.

25. **MP 3** Using the diagram, prove the exterior angle theorem.

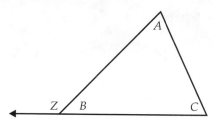

Prove: $m\angle Z = m\angle A + m\angle C$

26. What is the area of a triangle with sides measuring 5 and 6 and the angle between them measuring 39°? Give your answer to the nearest whole number.

27. What is the area of the triangle below, to the nearest square inch?

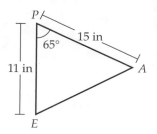

28. A triangle has side length $a = 6$ and angles $A = 16°$ and $B = 64°$. What is the length of side b? Express your answer to the nearest tenth.

---

29. **MP 3, 6** Use the law of cosines to prove the Pythagorean obtuse inequality theorem. Hint: What are the values of cos C if $m\angle C$ is between 0° and 90°? between 90° and 180°?

Pythagorean obtuse inequality theorem

If the square of the triangle's longest side is greater than the sum of the squares of the other two sides, then the triangle is obtuse.

If $c^2 > a^2 + b^2$, then $\triangle ABC$ is obtuse.

Chapter Content

Chapter Vocabulary

adjacent arc

arc

arc length

central angle

chord

circumscribed angle

circumscribed circle

common tangent

cyclic quadrilateral

inscribed angle

inscribed polygon

intercepted arc

major arc

minor arc

radians

secant

sector of a circle

semicircle

tangent

LESSON 8.1

8.1 Circles, Tangents, and Secants

Circles, Circumferences, and Areas

A circle is a figure in a plane that consists of all the points equidistant from a fixed point in the same plane, known as the *circle's center*.

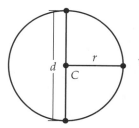

> You can assume in this chapter that a point C in a circle is at the circle's center.

The distance from the center to the points on the circumference of the circle is the *radius of the circle*. The center of a circle and its radius are labeled on the circle. Each point on the circle is the same distance, r, from the center. A diameter, d, is a segment that passes through a circle's center and has its endpoints on the circle. A diameter is twice the length of the radius.

We know from our previous studies of mathematics that the formula for the circumference of a circle is πd or $2\pi r$. To measure the value of pi, we can use a circular object, like a tire, and measure its radius. Then the distance of one revolution is noted, and the distance is divided by twice the radius.

$r = 35$ cm

220 cm

Measure radius	35 centimeters
Measure distance of one revolution	220 centimeters
Divide	$\pi = \dfrac{C}{2r}$
	$\pi = \dfrac{220 \text{ cm}}{2(35 \text{ cm})} \approx 3.14$

π was first calculated by the famous Greek mathematician Archimedes. Archimedes performed the calculation in the third century BCE. He calculated a minimum value for π by finding the area of an inscribed hexagon, which is made up of six congruent triangles.

As he increased the number of triangles, he got closer and closer to the value of π. The value π is a limit in his method—a number that is approached but never quite reached. With a large number of triangles—thousands or millions—the value calculated for π would be very close.

We show an example of his calculations below:

Draw a regular hexagon inside the circle to create equilateral triangles

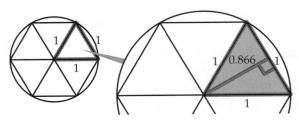

Find the height of the triangle

$$c = 1 \text{ and } b = \frac{1}{2}$$

$$a^2 = c^2 - b^2$$

$$a^2 = 1^2 - \left(\frac{1}{2}\right)^2$$

$$a = \sqrt{\frac{3}{4}} \approx 0.866$$

Area of triangle

$$A = \frac{1}{2}bh = \frac{1}{2}(1)(0.866) = 0.433$$

Multiply by number of polygons

$$A = 6 \cdot 0.433 = 2.58$$

Use formula for area of circle

$$\pi = \frac{A}{r^2}$$

$$\pi = \frac{2.58}{1^2} = 2.58$$

Approximations for the value of π have been known for about 4,000 years. While ancient societies, such as the Babylonians and Egyptians, used various methods for determining π, Archimedes is credited with one of the first formal approximations. He calculated a minimum value for π as shown above. He established a maximum value for π by setting a circle inside a polygon. To the right, we show a 24-sided polygon, which can be set in a circle to show π is approximately 3.11. Archimedes used a 96-sided polygon for his estimation.

One element of computing the circumference and area of a circle is having a value for π. Assuming we have a value for π, how does the area of a circle approximately relate to its circumference?

We dissect the circle into 8 slices to answer this question, but keep in mind that the more slices we use, the more rectangular and exact the rectangle will be. The base of the rectangle is approximately half the circumference of the circle.

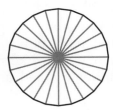

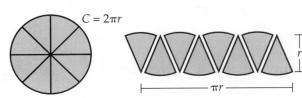

Calculate area of rectangle

$$\text{height} \approx r$$
$$A = hw$$
$$A \approx r(\pi r) = \pi r^2$$

Circles, Segments, and Lines

A **chord** is a line segment with its endpoints on the circle. A chord that passes through the center is a diameter.

A **secant** is a line that intersects a circle at two points. A **tangent** is a line that intersects a circle at only one point and is contained in the same plane as the circle it intersects.

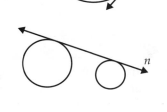

> Every secant contains a chord, and every chord is part of a secant.

A tangent shared by two circles is called a **common tangent.** The lines *m* and *n* are common tangents.

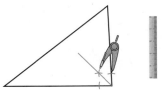

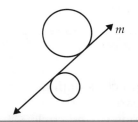

MODEL PROBLEM

MP 6 Determine whether the lines $\overleftrightarrow{XY}$ and $\overleftrightarrow{ZK}$ are chords, secants, or tangents.

SOLUTION

$\overleftrightarrow{XY}$ The line intersects the circle twice. This makes it a secant.

$\overleftrightarrow{ZK}$ This line intersects a circle at one point and lies in its plane. This makes it a tangent.

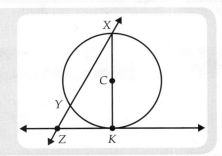

Construction: Inscribed and Circumscribed Circles

We can inscribe a circle within a triangle using a compass and a straightedge.

Inscribing a circle within a triangle:

1. Bisect an angle.

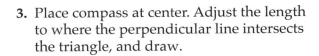

> We showed how to construct an angle bisector in chapter 6.

2. Bisect another angle. The bisectors intersect at the circle's center. Construct a perpendicular line from the center to the triangle's side.

3. Place compass at center. Adjust the length to where the perpendicular line intersects the triangle, and draw.

Circumscribing a triangle with a circle:

1. Construct a perpendicular bisector.

3. Place compass at center. Adjust the length to any vertex, and draw the circle.

2. Construct another perpendicular bisector. They intersect at the circle's center.

Paragraph Proof

In the second construction (circumscribing a triangle with a circle), the perpendicular bisectors define a circumcenter, which is equidistant from the triangle's vertices, as we learned earlier in the book. The vertices are equidistant from the center and lie on the constructed circle.

We state a theorem about tangents:

Tangent to a circle theorem

A line is tangent to a circle if and only if that line is perpendicular to the radius drawn at the point of tangency.

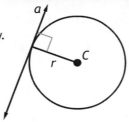

a is tangent to circle C in the same plane if and only if $a \perp r$.

We use the theorem to show that the result of our first construction is that the triangle's sides are tangents to the circle. The point where the angle bisectors meet is an incenter and is the center of the circle we drew. Refer to the diagram in the following proof.

Paragraph Proof

The additional segments we drew, such as segment DC, are all of equal length, as we learned earlier in the book, and are therefore radii of the circle that are perpendicular to triangle sides. The theorem then tells us that the sides are tangents to the circle.

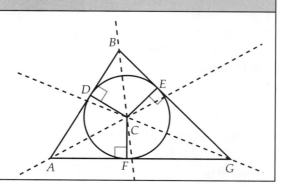

We construct a tangent line to a circle in the traditional manner, using a compass and straightedge.

How to construct a tangent line to a circle through a given point:

1. Start with circle C and point B on the circle. Use a straightedge to construct ray CB. The tangent line will intersect circle at B.

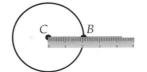

2. Create two arcs on the ray, centering the compass at point B. Label the points D and E.

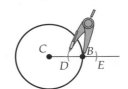

3. Create two more arcs using the new points. Center compass on D, and then on E.

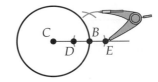

4. Draw tangent line. Use the straightedge to construct a line through the intersection of the new arcs and B. This line is the tangent line to circle C through B.

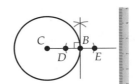

Paragraph Proof

Confirming the construction above is short work. The segment is a radius, and we constructed a perpendicular bisector of segment DE. As the theorem above states, lines perpendicular to radii at the points of intersection are tangents.

We also show how to construct two tangent lines from a given point <u>not</u> on the circle.

How to construct tangent lines through a point <u>not</u> on the circle:

1. Draw segment from circle's center to the given point.

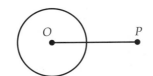

2. Construct perpendicular bisector.

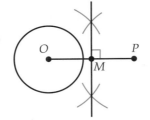

3. From the midpoint, M, set the compass width to the circle center. With the compass point on M, make two arcs on the circle. Label intersections A and B.

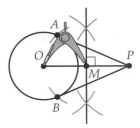

4. Draw tangent lines $\overline{AP}$ and $\overline{BP}$.

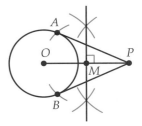

We prove the construction.

Statement	Reason	
$OM = MP = AM$	Perpendicular bisector theorem	As with an earlier construction, we created a perpendicular bisector, so $OM = MP$. $AM = OM$ since they were drawn with compass set to the same length.
$\triangle AOM$ is an isosceles triangle	Definition of isosceles triangle	Since $AM = OM$ as shown in step 1.
$\triangle AMP$ is an isosceles triangle	Definition of isosceles triangle	Since $AM = MP$ as shown in step 1.
$m\angle AMO = 180° - 2(m\angle OAM)$	Triangle sum theorem	Triangle angles sum to 180°, and base angles of an isosceles triangle are congruent.
$m\angle AMP = 180° - 2(m\angle MAP)$	Triangle sum theorem	Triangle angles sum to 180°, and base angles of an isosceles triangle are congruent.
$m\angle AMO + m\angle AMP = 180°$	Definition of a straight angle	Linear pairs sum to 180°.
$180° - 2(m\angle OAM) + 180° - 2(m\angle MAP) = 180°$	Substitute	Substitute expressions $m\angle AMO$ and $m\angle AMP$.
$m\angle OAM + m\angle MAP = 90°$	Simplify	Simplify the expression.
$\angle OAP$ is a right angle	Angle addition postulate	Angles form a right angle.
$\overline{AP}$ is tangent	Tangent to a circle theorem	$\overline{AP}$ is perpendicular to a radius and intersects the circle at only one point. We could use similar reasoning for $\overline{BP}$.

MODEL PROBLEMS

1. $\overline{AB}$ is tangent to circle C. What is its length?

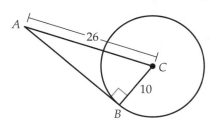

SOLUTION

$\triangle ABC$ is a right triangle   Tangent to a circle theorem

Use Pythagorean theorem to calculate AB

$$a^2 + b^2 = c^2$$
$$(AB)^2 + (BC)^2 = (AC)^2$$
$$(AB)^2 + (10)^2 = (26)^2$$
$$(AB)^2 = 576$$
$$AB = 24$$

Model Problems continue . . .

2. What is the radius of the circle? $\overline{AB}$ is tangent to the circle.

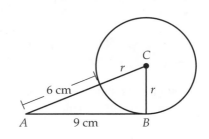

SOLUTION

Use Pythagorean theorem	$AB^2 + BC^2 = AC^2$
Substitute	$AC = 6 + r$
	$9^2 + r^2 = (6 + r)^2$
Simplify	$81 + r^2 = 36 + 12r + r^2$
	$45 = 12r$
Solve	$r = 3.75$ cm

> Triangle *ABC* is a right triangle according to the tangent to a circle theorem.

3. What is $m\angle D$? $\overline{AD}$ and $\overline{UD}$ are tangents to the circle.

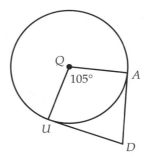

SOLUTION

Tangents form right angles	$m\angle U = m\angle A = 90°$
Quadrilateral *QUDA*	$m\angle Q + m\angle U + m\angle D + m\angle A = 360°$
Substitute and solve	$105° + 90° + 90° + m\angle D = 360°$
	$285° + m\angle D = 360°$
	$m\angle D = 75°$

4. **MP 2, 4, 5** What is the approximate distance to the horizon from the summit of Mount Everest? Earth's radius is about 6,400 kilometers, and Everest is approximately 8,000 meters high.

SOLUTION

Draw diagram

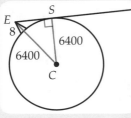

Create a construction of the view to the horizon as a tangent from the summit of Everest to Earth's surface. This means $\angle ESC$ is a right angle. We approximate Everest's height as 8 kilometers (or 8,000 meters) above Earth's surface.

Use Pythagorean theorem
$$EC^2 = ES^2 + SC^2$$
$$ES^2 = EC^2 - SC^2$$

Since the tangent forms a right angle with the radius, we have a right triangle and can use the Pythagorean theorem. Solve for the unknown.

Substitute
$$ES^2 = (6{,}400 + 8)^2 - 6{,}400^2$$
Substitute the values given to us.

Evaluate
$$ES^2 = 6{,}408^2 - 6{,}400^2$$
$$ES \approx 320 \text{ km}$$
Evaluate. The distance to the horizon atop Everest is about 320 kilometers.

Tangents with a Common Endpoint

The theorem below describes the relationship of tangents that share an endpoint:

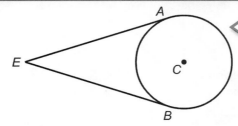

In the theorem diagram, ∠AEB is a **circumscribed angle**, an angle formed by two tangents drawn from one common endpoint.

Tangent endpoint theorem

If two tangent segments share a common endpoint, then they are congruent.

If $\overline{AE}$ and $\overline{BE}$ are both tangent to the circle, then $\overline{AE} \cong \overline{BE}$.

MODEL PROBLEM

What is the length of either of the tangents?

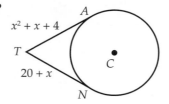

SOLUTION

Tangents with shared endpoint are congruent	$TA = TN$
Set expressions equal to one another	$x^2 + x + 4 = 20 + x$
Simplify and solve	$x^2 + 4 = 20$
	$x^2 = 16$
	$x = 4$
Calculate length of tangent	$TN = 20 + x$
	$TN = 20 + 4$
	$TN = TA = 24$

PRACTICE

Exercises 1–3: Provide the correct name for the line or segment shown in the diagram below.

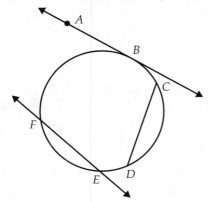

1. $\overleftrightarrow{AB}$ is a

   A. Chord.

   B. Tangent.

   C. Secant.

2. $\overline{CD}$ is a

   A. Chord.

   B. Tangent.

   C. Secant.

3. $\overrightarrow{EF}$ is a

   A. Chord.

   B. Tangent.

   C. Secant.

Practice Problems continue . . .

4. What is the radius of the circle shown in the diagram? The segment of length 45 is tangent to the circle.

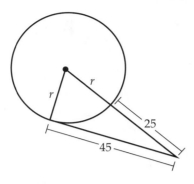

A. 24 C. 28
B. 26 D. 30

5. If $\overline{AB}$ is tangent to the circle, what is the length of $\overline{AC}$?

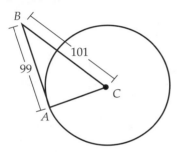

A. 16 C. 20
B. 18 D. 22

6. A line intersects a circle at exactly one point and is in the circle's plane. It is a

A. Secant.
B. Chord.
C. Tangent.

7. The sides of a triangle with a circle inscribed within it are

A. Tangents. C. Secants.
B. Chords. D. Radii.

8. Define the following: secant, chord, and tangent.

9. Is it possible for a secant to be in a different plane than a circle it intersects? Explain.

10. A secant intersects a circle once. Is this statement true or false? Explain.

11. A tangent of a circle is perpendicular to the radius of the circle. Is this statement true or false? Explain.

12. Consider a circle with center O, radii $\overline{OT}$ and $\overline{OA}$, and tangents $\overline{TD}$ and $\overline{AD}$. If $m\angle O = 122°$, then what is $m\angle D$?

13. $\overline{AB}$ is tangent to the circle below. What is the circle's radius? C is the circle's center.

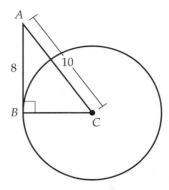

14. $\overline{RS}$ is tangent to the circle. What is the radius of the circle, with center T?

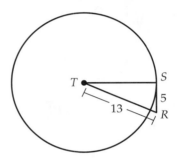

15. $\overline{AB}$ is tangent to the circle below with center C. What is the circle's radius?

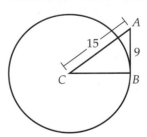

16. Two segments are tangent to the same circle and share an endpoint, T. $TA = 5x + 3$ and $TN = 6x - 6$. What is the length of $\overline{TA}$?

17. A line is perpendicular to the radius of a circle and in the same plane. This means the line is tangent to the circle. Is this statement true or false? Explain.

18. Provide a description of the step-by-step process used to construct a circle that circumscribes a triangle.

Practice Problems continue . . .

Practice Problems continued . . .

19. In the diagram below, is $\overline{XY}$ tangent to the circle? Explain.

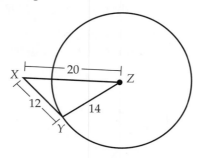

20. In the diagram below, is $\overline{AB}$ tangent to the circle? Explain.

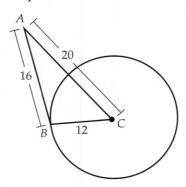

21. In the diagram below, is $\overline{RS}$ tangent to the circle? Explain.

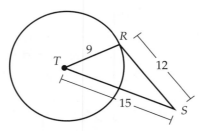

22. In the diagram below, is $\overline{AB}$ tangent to the circle? Explain.

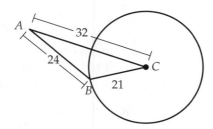

23. $\overline{AB}$ and $\overline{BD}$ are tangent to the circle below. In the diagram, what is the value of x?

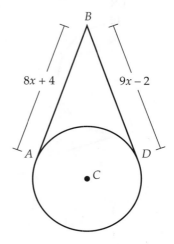

24. In the diagram below, $\overline{AB}$ and $\overline{BD}$ are tangent to the circle. What is the value of x?

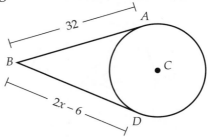

25. **MP 4, 6** Mars has a radius at the equator of about 3400 km. Its tallest mountain is Olympus Mons, with an estimated height of 21 km. What is the approximate distance to the horizon from the summit of Olympus Mons? Round your answer to the nearest kilometer.

26. **MP 2, 4** An architect creates a circular sunroof with a radius of 12 inches. He places one board that starts at the sunroof's center and ends 16 inches from the sunroof's center. Another board, tangent to the circle, extends from the sunroof's edge to the end of the first board. What is the length of the second board, to the nearest tenth of an inch?

27. The highest point on the San Francisco Peaks is 3.851 km above Earth's surface. Earth's radius is approximately 6,400 km. What is the approximate distance from the summit of the highest point on the San Francisco Peaks to the horizon? Round to the nearest kilometer.

Practice Problems continue . . .

28. Pikes Peak Mountain in Colorado is 4.302 km above Earth's surface. Earth's radius is approximately 6,400 km. What is the approximate distance from the summit of Pikes Peak to the horizon? Round to the nearest kilometer.

29. Draw a circle and illustrate a chord, a secant, and a tangent.

30. Compare a secant and a chord. How are they different? How are they similar?

31. Draw 3 circles that share a common tangent.

---

32. **MP 3, 7** Prove the tangent endpoint theorem. Hint: Construct auxiliary segments $\overline{AC}$, $\overline{BC}$, and $\overline{EC}$.

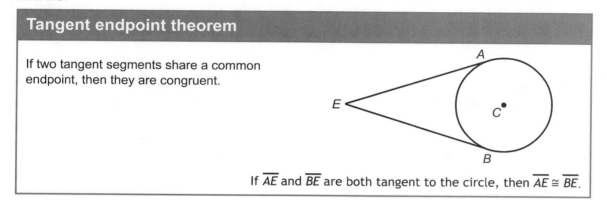

Tangent endpoint theorem

If two tangent segments share a common endpoint, then they are congruent.

If $\overline{AE}$ and $\overline{BE}$ are both tangent to the circle, then $\overline{AE} \cong \overline{BE}$.

LESSON 8.2

8.2 Chords and Arcs

Arc Measure

A **central angle** is an angle with its vertex at the circle's center. An **arc** is part of a circle's circumference and is defined by a central angle in that the sides of a central angle intercept the arc. The degree measure of a central angle is the same as the degree measure of the arc it intercepts. If the angle is less than 180°, the enclosed arc is called a **minor arc**, and the other part of the circle is a **major arc**.

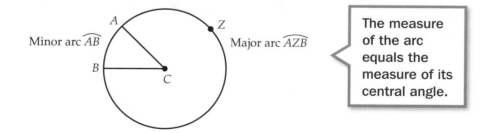

Minor arc $\overset{\frown}{AB}$

Major arc $\overset{\frown}{AZB}$

> The measure of the arc equals the measure of its central angle.

If the angle is 180°, then its arc is a **semicircle**, or one-half the circle. The chord for this angle is a diameter, as we show in the diagram to the right.

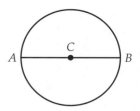

Two circles are congruent if their radii have the same length. Two arcs of the same circle are congruent if they have the same measure.

Arc addition postulate

The measure of an arc formed by two adjacent arcs in a circle is the sum of the measures of each arc.

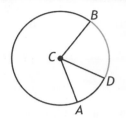

> The postulate states that the measures of two **adjacent arcs** can be added.

If $\overarc{AD}$ and $\overarc{DB}$ are adjacent, then $m\,\overarc{AD} + m\,\overarc{DB} = m\,\overarc{AB}$.

Properties of Chords

We state some theorems about chords:

Congruent minor arcs theorem

In the same or congruent circles, two minor arcs are congruent if and only if their chords are congruent.

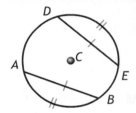

$\overarc{AB} \cong \overarc{DE}$ if and only if $\overline{AB} \cong \overline{DE}$.

Perpendicular chords theorem

If a radius is perpendicular to a chord, then it bisects the chord.

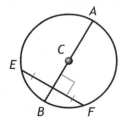

If $\overline{AB}$ is a $\perp$ bisector of $\overline{EF}$, then $\overline{AB}$ is a diameter.

Perpendicular chords theorem converse

A radius that bisects a chord is perpendicular to the chord.

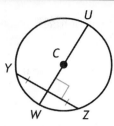

If $\overline{UW}$ is a diameter and $\overline{UW} \perp \overline{YZ}$, then it bisects $\overline{YZ}$.

We prove the perpendicular chords theorem converse:

Prove: $\overline{YD} \cong \overline{DZ}$
Given: $\overline{UW}$ is a diameter; $\overline{UW} \perp \overline{YZ}$

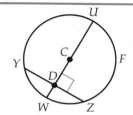

Paragraph Proof

Construct auxiliary line segments $\overline{CY}$ and $\overline{CZ}$ to form an isosceles triangle CYZ that is split by an altitude. Since $\overline{UW} \perp \overline{YZ}$, we have created two right triangles, CDY and CDZ. Thus $m\angle CDY = m\angle CDZ = 90°$, and since an isosceles triangle has equal base angles, $\angle DYC \cong \angle DZC$. The segments $\overline{CY}$ and $\overline{CZ}$ are both radii of the circle C, so $\overline{CY} \cong \overline{CZ}$. By angle-angle-side, $\triangle CDY \cong \triangle CDZ$ and $\overline{YD} \cong \overline{DZ}$.

Congruent chords theorem

Two chords are congruent if and only if they are the same distance from the circle's center.

> Two chords would also be congruent if they are the same distance from the centers of two congruent circles.

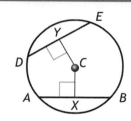

$\overline{AB} \cong \overline{DE}$ if and only if $CX = CY$.

MODEL PROBLEMS

1. If $m\widehat{MN} = 65°$, what is $m\widehat{XY}$?

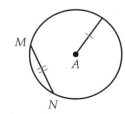 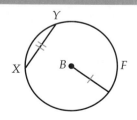

SOLUTION

Circles are congruent   Same radii

$\overline{MN} \cong \overline{XY}$ $m\widehat{MN} = m\widehat{XY} = 65°$; this is true by the congruent minor arcs theorem

Model Problems continue . . .

2. **MP 4, 5** Cell phone towers can be used to locate the position of cell phones. Find the location that is the same distance from the three towers shown in the diagram.

SOLUTION

Start by drawing a diagram, labeling the three cell towers. Connect the tower locations with line segments, which are three chords in a circle. Points *A*, *B*, and *D* are on the circle (see right). Now draw the bisectors of *AB* and *BD*. Since these lines are perpendicular to the chords, they are radii, which meet in the center of the circle. Thus the intersection of these two lines is the center of the circle and of equal distance from all three towers.

3. What is *CF*? *AB* and *DE* are both 24.5 cm.

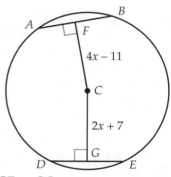

SOLUTION

The two distances are equal since the chord lengths are the same	$CF = CG$
	$4x - 11 = 2x + 7$
Calculate *x*	$2x = 18$
	$x = 9$
Substitute, evaluate	$CF = 4x - 11$
	$CF = 4(9) - 11$
	$CF = 25$

PRACTICE

1. The measure of a central angle of a circle is 124°. What is the measure of the major arc of the circle?

A. 124° C. 236°
B. 186° D. 248°

2. What is $m\angle ABC$, given that it is a central angle?

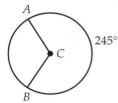

A. 245° C. 115°
B. 122.5° D. 163°

Practice Problems continue . . .

3. What is $m\widehat{AD}$?

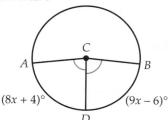

(8x + 4)°   (9x − 6)°

A. 78°   C. 88°
B. 84°   D. 96°

4. $\overline{AD}$ is a diameter.

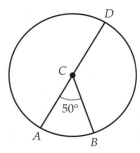

50°

a What is $m\widehat{BD}$?
b What is $m\widehat{ABD}$?

5. $\overline{AB}$ is a diameter that intersects the chord $\overline{DF}$ at a right angle at the point *E*. If *DE* = 4, what does *EF* equal?

6. A circle is composed of 3 arcs, and the measures of two of them are 29° and 212°. What is the measure of the circle's third arc?

7. A circle is composed of 3 arcs, and the measures of two of them are 81° and 171°. What is the measure of the circle's third arc?

8. What is $m\widehat{YW}$?

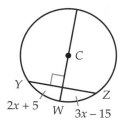

2x + 5   W   3x − 15

9. What is $m\widehat{AB}$?

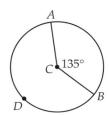

135°

10. If $m\widehat{AB}$ is 38° and $m\widehat{BD}$ is 105°, what is $m\widehat{AD}$?

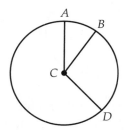

11. What is $m\widehat{AB}$?

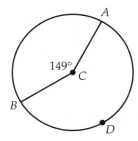

149°

12. What is $m\widehat{AZB}$?

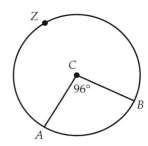

96°

13. What is $m\widehat{AZB}$?

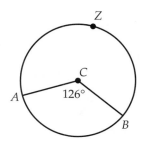

126°

14. The measure of a central angle of a circle is 89°. What is the measure of the major arc of the circle?

15. The measure of a minor arc of a circle is 148°. What is the measure of the smaller central angle of the circle?

16. The measure of a major arc of a circle is 220°. What is the measure of the smaller central angle of the circle?

Practice Problems continue . . .

17. What is $m\widehat{ADB}$?

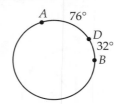

18. Given that $\overline{AD}$ is a diameter of the circle below, answer the following questions.

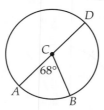

  a What is $m\widehat{BD}$?

  b What is $m\widehat{ADB}$?

19. **MP 2, 7** In the circle below, $m\widehat{AD} = m\widehat{BD}$.

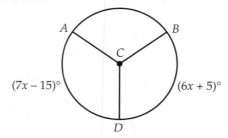

  a What is $m\widehat{AD}$?

  b What is $m\widehat{AB}$?

  c What is $m\widehat{ADB}$?

20. In the circle below, $\widehat{XZ} \cong \widehat{YZ}$. If $\overline{XZ}$ is 8 inches long, how long is $\overline{YZ}$?

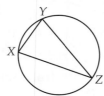

21. If C is the center of the circle below and $XY = 25$ cm, what is YZ?

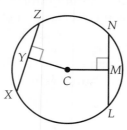

22. $\overline{AD}$ and $\overline{EF}$ are perpendicular in the circle below. The radius of the circle is 18 cm. $BE = 9$ cm and $BF = 9$ cm. What is the length of $\overline{AD}$?

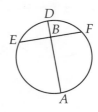

23. Given the two congruent circles below, what is $m\widehat{AB}$?

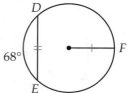

24. Given the circle below, what does EF equal? What is $m\widehat{AF}$?

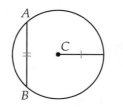

25. C is the center of the circle. $\overline{XZ} \cong \overline{LN}$. If $CY = 10x - 7$ and $CM = 3x + 42$, what is x?

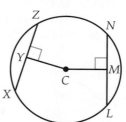

26. What is the length of $\overline{CY}$? What is the length of $\overline{CX}$?

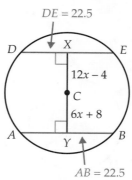

Practice Problems continue . . .

27. An artist includes a circular disk in one of his paintings. In order to add to the aesthetic beauty of the painting, he draws a central angle with a measure of 145° within the disk. What is the measure of the minor arc of the disk?

28. A bulls-eye of a target has a section colored red. The red section is formed by a central angle of 85° and its enclosed arc. What is the measure of the major arc of the bulls-eye?

29. **MP 1, 4** An architect wishes to include two boards inside a circular window. The first board will serve as a diameter of the circle and will intersect the other board (or chord) at a right angle. If one portion of the intersected board measures 14 inches, what is the length of the other portion of the intersected board?

30. Define and sketch the following: central angle, minor arc, and major arc.

31. Define congruent circles.

32. Draw and label an original circle that illustrates the perpendicular chords theorem.

33. Determine whether $\overline{AB}$ is a diameter of the circle or not. Explain.

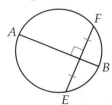

34. Given a circle with a center at $(0, 0)$, a radius r, and the point (x, y) located on the circle, prove $x^2 + y^2 = r^2$. Hint: Use the distance formula.

35. **MP 2, 3** Prove the congruent minor arcs theorem. Remember, since it is an "if and only if" theorem, there are two if/then statements to prove.

Congruent minor arcs theorem

In the same or congruent circles, two minor arcs are congruent if and only if their chords are congruent.

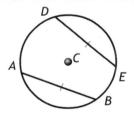

$\overset{\frown}{AB} \cong \overset{\frown}{DE}$ if and only if $\overline{AB} \cong \overline{DE}$.

36. **MP 3, 6** Prove the congruent chords theorem. Remember, since it is an "if and only if" theorem, there are two if/then statements to prove. Hint: Construct auxiliary segments $\overline{CA}$, $\overline{CD}$, $\overline{CB}$, and $\overline{CE}$.

Congruent chords theorem

Two chords are congruent if and only if they are the same distance from the circle's center.

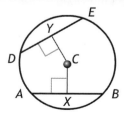

$\overline{AB} \cong \overline{DE}$ if and only if $CX = CY$.

37. **MP 3** Prove the perpendicular chords theorem. Hint: Let D be the intersection point of $\overline{AB}$ and $\overline{EF}$, and use an indirect proof.

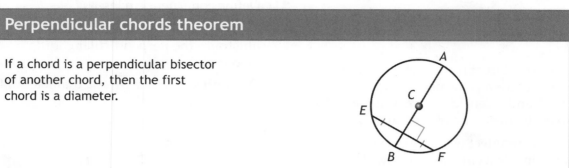

Perpendicular chords theorem

If a chord is a perpendicular bisector of another chord, then the first chord is a diameter.

If $\overline{AB}$ is a $\perp$ bisector of $\overline{EF}$, then $\overline{AB}$ is a diameter.

LESSON 8.3

8.3 Inscribed Figures

An **inscribed angle** is one with its vertex on a circle and with sides that contain chords of the circle. As the angle intersects (intercepts) the circle, it forms an **intercepted arc** between the rays. The intercepted arc is the arc between the chords.

We summarize the different types of angles related to circles we have discussed so far and then state two theorems:

Circumscribed angle   Central angle   Inscribed angle

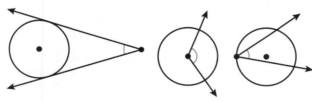

Inscribed angle case 1

In a circle, the measure of an inscribed angle is half the measure of the central angle with the same intercepted arc.

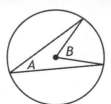

$$m\angle A = \frac{1}{2}m\angle B$$

Inscribed angle case 2

In a circle, two inscribed angles with the same intercepted arc are congruent.

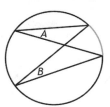

$m\angle A = m\angle B$

MODEL PROBLEMS

1. Identify the congruent angles.

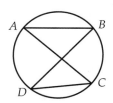

SOLUTION

Angles that intercept same arc are congruent

$\angle A \cong \angle D$
$\angle B \cong \angle C$

These angles intercept the same arc, so they are congruent.

2. If $m\angle ADE = 34°$, what is $m\angle ABE$?

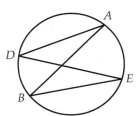

SOLUTION

The two inscribed angles intercept the same arc and are congruent. The angles are both 34°.

3. $\angle A$ is the inscribed angle for $\overset{\frown}{UQD}$. Calculate the angles.

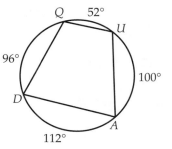

SOLUTION

Calculate $m\angle A$

$$m\angle A = \frac{1}{2}m\overset{\frown}{UQD}$$

$$m\angle A = \frac{1}{2}(96° + 52°) = 74°$$

Repeat the process for $m\angle D$, $m\angle Q$, and $m\angle U$

$$m\angle D = \frac{1}{2}m\overset{\frown}{AUQ}$$

$$m\angle D = \frac{1}{2}(52° + 100°) = 76°$$

$$m\angle Q = \frac{1}{2}m\overset{\frown}{DAU} = \frac{1}{2}(100° + 112°) = 106°$$

$$m\angle U = \frac{1}{2}(96° + 112°) = 104°$$

> One way to check the answer is to make sure that the four angle measures sum to 360°.

Model Problems continue . . .

4. What is $m\widehat{AB}$?

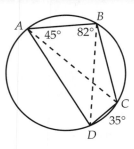

SOLUTION

Calculate other arcs
$$m\widehat{BC} = 2(m\angle BAC) = 90°$$
$$m\widehat{DA} = 2\,(m\angle ABD) = 164°$$

360° in a circle
$$m\widehat{AB} + m\widehat{BC} + m\widehat{CD} + m\widehat{DA} = 360°$$
$$m\widehat{AB} + 90° + 35° + 164° = 360°$$

Solve for $m\widehat{AB}$
$$m\widehat{AB} = 360° - 289°$$
$$m\widehat{AB} = 71°$$

5. What are $m\widehat{IC}$ and $m\angle CSI$?

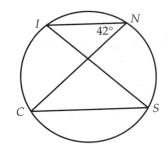

SOLUTION

Arc equals twice inscribed angle
$$m\widehat{IC} = 2 \cdot m\angle INC$$
$$m\widehat{IC} = 2 \cdot 42° = 84°$$

An inscribed angle is one-half its arc. This means the arc is twice the angle.

Inscribed angle equals half the arc
$$m\angle CSI = \frac{1}{2}m\widehat{IC}$$
$$m\angle CSI = \frac{1}{2}(84°) = 42°$$

An inscribed angle is one-half its arc. Substitute and multiply by $\frac{1}{2}$.

Construction: Regular Hexagon in a Circle

We construct a hexagon inscribed in a circle. The construction relies on the fact that the length of the side of a hexagon equals the distance from the circle's center to a vertex, which is the circle's radius.

Constructing a regular hexagon inscribed in a circle:

1. Draw a circle and place the compass on any point on the circle. Set the compass width to the circle radius.

2. Make an arc. The compass passes through the circle.

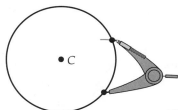

3. Repeat, moving to a new vertex. Create six vertices.

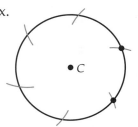

You may wonder how we know we will reach the initial point in step 3, rather than continuing around the circle forever with our compass. This happens in regular hexagons, because they can be split into 6 equilateral triangles where the radius of the circumscribed circle is the same length as each side of the regular hexagon. This is why we can use the radius as a side length in this construction.

4. Connect adjacent points with lines.

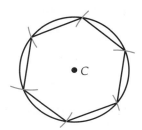

Inscribed Polygons and Cyclic Quadrilaterals

A circle that passes through all the vertices of a polygon is a **circumscribed circle**. An **inscribed polygon** is a polygon with all its vertices on a circle.

A quadrilateral with each vertex on a circle is known as a **cyclic quadrilateral**. Such quadrilaterals have various properties: for example, the cyclic quadrilateral has the maximum area of any quadrilateral with the same side lengths.

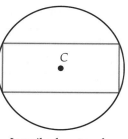

Inscribed rectangle

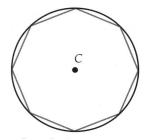

Inscribed octagon

We state a theorem about cyclic quadrilaterals.

Inscribed quadrilateral theorem

A quadrilateral can be inscribed in a circle if and only if its opposite angles are supplementary.

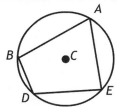

ABDE can be inscribed in circle C if and only if $m\angle A + m\angle D = 180°$ and $m\angle B + m\angle E = 180°$.

Since this theorem is a biconditional statement, there are two conditional statements, and we must prove them both in order to prove the entire theorem.

We begin by proving the conditional, "If a quadrilateral can be inscribed in a circle, then its opposite angles are supplementary."

Prove: $m\angle A + m\angle C = 180°$

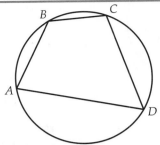

To complete the proof of the theorem, we would need to prove the other conditional, "If the opposite angles of a quadrilateral are supplementary, then it can be inscribed in a circle." However, we leave this to you in Practice Problem 34.

Statement	Reason	
$m\angle A = \dfrac{1}{2} m\widehat{BCD}$ and $m\angle C = \dfrac{1}{2} m\widehat{DAB}$	Inscribed angle case 1	Each of these angles is one-half the measure of its intercepted arc.
$2m\angle A = m\widehat{BCD}$ and $2m\angle C = m\widehat{DAB}$	Multiplication property of equality	Multiply both sides of each equation by 2 to get rid of the fraction.
$m\widehat{BCD} + m\widehat{DAB} = 360°$	Properties of a circle	A circle's interior angle measure is 360°, which means that its arc measures also sum to 360°.
$2m\angle A + 2m\angle C = 360°$	Substitution	Substitute the equivalent angle measures for the arc measures.
$2(m\angle A + m\angle C) = 360°$	Distributive property	Use the distributive property to separate the multiplication.
$m\angle A + m\angle C = 180°$	Multiplication property of equality	Divide both sides of the equation by 2 to simplify, and see that the opposite angles are supplementary.

MODEL PROBLEMS

1. What are $m\angle W$ and $m\angle Y$?

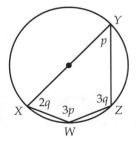

SOLUTION

Opposite angles are supplementary

$m\angle W + m\angle Y = 180°$
$3p + p = 180°$
$4p = 180°$
$p = 45°$

The opposite angles of an inscribed quadrilateral are supplementary. They sum to 180°.

Substitute

$m\angle W = 3p = 135°$
$m\angle Y = p = 45°$

Substitute and solve.

Model Problems continue . . .

2. What is $m\angle AED$?

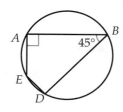

SOLUTION

Supplementary angles	$m\angle ABD + m\angle AED = 180°$	Opposite angles are supplementary.
Solve for $m\angle AED$	$45° + m\angle AED = 180°$ $m\angle AED = 135°$	Substitute, and solve for the angle.

3. What is $m\angle EDA$?

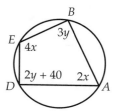

SOLUTION

Opposite angles are supplementary	$m\angle ABE + m\angle EDA = 180°$ $3y + 2y + 40° = 180°$	Opposite angles are supplementary. Substitute the values.
Combine like terms	$5y = 140°$	Combine like terms.
Solve for y	$y = 28°$	Divide both sides by 5.
Substitute value of y into expression for $m\angle EDA$	$m\angle EDA = 2y + 40°$ $m\angle EDA = 2 \cdot 28° + 40° = 96°$	Substitute the value you computed for y into the expression for the angle.

Cyclic Quadrilaterals and Their Diagonals

Cyclic quadrilaterals also have a special property related to angles formed by their diagonals and sides:

Cyclic quadrilateral inscribed angle theorem

The inscribed angle formed by one diagonal and side of a cyclic quadrilateral is congruent to the inscribed angle formed by the other diagonal and opposite side.

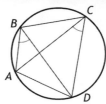

In cyclic quadrilateral $ABCD$, $m\angle ABD \cong m\angle ACD$.

We prove the theorem, which follows from the inscribed angle case 2

Prove: $\angle ABD \cong \angle ACD$

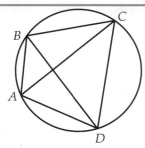

Statement	Reason	
$\angle ABD$ intercepts $\overset{\frown}{AD}$	Diagram	The diagram shows that $\angle ABD$ intercepts the arc.
$\angle ACD$ intercepts $\overset{\frown}{AD}$	Diagram	The diagram also shows that $\angle ACD$ intercepts the same arc.
$\angle ABD \cong \angle ACD$	Inscribed angle case 2	Because both angles intercept the same arc, they are congruent by the inscribed angle case 2.

MODEL PROBLEM

What is $m\angle BAC$?

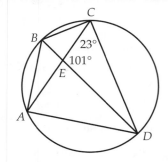

SOLUTION

Find $m\angle BDC$ $m\angle BDC = 56°$ The interior angles of a triangle sum to 180°. Since $m\angle DEC = 101°$ and $m\angle ACD = 23°$, then $m\angle BDC = 56°$.

Calculate $m\angle BAC$ $m\angle BAC = 56°$ By the cyclic quadrilateral inscribed angle theorem, $\angle BDC \cong \angle BAC$, so their measures are equal.

Inscribed Right Triangles

Since we can inscribe angles into a circle, we can also inscribe triangles. There are special theorems that relate to inscribed right triangles, one of which we state below.

Inscribed right triangle theorem

A side of an inscribed triangle is a diameter, if and only if the triangle is a right triangle with its right angle opposite the diameter.

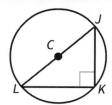

$\overline{JL}$ is a diameter if and only if $\triangle JKL$ is a right $\triangle$ with its right angle opposite $\overline{JL}$.

1. What is the length of $\overline{YZ}$? The circumference of circle C is 8π.

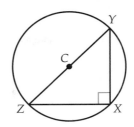

SOLUTION

$\overline{YZ}$ is a diameter	X is right angle	The diagram shows that X is a right angle. This means by the theorem in this lesson that $\overline{YZ}$ is a diameter.
Solve circumference formula for diameter	$C = \pi d$ $d = \dfrac{C}{\pi}$	Use the formula for the circumference of a circle and solve for the diameter.
Substitute	$YZ = \dfrac{8\pi}{\pi}$ $YZ = 8$	Substitute the circumference of the circle, and take advantage of the fact that $\overline{YZ}$ is a diameter.

2. **MP 2, 4, 5** A director wants to film the entire door. Her movie camera has a 90° field of vision. Where else can it be moved so that it films the door and films the same field of vision?

> The field of vision is all the points that can be filmed by the camera. We assume the camera stays on the same side of the door. We use the theorem that describes the relationship of circles and inscribed right triangles.

SOLUTION

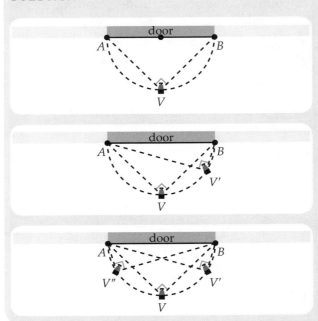

Draw the video camera in front of the middle of the door. $\triangle ABV$ is a right triangle. The camera is at a distance such that it shows the front of the door but no more. Draw a circle with the vertex of the right triangle on the circle.

A theorem says that the hypotenuse of an inscribed right triangle is a diameter. So we can shift the camera to this second location on the circle and it will still cover the entire door with a 90° field of vision.

Since we have a right triangle with the door as its hypotenuse, any point on the circle will allow for a 90° field of vision of the entire door.

PRACTICE

Exercises 1–4: Find the measure of the arc or angle.

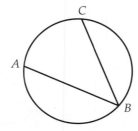

1. If $m\angle ABC = 44°$, what is $m\widehat{AC}$?

2. If $m\angle ABC = 52°$, what is $m\widehat{AC}$?

3. If $m\widehat{AC} = 80°$, what is $m\angle ABC$?

4. If $m\widehat{AC} = 118°$, what is $m\angle ABC$?

5. Triangle XYZ is inscribed in a circle, and $\angle X$ is a right angle. The length of $\overline{YZ}$ is 12.2. What is the circumference of the circle? Round your answer to the nearest tenth.

Exercises 6–15: Using the diagram, find the measure of the arc or angle.

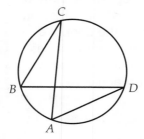

6. $m\widehat{CD} = 116°$ and $m\widehat{AB} = 40°$. What is $m\angle CBD$?

7. $m\widehat{CD} = 116°$ and $m\widehat{AB} = 60°$. What is $m\angle CBD$?

8. $m\widehat{CD} = 126°$ and $m\widehat{AB} = 52°$. What is $m\angle CAD$?

9. $m\widehat{CD} = 122°$ and $m\widehat{AB} = 52°$. What is $m\angle CAD$?

10. $m\angle CBD = 65°$ and $m\angle BDA = 26°$. What is $m\widehat{CD}$?

11. $m\angle CBD = 61°$ and $m\angle BDA = 21°$. What is $m\widehat{CD}$?

12. $m\angle CBD = 56°$ and $m\angle BDA = 22°$. What is $m\widehat{AB}$?

13. $m\angle CBD = 63°$ and $m\angle BDA = 25°$. What is $m\widehat{AB}$?

14. $m\widehat{CD} = 126°$ and $m\widehat{AB} = 48°$. What is $m\angle BCA$?

15. $m\widehat{CD} = 118°$ and $m\widehat{AB} = 54°$. What is $m\angle BCA$?

16. Given the diagram below, what is $m\angle ADE$?

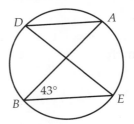

17. Use the diagram to answer the questions.

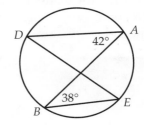

a What is $m\angle DEB$?
b What is $m\angle ADE$?

18. **MP 5** Construct a regular hexagon in a circle and describe any difficulties encountered or notable understanding achieved during the construction process.

19. Describe the connection between the sides of a hexagon inscribed in a circle and the radius of the circle.

20. **MP 2** Use the diagram to answer the questions.

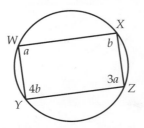

a What is $m\angle W$? What is $m\angle Z$?
b What is $m\angle X$? What is $m\angle Y$?

Practice Problems continue . . .

21. What is $m\angle B$? What is $m\angle A$?

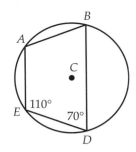

22. What is $m\angle E$? What is $m\angle D$?

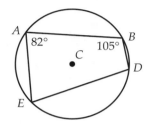

23. ▨ MP 2, 7 ▨ What is $m\angle EBA$? What is $m\angle DAB$?

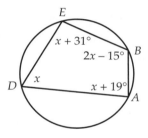

24. ▨ MP 2 ▨ Use the diagram to answer the following questions.

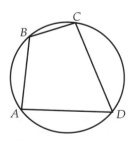

a If $m\angle C = 8x + 57°$ and $m\angle A = 10x + 69°$, what is $m\angle C$?

b If $m\angle C = 8x + 68°$ and $m\angle A = 9x + 78°$, what is $m\angle C$?

25. Draw a cyclic quadrilateral and explain the inscribed quadrilateral theorem using your drawing.

Exercises 26–30: Assume that C is the center of the circle.

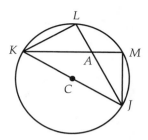

26. If $m\angle MKJ = 23°$, what is the measure of $\angle JMK$?

27. If $m\angle MKJ = 27°$, what is the measure of $\angle JMK$?

28. If $m\angle MKJ = 29°$, what is the measure of $\angle KJM$?

29. If $m\angle MKJ = 28°$, what is the measure of $\angle KJM$?

30. If $m\angle LJM = 30°$, what is $m\angle KAJ$?

31. What is AB, given the circumference of the circle below is 3π?

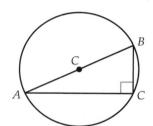

32. ▨ MP 2, 6 ▨ What is the approximate length of $\overline{BC}$, given the circumference of the circle below is 25 inches? Round your answer to the nearest whole number.

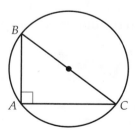

33. $\triangle ABC$ is inscribed in a circle and $m\angle C$ is 90°. The length of $\overline{AB}$ is 20.6 cm. What is the circumference of the circle, to the nearest tenth?

Practice Problems continue . . .

34. Prove the other half of the inscribed quadrilateral theorem using the diagram below: If $m\angle A + m\angle D = 180°$ and $m\angle B + m\angle E = 180°$, then $ABDE$ can be inscribed in a circle.

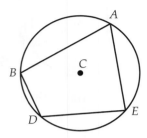

• Multi-Part PROBLEM Practice •

MP 3 Jen and Annie are discussing the following problem: "Given that $ABCD$ is an isosceles trapezoid inscribed in circle O, with $\overline{AD} \parallel \overline{BC}$, and $m\widehat{BCD} = 210°$, find the measures of all of the angles in the trapezoid." A trapezoid is a quadrilateral with one pair of sides parallel. Annie says there isn't enough information to solve the problem. Jen disagrees.

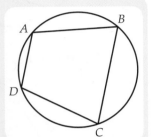

a Decide who is right, and explain why.

b If Annie is correct, then explain what additional information is needed in order to solve the problem. If Jen is correct, then find the measures of all the angles in the trapezoid.

LESSON 8.4

8.4 More on Chords and Angles

Tangents, Chords, and Circles

An inscribed angle equals one half the measure of its intercepted arc. This holds true when the angle and arc are formed in part by a tangent.

Tangent and chord theorem

If a tangent and chord intersect on a circle, then the measure of each angle formed is one-half the measure of its intercepted arc.

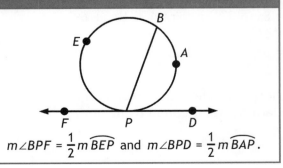

$m\angle BPF = \dfrac{1}{2} m\widehat{BEP}$ and $m\angle BPD = \dfrac{1}{2} m\widehat{BAP}$.

What are $m\angle BAD$ and $m\overparen{BOA}$?

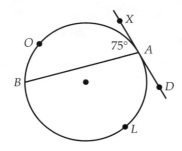

SOLUTION

Relationship of inscribed angle, intercepted arc	$\frac{1}{2}m\overparen{BOA} = m\angle BAX$	The inscribed angle will be half the arc it intercepts. This holds true with a pair of chords, or a chord and a tangent.
	$m\overparen{BOA} = 2(m\angle BAX)$	
	$m\overparen{BOA} = 2\cdot75° = 150°$	
Use number of degrees in a circle to find $m\overparen{BLA}$	$m\overparen{BLA} = 360° - 150° = 210°$	The two intercepted arcs must sum to 360°.
Relationship of intercepted arc, inscribed angle	$m\angle BAD = \frac{1}{2}m\overparen{BLA}$	Start with the same relationship, and solve for the unknown, the arc measure. Substitute and evaluate.
	$m\angle BAD = \frac{1}{2}(210°)$	
	$m\angle BAD = 105°$	

> The sum of two intercepted arcs will equal 360°, and the adjacent angles formed by the chord and the tangent line sum to 180°.

Angles Inside and Outside a Circle

Several theorems relate arcs and angles. We start with a theorem that concerns angles formed by chords within a circle:

Chord angles inside circle theorem

If two chords intersect inside a circle to form an angle, then the measure of the angle equals one-half the sum of the measures of the arcs intercepted by the angle and its vertical angle.

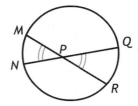

> In this case, the angle equals one-half the *sum* of two arcs.

If $\overline{MR}$ intersects $\overline{NQ}$ at P, then $m\angle MPN = \frac{1}{2}(m\overparen{MN} + m\overparen{QR})$.

So far, we have been working with angles formed within circles. We now turn to the angles formed by secants and tangents that intercept each other outside a circle.

Angles formed outside circle theorems

Angle formed by a secant line and a tangent line

When a secant and a tangent intersect outside a circle, the measure of the angle they form is equal to one-half the difference of the intercepted arcs.

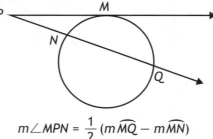

$$m\angle MPN = \frac{1}{2}(m\,\widehat{MQ} - m\,\widehat{MN})$$

> In these cases, the angle equals one-half the **difference** of the intercepted arcs.

Angle formed by two secant lines

When two secants intersect outside a circle, the measure of the angle they form equals one-half the difference of their intercepted arcs.

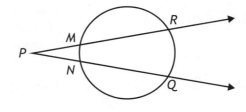

$$m\angle MPN = \frac{1}{2}(m\,\widehat{RQ} - m\,\widehat{MN})$$

Angle formed by two tangent lines

When two tangent lines intersect outside a circle, the measure of the angle they form equals one-half the difference of their intercepted arcs.

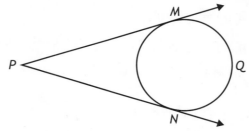

$$m\angle MPN = \frac{1}{2}(m\,\widehat{MQN} - m\,\widehat{MN})$$

MODEL PROBLEMS

1. What is $m\angle XYZ$?

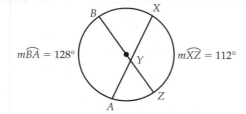

$m\widehat{BA} = 128°$ $m\widehat{XZ} = 112°$

SOLUTION

Use formula $m\angle XYZ = \dfrac{1}{2}(m\widehat{BA} + m\widehat{XZ})$ The angle equals half the sum of these arcs.

Substitute, evaluate $m\angle XYZ = \dfrac{1}{2}(128° + 112°)$ Substitute and evaluate.

$m\angle XYZ = 120°$

Model Problems continue . . .

2. Write an expression for x in terms of $m\angle PQR$.

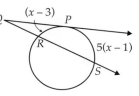

SOLUTION

Angle equals difference of arcs	$m\angle PQR = \frac{1}{2}(m\widehat{PS} - m\widehat{PR})$	The tangent and secant intersect outside the circle. This means the angle measure equals one-half the difference of the measures of these arcs.
Substitute	$m\angle PQR = \frac{1}{2}[5(x-1) - (x-3)]$	Substitute the expressions for the arcs.
Distribute and simplify	$m\angle PQR = \frac{1}{2}(4x - 2)$	Distribute and combine like terms.
	$m\angle PQR = 2x - 1$	
Solve for x	$x = \frac{m\angle PQR + 1}{2}$	Solve for x.

Secants, Tangents, and Circles

The theorem below is an extension of one of the "angle formed outside circle" theorems presented on the previous page.

Secants and tangents theorem

If secant and tangent segments intersect outside a circle, then the product of the lengths of the entire secant segment and the secant segment outside of the circle equals the square of the tangent segment's length.

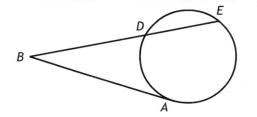

If secant $\overline{BE}$ and tangent $\overline{AB}$ share endpoint B, then $(AB)^2 = BD \cdot BE$.

MODEL PROBLEMS

1. Select the true statement below.

    A.   All tangents are also chords.
    B.   A chord that passes through a circle's center is a diameter.
    C.   All chords are also tangents.
    D.   A tangent intercepts a circle at twice as many points as a secant.

SOLUTION

The answer is B. Chords are segments with two endpoints on a circle, and tangent is a line that intercepts a circle once, while a secant is a line that does so twice. This makes A, C, and D false. A segment that passes through a circle's center is both a chord and a diameter, so B is true.

Model Problems continue . . .

2. What is the length of $\overline{MY}$, to the nearest tenth?

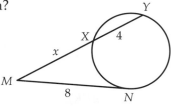

SOLUTION

Use theorem	$(MN)^2 = MX \cdot MY$ $8^2 = x \cdot (x + 4)$	We are told the length of the tangent. The length of the part of the secant outside the circle is represented by x. Its entire length is $x + 4$.
Simplify, write in standard form	$x^2 + 4x - 64 = 0$	Simplify the equation and then write in standard form.
Use quadratic formula	$x = \dfrac{-b \pm \sqrt{b^2 - 4ac}}{2a}$ $x = \dfrac{-4 \pm \sqrt{4^2 - 4(1)(-64)}}{2(1)}$	Use the quadratic formula, substituting from the equation above.
Evaluate	$x = -2 \pm 2\sqrt{17}$	Evaluate the expression from the formula.
Choose positive value	$x \approx 6.2$ $MY = x + 4 \approx 10.2$	x has to be positive, so add the radical.

 3. MP 2 A satellite needs line-of-sight access to receivers. In other words, a straight line must connect the two. How far is the satellite from the cell tower shown to the right? Assume the height of the receiver can be ignored, and that the line of sight access is tangent to the surface of Earth.

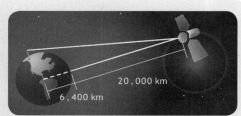

20,000 km

6,400 km

SOLUTION

Draw diagram		We can use the relationship of secant and tangent segment lengths.
Calculate length of secant	secant $= 20,000 + 2(6,400)$ $= 32,800$	The secant in this case passes through the center of the earth. It equals the distance to the earth, 20,000 kilometers, plus the diameter of the earth. The diameter is twice the radius, which we were told.
Use the relationship of secant and tangent segment lengths	$AB^2 = BD \cdot BE$ $AB = \sqrt{BD \cdot BE}$ $AB = \sqrt{20,000 \cdot 32,800}$ $AB \approx 25,600$ km	The secant and tangent share an endpoint, the satellite, so this formula holds true. Substitute and evaluate. Another way to calculate AB would be to realize that a right triangle is formed from B to A to the center of the earth, and that the vertical leg equals the earth's radius.

Chord Lengths in Circles

The theorem below states the relationship between the lengths of chords in a circle:

Intersecting chords theorem

The products of the segment lengths of each of two chords that intersect inside a circle equal one another.

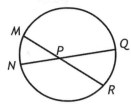

$$MP \cdot PR = NP \cdot PQ.$$

 In this activity, you will discover a relationship concerning the lengths of chord segments formed.

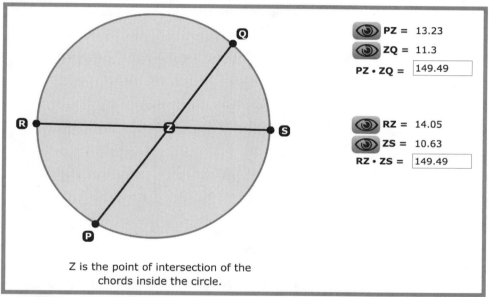

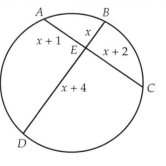	PZ =	13.23
	ZQ =	11.3
PZ · ZQ =	149.49

	RZ =	14.05
	ZS =	10.63
RZ · ZS =	149.49

Z is the point of intersection of the chords inside the circle.

MODEL PROBLEM

The length of $\overline{AE}$ is one unit longer than the length of $\overline{BE}$, and the length of $\overline{CE}$ is two units longer than that of $\overline{BE}$, while the length of $\overline{DE}$ is four units longer than the length of $\overline{BE}$. What are the lengths of $\overline{BE}$ and $\overline{DE}$?

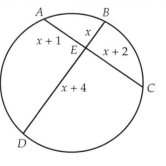

SOLUTION

Let x represent BE

$AE = x + 1; CE = x + 2;$
$DE = x + 4$

Use relationship of segments of intersecting chords

$AE \cdot CE = BE \cdot DE$
$(x + 1)(x + 2) = x(x + 4)$

Multiply

$x^2 + 3x + 2 = x^2 + 4x$

Combine like terms

$x = 2$

Substitute

$BE = x = 2$
$DE = x + 4 = 6$

> You can check the answers. The other segments lengths equal 3 and 4, so the product of each pair of segment lengths is 12.

PRACTICE

1. Given the diagram below, what is $m\widehat{RQ}$?

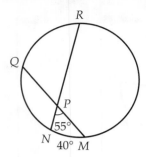

2. Given the diagram below, what is $m\widehat{RQ}$?

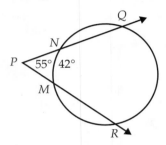

Exercises 3–4: Find the measure of the arc or angle.

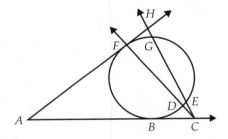

3. $m\widehat{FBD} = 140°$ and $m\widehat{FGD} = 220°$. What is $m\angle AFD$?

4. $m\widehat{FBD} = 136°$ and $m\widehat{FGD} = 224°$. What is $m\angle AFD$?

5. Given the diagram below, what is $m\angle BDE$? $m\widehat{BAD} = 240°$.

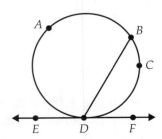

6. Given the diagram below, what is $m\widehat{ACB}$? $m\angle BAD = 78°$.

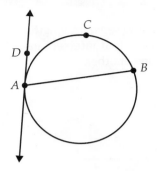

7. Sketch and fully label an original diagram to illustrate the tangent and chord theorem. Then explain the theorem in your own words.

Exercises 8–11: Use the diagram to answer the questions.

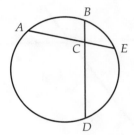

8. If $m\widehat{AB} = 28°$ and $m\widehat{DE} = 120°$, what is $m\angle ECD$?

9. If $m\widehat{AB} = 28°$ and $m\widehat{DE} = 118°$, what is $m\angle ECD$?

10. If $m\widehat{AB} = 65°$ and $m\angle ECD = 60°$, what is $m\widehat{DE}$?

11. If $m\widehat{AB} = 73°$ and $m\angle ECD = 67°$, what is $m\widehat{DE}$?

12. What is the value of a?

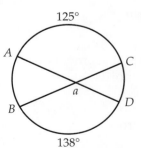

Practice Problems continue . . .

13. What is the value of *b*?

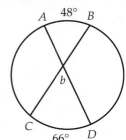

14. Given the diagram below, what is $m\angle MPN$?

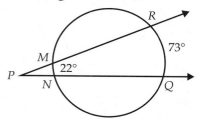

15. Given the diagram below, what is $m\angle MPN$?

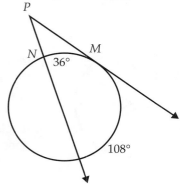

Exercises 16–19: Use the diagram to answer the questions.

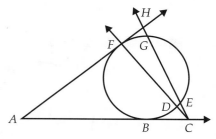

16. If $m\widehat{GF} = 42°$, $m\widehat{GE} = 166°$, and $m\widehat{FBE} = 152°$, what is $m\angle FHG$?

17. If $m\widehat{GF} = 40°$, $m\widehat{GE} = 170°$, and $m\widehat{FBE} = 150°$, what is $m\angle FHG$?

18. If $m\angle ECD = 11°$, $m\widehat{GF} = 44°$, what is $m\widehat{DE}$?

19. If $m\angle ECD = 11°$, $m\widehat{GF} = 38°$, what is $m\widehat{DE}$?

20. MP 3, 6 Adam states, "When a secant and a tangent intersect at a point outside a circle, the square of the tangent's length is equal to the product of the length of each line segment of the secant." Is he correct? Why or why not?

21. MP 6 Given the diagram below, what measures are *AE*, *EC*, *BE*, and *DE*?

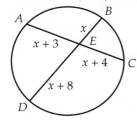

22. MP 6 Use the diagram below to answer the following questions.

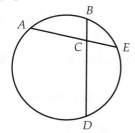

a $AC = 6$ cm, $CE = 4$ cm, and $BC = 2$ cm. How long is $\overline{CD}$?

b $AC = x + 1$, $CE = x$, $BC = x − 2$, and $CD = x + 6$. What is *x*?

23. Sketch and fully label an original diagram to illustrate the intersecting chord lengths theorem. Then explain the theorem in your own words.

24. Given the diagram below, what is $m\widehat{DE}$?

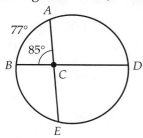

25. What is $m\angle ACB$?

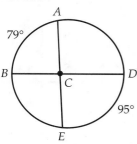

MP 2 When two secants meet outside a circle, the lengths of their legs can be determined by the formula $MA \cdot BA = MD \cdot CD$. In the circle to the right, $AB = 2x$; $BM = 10$; $CD = 2x + 3$; $CM = 9$; $m\overset{\frown}{AB} = 2y$; $m\overset{\frown}{BC} = y$; $m\overset{\frown}{CD} = 3y$; and $m\overset{\frown}{DA} = 2y$. Note: The diagram is not to scale.

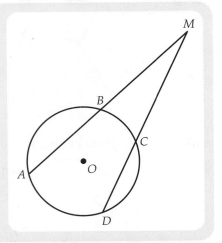

a Find the length of each secant, $\overline{AM}$ and $\overline{DM}$. Show your work and justify your steps.

b Find $m\angle M$. Show your work and justify your steps.

LESSON 8.5

8.5 Arc Lengths and Area

Recall that a circle's perimeter is called a circumference, and it is calculated by the formula $C = 2\pi r$. Circumference and arc length, defined in previous lessons, have a proportional relationship as shown to the right.

$$\frac{\text{arc length}}{2\pi r} = \frac{\text{central angle}}{360°}$$

> Remember, the measure of the complete revolution describing a circle is 360°.

We solve the equation for the **arc length**, since that is often helpful to know.

$$\text{arc length} = \left(\frac{\text{central angle}}{360°}\right) \cdot 2\pi r$$

MODEL PROBLEMS

1. Using the diagram to the right, what is the arc length, S, in feet? Use 3.14 for π and round to the nearest hundredth.

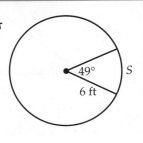

SOLUTION

Use arc length equation

$$\text{arc length} = \left(\frac{\text{central angle}}{360°}\right) \cdot 2\pi r$$

$$S = \left(\frac{49°}{360°}\right) \cdot 2\pi(6 \text{ ft})$$

Start with the arc length equation and substitute the values given in the diagram.

Calculate s

$$S = \left(\frac{49°}{360°}\right) \cdot 2 \cdot (3.14)(6 \text{ ft})$$

Divide and multiply to simplify the right side of the equation.

$$S \approx 5.13 \text{ ft}$$

Model Problems continue . . .

2. **MP 4** A race uses a section of a racetrack as shown. One curve is 180°, and the other curve is 60°. How long is this section of the track?

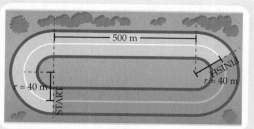

SOLUTION

By calculating the arcs' lengths, we can calculate the length of the track section.

Calculate 180° arc length	arc length $= \left(\dfrac{\text{angle}}{360°}\right) \cdot 2\pi r$	Use the equation for arc length. Substitute the radius of the 180° angle section.
	arc length $= \dfrac{180°}{360°} \cdot 2\pi \cdot 40 \approx 125.7$ meters	
Calculate 60° arc length	arc length $= \dfrac{60°}{360°} \cdot 2\pi \cdot 40 \approx 41.9$ meters	Substitute the radius of the 60° angle section.
Add lengths	$125.7 + 41.9 + 500 \approx 667.6$ meters	Add the lengths, including the straight section.

Area of a Sector

Similar to the relationship between circumference and arc length, the area of a circle and the area of a sector also share a proportionality relationship. Note that a **sector of a circle** is a region defined by two radii and the arc they intercept.

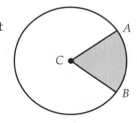

Proportion	$\dfrac{\text{sector area}}{\text{circle area}} = \dfrac{\text{central angle}}{\text{one revolution}}$
	$\dfrac{\text{sector area}}{\pi r^2} = \dfrac{\text{central angle}}{360°}$
Solved for sector area	sector area $= \left(\dfrac{\text{central angle}}{360°}\right) \cdot \pi r^2$

1. Select the true statement.

   A. Inscribed angles on a diameter are right angles, and the radius of a circle is perpendicular to the tangent where the radius intersects the tangent and the circle.
   B. The area of a sector of a circle will increase linearly with the circle's radius.
   C. The measure of an intercepted arc equals the measure of the inscribed angle that defines it.
   D. An arc length of a circle increases proportionally to the square of a circle's radius.

SOLUTION

The answer is A; both those statements are true. A sector's area increases proportionally to the square of the radius (as does the area of the circle), so B is false. The intercepted arc has twice the measure of the inscribed angle that defines it, so C is false, and D is false since that relationship is linear, as it is related to the equation for the circumference of a circle.

Model Problems continue . . .

2. To the nearest tenth, what are the areas of the sectors?

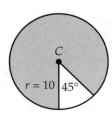

SOLUTION

Area of 45° sector

$$\text{sector area} = \left(\frac{\text{central angle}}{360°}\right) \cdot \pi r^2$$

$$\text{sector area} = \left(\frac{45°}{360°}\right) \cdot \pi(10)^2$$

$$\text{sector area} \approx 39.3$$

We want to find the area of the two sectors. Start with the one labeled 45°. Use the equation for the area of a sector and substitute in the angle and the radius, 10.

Calculate other angle

$$360° - 45° = 315°$$

There are 360° in a circle. Subtract 45°, the measure of the one sector, to find the angle of the other.

Use equation again

$$\text{sector area} = \left(\frac{315°}{360°}\right) \cdot \pi(10)^2$$

$$\text{sector area} \approx 274.9$$

Substitute the angle we calculated into the formula, substitute the radius again, and evaluate. We could check the answer by calculating the area of the entire circle, which is about 314. The area of the two sectors do approximately sum to this area.

3. The gray sector area equals 30π in^2.

    a What is the radius of the circle?
    b What is the area of the circle?

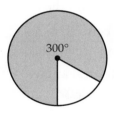

SOLUTION

a Substitute values

$$\text{sector area} = \left(\frac{\text{central angle}}{360°}\right) \cdot \pi r^2$$

$$30\pi = \left(\frac{300°}{360°}\right) \cdot \pi r^2$$

We want to calculate the radius. Substitute the values we are told.

Solve for radius squared

$$30 = \left(\frac{300}{360}\right)r^2$$

$$\left(\frac{6}{5}\right)30 = \left(\frac{6}{5}\right)\left(\frac{5}{6}\right)r^2$$

$$36 = r^2$$

Solve for r. Cancel out π since it appears on both sides of the equation.

Take square root

$$r = 6 \text{ inches}$$

Take the positive square root of 36 square inches.

Model Problems continue . . .

b Use the equation for a circle's area $\qquad A = \pi r^2$

Substitute $\qquad\qquad\qquad\qquad\qquad\qquad A = \pi \cdot 6^2$

Solve $\qquad\qquad\qquad\qquad\qquad\qquad\qquad A = 36\pi$ square inches

4. For a sculpture, an artist removes four 45° sectors as shown on the square. What is the remaining area on the surface you see?

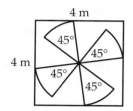

SOLUTION

Calculate radius

$$\text{radius} = \left(\frac{1}{2}\right) \text{diameter}$$

$$\text{radius} = \left(\frac{1}{2}\right) 4 = 2 \text{ meters}$$

We will subtract the areas of the four sectors from the area of the square. We need to calculate the radius to calculate the sector areas. The radius is one-half the diameter.

Calculate area of sectors

$$\text{sector area} = \left(\frac{\text{central angle}}{360°}\right) \cdot \pi r^2$$

$$4 \text{ sector areas} = 4\left(\frac{45°}{360°}\right) \cdot \pi r^2$$

$$\text{sector area} \approx 6.3 \text{ square meters}$$

There are 4 sectors in the sculpture. So use the equation for the area of a sector, multiplying by four.

Calculate area of square

$$A = s^2$$
$$A = 4^2 = 16 \text{ square meters}$$

We are asked to calculate the area of the sculpture after the four sectors are removed. To do this, first calculate the area of the square.

Subtract sectors from square

$$16 - 6.3 \approx 9.7 \text{ square meters}$$

And subtract the sector areas from the square.

5. Select the true statement.

   A.   The angle measure of an arc remains constant when a circle is dilated, but the length of its arc changes.

   B.   Both the angle measure of an arc and the length of its arc change when a circle is dilated.

   C.   Neither the angle measure of an arc nor the length of its arc change when a circle is dilated.

   D.   The angle measure of an arc and its arc change proportional to the scale factor of the dilation.

SOLUTION

The answer is A. Like other angles, the angle measure of an arc stays the same when dilated. However, as the circumference of the circle changes (due to the dilation), the length of the arc changes (by the scale factor).

Radian Measure of Angles

Instead of degrees, angles can be measured in **radians**, with the angle often represented with the Greek letter theta, θ. The radian measure of an angle is defined as the measure of the central angle of a circle whose center is the vertex of the angle. The radian measure of the angle is the ratio of the length of the arc intercepted by the angle to the radius of the circle. This ratio remains constant for a given angle, as we illustrated in an earlier problem and will illustrate again in the model problems in this lesson. One radian is defined as the angle created when the arc length equals the radius.

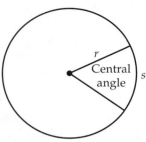

The circumference of a circle with radius r is $2\pi r$. When the radius of a circle is one, the circumference and the arc length of the full circle are both 2π. This means that the radian measure of a 360° angle is 2π. Since 360° equals 2π radians, 180° equals π radians.

Derive: The proportion for finding arc length with a central angle measured in radians.		
Proportion using degrees	$\dfrac{s}{2\pi r} = \dfrac{\text{central angle (degrees)}}{360°}$	This is the proportion used for finding arc length s with a central angle measured in degrees.
Solve for $\dfrac{s}{r}$	$\dfrac{s}{r} = 2\pi \cdot \dfrac{\text{central angle (degrees)}}{360°}$	Multiply both sides of the equation by 2π and simplify.
2π radians = 360°	$\dfrac{s}{r} = \text{central angle (radians)}$	The central angle in degrees, divided by 360° gives us the fraction of the full circle that the angle forms. 2π radians is a full circle (expressed in radians), so multiplying 2π radians by the fraction gives the central angle expressed in radians.
Ratio equals angle in radians	$\dfrac{s}{r} = \theta$ in radians	We are left with the central angle measure in radians on the right side of the equation.

 In this activity, you can experiment with common angles in degrees and radians.

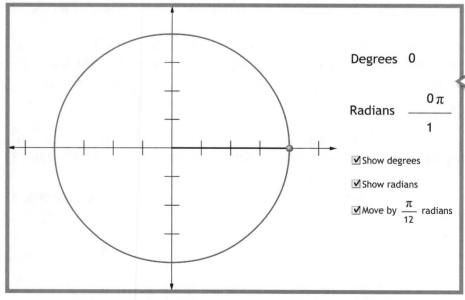

Since the radian is a ratio of two lengths, the units (say, centimeters or inches) cancel out, and the radian itself has no units. Angle measures with no ° symbol are assumed to be expressed in radians.

Conversion factors:

Degrees to radians	Multiply degrees by $\dfrac{\pi \text{ radians}}{180°}$
Radians to degrees	Multiply radians by $\dfrac{180°}{\pi \text{ radians}}$

> The conversion factors here enable you to convert from degrees to radians and radians to degrees.

Using similarity, we derive the fact that the length of the arc intercepted by an angle is proportional to the radius, and define the radian measure of the angle as the constant of proportionality, or scale factor, between the two similar triangles within the circles shown in the diagram.

Derive: $\dfrac{s_1}{r_1} = \dfrac{s_2}{r_2} = \theta$

Given: $\angle ACB \cong \angle DFE$

 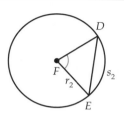

Statement	Reason	
$\angle ACB \cong \angle DFE$	Given	The central angles of the two circles are congruent.
$\overline{AC} \cong \overline{BC}$ and $\overline{DF} \cong \overline{EF}$	Definition of circle radius	Because all radii in a circle are congruent, we know that the radii in each circle are congruent as well.
$\angle CAB \cong \angle CBA$ and $\angle FDE \cong \angle FED$	Base angles theorem	Because the two triangles are made up of their circles' radii, they are isosceles triangles and have congruent base angles.
$\angle CAB \cong \angle CBA \cong$ $\angle FDE \cong \angle FED$	Triangle sum theorem, and substitution	Since we know that the isosceles triangles' central angles are congruent, their base angles must be congruent as well.
$\triangle ABC \sim \triangle DEF$	AA similarity postulate	The triangles are similar, because their corresponding angles are congruent.
Arc lengths and radii of circles are proportional	$\dfrac{s_1}{r_1} = \dfrac{s_2}{r_2}$	Because the triangles are similar, the central angles are congruent. The arc length equals the circumference times the ratio of the central angle to the angle of a full circle. Both the arc lengths of the central angles and radii are proportional.
The scale factor is the central angle	$\dfrac{s_1}{r_1} = \dfrac{s_2}{r_2} = \theta$	The scale factor between the arc length and radius for both triangles is the congruent central angle in radians, since the ratio of the arc length to the radius defines the central angle.

MODEL PROBLEMS

1. What are the radian measures for 30°, 45°, 60°, and 90°?

SOLUTION

Use conversion factor

$$30° \cdot \frac{\pi \text{ radians}}{180°} = \frac{\pi}{6} \text{ radians}$$

To convert from degrees to radians, multiply by the conversion factor,

$$45° \cdot \frac{\pi \text{ radians}}{180°} = \frac{\pi}{4} \text{ radians}$$

$$\frac{\pi \text{ radians}}{180°}.$$

$$60° \cdot \frac{\pi \text{ radians}}{180°} = \frac{\pi}{3} \text{ radians}$$

$$90° \cdot \frac{\pi \text{ radians}}{180°} = \frac{\pi}{2} \text{ radians}$$

2. Convert one radian and $-\frac{5}{4}\pi$ radians into degrees.

SOLUTION

Use conversion factor

$$1 \text{ radian} \cdot \frac{180°}{\pi \text{ radians}} \approx 57.3°$$

We are asked to convert two angles measured in radians to degrees.

$$-\frac{5}{4}\pi \cdot \frac{180°}{\pi \text{ radians}} = -225°$$

3. The circle to the right is dilated by a scale factor of 3. How does this affect the measure of the angle you see, and the length of $\overarc{XY}$?

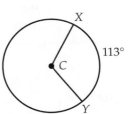

SOLUTION

Dilation does not change angle measures, so the angle stays 113°. The circumference is given by the equation $2\pi r$. The arc length will increase by a factor of 3, since $\frac{2\pi(3r)}{2\pi r} = 3$.

4. The circle is dilated by a scale factor 0.5. How does this change the ratio of the arc length, s, to the circle's circumference?

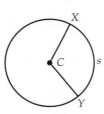

SOLUTION

Use the equation for a circle's circumference, $2\pi r$, and determine the initial ratio

$$\frac{s}{2\pi r}$$

Both are dilated by the same scale factor, 0.5

$$\frac{0.5s}{2\pi(0.5)r} = \frac{s}{2\pi r}$$

The dilation does not change the ratio.

Area of a Sector with Angle in Radians

Earlier in this lesson, we calculated the area of a circle's sector using the degree measure of the central angle. Since we can convert from degrees to radians, we can also calculate sector area in radians. Below we show how the formula is derived.

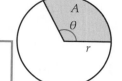

Derive the formula for the area of a sector whose angle is expressed in radians:

$$A = \frac{1}{2}r^2\theta$$

Radian measure and sector area are proportional	$\dfrac{\text{sector area}}{\text{circle area}} = \dfrac{\text{measure of central angle}}{\text{measure of one full rotation}}$
Substitute values	$\dfrac{A}{\pi r^2} = \dfrac{\theta}{2\pi}$
Solve for A	$A = \dfrac{1}{2}r^2\theta$

MODEL PROBLEM

Calculate the area, A, of the indicated sector.

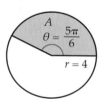

SOLUTION

Formula for area of sector	$A = \dfrac{1}{2}r^2\theta$	Start with the formula for the area of a sector.
Substitute	$A = \dfrac{1}{2} \cdot 4^2 \cdot \dfrac{5\pi}{6}$	Substitute the values for the radius and the measure of the central angle.
Evaluate	$A = \dfrac{20\pi}{3}$	Square 4 and simplify the expression. The area is $\dfrac{20\pi}{3}$.

PRACTICE

1. A circle has a radius of 8 in. What is the area of the circle, rounded to the nearest hundredth?

    A. 631.65 in²

    B. 201.06 in²

    C. 50.26 in²

    D. 25.13 in²

2. Which of the following best represents the arc length of $\overset{\frown}{AB}$?

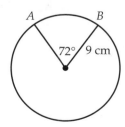

    A. 10.3 cm   C. 11.3 cm

    B. 10.9 cm   D. 11.8 cm

Practice Problems continue . . .

3. Ana creates a circular spinner. One section of the spinner has an angle measure of 45°. If the radius of the spinner is 10 inches, what is the approximate area of that section of the spinner?

    A. 41.25 in²

    B. 39.25 in²

    C. 43.75 in²

    D. 42.75 in²

4. Convert 80° to radians.

5. Convert 240° to radians.

6. Convert $\frac{2}{3}\pi$ radians into degrees.

7. Convert $\frac{8}{5}\pi$ radians into degrees.

8. Convert 135° to radians.

9. What is the area of the sector cut through a circle of radius 6 by a central angle with measure $\frac{6}{5}\pi$ radians?

10. A circle has a radius of 3. What is the arc length of the segment cut by a central angle with a measure of $\frac{3}{4}\pi$ radians?

11. What is the arc length of an arc with a central angle of 60°? The radius of the circle is 5 inches.

12. What is the arc length of an arc with a central angle of 70°? The radius of the circle is 3 inches.

13. What is the central angle, in degrees, of an arc with arc length 4? The radius of the circle is 9 inches.

14. What is the central angle, in degrees, of an arc with arc length 4? The radius of the circle is 11 inches.

15. A circle has a central angle measure of 120° and a radius of 6 inches. What is the length of the arc that is intercepted by the central angle?

16. A circle has a central angle measure of 86° and a circumference of 26 cm. What is the length of the arc that is intercepted by the central angle?

17. A circle has a central angle measure of 136° and a radius of 14 inches. What is the length of the arc that is intercepted by the central angle?

18. A circle has a central angle measure of 172° and a circumference of 24 inches. What is the length of the arc that is intercepted by the central angle?

19. In the diagram below, the radius of the circle is 11 cm and the central angle measure is 108°. What is the arc length of $\overset{\frown}{AB}$?

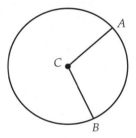

20. The circumference of the circle below is 16 inches and $m\angle ACB = 74°$. What is the arc length of $\overset{\frown}{AB}$?

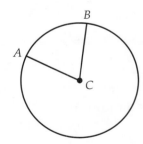

21. What is the arc length of $\overset{\frown}{AB}$ in the diagram below? Round to the nearest tenth.

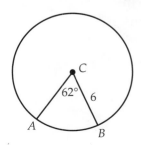

22. Laurie states, "An arc length can be determined if the measure of the central angle and circumference of the circle are known." Is she correct? Why or why not?

23. What is the area of the shaded sector in the circle below?

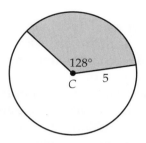

24. What is the area of the shaded sector in the circle below?

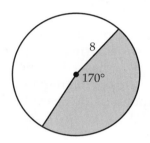

25. What are the areas of the sectors in the circle below?

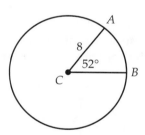

26. What is the area of the sector of a circle with radius 6 cm, when the central angle of the sector is 20°?

27. What is the area of the sector of a circle with radius 10 cm, when the central angle of the sector is 60°?

28. A circle has a radius of 4 cm and a central angle measure of 112°. What are the areas of the two sectors formed inside the circle?

29. A circle has a radius of 7 cm and a central angle measure of 103°. What are the areas of the two sectors formed inside the circle?

30. `MP 2, 6` $x = 3$ inches. What is the area of the shaded region below?

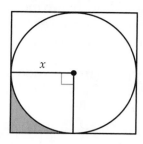

31. The sector area, shaded in the circle below, equals 24π square inches. What is the radius of the circle?

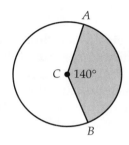

32. The sector area, shaded in the circle below, equals 16π square cm. What is the radius of the circle?

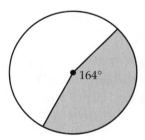

33. The sector area, shaded in the circle below, equals 18π square inches. What is the radius of the circle?

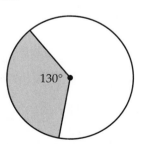

Practice Problems continue . . .

34. **MP 4, 6** A speed skater races on a circular track with a diameter of 20 meters. If the race is 50 laps, how many meters in total does the speed skater race? Round your answer to the nearest meter.

35. A woodworker is using wood stain to finish a circular mirror frame. The diameter of the frame is 24 inches. Before choosing the stain, she tests three different stains, each on $\frac{1}{16}$ of the frame. How many inches of the frame remain unstained after the woodworker tests the three different stains? Round your answer to the nearest hundredth of an inch.

36. A pumpkin pie has a radius of 4.5 in. In the oven, one-third of the crust falls off, one-third burns, and one-third cooks perfectly. If Brad only eats the crust that cooks perfectly, what is the length of the crust he eats to the nearest tenth of an inch?

37. A dog walks on a circular track. The track has a radius of 5 feet and one arc of the track is intercepted by a central angle of 80°. Approximately how many feet must the dog walk along that portion of the track? Round to the nearest foot.

38. A spherical rock hits the windshield of a car and creates a circular hole with radius 0.75 cm. The repair company can fill the hole in the windshield with glass. What is the area of the hole that will need to be filled with glass? Find the area to the nearest hundredth of a square centimeter.

39. A carnival game consists of a large circle filled with balloons at which contestants throw darts. The large circle has a diameter of 8 feet. If each balloon has an area of approximately 1.2 square feet, about how many balloons can fill the circle? Round your answer to the nearest balloon.

40. A new resort will have three circular pools. The diameters of the pools are 6 m, 12 m, and 18 m. The construction crew wants to paint the bottom of the pools with textured paint. However, the budget only allows for enough paint to cover 290 square meters. Which two pools should get the textured paint? Explain your answer. Then propose how the resort can change the diameter of one of the pools so that all three pools can have the textured paint.

41. A family eats a portion of a pizza. The remaining slices form an angle measuring 30°. If the pizza has a diameter of 16 inches, what is the area of the remaining pizza slices, rounded to the nearest tenth of a square inch?

42. Two circles are concentric, with the radius of the larger circle being equal to twice the radius of the smaller circle. Each circle is divided into six equal sectors. The difference between the area of one sector of the larger circle and one sector of the smaller circle is equal to what portion of the total area of the larger circle?

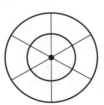

1. Which of the following lines or segments represents a secant?

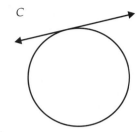

A

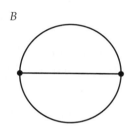

B

C

D

A. *A*   C. *C*
B. *B*   D. *D*

2. What is the value of *x*?

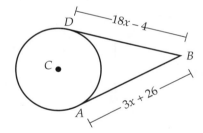

A. 1   C. 4
B. 2   D. 5

3. A pie chart is divided into two semicircles. A portion of one semicircle has an arc measuring 80°. What is the measure of the other arc in the same semicircle?

A. 80°   C. 100°
B. 280°   D. 180°

4. A student wants to draw an inscribed angle with a measure of 40°. To accomplish this, he can draw an intercepted arc with a measure of

A. 20°.   C. 60°.
B. 40°.   D. 80°.

5. A hexagon is inscribed in a circle of radius *r*. Which of the following are true statements? Select all that apply.

A. Each vertex is separated from its neighboring vertices by a distance 2*r*.
B. The hexagon's sides have length *r*.
C. Each vertex is a distance *r* from the circle's center.
D. The hexagon has 6 sides and 7 vertices.

6. A circle is dilated by a factor of 0.73, translated 2 units to the left, and then rotated 90°. Which statement supplies the most correct information about the resulting circle?

A. It is congruent with the initial circle.
B. It is similar to the initial circle.
C. Both A and B are correct.
D. Neither A nor B are correct.

7. **MP 2** $\overline{AB}$ is tangent to the circle. What is the radius of the circle, with center *C*?

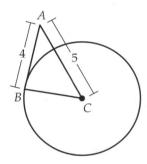

8. **MP 2** $\overline{XY}$ is tangent to the circle. What is the radius of the circle, with center *Z*?

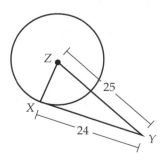

Chapter Review continues . . .

9. $\overline{AB}$ is tangent to the circle below. What is the radius of the circle, whose center is C?

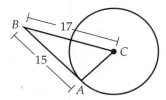

10. $\overleftrightarrow{AB}$ is tangent to the circle below. AB is 20 inches and AC is 25 inches. What is the radius of the circle, with center C?

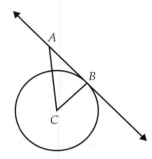

11. $\overline{AB}$ and $\overline{BD}$ are both tangent to the circle. What is the value of x?

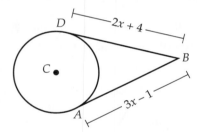

12. **MP 4** The Rocky Mountains' tallest mountain, Mt. Elbert, is 4.401 km above Earth's surface. Earth's radius is approximately 6,400 km. What is the approximate distance from the summit of Mt. Elbert to the horizon? Round to the nearest kilometer.

13. Draw a circle with two tangent segments that meet at a common point.

Exercises 14–15: Use the diagram to answer the questions.

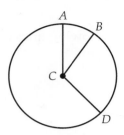

14. If $m\widehat{ABD}$ is 135° and $m\widehat{BD}$ is 101°, what is $m\widehat{AB}$?

15. If $m\widehat{ABD}$ is 137° and $m\widehat{BD}$ is 104°, what is $m\widehat{AB}$?

16. The measure of a central angle of a circle is 125°. What is the measure of the minor arc of the circle?

17. The measure of a minor arc of a circle is 165°. What is the measure of the major arc of the circle?

18. **MP 2** In the circle below, $m\widehat{AD} = m\widehat{BD}$.

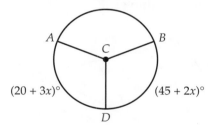

  a What is $m\widehat{AD}$?
  b What is $m\widehat{AB}$?
  c What is $m\widehat{ADB}$?

19. Use the diagram below to answer the questions.

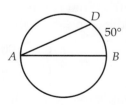

  a What is $m\angle DAB$?
  b If in the diagram, $m\angle DAB$ were 35°, what would $m\widehat{BD}$ equal?

Chapter Review continues . . .

20. Given the diagram below, what is the approximate value of x?

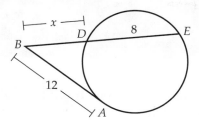

21. Given the diagram below, what is the value of x?

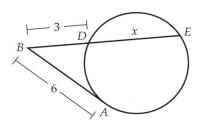

22. **MP 2** What is $m\widehat{DE}$?

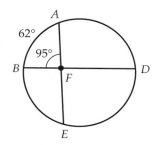

Exercises 23–25: Use the diagram to answer the questions.

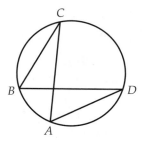

23. If $m\widehat{CD} = 114°$ and $m\widehat{AB} = 54°$, what is $m\angle CBD$?

24. If $m\widehat{CD} = 110°$ and $m\widehat{AB} = 42°$, what is $m\angle CBD$?

25. If $m\angle CBD = 56°$ and $m\angle BDA = 28°$, what is $m\angle CAD$?

26. **MP 2** C is the center of the circle.

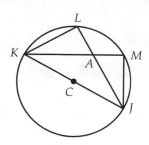

   a If $m\angle MKJ = 29°$, what is the measure of $\angle JMK$?

   b If $m\angle LJM = 29°$, what is $m\angle KAJ$?

27. **MP 2** If the radius of a circle is 6.8 and the circle contains a 75° arc, what is the area of the smaller sector, to the nearest whole number?

28. **MP 1, 2, 4** Find the distance between the cities to the nearest mile. Their latitudes are given; assume that the cities are on the same meridian (that means one city is due north of the other). Assume the circumference of the earth is 25,000 miles.

   a Berlin, Germany 52.5° N; Tripoli, Libya 32.9° N

   b Boston, MA 42.3° N; Santiago, Chile 33.4° S

   c Find the difference in the latitudes of two cities, one of which is 700 kilometers due north of the other. Assume the earth is a sphere with a radius of 6378 kilometers.

1. A triangle has vertices at the points (2, 4), (3, −2), and (−2, −1). What is the reflection of the triangle about the *x*-axis?

   A. (−2, 4), (−3, −2), and (2, −1)
   B. (2, −4), (3, 2), and (−2, 1)
   C. (−2, −4), (−3, 2), and (2, 1)

2. In $\triangle DEF$, the $m\angle D = 30°$, and $m\angle E$ is 3 times $m\angle D$. What type of triangle is this? Choose all descriptions that apply.

   A. Scalene
   B. Isosceles
   C. Equilateral
   D. Acute
   E. Right
   F. Obtuse

3. Eunice uses a paragraph proof to show $\triangle WXZ \cong \triangle WYZ$. She says, "It is given that $\angle XZW \cong \angle YZW$. It is also given that $\angle XWZ \cong \angle YWZ$. $\overline{WZ} \cong \overline{WZ}$ due to the reflexive congruence property." What postulate or theorem is she using?

   A. SSS
   B. SAS
   C. Hypotenuse-leg
   D. ASA
   E. AAS

4. Charlie graphs the ratio of the area of a circle to its circumference as a function of its radius. The graph would be

   A. A parabola.
   B. A curve but not a parabola.
   C. A line with a slope of 0.5.
   D. None of the above.

5. There exist two scalene triangles, $\triangle ABC$ and $\triangle DEF$. Which two statements contradict each other?

   A. Scalene $\triangle ABC$ is congruent to scalene $\triangle DEF$.
   B. $\angle C \cong \angle F$
   C. $\overline{AB} \cong \overline{DE}$
   D. $\angle A \cong \angle E$

6. Based on the diagram below and the knowledge that $m\angle B = 104°$, which of the following could be the measure of $\angle Y$?

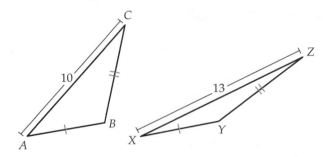

   A. 91°
   B. 98°
   C. 104°
   D. 115°

7. A unit radian has the dimensions

   A. Length per degree, since it is the ratio of the circumference divided by measure of the angle.
   B. It has no units, since it is the ratio of arc length to radius of the circle.
   C. Degree per length, since it is the ratio of the circumference divided by the measure of the angle.
   D. Degrees, since it is the measure an angle.

8. Michele uses a paragraph proof to show $\triangle ABC \cong \triangle ABD$. She says, "It is given that $\angle ABD$ is a right angle, and C, B, and D are collinear, so $\angle ABD \cong \angle ABC$ by the perpendicular line and right angle converse. It is also given that $\overline{AC} \cong \overline{AD}$. $\overline{AB} \cong \overline{AB}$ due to the reflexive congruence property." What postulate or theorem is she using?

A. SSS

B. SAS

C. SSA

D. Hypotenuse-leg

E. AAS

9. A carpenter places a wooden beam across a triangular skylight. What is the length of $\overline{BY}$?

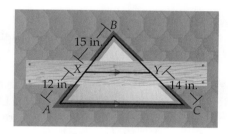

A. 15.5 inches

B. 16 inches

C. 17.5 inches

D. 18 inches

10. A triangle has sides of 12, 15, and 20. What kind of triangle is it?

A. Acute   C. Right

B. Obtuse   D. Cannot tell

11. In a 45-45-90 triangle, each leg measures 9 units. How long is the hypotenuse of the triangle?

A. 9 units   C. $9\sqrt{3}$ units

B. $9\sqrt{2}$ units   D. 18 units

12. What is the length of a 21° arc in a circle with a 3-inch radius, to the nearest tenth of an inch?

13. What is the measure of angle B in the diagram below? Express your answer to the nearest degree.

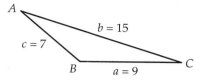

14. I am a triangle whose orthocenter is located on one of my vertices, and whose circumcenter is located on my longest side. Two of my medians are congruent. What type of triangle am I?

15. An arc has a length of 7 kilometers in a circle with a radius of 12 kilometers. What is the measure of the arc's central angle, to the nearest degree?

16. A triangle has sides of length $b = 2$ and $a = 3$. If the measure of angle C is 28°, what is the area of the triangle, to the nearest tenth?

17. The area of the circle below is 24 cm². What is the measure of the central angle ACB? Hints: Solve the equation for sector area for the angle, and remember what the formula πr^2 represents.

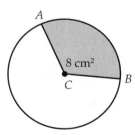

18. $\overleftrightarrow{AB}$ is tangent to the circle below. AB is 12 inches and AC is 15 inches. What is the radius of the circle, with center C?

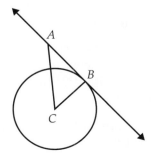

19. Given the diagram below, the line pairs p and q, a and c, and b and c intersect; the line pairs m and n, and a and b do not intersect. List all the pairs of parallel lines.

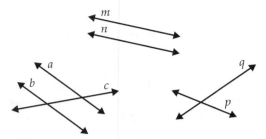

20. The leg opposite the 30° angle of a 30-60-90 triangle has a length of $\dfrac{\sqrt{2}}{3}$. What is the length of the hypotenuse?

21. What is the length $\overline{GC}$?

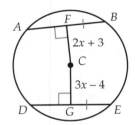

22. MP 2, 3 Prove the consecutive interior angles theorem.
Prove: $m\angle D + m\angle E = 180°$
Given: $m \parallel n$, t is a transversal

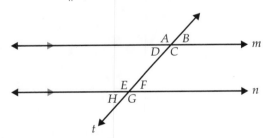

23. What is sin 42° to the nearest thousandth?

24. Can a triangle be both obtuse and isosceles? Justify your answer.

25. A right triangle has a hypotenuse of 7. How long is the leg adjacent to angle A if the angle's measure is 70°? State your answer to the nearest hundredth.

26. MP 4 11 feet from a street lamp, the angle from the ground to its tip is 42°. What is the height of the lamp? Give your answer to the nearest tenth of a foot.

27. MP 2, 7 One could prove that, given two parallel lines, the distance from a point on one line to the other line is the same for any point. That distance, the length of a perpendicular segment connecting parallel lines, is called the *distance between two parallel lines*.

a Parallel lines l, k, and n are on the same plane. Line k is 4 inches away from line l and is 6 inches from line n. What is the distance between the lines l and n? Give all possible answers.

b What is the distance between the coplanar lines that are 5 units away from the x-axis in either direction?

c What is the distance between the coplanar lines that are 4.69 units away from the x-axis in either direction?

28. MP 3 Is it possible to use the law of cosines to solve a right triangle? Explain your reasoning.

29. MP 4, 5 An airplane is at an altitude of 2 miles over the city of Mt. Dora. Mt. Dora is 7 miles away from the airport where the plane will land. At what angle from the horizontal should the plane descend?

30. In circle O below, given that $AC = 8$, $DE = 2$, and $\overline{DB}$ is a perpendicular bisector of $\overline{AC}$, find the following:

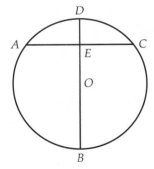

a The length of $\overline{AE}$.

b The radius of circle O

c The area of the segment of the circle enclosed by $\overline{AC}$ and $\overarc{ADC}$, rounded to the nearest tenth. (Hint: To start, use trigonometry to find the measure of the central angle enclosing $\overarc{AD}$.)

31. MP 3 Prove the transversal and parallel lines theorem for the case that $\overleftrightarrow{AN}$ and $\overleftrightarrow{SM}$ are not parallel. Hint: Use the triangle proportionality theorem.

A transversal and parallel lines theorem

When parallel lines pass through transversals, they divide the transversals into proportional line segments.

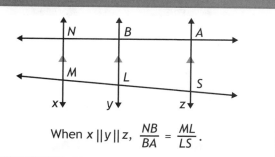

When $x \parallel y \parallel z$, $\dfrac{NB}{BA} = \dfrac{ML}{LS}$.

Statement	Reason
1. Extend $\overleftrightarrow{AN}$ and $\overleftrightarrow{SM}$ so that they intersect at T	1. Auxiliary construction
2. $TA = TN + NB + BA$ and $TS = TM + ML + LS$	2. Segment addition postulate
3. $\dfrac{TN}{TM} = \dfrac{TN + NB}{TM + ML} = \dfrac{TN}{TM} = \dfrac{TN + NB + BA}{TM + ML + LS}$	3. Triangle proportionality theorem
4. $(TN)(TM) + (TN)(ML) = (TN)(TM) + (NB)(TM)$ and $(TN)(TM) + (TN)(ML) + (TN)(LS) = (TN)(TM) + (NB)(TM) + (BA)(TM)$	4. Multiplication property of equality
5. $(TN)(ML) = (NB)(TM)$ and $(TN)(ML) + (TN)(LS) = (NB)(TM) + (BA)(TM)$	5.
6.	6. Multiplication property of equality
7. $(NB)(TM) + (TN)(LS) = (NB)(TM) + (BA)(TM)$ (from step 5)	7. Substitution property of equality
8. $(TN)(LS) = (BA)(TM)$	8.
9. $(LS)\dfrac{(NB)(TM)}{ML} = (BA)(TM)$	9.
10.	10. Multiplication property of equality and reflexive property

Chapter Content

Chapter Vocabulary

apothem	parallelogram	regular polygon
concave polygon	quadrilateral	rhombus
convex polygon	rectangle	square
isosceles trapezoid	rectilinear figure	trapezoid
kite		

LESSON 9.1

9.1 Parallelograms and Their Diagonals

Recall that a polygon is any closed figure with straight sides. When all of the sides of a polygon have the same lengths and all of the angles have the same measure, the figure is a **regular polygon**. The polygons we show to the right are all examples of regular polygons. Polygons can have sides and angles of different measures, as the table below shows. A polygon is a closed figure of at least three sides. A polygon can be named based on the number of its sides. We show the names of some figures that end in "gon."

| Pentagon | Hexagon | Heptagon | Octagon |
| 5 sides | 6 sides | 7 sides | 8 sides |

Quadrilaterals are four-sided polygons. Quadrilaterals have specific names based on the properties of their sides and angles.

Types of Quadrilaterals		Properties
Trapezoid		Quadrilateral with at least 1 pair of parallel sides
Parallelogram		Opposite sides are parallel and equal in length
Rhombus		Parallelogram with 4 congruent sides
Rectangle		Parallelogram with 4 right angles
Square		Rhombus with 4 right angles Rectangle with 4 congruent sides

> A **rectilinear figure** is a polygon in which all its edges meet at right angles. Squares and rectangles are examples of rectilinear figures.

The relationship between quadrilaterals is:

- All four-sided figures are quadrilaterals
- All trapezoids are quadrilaterals
- All parallelograms are quadrilaterals
- All rhombuses are parallelograms
- All rectangles are parallelograms
- All squares are rectangles and rhombuses

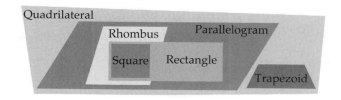

Sides and Angles in a Parallelogram

Earlier, we stated that the opposite sides of a parallelogram are congruent. This is a direct result of the following theorem.

Parallelogram opposite sides theorem

If a quadrilateral is a parallelogram, then its opposite sides are congruent.

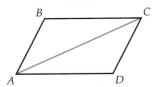

If *ABCD* is a parallelogram, then $\overline{AB} \cong \overline{CD}$ and $\overline{BC} \cong \overline{AD}$.

Below, we prove this theorem.

Prove: $\overline{AB} \cong \overline{CD}$ and $\overline{AD} \cong \overline{BC}$
Given: *ABCD* is a parallelogram

> The proof relies on a diagonal of the parallelogram. We draw the orange diagonal as an auxiliary segment, $\overline{AC}$, which we treat as a transversal of two parallel lines.

Statement	Reason	
ABCD is a parallelogram	Given	We are told that quadrilateral *ABCD* is a parallelogram.
Draw $\overline{AC}$	Auxiliary line segment construction	Draw an auxiliary line segment to divide the parallelogram into two triangles.
$\overline{AB} \parallel \overline{CD}$, $\overline{AD} \parallel \overline{BC}$	Definition of parallelogram	By definition, a parallelogram's opposite sides are parallel.
$\angle DAC \cong \angle BCA$, $\angle BAC \cong \angle DCA$	Alternate interior angles theorem	The auxiliary line acts as a transversal to the parallel sides $\overline{AD}$ and $\overline{BC}$ and to the parallel sides $\overline{AB}$ and $\overline{CD}$. Use the alternate interior angles theorem to show that the alternate interior angles are congruent.
$\overline{AC} \cong \overline{AC}$	Reflexive property of congruence	A segment is congruent to itself.
$\triangle DAC \cong \triangle BCA$	ASA postulate	Since we have shown that two corresponding angles and the side between them are congruent, use ASA to prove that the two triangles are congruent.
$\overline{AB} \cong \overline{CD}$, $\overline{AD} \cong \overline{BC}$	Definition of congruent triangles	Because the two triangles are congruent, their corresponding sides are as well.

We apply the theorem in our proof that parallel lines have the same slope.

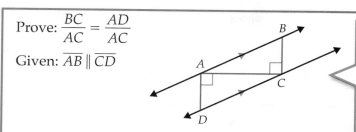

Prove: $\dfrac{BC}{AC} = \dfrac{AD}{AC}$

Given: $\overline{AB} \parallel \overline{CD}$

> We begin by drawing a gray horizontal auxiliary segment $\overline{AC}$ and two gray vertical auxiliary segments $\overline{AD}$ and $\overline{BC}$ that connect the parallel lines. This means that we can represent the slopes of the two parallel lines $\overleftrightarrow{AB}$ and $\overleftrightarrow{CD}$ with $\dfrac{BC}{AC}$ and $\dfrac{AD}{AC}$, respectively.

Statement	Reason	
$\overline{AB} \parallel \overline{CD}$	Given	We are proving that if a pair of lines is parallel, then they have the same slope. The hypothesis that the lines are parallel is given.
$\overline{AD} \parallel \overline{BC}$	Given	These auxiliary segments were drawn as vertical segments, so they are also parallel.
$ABCD$ is a parallelogram	Definition of a parallelogram	Since opposite sides are parallel, the quadrilateral is a parallelogram.
$AD = BC$	Parallelogram opposite sides theorem	If a figure is a parallelogram, then its opposite sides are congruent and have equal lengths.
$\dfrac{BC}{AC} = \dfrac{AD}{AC}$	Multiplication property of equality	Divide both sides of the equation by the same amount, and the equation will remain true. This means that we have shown the slopes of two parallel lines are equal.

Adjacent angles of a parallelogram are supplementary, summing to 180°, and opposite angles are congruent. We summarize this in two theorems:

Parallelogram angle theorems

If a quadrilateral is a parallelogram, then its opposite angles are congruent.

If $ABCD$ is a parallelogram, then $\angle A \cong \angle C$ and $\angle B \cong \angle D$.

If a quadrilateral is a parallelogram, then its adjacent angles are supplementary.

If $ABCD$ is a parallelogram, then $m\angle A + m\angle D = 180°$,
$m\angle D + m\angle C = 180°$, $m\angle C + m\angle B = 180°$ and $m\angle B + m\angle A = 180°$.

We prove the theorem about congruent opposite angles. It is very similar to the proof we did before for showing congruent opposite sides in a parallelogram.

Prove: $\angle A \cong \angle C$ and $\angle B \cong \angle D$
Given: $ABCD$ is a parallelogram

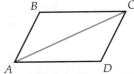

Statement	Reason	
$ABCD$ is a parallelogram	Given	We are told that quadrilateral $ABCD$ is a parallelogram.
Draw $\overline{AC}$	Auxiliary line segment construction	Draw an orange auxiliary line segment to divide the parallelogram into two triangles.
$\overline{AB} \parallel \overline{CD}, \overline{AD} \parallel \overline{BC}$	Definition of parallelogram	By definition, a parallelogram's opposite sides are parallel.
$\angle DAC \cong \angle BCA$, $\angle BAC \cong \angle DCA$	Alternate interior angles theorem	The auxiliary line acts as a transversal to the parallel sides $\overline{AD}$ and $\overline{BC}$ and to the parallel sides $\overline{AB}$ and $\overline{CD}$. Use the alternate interior angles theorem to show that the alternate interior angles are congruent.
$\overline{AC} \cong \overline{AC}$	Reflexive property of congruence	A segment is congruent to itself.
$\triangle DAC \cong \triangle BCA$	ASA postulate	Since we have shown that two corresponding angles and the side between them are congruent, use ASA to prove that the two triangles are congruent.
$\angle B \cong \angle D$	Definition of congruent triangles	Because the two triangles are congruent, their corresponding angles are as well.
$\angle A \cong \angle C$	Same as above	We can prove $\angle A \cong \angle C$ by drawing an auxiliary line segment $\overline{BD}$ and using the same series of steps as we used above.

MODEL PROBLEMS

1. In all parallelograms

    A. All four sides are congruent.

    B. Opposite sides are congruent.

    C. Adjacent angles are congruent.

    D. All angles are congruent.

SOLUTION

The answer is B. The other statements are not true.

2. *ABCD* is a parallelogram. If $m\angle A = 63°$, what are the other angles?

SOLUTION

Opposite angles congruent	$m\angle A = m\angle C = 63°$	Opposite angles are congruent in a parallelogram.
Adjacent angles supplementary	$m\angle A + m\angle B = 180°$ $63° + m\angle B = 180°$ $m\angle B = 117°$	Adjacent angles are supplementary. Substitute for $m\angle A$ and solve.
Opposite angles congruent	$m\angle B = m\angle D = 117°$	Again, use the fact that opposite angles are congruent. To check our answer, sum the four angles, and they total 360°.

3. *EFGH* is a parallelogram. What is $m\angle E$?

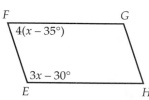

SOLUTION

Angles are supplementary	$m\angle E + m\angle F = 180°$ $3x - 30° + 4(x - 35°) = 180°$	Adjacent angles are supplementary.
Calculate x	$3x - 30° + 4x - 140° = 180°$ $7x = 350°$ $x = 50°$	Distribute, combine like terms, then divide.
Substitute and evaluate	$m\angle E = 3x - 30°$ $m\angle E = 3(50)° - 30° = 120°$	We are asked for $m\angle E$, so substitute the value for x into the expression for $m\angle E$ in the diagram. To check our answer, substitute our value for x into the expression for $m\angle E$ and we get 60°. The angles are supplementary, as they must be.

Model Problems continue . . .

4. **MP 2, 4** You are asked to design a racecourse in the shape of a parallelogram with a 3.6-mile perimeter. One angle is supposed to have triple the measure of the other, and one side is supposed to be twice as long as the other. Calculate the lengths of the sides and measures of the angles in the track.

SOLUTION

Draw diagram

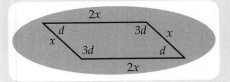

We represent the sides of the track with x (the shorter side) and $2x$, since we are told one side is twice as long as another.

Calculate length of sides

$$x + 2x + x + 2x = 3.6$$
$$6x = 3.6$$
$$x = 0.6, 2x = 1.2$$

Sum the sides to 3.6, the given perimeter. Calculate x. Multiply by 2 to get the longer sides. The side lengths are 0.6 and 1.2 miles.

Calculate angles

$$3d + d = 180°$$
$$d = 45°$$
$$3d = 3(45°) = 135°$$

The problem says that one angle is triple another, so we represent the angles with d and $3d$. Adjacent angles are supplementary in a parallelogram, so they sum to 180°. Calculate d. Then, substitute and calculate the other angle. The measures of the angles are 45° and 135°.

Diagonals in a Parallelogram

The diagonals of a parallelogram bisect one another:

Parallelogram diagonals theorem

If the quadrilateral is a parallelogram, then its diagonals bisect one another.

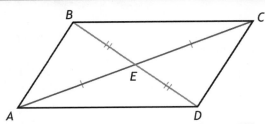

If *ABCD* is a parallelogram, then $\overline{AE} \cong \overline{EC}$ and $\overline{DE} \cong \overline{EB}$.

We prove the theorem:

Prove: Prove the diagonals bisect each other

Given: *ABCD* is a parallelogram

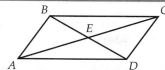

Statement	Reason	
ABCD is a parallelogram	Given	We are told that quadrilateral *ABCD* is a parallelogram.
$\overline{AD} \parallel \overline{BC}$	Definition of a parallelogram	By definition of a parallelogram, opposite sides are parallel.
$\overline{AD} \cong \overline{BC}$	Parallelogram opposite sides theorem	Opposite sides of a parallelogram are congruent.
$\angle CBE \cong \angle ADE$ and $\angle BCE \cong \angle DAE$	Alternate interior angles theorem	The diagonals act as transversals for the pairs of parallel sides $\overline{AD}$ and $\overline{BC}$, and $\overline{AB}$ and $\overline{CD}$. This means that the alternate interior angles created by the diagonals and these sides are congruent.
$\triangle BCE \cong \triangle DAE$	ASA postulate	Since two corresponding angles and the sides in between them are congruent, the triangles are congruent.
$\overline{AE} \cong \overline{EC}$ and $\overline{BE} \cong \overline{ED}$	Definition of congruent triangles	Because the two triangles are congruent, their corresponding sides are congruent as well.
Diagonals bisect each other	Definition of bisectors	Since the segments on a diagonal that are formed by the intersection are congruent, each diagonal bisects the other.

MODEL PROBLEM

Where do the parallelogram's diagonals intersect?

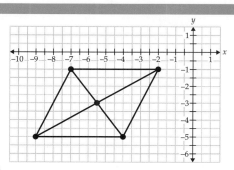

SOLUTION

Use the midpoint formula

$$\text{midpoint} = \left(\frac{x_1 + x_2}{2}, \frac{y_1 + y_2}{2} \right)$$

Diagonals in a parallelogram intersect at their midpoints. Start with the formula for midpoints.

Pick a pair of opposite vertices

$$\text{midpoint} = \left(\frac{-7 + (-4)}{2}, \frac{-1 + (-5)}{2} \right)$$

$$\text{midpoint} = (-5.5, -3)$$

Pick a pair of opposite vertices and use the formula to calculate their midpoint. We can check the answer by calculating the midpoint of the other vertices. The midpoint of $(-9, -5)$ and $(-2, -1)$ is the same point.

1. Which of the following statements are true? Select all that apply.

   A. A rhombus has two pairs of parallel sides.
   B. A rectangle has four congruent sides.
   C. A rhombus has four congruent sides.
   D. A rhombus is a parallelogram.

2. Choose all of the following that describe the figure.

   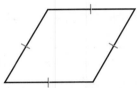

   A. Rhombus   C. Quadrilateral
   B. Parallelogram D. Rectangle

3. In a rectangle, mark the point in the middle of each of the 4 sides. Proceeding around the rectangle, connect the midpoints in order. Which of these figures is the result?

   A. Square   C. Trapezoid
   B. Rectangle   D. Rhombus

Exercises 4–5: Use the diagram to answer the questions. *ABCD* is a parallelogram. *O* is the intersection point of the diagonals.

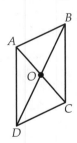

4. The perimeter of triangle *AOB* is 56 inches. The perimeter of triangle *AOD* is 60 inches. How much longer is $\overline{AD}$ than $\overline{AB}$?

   A. 2 in
   B. 4 in
   C. 58 in
   D. The sides are the same.

5. Which of the following must be true for parallelogram *ABCD*? *O* is the point of intersection of the diagonals in the parallelogram.

   A. $m\angle OAD = m\angle OBC$
   B. $BD \perp AC$
   C. $m\angle A + m\angle C = 180°$
   D. $OA = OC$

6. In quadrilateral *SODA*, *OD* ∥ *SA*. Dorothy thinks that *SODA* might be a parallelogram. Which of the following should she check to give her enough information to conclude that *SODA* is indeed a parallelogram?

   A. $m\angle D = m\angle S$
   B. $SD = OA$
   C. $OS = DA$
   D. $OD = SA$

7. How many sides does a heptagon have?

8. What quadrilateral figure has only 1 pair of parallel sides?

9. In a parallelogram, one interior angle is 58°. What is the measure of the angle opposite it?

10. In a parallelogram, one interior angle is 67°. What is the measure of the angle adjacent to it?

11. One of the angles of a parallelogram is 75°. Find the measures of the other three angles.

12. One interior angle in a parallelogram is 33°. What is the angle opposite it?

13. The perimeter of a parallelogram is 38 inches. Find the lengths of its sides if one side is 5 inches longer than another.

14. The perimeter of a parallelogram is 48 inches. Find the side lengths of the parallelogram when one side of the parallelogram is 4 inches longer than the other.

15. The perimeter of a parallelogram is 78 inches. Find the side lengths of the parallelogram when one side of the parallelogram is twice as long as the other.

16. A parallelogram has vertices at (1, 1), (5, 5), (2, 1), and (4, 5). Where do the parallelogram's diagonals intersect?

Practice Problems continue . . .

17. Ann states, "All squares are rectangles, but not all squares are rhombi." Is she correct? Explain.

18. What are the measures of the angles in the parallelogram *DARE*?

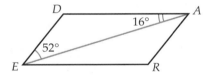

19. Find the measures of the angles between the diagonals of the parallelogram *SOFT*.

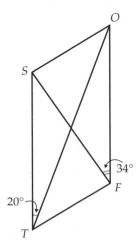

20. The ratio of two sides of a parallelogram is 3 : 4. Find the sides if the perimeter of the parallelogram is 2.8 inches.

21. The perimeter of the parallelogram *ABCD* is 10 meters. The perimeter of the triangle *ABD* is 8 meters. Find the length of the diagonal $\overline{BD}$.

22. Dina found two angles of a parallelogram to be equal to 40° and 50°. What should we conclude about Dina's calculations and why?

23. What is the largest integer value an angle of a parallelogram can have?

24. In a quadrilateral *ABCD*, ∠*A* ≅ ∠*C* and *BC* = *AD*. Can we conclude that *ABCD* must be a parallelogram?

25. In a quadrilateral *TERM*, *TE* = *RM* and *ER* = *TM*. Can we conclude that *TERM* is a parallelogram?

26. Using the diagram below, what can we conclude about quadrilateral *ABCD* based on its diagonals? Why?

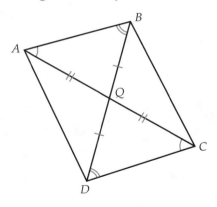

27. **MP 3** In a parallelogram *ABCD*, the diagonals intersect at point *O*. Prove that ∠*ABO* ≅ ∠*CDO* without using the alternate interior angles theorem.

28. A city plaza is formed between two pairs of parallel streets, as shown in the picture. One side of the plaza is 3 times as long as the other, and one angle between intersecting streets is 50° greater than the other angle. The walk around the plaza is 160 meters long. What are the measures of the sides and the angles of the plaza?

29. **MP 2, 4** Aran wants to bend a wire that is 84 inches long to form a parallelogram. One side should be 50% shorter than the other, and the angles have the ratio of 2 : 3. What are the measures of the sides and angles of Aran's parallelogram?

Practice Problems continue . . .

30. Two identical wheels with rods are connected, as shown below. The lengths of the rods *MN* and *AB* are equal. The connecting pivot translates rotation from one wheel to another. Prove that segments $\overline{AB}$ and $\overline{MN}$ are either parallel or lie on the same line.

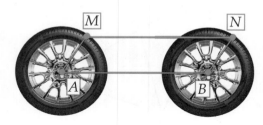

Exercises 31–34: Find the point of intersection of the diagonals of the parallelogram *ABCD* with the given coordinate of the vertices.

31. $A(-3, -1)$; $B(-1, -1)$; $C(3, -3)$; $D(1, -3)$

32. $A(-1, 2)$; $B(2, -5)$; $C(1, -2)$; $D(-2, 5)$

33. $A(6, -4)$; $B(-2, 5)$; $C(-9, 4)$; $D(-1, -5)$

34. $A(-2, 5)$; $B(4, 8)$; $C(7, 6)$; $D(1, 3)$

35. All vertices of the quadrilateral *ABCD* lie in quadrant I. Three of its vertices are $A(1, 1)$, $B(6, 1)$, and $D(2, 4)$. What should the coordinates of the fourth vertex *C*, be so that *ABCD* is a parallelogram?

36. **MP 3** The coordinates of quadrilateral *MNPQ* are $M(-5, 1)$, $N(-4, 4)$, $P(-1, 5)$, and $Q(-2, 2)$. Prove that *MNPQ* is a parallelogram.

37. The diagonals of a parallelogram intersect at the origin. If two vertices of the parallelogram are $(-7, 0)$ and $(0, 8)$, find the coordinates of the two other vertices.

38. Is it possible to draw a parallelogram so that all of its sides are equal to one of its diagonals? If it is, what would the angles of such a parallelogram be?

39. The sides of the parallelogram below are equal to 7 inches and 3 inches. The angle bisectors of angles *A* and *D* divide the opposite side of the parallelogram into three segments. Find the length of segment $\overline{MN}$.

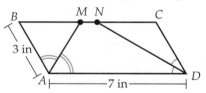

40. *ABDC* and *DEGF* are parallelograms, and $\overline{BF}$ and $\overline{CE}$ are continuous line segments. Prove that $AC \parallel EG$.

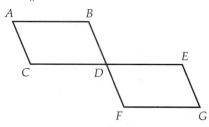

41. The diagonals of a parallelogram *ABCD* intersect at point *O*. The line $\overleftrightarrow{MN}$ passes through point *O* and intersects the sides $\overline{BC}$ and $\overline{AD}$ at points *M* and *N*. Make a sketch and then write a proof that $OM = ON$.

42. One of the sides of a parallelogram is 5 inches. Can the diagonals of the parallelogram be equal to 4 inches and 6 inches? Why or why not?

43. Three points that are not on the same line are marked on a plane. How many parallelograms with three of its vertices on the marked points can be drawn? Make a sketch of all possible options.

44. The difference of two angles of a parallelogram is 30°. Find all angles of the parallelogram.

45. A diagonal of a parallelogram divides it into two triangles. The perimeter of each triangle is 8.51 meters, while the perimeter of the parallelogram is 10.22 meters. What is the length of the diagonal?

46. Consider a quadrilateral *ABCD* whose interior angles all measure less than 180°. Prove that if $\angle BAC \cong \angle ACD$ and $\angle BCA \cong \angle DAC$, then *ABCD* is a parallelogram. Make a sketch and use it in your proof.

Practice Problems continue . . .

47. Prove the second parallelogram angle theorem using the diagram below.

Given: *ABCD* is a parallelogram

Prove: Adjacent angles in the parallelogram are supplementary

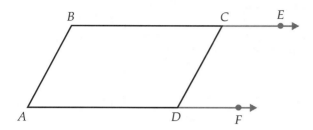

48. The angle between two heights drawn from a vertex of an acute angle of a parallelogram is equal to 116°. Find the angles of the parallelogram.

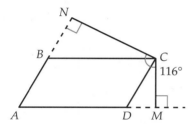

49. The perimeter of a parallelogram *ABCD* is 50 feet and $m\angle C = 30°$. The height *BH*, where *H* lies on side *CD*, is equal to 6.5 feet. Find the measures of the sides of the parallelogram.

50. **MP 1, 3** You are given two numbers. Can you uniquely define a parallelogram with these two numbers as its side lengths? Why or why not? If not, what else is needed to uniquely define a parallelogram? Can we use the same two numbers to uniquely identify a rectangle?

51. **MP 2** Represent all subsets of the set of quadrilaterals using a Venn diagram. Discuss whether trapezoids are a subset of parallelograms. Justify your reasoning.

52. A rectangle has vertices located at (4, 5), (8, 2), (2, −6), and (−2, −3). What is the area of the quadrilateral formed by connecting the midpoints of each side of this rectangle, expressed in square units?

LESSON 9.2

9.2 Deciding If a Parallelogram Is Also a Rectangle, Square, or Rhombus

In Lesson 9.1, we stated that rectangles, squares, and rhombi are all parallelograms. In this lesson, we provide the theorems needed to determine if parallelograms are also rectangles, squares, and/or rhombi.

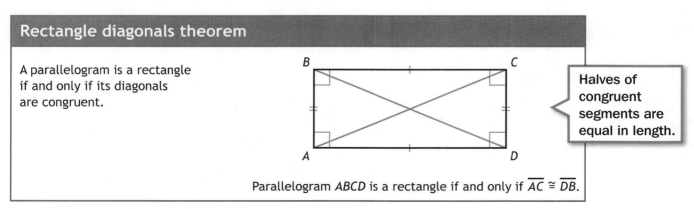

Rectangle diagonals theorem

A parallelogram is a rectangle if and only if its diagonals are congruent.

Halves of congruent segments are equal in length.

Parallelogram *ABCD* is a rectangle if and only if $\overline{AC} \cong \overline{DB}$.

Below, we prove one piece of the previous theorem.

Prove: $m\angle A \cong m\angle B \cong m\angle C \cong m\angle D = 90°$
Given: $ABCD$ is a parallelogram and $\overline{AC} \cong \overline{BD}$

> By definition, a rectangle is a parallelogram with four right angles.

Statement	Reason
$ABCD$ is a parallelogram	Given
$\overline{AB} \cong \overline{CD}$, $\overline{AD} \cong \overline{BC}$	Parallelogram opposite sides theorem
$\overline{AC} \cong \overline{BD}$	Given
$\overline{CD} \cong \overline{CD}$	Reflexive property
$\triangle ADC \cong \triangle BCD$	SSS postulate
$\angle D \cong \angle C$	Definition of congruent triangles
$\overline{AD} \cong \overline{AD}$	Reflexive property
$\triangle ADC \cong \triangle DAB$	SSS postulate
$\angle D \cong \angle A$	Definition of congruent triangles
$\overline{AB} \cong \overline{AB}$	Reflexive property
$\triangle DAB \cong \triangle CBA$	SSS postulate
$\angle A \cong \angle B$	Definition of congruent triangles
$\angle A \cong \angle B \cong \angle C \cong \angle D$	Transitive property of congruence
$m\angle A \cong m\angle B \cong m\angle C \cong m\angle D = 90°$	Sum of interior angles in a quadrilateral

Parallelogram and rhombus theorems

> A rhombus is a parallelogram with four congruent sides. These theorems provide two additional ways to know if a parallelogram is a rhombus.

A parallelogram is a rhombus
if and only if its diagonals are perpendicular.

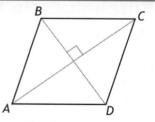

Parallelogram $ABCD$ is a rhombus if and only if $\overline{AC} \perp \overline{BD}$.

A parallelogram is a rhombus if and only if
its diagonals bisect the figure's angles.

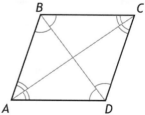

Parallelogram $ABCD$ is a rhombus if and only if $\angle BAC \cong \angle DAC$,
$\angle ABD \cong \angle CBD$, $\angle BCA \cong \angle DCA$, and $\angle CDB \cong \angle ADB$.

If a parallelogram is both a rectangle and a rhombus, then it is a square. It will have four right angles, and four congruent sides.

MODEL PROBLEMS

1. The diagonal of a rectangle starts at (2, 4) and ends at (2, 10). What other segment with the endpoints described below could also be a diagonal?

    A. (2, 4) and (2, −1)   C. (4, 4) and (4, 10)

    B. (−1, 7) and (5, 7)   D. (−2, 6) and (2, 6)

SOLUTION

The answer is B. Diagonals in a rectangle are congruent, so we need one with a length of 6 (the difference in the *y*-coordinates is the length of the one described in the problem). Only B and C are 6 long. Choice C describes a segment parallel to the one in the problem statement, and diagonals need to intersect. Choice A also describes a line segment parallel to the one in the problem statement. Choice D is too short. Choice B bisects and is bisected by the line segment described in the problem statement. The diagonals happen to be perpendicular, so this retangle is also a rhombus and, thus, a square.

 2. **MP 1, 4** A rope has traditionally been used to lay out a rectangle. In many parts of the world, this method is still used to create a rectangular plot. In the diagram, four people stand at the corners of the plot. Along one side of the plot is a bamboo pole. Each person holds the end of the rope. How might a rope be used to create a rectangle?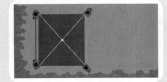

SOLUTION

One side of plot is bamboo pole

The method starts with a bamboo pole. Each end of the bamboo pole is a vertex of the rectangle.

Take two equal-length ropes and knot them together in their middles

Two equal-length ropes are then knotted in their middles.

Pull them taut and straight to locate the other two vertices

The ropes are then pulled taut. This locates the other two vertices. Why does this method work? The diagonals of a rectangle bisect one another. This approach gives you a sense of the size of plots of land in the developing world (not very large—with this method, not longer than a piece of bamboo).

Model Problems continue . . .

3. What are the measures of x and y in the rhombus?

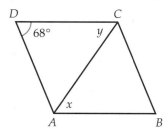

SOLUTION

Draw diagonal	Diagonal bisects interior angle	We find the measures of x and y by using the two parallelogram and rhombus theorems and the alternate interior angle theorem. Start by drawing the second diagonal. The two adjacent angles equal 34°, since the diagonals of a rhombus bisect its interior angles, and half of 68° is 34°.
Diagonals are perpendicular	$y = 180° - 34° - 90° = 56°$	Diagonals in a rhombus are perpendicular, which gives us two angles in a triangle. Triangle angles sum to 180°. Subtract to calculate the measure of the third angle, y, which is equal to 56°.
Alternate interior angles	$x = y = 56°$	Segments $\overline{AB}$ and $\overline{CD}$ of the rhombus are opposite sides of the rhombus and are parallel, so the diagonal acts as a transversal. This means that the measures of x and y are equal since their angles are congruent alternate interior angles.
Draw diagram	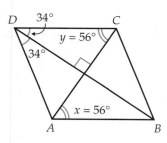	Complete the problem by drawing a diagram.

> There are other ways to answer this question. For instance, we can calculate x by noting that its angle is the third angle in a triangle where you know two angles. This means we could subtract:
> $180° - 90° - 34° = 56°$

Identifying Rectangles, Rhombuses, and Squares

Using the properties and theorems of parallelograms, we can decide whether a figure is a rectangle, rhombus, or both—which would make it a square.

MODEL PROBLEM

What type of figures are *MINE* and *YOUR*?

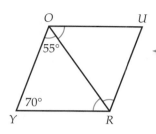

> We determine the types of quadrilaterals. However, we have to be careful because the figures are not drawn to scale. We can only rely on the hash marks and congruent angle arcs provided in the diagrams.

SOLUTION

MINE diagonals	The single hash marks on the diagonals show not only that the diagonals bisect each other, but that they are congruent. This means that *MINE* is a parallelogram and a rectangle.
MINE is a rectangle	However, the double and triple hash marks on the sides show that *MINE* cannot also be a rhombus (which would make it a square). *MINE* must be a rectangle.

YOUR angles

$2(55°) + 70° = 180°$

Double the 55° angle and add it to 70° to calculate the sum of two consecutive angles. They sum to 180°.

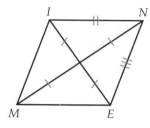 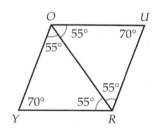

The angles opposite the 55° angles also have a measure of 55°. This means that the measure of the remaining angle is 70°. Because consecutive angles are supplementary, *YOUR* is a parallelogram.

YOUR sides

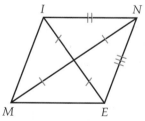 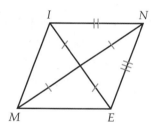

YOR is an isosceles triangle. ∠*ORY* and ∠*YOR* are congruent, so sides *OY* and *RY* are also congruent.

Triangles *YOR* and *OUR* are congruent, so all sides opposite an angle of 55° are congruent, which means that *YOUR* is also a rhombus.

YOUR is a rhombus

Angles not equal to 90° (not a square)

However, because the angles are not equal to 90°, the figure cannot be a square, and is only a rhombus.

PRACTICE

1. The diagonals of a parallelogram *ABCD* are perpendicular to each other. Which of the following must be true about *ABCD*?

   A. *ABCD* is a rectangle.
   B. *ABCD* is a rhombus.
   C. *ABCD* is a square.

2. The lengths of the diagonals of a parallelogram *ABCD* are equal to each other. Which of the following must be true about *ABCD*?

   A. *ABCD* is a rectangle.
   B. *ABCD* is a rhombus.
   C. *ABCD* is a square.

3. Which of the following must be true about the rhombus *TORN*? Choose all that apply.

   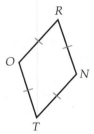

   A. $TR = ON$
   B. $\overline{TR} \perp \overline{ON}$
   C. $m\angle ROT = m\angle RNT$
   D. $NO = RT$

4. A quadrilateral is a square if its diagonals are

   A. Congruent and perpendicular.
   B. Perpendicular and bisect each other.
   C. Congruent and bisect each other.
   D. Any two of the above.

5. The right triangles *ABC* and *DEC* are congruent, and $\overline{AB} \parallel \overline{DE}$. What must be true about the quadrilateral *ABDE*?

   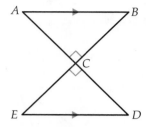

   A. *ABDE* is a rhombus.
   B. *ABDE* is a rectangle.
   C. *ABDE* is a square.

6. Given rhombus *ABCD*, with diagonal $\overline{BD}$ and $m\angle ABD = 40°$, what is the $m\angle A$?

7. The figure below is a rhombus. What are the measures of *x* and *y* if $z = 54°$?

   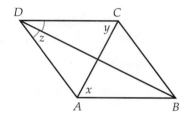

8. Explain how if all angles of a parallelogram are congruent then it is a rectangle.

9. Explain how if one angle of a parallelogram is a right angle then the parallelogram is a rectangle.

10. Explain how a rhombus with a right angle is also a square.

11. The diagonals of a rectangle *EFGH* below intersect at point *A*. Prove that the triangles *EAH* and *EAF* are isosceles.

    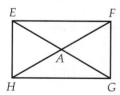

12. Prove that in a rhombus the diagonals bisect the rhombus's angles and are perpendicular to each other.

   Practice Problems continue . . .

13. In the parallelogram *KLMN*, the diagonal $\overline{KM}$ is 7 inches long. How long would $\overline{LN}$ have to be to ensure that *KLMN* is a rectangle?

Exercises 14–15: Use the diagram to answer the questions.

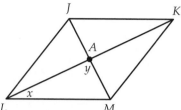

14. $m\angle JLA$ is 27°. What value of *x* would make the parallelogram a rhombus?

15. $m\angle JLA$ is 34°. What value of *y* would make the parallelogram a rhombus?

16. One of the angles formed by the diagonal of a rhombus and its side is equal to 29°. Find the angles of the rhombus.

17. The angles formed by the side of a rhombus and each of its two diagonals have a ratio of 4 to 5. Find the angles of the rhombus.

18. Use the properties of rhombuses to find the angles of the rhombus in the diagram below. Note: The diagram is not drawn to scale.

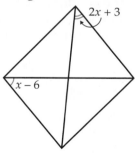

19. Use the properties of rhombuses to find the angles of the rhombus in the diagram below. Note: The diagram is not drawn to scale.

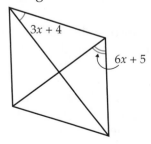

20. The diagonals of a parallelogram are perpendicular to each other. The perimeter of the parallelogram is 48 feet. Find the lengths of the sides of the parallelogram.

21. Two isosceles triangles *ABC* and *DEC* are congruent. Can you conclude that the quadrilateral *ABDE* must be a rhombus? A rectangle? Why or why not?

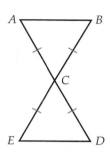

22. MP 3 Prove that the midpoints of the sides of a rectangle are the vertices of a rhombus. Make a sketch and refer to it in your proof.

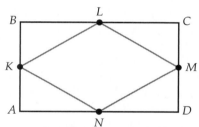

23. To create a square out of a rectangular piece of paper, Mariah folds it as shown below and cuts out a strip of paper in the bottom. Then she unfolds the piece to get a square. Explain why this method produces a square.

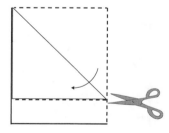

24. $m\angle AJL$ is 63°. What value of *x* would make the parallelogram a rhombus?

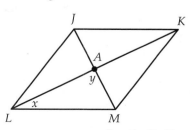

25. **MP 3** Prove the distances from the point of intersection of the diagonals of a rhombus to all its sides are equal.

Prove: $OA = OB = OC = OD$

Given: $KLMN$ is a rhombus, $\overline{KM}$ and $\overline{LN}$ are diagonals, and the diagonals intersect at O.

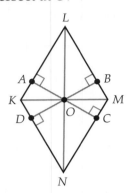

26. **MP 1, 2** Exterior to the vertices of a square $ABCD$, the lines parallel to its diagonals are drawn. Make a sketch and determine the type of the quadrilateral $EFGH$ that is formed. Justify your answer.

27. One of the angles of a rhombus is equal to 36°. Find the angles that the diagonals of the rhombus form with its sides.

28. One of the angles of a rhombus is equal to 51°. Find the angles that the diagonals of the rhombus form with its sides.

29. $ABCD$ is a square. $\overline{AE}$, $\overline{BF}$, $\overline{CG}$, and $\overline{DH}$ are all congruent. Prove that $EFGH$ is a square.

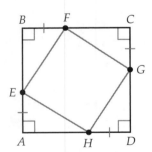

30. Prove that the midpoints of the sides of a rhombus are the vertices of a rectangle. In other words, if $MORE$ is a rhombus and D, U, S, and T are the midpoints of its sides, prove that $DUST$ is a rectangle.

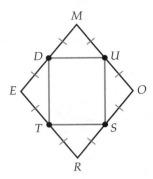

31. The side of a rhombus forms two angles with its diagonals such that their difference is equal to 30°. What are the angles of the rhombus?

32. A height of a rhombus divides its base into two equal segments. What are the angles of the rhombus?

33. Prove that a parallelogram is a rhombus if and only if its diagonals bisect its angles.

34. **MP 2, 6** A square is inscribed into an isosceles right triangle with a hypotenuse of 2 centimeters. What is the perimeter of the square? Give your answer to the nearest tenth.

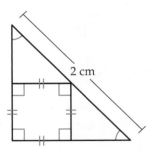

35. The perimeter of a rhombus is 8 inches and its height is 1 inch. Find the obtuse angle of the rhombus.

36. **MP 2, 5** Let $ABCD$ be a rhombus. If $m\angle B = 60°$ and $AC = 12.5$ inches, find the perimeter of the rhombus $ABCD$.

37. One angle of a rhombus is 120° and its sides are 3 centimeters each. Find the length of the shortest diagonal of the rhombus.

9.3 Deciding If a Quadrilateral Is a Parallelogram

Earlier, we stated theorems about quadrilaterals, such as opposite sides of a parallelogram are congruent. In this lesson, we begin to state the converses of those theorems. We use them to decide if a quadrilateral is a parallelogram. In other words, *if* a quadrilateral has certain properties, such as congruent opposite sides, we *then* know it is a parallelogram.

Parallelogram opposite sides theorem converse

If both pairs of opposite sides of a quadrilateral are congruent, then the quadrilateral is a parallelogram.

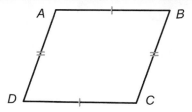

If $\overline{AB} \cong \overline{CD}$ and $\overline{AD} \cong \overline{BC}$, then *ABCD* is a parallelogram.

Parallelogram opposite angles theorem converse

If both pairs of opposite angles of a quadrilateral are congruent, then the quadrilateral is a parallelogram.

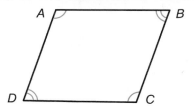

If $\angle A \cong \angle C$ and $\angle B \cong \angle D$, then *ABCD* is a parallelogram.

Parallelogram supplementary angles theorem converse

If all angles in a quadrilateral are supplementary to their consecutive angles, then the quadrilateral is a parallelogram.

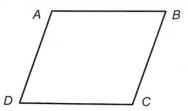

If $m\angle A + m\angle B = 180°$, $m\angle B + m\angle C = 180°$, $m\angle C + m\angle D = 180°$, $m\angle D + m\angle A = 180°$, then *ABCD* is a parallelogram.

Parallelogram diagonals theorem converse

If the diagonals of a quadrilateral bisect one another, then it is a parallelogram.

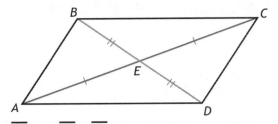

If $\overline{AE} \cong \overline{EC}$ and $\overline{DE} \cong \overline{EB}$, then $ABCD$ is a parallelogram.

Parallelogram and quadrilateral theorem

If one pair of sides of a quadrilateral is congruent and parallel, then the quadrilateral is a parallelogram.

> If two sides of a quadrilateral are both parallel and congruent, then the figure is a parallelogram.

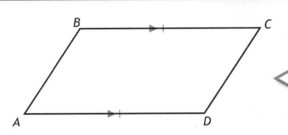

If $\overline{BC} \cong \overline{AD}$ and $\overline{BC} \parallel \overline{AD}$, then $ABCD$ is a parallelogram.

We prove the parallelogram and quadrilateral theorem stated above:

Prove: $ABCD$ is a parallelogram
Given: $\overline{AD} \cong \overline{BC}$ and $\overline{AD} \parallel \overline{BC}$

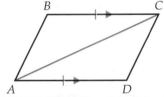

Statement	Reason	
$\overline{AD} \cong \overline{BC}$, $\overline{AD} \parallel \overline{BC}$	Given	This information is given in the hypothesis of the parallelogram and quadrilateral theorem.
$\angle ACB \cong \angle CAD$	Alternate interior angles theorem	Because the opposite sides are parallel, the diagonal acts as a transversal and creates these congruent alternate interior angles.
$\overline{AC} \cong \overline{AC}$	Reflexive property of congruence	A segment is congruent to itself.
$\triangle DAC \cong \triangle BCA$	SAS postulate	The two triangles are congruent, because two of their corresponding sides and the angle between them are congruent.
$\overline{AB} \cong \overline{CD}$	Definition of congruent triangles	Corresponding sides of congruent triangles are congruent.
$ABCD$ is a parallelogram	Parallelogram opposite sides theorem converse	Because we have shown that the opposite sides in the quadrilateral are congruent, the quadrilateral must be a parallelogram.

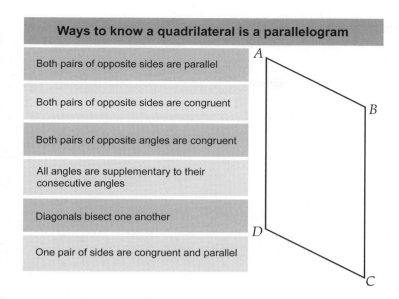

Ways to know a quadrilateral is a parallelogram
Both pairs of opposite sides are parallel
Both pairs of opposite sides are congruent
Both pairs of opposite angles are congruent
All angles are supplementary to their consecutive angles
Diagonals bisect one another
One pair of sides are congruent and parallel

MODEL PROBLEMS

1. Are either of the quadrilaterals below parallelograms?

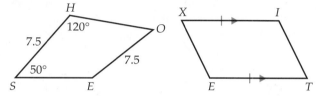

SOLUTION

SHOE is not a parallelogram. The consecutive angles would add up to 180°.

EXIT is a parallelogram because a set of opposite sides are both parallel and congruent.

2. Is this quadrilateral a parallelogram? What does x equal?

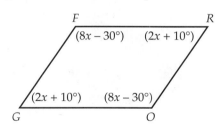

SOLUTION

Opposite angles are congruent	Figure is a parallelogram	The figure is a parallelogram since its opposite angles are congruent. The same expression represents each pair of opposite angles.
Consecutive angles are supplementary	$(2x + 10°) + (8x - 30°) = 180°$	Consecutive angles are supplementary in a parallelogram. This means, write an equation summing the two angle expressions to 180°.
Evaluate the expression for x	$10x - 20° = 180°$ $10x = 200°$ $x = 20°$	Calculate x. Combine like terms, isolate the variable, and divide.

Model Problems continue . . .

3. State all properties of angles for *NEXT*, and sides for *LAST*, that would make each quadrilateral a parallelogram.

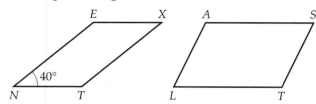

SOLUTION

NEXT $m\angle E = 140°$, $m\angle T = 140°$, and $m\angle X = 40°$ There are two ways based solely on angle measures to know that *NEXT* is a parallelogram. One is that all consecutive angles are supplementary, which in this case means angles *T* and *E* both must be 140°, and angle *X* must be 40°. These angles also match the second condition: all opposite angles are congruent.

LAST $\overline{LA} \parallel \overline{ST}$ and $\overline{LA} \cong \overline{ST}$, or $\overline{LA} \cong \overline{ST}$ and $\overline{AS} \cong \overline{TL}$, or $\overline{LA} \parallel \overline{ST}$ and $\overline{AS} \parallel \overline{TL}$ There are three conditions that would each make the figure a parallelogram. First, a pair of sides are both congruent and parallel. Second, if both pairs of opposite sides are congruent. Third, if both pairs of opposite sides are parallel.

4. **MP 4** In the figure below, it is important for the platform to remain parallel to the ground as it rises so packages do not slide off. Will this design accomplish that goal? Why?

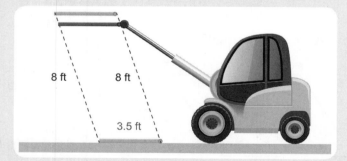

SOLUTION

Opposite sides congruent	Lift's path makes parallelogram	The lift stays the same length, and the distance each end travels from the floor to its highest point is the same. This means the lift and its path create a parallelogram.
Parallelogram opposite sides are parallel	Platform will always be parallel to ground	The definition of a parallelogram is that its opposite sides are parallel. This means that as the platform rises up, it will remain parallel to the ground.

1. *TRAM* is a quadrilateral. Which of the following would allow us to conclude that *TRAM* is a parallelogram?

A. $TR = MT$

B. $AT = RM$

C. $m\angle T = m\angle A$ and $m\angle M + m\angle A = 180°$

D. None of the above

2. If two pairs of opposite sides of a quadrilateral are congruent and the angle at one vertex of the quadrilateral is 56°, which of these could be the angle at another vertex?

A. 34°   C. 112°

B. 248°   D. 56°

3. What is the length of the side $\overline{CD}$ of the quadrilateral *ABCD* below?

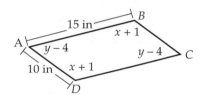

A. 10 in   C. 15 in

B. 20 in   D. 5 in

4. Congruent elements are marked on the diagrams showing the quadrilaterals *LIMB*, *CARD*, and *SPOT*. Which of these quadrilaterals must be parallelograms? Check all that apply.

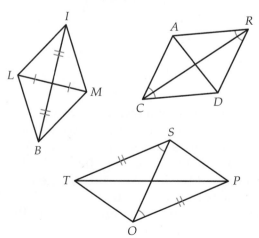

A. *LIMB*   C. *SPOT*

B. *CARD*   D. None of them

5. Is the figure below a parallelogram? Find its angle measures.

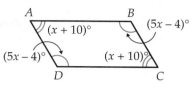

6. Is the figure below a parallelogram? Find its angle measures.

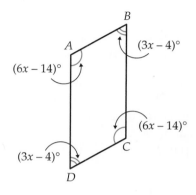

7. The opposite angles of a quadrilateral are congruent, and its perimeter is equal to 188 inches. Two of its sides are equal to $x + 3$ inches and $2x + 4$ inches. Find the lengths of the sides in inches.

8. The opposite angles of a quadrilateral are congruent. Also, the measure of the larger angle of the quadrilateral is 26° greater than the measure of the smaller angle. Find the angles of the quadrilateral.

9. The opposite angles of a quadrilateral are congruent. If one angle of the quadrilateral is three times as large as another, find the angles.

10. In a quadrilateral *ABCD*, $\angle BAC \cong \angle ACD$ and $\angle BCA \cong \angle DAC$. Prove that *ABCD* is a parallelogram.

Practice Problems continue . . .

11. A bookcase without a back panel can sometimes bend, as shown in the diagram below. What will happen to tennis balls that are kept on the shelves of the bookcase—will they roll from the shelves or stay there? Justify your answer.

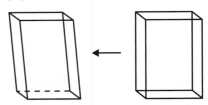

12. Two interior angles of a quadrilateral are right angles. Is this quadrilateral a parallelogram? Why or why not?

13. Kaya said to Marcus: "Two of the sides of the quadrilateral I drew are equal to 5 inches each, and two other sides are equal to 6 inches each." Marcus says: "I know! You drew a parallelogram!" Is Marcus right? Explain.

14. The pattern shown below is made of two pairs of identical triangular tiles. Is the shape shown a parallelogram? Why or why not?

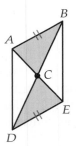

15. Michael has a parallelogram-shaped wooden board. He measures out the same distance on each side of his board, starting from each vertex, and nails in the pegs. After he stretches a rubber band on the pegs, he gets the shape shown below. Prove that the shape Michael obtained is a parallelogram.

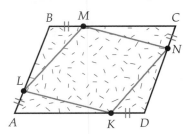

16. In a parallelogram *BEST*, the point *A* is the midpoint of $\overline{ES}$ and point *M* is the midpoint of $\overline{BT}$. Make a sketch and prove that the quadrilateral *EATM* is a parallelogram.

17. In the diagram below, *ABCD* and *AMND* are parallelograms. Prove that *MBCN* is also a parallelogram.

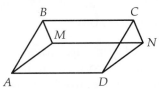

18. *ROSE* is a parallelogram. The points *A*, *B*, *C*, and *D* are midpoints of the segments $\overline{XR}$, $\overline{XO}$, $\overline{XS}$, and $\overline{XE}$, respectively. Prove that *ABCD* is also a parallelogram.

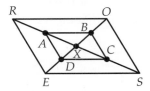

19. In the parallelogram *EFGH*, the diagonals intersect at point *O*. A line passes through the point *O* and intersects the sides of parallelogram at points *M* and *N*. Prove that *OM* = *ON*.

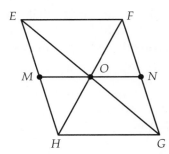

20. A midsegment of a triangle is a segment connecting the midpoints of two of the triangle's sides. In the triangle *ABC*, $\overline{MN}$ is a midsegment connecting the sides $\overline{AB}$ and $\overline{BC}$. Extend the line $\overline{MN}$ outside the triangle and mark the point *P* such that *MN* = *NP*. Prove that *AMPC* is a parallelogram. Refer to your sketch in your proof.

Practice Problems continue . . .

21. MP 1, 7 In a quadrilateral $ABCD$, $m\angle A + m\angle B = 180°$ and $m\angle B + m\angle C = 180°$. The diagonals $\overline{AC}$ and $\overline{BD}$ intersect at point O. A line passes through the point O and intersects the sides $\overline{BC}$ and $\overline{AD}$ at the points M and K, respectively, so the $m\angle BOM = 90°$. Make a sketch and state why $BK = BM$.

22. MP 4, 5 The perimeter of a parallelogram is 90 feet. A diagonal of the parallelogram makes angles of 90° and 30° with the sides. Find the lengths of the sides of the parallelogram.

23. Use the diagram below to prove the parallelogram opposite angles theorem converse. Hint: Begin by using the fact that $2a + 2b = 360°$.

Given: $\angle A \cong \angle BCD$ and $\angle D \cong \angle ABC$
Prove: $ABCD$ is a parallelogram

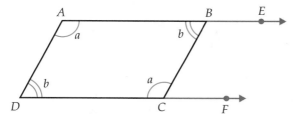

24. Use the diagram below to prove the parallelogram supplementary angles theorem converse. Hint: First prove that $\overline{AB} \parallel \overline{CD}$ by showing $\overrightarrow{AE} \parallel \overrightarrow{DF}$. Then, write a similar series of steps to prove $\overline{AD} \parallel \overline{BC}$ by showing $\overrightarrow{AG} \parallel \overrightarrow{BH}$.

Given: Consecutive interior angles are supplementary
Prove: $ABCD$ is a parallelogram

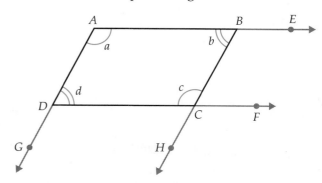

25. MP 1, 3 Prove that, in a parallelogram, the sum of the squares of the diagonals is equal to the sum of the squares of all its sides. In other words, in parallelogram $ABCD$: $AC^2 + BD^2 = AB^2 + BC^2 + CD^2 + AD^2$

26. Prove the parallelogram diagonals theorem converse. Hint: Prove that the opposite sides of the quadrilateral are congruent, then use the parallelogram opposite sides theorem converse.

Parallelogram diagonals theorem converse

If the diagonals of a quadrilateral bisect one another, then it is a parallelogram.

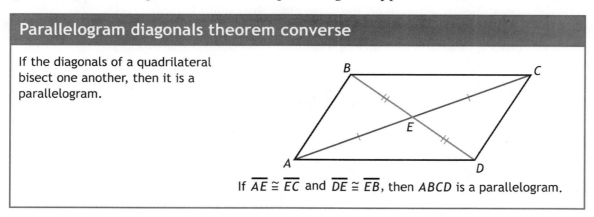

If $\overline{AE} \cong \overline{EC}$ and $\overline{DE} \cong \overline{EB}$, then $ABCD$ is a parallelogram.

Practice Problems continue . . .

27. **MP 3** Prove the parallelogram opposite sides theorem converse. Hint: Construct $\overline{BD}$ and work backward through the proof for the parallelogram opposite sides theorem (non-converse).

Parallelogram opposite sides theorem converse

If both pairs of opposite sides of a quadrilateral are congruent, then the quadrilateral is a parallelogram.

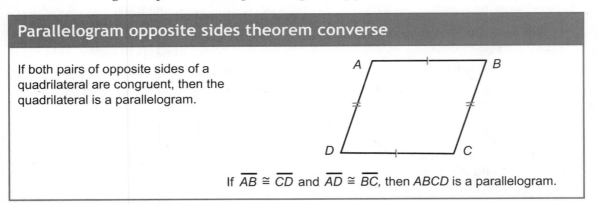

If $\overline{AB} \cong \overline{CD}$ and $\overline{AD} \cong \overline{BC}$, then $ABCD$ is a parallelogram.

LESSON 9.4

9.4 Optional: Polygons and Their Angles

Interior Angles in a Polygon

Interior angles, the angles inside a polygon, are formed by each pair of adjacent sides in a polygon. The sum of the interior angle measures for a triangle is 180°. The sum of the interior angle measures for a square, a rectangle, or any quadrilateral is 360°.

To calculate the sum of interior angles:

$$\text{sum} = 180°(n-2)$$
$$n = \text{number of sides}$$

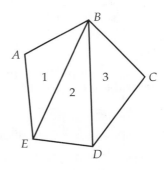

One informal derivation of this formula is to note the number of triangles, such as the ones shown in the diagram, is two less than the number of vertices. (For instance, the diagram shows three triangles when there are five vertices) Since the measure of a triangle's angles sum to 180°, we have an informal derivation of the formula.

There is also a formula for calculating the measure of each angle in a regular polygon. The formula follows from the fact that the angles in a regular polygon are congruent.

To calculate each interior angle:

$$\text{angle} = \frac{180°(n - 2)}{n}$$
$$n = \text{number of sides}$$

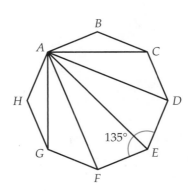

The formula has the expression we just showed for the sum of the figure's angle measures, divided by the number of sides, with the number of sides equal to the number of angles.

The measures of interior angles are used to define convex and concave polygons.

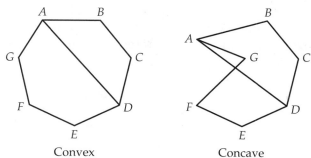

Convex   Concave

In a **convex polygon**, all diagonals connecting vertices are inside the polygon. All the interior angles of a convex polygon are less than 180°. All the vertices point outward, away from the interior.

In a **concave polygon**, some diagonals connecting vertices will be outside the polygon. One or more interior angles of a concave polygon are greater than 180°. Some vertices point inward, toward the interior.

MODEL PROBLEMS

1. What is $m\angle F$?

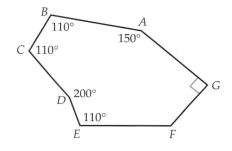

SOLUTION

Angles in 7-sided polygon	sum = $180°(n-2)$ sum = $180°(7-2) = 900°$	The polygon has 7 sides. Substitute that value into the equation for the sum of the angles in a polygon and calculate.
Calculate $m\angle F$	$m\angle F = 900° - (150° + 200° + 90° + 3 \cdot 110°)$ $m\angle F = 900° - 770° = 130°$	$m\angle F$ is equal to 900° minus the sum of the other angles. Take advantage of the fact that there are three 110° angles when doing the subtraction. Sum the expression in the parentheses and subtract.

2. A polygon's interior angles sum to 1080°. What type of polygon is it?

SOLUTION

Angles sum to 1080°	sum = $180°(n-2) = 1080°$	We know the sum of the angles, but not the number of sides.
Substitute and solve	$n - 2 = \dfrac{1080°}{180°}$ $n - 2 = 6$ $n = 8$ sides Octagon	Substitute and solve the equation for n. The polygon is an octagon.

Exterior Angles of a Convex Polygon

We show the exterior angles of a convex polygon made by extending each of its sides. The sum of these exterior angles does not depend on the number of sides of a polygon—the sum always equals 360°.

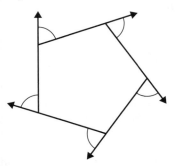

> Exterior angles are angles formed by a side of a convex polygon and the extension of its adjacent side.

MODEL PROBLEMS

1. What is $m\angle BCX$?

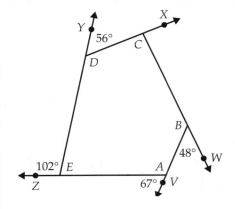

SOLUTION

Sum of exterior angles

$360° = m\angle BCX + 67° + 56° + 48° + 102°$
$m\angle BCX = 360° - 273°$
$m\angle BCX = 87°$

The sum of the exterior angles of a convex polygon is always 360°. Add the other angles and subtract them from 360°.

2. Climbers use chocks to attach ropes by placing them in rocks. What are the measures of each interior and exterior angle of a regular, six-sided chock?

SOLUTION

Equation for interior angle measures

$$\text{angle} = \frac{180°(n-2)}{n} = \frac{180°(6-2)}{6}$$
$$\text{angle} = 120°$$

Use the equation for the measure of interior angles, substituting 6 for the number of sides and evaluate. The interior angles each have a measure of 120°.

Exterior angle measures sum to 360°

$$\frac{360°}{6} = 60°$$

Divide by the number of sides to find the measure of each exterior angle. The exterior angles are 60°.

Number of Diagonals in a Polygon

A diagonal is a line segment connecting two non-adjacent vertices. The number of diagonals in a polygon does not depend on whether the polygon is regular or irregular, only on the polygon's number of sides.

To calculate the number of diagonals in a polygon:

$$\text{number of diagonals} = \frac{n(n-3)}{2}$$

$n = \text{number of sides}$

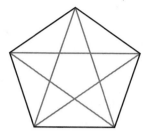

PRACTICE

1. What is the sum of the interior angles of a pentagon with sides measuring 3 in, 4 in, 5 in, 7 in, and 6 in?

A. 250°
B. 540°
C. 360°
D. 180°

2. A modern building façade has the shape of a regular nonagon. What is the measure of the angle between adjacent sides of the façade?

A. 1360°
B. 140°
C. 160°
D. 136°

3. The measure of each exterior angle of a polygon is 30°. How many sides does the polygon have?

A. 6
B. 10
C. 12
D. 36

4. The measure of each interior angle of a polygon is equal to 144°. What type of polygon is it?

A. Octagon
B. Nonagon
C. Decagon
D. Heptagon

5. Which statement is correct? Choose all that apply.

A. A regular polygon is always convex.
B. A polygon with congruent angles is always regular.
C. A regular polygon has congruent angles and congruent sides.
D. The sum of the interior angles of a polygon is always greater than the sum of its exterior angles.

6. One of the interior angles of a polygon is equal to 210°. What type of polygon is it?

A. Convex polygon
B. Concave polygon
C. Triangle

7. *ABCDE* is a concave pentagon with congruent sides. Which of the following must be true about *ABCDE*?

A. *ABCDE* is a regular pentagon.
B. The sum of its interior angles is greater than 540°.
C. Each interior angle of the pentagon *ABCDE* is equal to 108°.
D. One of the interior angles of *ABCDE* is greater than 180°.

8. What is the measure of each interior angle in a regular 10-sided polygon?

9. A polygon's interior angles sum to 360°. How many sides does it have?

Practice Problems continue . . .

10. How many diagonals are in a pentagon?

11. What is the sum of the interior angles of a polygon with 7 sides?

12. What is the sum, in degrees, of the interior angles of the polygon below?

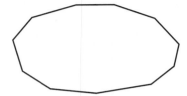

13. What is the sum, in degrees, of the interior angles of an octagon?

14. What is the sum, in degrees, of the interior angles of a rhombus?

15. What is the sum, in degrees, of the interior angles of a hexagon?

16. For simplicity, mathematicians sometimes refer to polygons that have many sides as *n*-gons, where *n* stands for the number of sides. What is the sum of the interior angles of a 16-gon?

17. A 19-sided figure is called an enneadecagon. What is the degree sum of its interior angles?

18. What is the measure of each interior angle of a regular pentagon?

19. What is the measure of each interior angle of a regular hexagon?

20. The sum of the angles of a convex polygon with equal angles is equal to 1260°. What is the measure of each angle of the polygon?

21. How many sides does a regular polygon with an interior angle of 60° have?

22. How many sides does a regular polygon with an interior angle of 90° have?

23. How many sides does a regular polygon with an interior angle of 108° have?

24. Four angles of a convex pentagon are congruent, and the fifth angle is 80°. Find the measure of each of the four congruent angles.

25. What is the measure of each exterior angle of a regular polygon with 9 sides?

26. What is the measure of each exterior angle of a regular polygon with 6 sides?

27. What is the measure of each exterior angle of a regular polygon with 8 sides?

28. The measure of each exterior angle of a polygon is 72°. How many sides does the polygon have?

29. The measure of each exterior angle of a polygon is 40°. How many sides does the polygon have?

30. The measure of each exterior angle of a polygon is 60°. How many sides does the polygon have?

31. A 19-sided figure is called an *enneadecagon*. What is the sum of the measures of the exterior angles of an enneadecagon?

32. The sum of the interior angles of a convex polygon is equal to the sum of its exterior angles. How many sides does the polygon have?

33. In the figure below, the interior angle at *A* measures 75° and the interior angle at *B* measures 102°. What is the sum of the angles 1, 2, and 3?

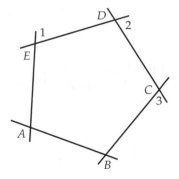

34. The measure of each exterior angle of a convex polygon is *x* degrees. Find an expression for the sum of the interior angles of the polygon in terms of *x*.

35. Is it possible to draw a convex quadrilateral so that all four of its angles are acute? If it is, show how. If not, explain why.

Practice Problems continue . . .

36. **MP 2, 6** Explain how you know that the figure obtained by connecting every other vertex of a regular octagon is a square. Make a sketch to support your explanation.

37. **MP 4, 5** In a video game, two pirates stand on adjacent corners of a field that has the shape of a regular decagon. When they direct their laser beams along the extensions of the sides of the field, as shown below, the points of the beams' intersection shows the place where treasure is hidden. Find the obtuse angle between the pirates' beams.

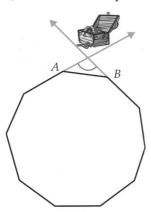

38. A convex polygon has 20 diagonals. How many sides does the polygon have?

39. **MP 3** Prove that the sum of the interior angles of a convex polygon with n sides is $(n - 2) \cdot 180°$.

40. The vertices of a triangle are $(0, 0)$, $\left(\dfrac{1}{a} - \dfrac{1}{a^2}, 0 \right)$, and $(0, y)$ when $a > 1$. Sketch the triangle and find the value of y if the area of the triangle is $\dfrac{3}{a(a - 1)}$.

41. **MP 1, 2** A blacksmith holds an iron piece, shaped as a regular hexagon, with his tongs. Determine the size, d, of the opening of the tongs, if each side of the piece has a length of s inches.

LESSON 9.5

9.5 Trapezoids and Kites

Trapezoids

A **trapezoid** is a quadrilateral with at least one pair of parallel sides. The parallel sides of a trapezoid are called *bases*, and the other sides are called *legs*. A pair of angles formed in part by the same base are called *base angles*. Since a trapezoid has two bases, it has two pairs of base angles.

An **isosceles trapezoid** has congruent legs, as shown below in the theorem diagram:

Isosceles trapezoid theorem

If the quadrilateral is an isosceles trapezoid, then each pair of base angles is congruent.

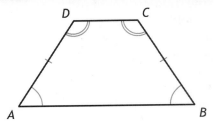

> The theorem describes the relationship of each pair of base angles in an isosceles trapezoid.

If *ABCD* is a trapezoid with $\overline{AD} \cong \overline{BC}$, then $\angle A \cong \angle B$ and $\angle C \cong \angle D$.

Isosceles trapezoid diagonals theorem

If a quadrilateral is an isosceles trapezoid, then its diagonals are congruent.

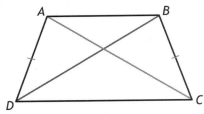

If *ABCD* is an isosceles trapezoid, then $\overline{AC} \cong \overline{BD}$.

We prove the theorem:

Prove: $\overline{AC} \cong \overline{BD}$
Given: *ABCD* is isosceles trapezoid

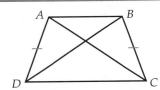

Statement	Reason	
ABCD is isosceles trapezoid	Given	The hypothesis of the theorem states that the figure is an isosceles trapezoid.
$\overline{AD} \cong \overline{BC}$	Definition of isosceles trapezoid	By definition, the two legs of an isosceles trapezoid are congruent.
$\overline{CD} \cong \overline{CD}$	Reflexive property of congruence	The segment is congruent to itself.
$\angle BCD \cong \angle ADC$	Isosceles trapezoid theorem	Base angles in an isosceles trapezoid are congruent.
$\triangle ADC \cong \triangle BCD$	SAS postulate	Two corresponding sides and their included angle are congruent, so the two triangles are congruent.
$\overline{AC} \cong \overline{BD}$	Definition of congruent triangles	Corresponding sides of congruent triangles are congruent.

What are the measures of the three other angles in the isosceles trapezoid?

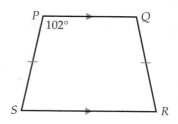

SOLUTION

Base angles are congruent	$m\angle P = m\angle Q = 102°$	In an isosceles trapezoid, the two angles that form a pair of base angles are congruent.
Two interior angles are supplementary	$m\angle P + m\angle S = 180°$ $102° + m\angle S = 180°$ $m\angle S = 78°$	These two angles are consecutive interior angles formed by a transversal and a pair of parallel lines. This means they are supplementary. Substitute for $m\angle P$ and calculate $m\angle S$.
Base angles are congruent	$m\angle S = m\angle R = 78°$	$\angle S$ and $\angle R$ are also a pair of base angles, so they too are congruent in an isosceles trapezoid.

Midsegments and Trapezoids

A midsegment of a triangle connects the midpoints of two sides of a triangle. A midsegment of a trapezoid connects the midpoints of the legs—the sides that are not parallel.

Trapezoid midsegment theorems

A trapezoid's midsegment is parallel to each base.

Midsegment's length is one half the sum of the bases' lengths.

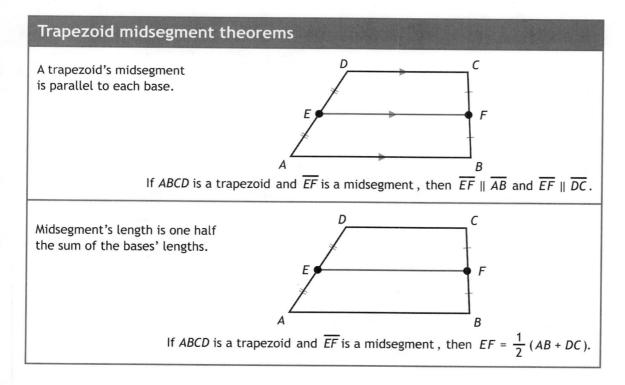

If $ABCD$ is a trapezoid and $\overline{EF}$ is a midsegment, then $\overline{EF} \parallel \overline{AB}$ and $\overline{EF} \parallel \overline{DC}$.

If $ABCD$ is a trapezoid and $\overline{EF}$ is a midsegment, then $EF = \frac{1}{2}(AB + DC)$.

We prove that the length of the midsegment is one half the sum of the lengths of the bases:

Prove: $NQ = \dfrac{1}{2}(MR + OP)$

Given: $\overline{NQ}$ is a midsegment of $MOPR$

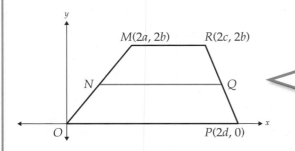

> We can assign whatever variables we like for the coordinates, so we choose variables that are simple to divide by two (since we use the midpoint formula). We place one vertex at the origin to make calculations simpler, and we also note that *M* and *R* must have the same *y*-coordinate, since we draw the bases as horizontal.

Statement	Reason	
$N = \left(\dfrac{0 + 2a}{2}, \dfrac{0 + 2b}{2}\right) = (a, b)$	Midpoint formula	N is the midpoint of $\overline{MO}$, so use the midpoint formula with the coordinates of M and O to calculate the simplified coordinates for N.
$Q = \left(\dfrac{2d + 2c}{2}, \dfrac{0 + 2b}{2}\right) = (d + c, b)$	Midpoint formula	Q is the midpoint of $\overline{RP}$, so use the midpoint formula to calculate the coordinates for Q and simplify.
$MR = 2c - 2a$, $NQ = d + c - a$, and $OP = 2d$	Ruler postulate	The length of each of these horizontal segments is the diffference of its endpoints' x-coordinates.
$MR + OP = 2c - 2a + 2d$	Addition	Add the lengths of the two bases to begin deriving the equation we are trying to prove.
$MR + OP = 2(d + c - a)$	Distributive and commutative properties	The right side of the equation can be rearranged so that it more closely resembles NQ.
$\dfrac{1}{2}(MR + OP) = d + c - a$	Multiplication property of equality	Divide both sides by 2.
$\dfrac{1}{2}(MR + OP) = NQ$	Substitution	Substitute NQ for its expression to finish our proof.

In the trapezoid, $\overline{CD}$ is a midsegment and $\overline{AB}$ has half the length of $\overline{CD}$. What is the length of $\overline{EF}$?

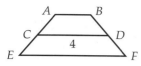

SOLUTION

Given	$\overline{CD}$ is a midsegment	This is given in the problem statement.
One base	$AB = \dfrac{1}{2} CD = \dfrac{1}{2} \cdot 4 = 2$	Since AB is half of CD, AB is 2.
Midsegment theorem	$CD = \dfrac{1}{2}(AB + EF)$	To find the length of the other base, use the midsegment theorem about lengths.
Substitute and evaluate	$4 = \dfrac{1}{2}(2 + EF)$ $4 = 1 + \dfrac{1}{2} EF$ $EF = 6$	Substitute the midsegment length and the length of one base, distribute the fraction and combine like terms. The other base is 6. We can check our solution: the sum of the bases is 8, and one-half that is 4, the length of the midsegment.

Kites

A geometric **kite** looks like a traditional kite. A kite is a quadrilateral with two pairs of adjacent congruent sides, each pair having a different length. In the diagram, that means $AB = AC$ and $BD = CD$, but AB does not equal BD. If a figure is a kite, then its diagonals are perpendicular. The angles formed by the unequal sides are congruent.

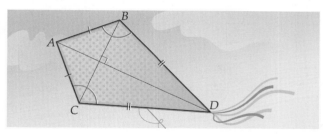

What is $m\angle CBA$?

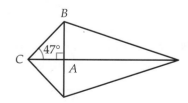

SOLUTION

Diagonals of a kite are perpendicular	$m\angle CAB = 90°$	The diagonals of a kite are perpendicular, so we can conclude this angle is 90°.
Triangle angles sum to 180°	$90° + m\angle CBA + 47° = 180°$ $m\angle CBA = 43°$	The triangle angles sum to 180°. Calculate $m\angle CBA$.

PRACTICE

1. Which of the following statements is true for any trapezoid?

   A. Two adjacent sides are parallel.
   B. Two opposite sides are congruent.
   C. Two opposite sides are parallel.
   D. Opposite angles are equal.

2. Which of the following statements must be true for a trapezoid $ABCD$ with bases $\overline{AD}$ and $\overline{BC}$? Check all that apply.

   A. $m\angle A + m\angle B = 180°$
   B. The legs $\overline{AB}$ and $\overline{CD}$ are congruent.
   C. The bases $\overline{AD}$ and $\overline{BC}$ are parallel.
   D. Opposite angles are supplementary.

3. Based on the markings on the diagram below, which of the quadrilaterals $MOLE$, $ANDY$ and $GRIT$ are trapezoids? Check all that apply.

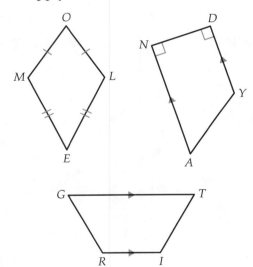

   A. $MOLE$
   B. $ANDY$
   C. $GRIT$
   D. None of them

4. In the diagram, $LIME$ is a kite. If $m\angle 1 = 56°$, what is the measure of $\angle 2$?

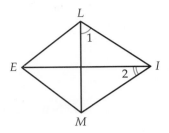

   A. 56°   C. 124°
   B. 34°   D. 68°

5. The vertices of a quadrilateral $KLMN$ are $K(-a, 0)$, $L(-b, c)$, $M(b, c)$, and $N(a, 0)$, where a, b, and c are positive numbers. What is the best description of $KLMN$?

   A. Trapezoid
   B. Parallelogram
   C. Isosceles trapezoid
   D. Rectangle

6. The length of a leg of an isosceles trapezoid is 5 inches and the sum of the lengths of the bases is 19 inches. What is the perimeter of the trapezoid?

7. In the trapezoid $ABCD$, $m\angle B = 119°$ and $m\angle D = 35°$. Find the other angles of the trapezoid. Trapezoid $ABCD$ is not an isosceles trapezoid.

8. $ABCD$ is an isosceles trapezoid. The lengths on the diagram are given in feet. Find the lengths of the trapezoid's legs in feet.

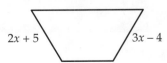

9. In the diagram of a trapezoid below, what is the measure of angle x?

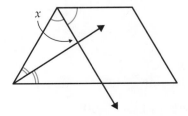

Practice Problems continue . . .

10. The diagram shows an isosceles trapezoid. Find the length of the diagonals. All lengths are shown in inches.

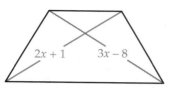

11. In an isosceles trapezoid, one angle is 40° smaller than another angle. Find the two different base angles of the trapezoid.

12. Trapezoid *ABCD* is an isosceles trapezoid where ∠*A* and ∠*B* are one pair of base angles and ∠*C* and ∠*D* are the other. *m*∠*A* is 70°. What is *m*∠*B*?

13. In an isosceles trapezoid with the bases measuring 3 inches and 5 inches, one of the diagonals is equal to 4.3 inches. What is the length of the other diagonal?

14. In an isosceles trapezoid *ABCD*, $\overline{BH}$ and $\overline{CG}$ are the heights from one base to another. Make a sketch. If *AH* = 2 cm, what is the length of $\overline{GD}$?

15. Show that in an isosceles trapezoid *ABCD* where $\overline{AD}$ and $\overline{BC}$ are the bases, △*ABD* ≅ △*DCA*. Use the theorem of base angles of an isosceles trapezoid.

16. In the diagram, *KLMN* is an isosceles trapezoid. What is the measure of ∠*KMN*?

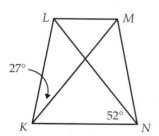

17. A design for a square photo frame with a square opening is shown below. If Mikala wants to cut the identical trapezoids that make up the frame, what should the measures of the angles in these trapezoids be?

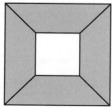

18. Cindy baked flatbread in the shape of a trapezoid. She wants to divide it into 4 congruent pieces, each having the shape of an isosceles trapezoid, as shown in the diagram. What should the measures of the angles of these pieces be?

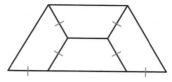

19. The bases of a trapezoid have lengths of 19 inches and 41 inches. Find the length of the midsegment of the trapezoid.

20. The bases of a trapezoid have lengths of 15 inches and 47 inches. Find the length of the midsegment of the trapezoid.

21. The lengths of $\overline{FG}$ and $\overline{JK}$ are 8 and 20 inches, respectively. How long is $\overline{HI}$?

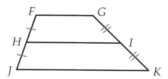

22. The midsegment of a trapezoid is 6 feet long, and one of the bases is 20% shorter than that. Find the longer base of the trapezoid.

23. The midsegment of an isosceles trapezoid is as long as its leg. The perimeter of the trapezoid is 48 inches. Find the measures of the legs of the trapezoid.

24. Make a sketch. The coordinates of the vertices of a trapezoid are (−4, 7), (3, 7), (−8, −1), and (5, −1). What is the length of the midsegment of the trapezoid?

25. The vertices of a quadrilateral are *A*(−3, 2), *B*(3, 4), *C*(5, −2), and *D*(−4, −5). Make a sketch and show that *ABCD* is a trapezoid.

Practice Problems continue . . .

Practice Problems continued . . .

26. **MP 3** Consider a trapezoid with vertices at the points $A(0, 0)$, $B(2a, 2b)$, $C(2c, 2b)$, and $D(2d, 0)$. Show that the midsegment $\overline{MN}$ of the trapezoid is parallel to its bases.

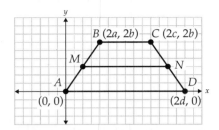

27. The diagram shows the kite $ABCD$.

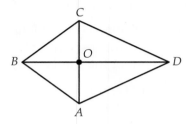

a If $m\angle ABO = 37°$, what is the measure of $\angle BCA$?

b If $m\angle ABO = 40°$ and $m\angle CDO = 25°$, find the angles of the kite.

28. The perimeter of a kite is 15 feet. If one side is 50% longer than the other, what are the lengths of the kite's sides?

29. What are the lengths of the sides of the kite $KITE$ shown in the diagram?

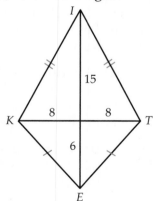

30. **MP 3** Prove that the base angles of an isosceles trapezoid are congruent.

31. **MP 3** Prove that the diagonals of a kite are perpendicular to each other. Hint: Consider perpendicular bisectors.

32. In kite $ABCD$, $AB = BC$ and $CD = DA$. Prove that diagonal $\overline{BD}$ of the kite is an angle bisector of $\angle B$ and $\angle D$.

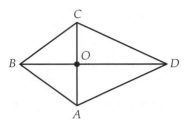

33. **MP 1, 2** A quadrilateral is obtained by connecting the midpoints of all sides of an isosceles trapezoid. Determine the type of quadrilateral, being as specific as possible. Justify your reasoning.

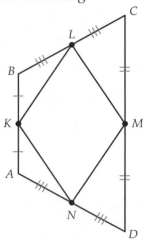

34. Show that the part of a midsegment of a trapezoid between its diagonals is equal to half of the difference of the trapezoid's bases. Make a sketch and refer to it in your proof.

35. The midsegment of a trapezoid is 8 ft long. Each diagonal of the trapezoid divides the midsegment into two parts, such that the distance between the midsegment's points of intersection with the diagonals is 2 ft. Find the base lengths of the trapezoid.

36. **MP 2, 3** The diagonals of a trapezoid divide its midsegment into three congruent segments. Show that one base of the trapezoid is twice as long as the other.

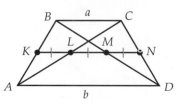

Practice Problems continue . . .

444 Chapter 9: Polygons

Practice Problems continued . . .

37. `MP 5, 6` In an isosceles trapezoid, the diagonals are perpendicular and the height is 10 inches. Find the length of the midsegment of the trapezoid.

38. `MP 1, 5` Two base angles of a trapezoid are 90° and 120°. The shorter diagonal is equal in length to the longer leg of the trapezoid, and they are each 12 meters. Find the length of the midsegment of the trapezoid.

LESSON 9.6

9.6 Areas and the Coordinate Plane

Area of a Parallelogram and Rhombus

We can call any side of a parallelogram or rhombus a base. Once we name the base, we can define its height, also known as its *altitude* (we use both terms interchangeably). It stretches perpendicularly from its base to the opposite side. An altitude can be inside or outside the figure.

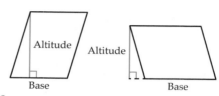

The formula for the area of these figures is shown below:

$$A = bh$$
$$A = \text{area}$$
$$b = \text{base}$$
$$h = \text{height}$$

MODEL PROBLEMS

1. What is the area of the rhombus?

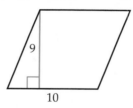

SOLUTION

Formula $A = bh$

The area of a rhombus is the product of its base and height. The base is the length of any side. The height is the length of a line segment that is perpendicular to that base and stretches to the side opposite the base.

Calculate area of figure $A = 10 \cdot 9 = 90$

To calculate the area, substitute for the variables and multiply. The area is 90.

Model Problems continue . . .

9.6 Areas and the Coordinate Plane **445**

2. What is the area of the figure?

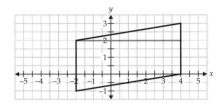

SOLUTION

Figure is parallelogram	Parallel sides are same length	The figure is a parallelogram, because each of its pairs of parallel sides are the same length.
Calculate base	$b = \lvert y_2 - y_1 \rvert$ $b = \lvert (2 - (-1) \rvert = 3$	The bases are vertical. Subtract the y-coordinates to find their length.
Calculate height	$h = \lvert x_2 - x_1 \rvert$ $h = \lvert -2 - (4) \rvert = 6$	Subtract the x-coordinates to calculate the distance between the bases.
Calculate area	$A = bh = 3 \cdot 6 = 18$	Multiply the base by the height to calculate the area.

3. **MP 3, 6** What are the area and perimeter of the figure?

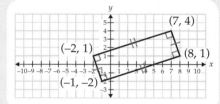

SOLUTION

Calculate length of base using distance formula	$d = \sqrt{(x_2 - x_1)^2 + (y_2 - y_1)^2}$	Use the distance formula.
Substitute and evaluate	$b = \sqrt{(-1 - 8)^2 + (-2 - 1)^2}$ $b = \sqrt{81 + 9} = \sqrt{90}$	Substitute and evaluate.
Calculate height using distance formula	$h = \sqrt{(-2 - (-1))^2 + (1 - (-2))^2}$ $h = \sqrt{(-1)^2 + (3)^2} = \sqrt{10}$	Calculate the height, again using the distance formula.
Calculate area	$A = bh = (\sqrt{90})(\sqrt{10}) = \sqrt{900} = 30$	Multiply the base by the height.
Calculate perimeter	$P = 2h + 2w = 2\sqrt{10} + 2\sqrt{90}$ $\quad = 2\sqrt{10} + 2\sqrt{9} \cdot \sqrt{10}$ $\quad = 2\sqrt{10} + 6\sqrt{10}$ $\quad = 8\sqrt{10}$	To find the perimeter, double both the base (or width, in this case) and the height. Then find their sum.

Construction: Two Ways to Construct a Square

We explain how to construct a square with a compass and straightedge.

Constructing a square with a compass and straightedge:

1. Construct a segment. Label endpoints A and B.

2. Construct a perpendicular line to $\overline{AB}$, passing through A.

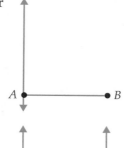

3. Repeat for B.

4. Measure AB using a compass.

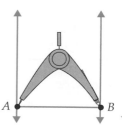

5. Use compass width to locate C and D.

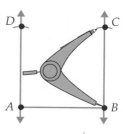

It is also possible to construct a square within a circle.

Constructing a square with a circle:

1. Construct a segment.

2. Create a perpendicular line passing through A.

3. Create a perpendicular line passing through B.

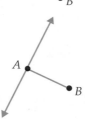

4. Create circle with center A, passing through B.

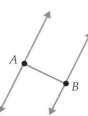

5. Label point C as shown.

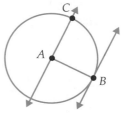

6. Through point C construct a line parallel to segment $\overline{AB}$.

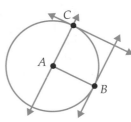

7. Label point D.

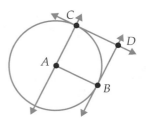

Why is the figure a square? $\angle CAB$ and $\angle DBA$ are right angles since $\overleftrightarrow{CA}$ and $\overleftrightarrow{DB}$ were constructed perpendicular to $\overline{AB}$. Since $\overleftrightarrow{CD}$ was constructed parallel to $\overline{AB}$, $\angle ACD$ and $\angle BDC$ are also right angles. This means that $ABDC$ is either a rectangle or square, because all of its interior angles are right angles. Finally, $AB = AC$, because they are both radii of the same circle. Because these adjacent sides are congruent, the figure must be a square.

MODEL PROBLEMS

1. **MP 2, 4** Anna, a beekeeper, is evaluating two parallelogram-shaped bee frames. The first one has a base of 20 inches, a height of 6 inches, and 234 bees. The other one has a base of 22 inches, a height of 8 inches, and 292 bees. Which has a higher density of bees? "Bee density" means the number of bees per square inch.

SOLUTION

Draw diagram

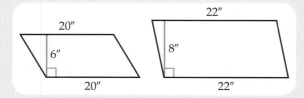

Smaller frame

$A = bh$
$A = 20 \cdot 6 = 120$ square inches

To calculate the bee densities, first calculate the areas of the bee frames, and then divide the number of bees on each frame by the area. Calculate the area of the smaller frame.

Larger frame

$A = 22 \cdot 8 = 176$ square inches

Now calculate the area of the larger frame.

Density smaller frame

$\text{density}_{\text{smaller}} = \dfrac{234 \text{ bees}}{120 \text{ square inches}}$

$\text{density}_{\text{smaller}} \approx 2.0$ bees per square inch

Divide the number of bees on the smaller frame by the area of the smaller frame. Do the division. There are about 2 bees per square inch.

Density larger frame

$\text{density}_{\text{larger}} = \dfrac{292 \text{ bees}}{176 \text{ square inches}}$

$\text{density}_{\text{larger}} \approx 1.7$ bees per square inch
Smaller frame has greater density

Do the same operation for the larger frame. It has 1.7 bees per square inch, so the smaller frame has a greater density of bees. It has more bees per square inch.

Model Problems continue . . .

2. Fonts are different designs of letters—you find them in computer programs, usually under a "Font" command. Pixels are the tiny elements that make up a computer display. A computer display might have 1280 pixels horizontally and 800 vertically. A designer wants to use simple geometric shapes to begin designing a new font. She wants to design the letter 'd' with a height of 15 pixels. How might she do this? What would be the area the user sees?

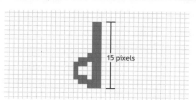

SOLUTION

The designer creates one design for the letter—you might come up with a different one, depending on your sense of design. We model two of the shape components as parallelograms—when viewed from a distance, the components appear to be parallelograms.

Vertical as rectangle	$b = 2$ pixels $h = 15$ pixels	To design the letter 'd' with a height of 15, we start with a rectangle 15 high by 2 wide. It could be wider or narrower—the width of 2 is a design choice.

Approximate areas as parallelograms	$b = 2$ pixels $h = 4$ pixels	Use two congruent parallelograms where the vertical segments are the bases. Each base has a length of 2 pixels. The altitude, or height, is a horizontal length of 4 pixels. Since we must use whole pixels, convert the parallelograms to pixelated parallelograms.

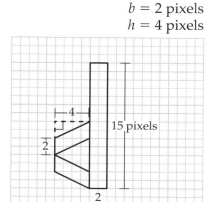

Areas of rectangle and parallelogram	rectangle $= bh = 2 \cdot 15 = 30$ parallelogram $= bh = 2 \cdot 4 = 8$	To calculate the area, start with the rectangle, whose area is the product of the base and height. Calculate the area of one of the parallelograms.

Total	letter area = rectangle + 2 parallelograms letter area $= 30 + 2(8) = 46$ pixels	The area of the letter equals the sum of the areas of the rectangle and the two parallelograms. We could have also solved this problem by simply counting pixels. However, we wanted to apply the rectangle and parallelogram area formulas.

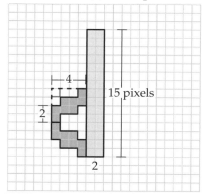

Area of a Trapezoid

The bases are the parallel sides of the trapezoid. The variables b_1 and b_2 represent the bases. H is the altitude, or height, between the two bases and is perpendicular to them both. To the right, we can see how the area for a trapezoid is derived from the area of a parallelogram; the figure is one-half the area of a parallelogram of those dimensions.

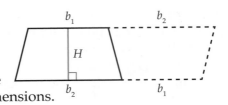

The area of a trapezoid is calculated using the formula:

$$A = \frac{1}{2}(b_1 + b_2)H$$

A = area

b_1 = base 1

b_2 = base 2

H = height

MODEL PROBLEMS

1. Calculate the area of a trapezoid.

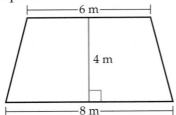

SOLUTION

Calculate area of figure

$$A = \frac{1}{2}(b_1 + b_2)H$$

$$A = \frac{1}{2}(8 + 6)4$$

$$A = \frac{1}{2} \cdot 14 \cdot 4$$

$$A = 28 \text{ m}^2$$

To calculate the area, substitute for the variables. Evaluate by first doing the operation in the parentheses, then multiplying. The area is 28 square meters.

2. **MP 7** In the diagram to the right, what is the area of the entire yard? All measurements are in meters.

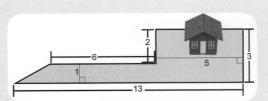

SOLUTION

Method 1

Split figure into trapezoids

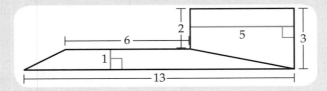

We have no formula for the area of the lawn above, but if we split it into two trapezoids, then we can calculate its area.

Model Problems continue . . .

Trapezoid at the bottom	$A = \frac{1}{2}(b_1 + b_2)H$	First calculate the area of the bottom trapezoid. Its bases are 6 and 13. Its height is 1. Add and then multiply.
	$A = \frac{1}{2}(6 + 13)1$	
	$A = \frac{1}{2}(19) = 9.5$	
Trapezoid on the right	$A' = \frac{1}{2}(2 + 3)5$	Now calculate the area of the trapezoid to the right. Its bases are 2 and 3. Its height is 5. Add and then multiply.
	$A' = \frac{1}{2} \cdot 5 \cdot 5 = 12.5$	
Add the two areas	Lawn area $= A + A'\ $ $= 9.5 + 12.5$ $= 22 \text{ m}^2$	The area of the lawn equals the sum of the two trapezoids' areas, 22 square meters.

Method 2

Split figure into rectangles, triangle	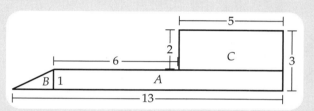	Instead of calculating areas of trapezoids, we will calculate the areas of two rectangles and a triangle.
Figure A	Base $= 6 + 5 = 11$ Area of figure $A = bh = 11 \cdot 1 = 11$	Calculate the base of figure A. It equals the sum of two lengths, which are 6 and 5. Then, calculate the area of the rectangle. It has base 11 and height 1.
Figure B	Base $= 13 - 11 = 2$ Area of figure $B = \frac{1}{2}b \cdot h = \frac{1}{2} \cdot 2 \cdot 1 = 1$	To calculate the area of triangle B, first calculate its base. Its base is the difference of two segment lengths, which is $13 - 11$. Then, use the formula for the area of a triangle.
Figure C	Area of figure $C = bh = 5 \cdot 2 = 10$	Again, apply the formula for the area of a rectangle.
Lawn area equals sum	Lawn area $= A + B + C$ Lawn area $= 11 + 1 + 10$ Lawn area $= 22 \text{ m}^2$	The area of the lawn equals the sum of the three areas we calculated.

Area of a Kite and Rhombus Using Diagonals

The formula for a kite or rhombus can be derived by considering the area of a figure as the sum of the areas of two triangles. One diagonal is the base of both triangles, and the other is twice the height of each triangle.

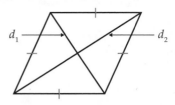

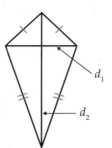

The same formula can be used to calculate the area of a rhombus or a kite:

$$A = \frac{1}{2} d_1 d_2$$
$$A = \text{area}$$
$$d_1 = \text{diagonal 1}$$
$$d_2 = \text{diagonal 2}$$

MODEL PROBLEMS

1. What is the area of the kite?

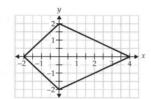

SOLUTION

Calculate diagonals

$\text{horizontal} = |-2 - 4| = 6$
$\text{vertical} = |2 - (-2)| = 4$

Calculate the diagonals' lengths. They are horizontal and vertical segments, so subtract and take the absolute values.

Use formula

$$A = \frac{1}{2} d_1 d_2$$

$$A = \frac{1}{2}(4)(6) = 12$$

Now use the area formula.

2. The area of a rhombus is 8 cm². What is the length of the longer diagonal?

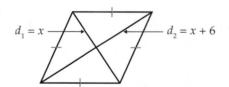

SOLUTION

Rhombus area

$$A = \frac{1}{2} d_1 d_2$$

$$8 = \frac{1}{2} x (x + 6)$$

The area of a rhombus equals half the product of its diagonals' lengths. The problem says the area is 8 cm². One diagonal has a length of x, and the other has a length of $x + 6$.

Factor

$16 = x^2 + 6x$
$x^2 + 6x - 16 = 0$
$(x + 8)(x - 2) = 0$

To solve the equation, multiply and then factor.

Solve

$x + 8 = 0$
$x - 2 = 0$
-8 and 2

Set each factor equal to zero. A length cannot be negative, so the solution -8 is not relevant to this problem. The shorter diagonal, x, has a length of 2 cm.

Positive lengths

$x + 6 = \text{longer diagonal}$
$2 + 6 = 8 \text{ cm}$

The longer diagonal is 6 cm longer than the shorter one.

Model Problems continue . . .

3. **MP 2, 4, 5** You want to design a kite with the maximum amount of area. You are told the diagonals' lengths sum to 12 inches. What should their lengths be to maximize the area?

SOLUTION

Draw diagram

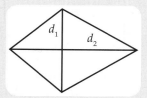

Write expressions for diagonals

$d_1 = x$
$d_2 = 12 - x$

We want to maximize the area of a kite which has diagonals' lengths that sum to 12. If $d_1 = x$, then $d_2 = 12 - x$.

Use equation for area

$A = \dfrac{1}{2} d_1 d_2$

$A = \dfrac{1}{2} x(12 - x)$

$A = 6x - \dfrac{1}{2} x^2$

Use the equation for the area of a kite. Substitute the expressions for the two diagonals and multiply.

Graph expression

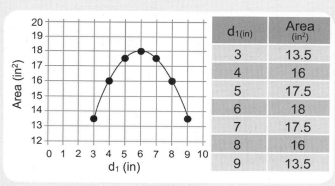

$d_{1(in)}$	Area (in²)
3	13.5
4	16
5	17.5
6	18
7	17.5
8	16
9	13.5

We graph the expression to determine its maximum value, with area on the vertical axis. Its maximum value occurs at the peak (vertex) of the parabola.

Maximum value

$x = 6$
$d_1 = 6$ inches

The maximum area of a kite is shown on the graph.

Compute other diagonal's length

$d_2 = 12 - x$
$d_2 = 12 - 6 = 6$ inches

Use the expression for the length of the other diagonal. The maximum area of a kite occurs when the diagonals are made to be the same length.

PRACTICE

1. What is the area of a trapezoid with bases of 12 cm and 14 cm and a height of 8 cm?

    A. 104 cm²

    B. 162 cm²

    C. 208 cm²

    D. 236 cm²

2. What is the area of the figure shown below? The numbers in the diagram refer to the entire length of each diagonal.

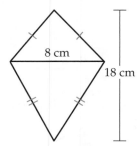

    A. 72 cm²   C. 128 cm²

    B. 96 cm²   D. 144 cm²

3. A trapezoid has an area of 104 cm², a base of 15 cm, and a height of 8 cm. What is the length of the other base of the trapezoid?

    A. 8 cm

    B. 11 cm

    C. 12 cm

    D. 14 cm

4. George wants to create a kite with a maximum area. The lengths of the diagonals of the kite sum to 18 inches. Which of the following represents the maximum area of the kite?

    A. 40 in²

    B. 40.5 in²

    C. 41 in²

    D. 41.5 in²

5. What is the area of the parallelogram below?

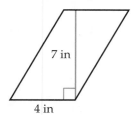

Exercises 6–12: Calculate the area of the figure.

6.

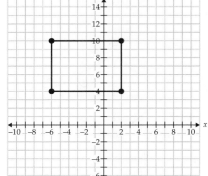

7.

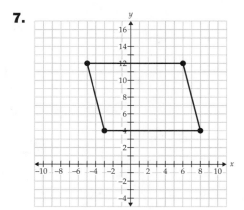

8.

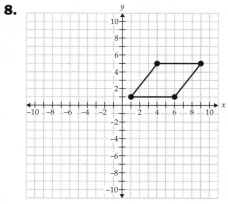

9.

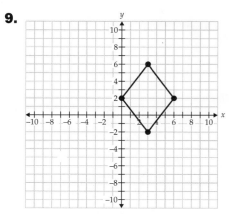

Practice Problems continue . . .

10.

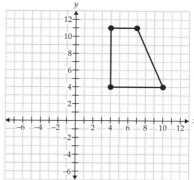

11.

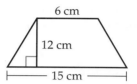

12.

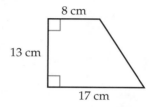

13. What is the area of a trapezoid with base lengths of 9 inches and 12 inches and a height of 5 inches?

14. What is the area of a trapezoid with base lengths of 6 inches and 5 inches and a height of 9 inches?

15. The top of a trapezoid is 10 centimeters and its bottom is 2 centimeters. It is 11 centimeters tall. What is its area?

16. The trapezoid below has an area of 88 square centimeters. What is the length of b_1?

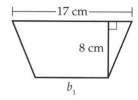

17. The area of a parallelogram is 72 in² and its height is 8 in. What is the length of its base, in inches?

18. The bases of a trapezoid are equal to 4 and 8 ft. The area of the trapezoid is 60 ft². Find the length of the trapezoid's height.

19. The height of a parallelogram is 6 times its base. Its area is 54 cm². What is the height, in centimeters?

20. If $x = 6.5$ inches, what is the area of the entire figure below? The lengths shown in the figure are in inches.

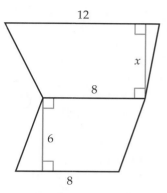

21. What is the area of the figure below?

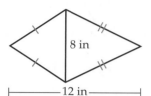

22. $\overline{AC}$ is 14 inches long, and $\overline{BD}$ is 7 inches long. What is the area of the shape below?

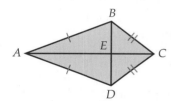

Exercises 23–26: Determine the figure's area given the measures of its diagonals.

23. A kite: 5 cm and 8 cm

24. A kite: 5 cm and 6 cm

25. A rhombus: 12 cm and 8 cm

26. A rhombus: 10 cm and 6 cm

27. A rhombus has diagonals represented by the expressions x and $x + 2$. If the area of the rhombus is 12 square inches, what is the length of the longer diagonal?

28. A rhombus has one diagonal that is 4 centimeters longer than the other diagonal. If the rhombus has an area of 38.5 square centimeters, what is the length of the shorter diagonal?

Practice Problems continue . . .

29. Amy's screen saver shows 148 tangent circles. Robert chooses the same screen saver but alters it to include 196 tangent circles. If both computer screens are 12 inches by 6.5 inches, how many more circles per square inch does Robert's screen saver have?

30. MP 2, 4 A rectangular puzzle *A* with dimensions of 10 inches by 8 inches contains 18 puzzle pieces. A different rectangular puzzle *B* with dimensions of 12 inches by 10 inches contains 24 puzzle pieces. What is the density of puzzle pieces for each puzzle, in pieces per square inch?

31. An artist wishes to create a drawing that includes a rectangle composed of two right triangles. If the base and height of each triangle are 18 inches and 12 inches, respectively, what will the overall area of this portion of the drawing be?

32. Macy states, "A kite is another term used to describe a rhombus. A kite and a rhombus are the same polygon." Is she correct? Why or why not?

33. MP 1, 3 Explain how a kite can be differentiated from a rhombus on a coordinate grid. Explain how a rhombus can be differentiated from a square on a coordinate grid.

34. Arlan wishes to create a kite with a maximum area. His kite will have diagonals with a combined length of 28 centimeters. What diagonal lengths should he choose in order to create a kite with a maximum area? What is the maximum area?

35. The area of a triangle is 42 square units. If the base of the triangle is five units longer than its height, what is the length of the triangle's base?

36. MP 6 A parallelogram has vertices located at $(a, 0)$, $(2a, b)$, $(a, 2b)$, and $(0, b)$. What is the area of the parallelogram, in terms of a and b?

37. MP 3 Prove the diagonals of a parallelogram divide the parallelogram into four triangles with equal area.

38. The shorter base of a trapezoid is six inches greater than its height, and the longer base is four inches greater than the shorter base. If the area of the trapezoid is 65 square inches, what is the height of the trapezoid?

39. MP 1, 5 The ratio of the lengths of the diagonals of a rhombus is 4 : 3. If the perimeter of the rhombus is 40 meters, what is its area?

• Multi-Part PROBLEM Practice •

MP 1, 2, 3, 4, 5, 6 The residents of Mudville want to landscape a park for the children and have chosen a plot of land bounded by 4 streets—Ash Avenue, Birch Boulevard, Deodar Drive, and Fir Fairway. The streets of Mudville do not intersect at right angles, but these four streets do form a quadrilateral. If you mapped the streets on a coordinate plane, with each square representing one square meter, the streets would intersect as follows:

Ash and Birch at $(4, 1)$; Birch and Deodar at $(6, -1)$; Deodar and Fir at $(0, -3)$;
Fir and Ash at $(-2, -1)$

a Plot the streets on the coordinate plane.

b What kind of quadrilateral do the streets enclose? How do you know?

c Find the area of the new park.

d How much fencing would be needed to enclose the park, rounded up to the next highest meter?

e If the residents want to plant a tree as close as possible to the center of the park, describe what kind of point you would find to locate this center. Find the coordinates of this point.

9.7 Area of Regular Polygons

In a regular polygon, the line from the center of the polygon to any of its sides is called the **apothem**. It forms a right angle with the side, as shown in the diagram to the right. The radius of a regular polygon is the distance from the center to a vertex. The apothem is the altitude of an isosceles triangle formed by two adjacent radii (radii is the plural of radius). The central angle of a regular polygon is also formed by these two radii. Its measure equals 360° divided by the number of sides.

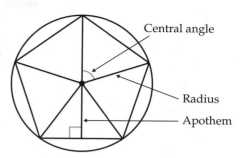

Central angle

Radius

Apothem

Using triangles like the ones in the diagram, we can calculate the area of any regular n-gon, a regular polygon with n sides.

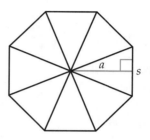

$$A_{\text{one triangle}} = \frac{1}{2} a \cdot s$$

$$A_{\text{regular polygon}} = \frac{1}{2} a \cdot s \cdot n$$

a = apothem
s = length of side
n = number of sides

An equivalent formula is the area equals one-half the product of the apothem and the perimeter.

$$A = \frac{1}{2} a \cdot p$$

a = apothem
p = perimeter

MODEL PROBLEMS

1. What are the perimeter and the area of the regular polygon below?

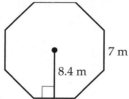

7 m

8.4 m

SOLUTION

Perimeter

$p = ns$
$p = 8 \cdot 7 = 56$ meters

The perimeter is the product of the number of sides and the length of each side. An octagon has 8 sides, so multiply by 8.

Area

$A = \frac{1}{2} ap$

$A = \frac{1}{2} (8.4)(56)$

$A = 235.2$ m^2

The area equals one-half the product of the apothem and perimeter. Substitute those values and multiply.

Model Problems continue . . .

2. What is the apothem of this regular figure?
Its area is 7 square inches.

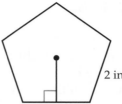

2 in

SOLUTION

Equation for area in terms of apothem, sides	$A = \dfrac{1}{2} a \cdot s \cdot n$	Use the equation for the area of a regular polygon as a function of its apothem, side length, and number of sides.
Solve equation for apothem	$a = 2 \dfrac{A}{ns}$	Solve for the apothem.
Substitute and evaluate	$a = 2 \left(\dfrac{7}{5 \cdot 2} \right)$	Substitute 5 for n since the figure is a pentagon, a five-sided figure and evaluate.
	$a = 1.4$ inches	

3. What is the area of the game board? All of its side lengths
are equal. Also, the distance from the center of the board
to any of its vertices is equal to one of its side lengths.

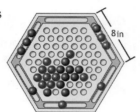

8 in

SOLUTION

Draw diagram

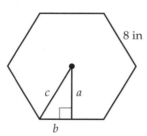

8 in

c a

b

Calculate apothem using Pythagorean theorem	$a^2 + b^2 = c^2$ $a = \sqrt{c^2 - b^2}$ $a = \sqrt{8^2 - 4^2} \approx 6.9$	We need to calculate the apothem in order to calculate the area. The apothem is a leg in a right triangle, so use the Pythagorean theorem, and solve for the leg a. b is half the length of a side, and c is equal to a side length, according to the problem. Substitute and evaluate to calculate the apothem.
Use formula for area	$A = \dfrac{1}{2} a \cdot s \cdot n$ $A \approx \dfrac{1}{2} \cdot 6.9 \cdot 8 \cdot 6$ $A \approx 166 \text{ in}^2$	Use the formula for area.

PRACTICE

1. What is the area of the regular polygon below?

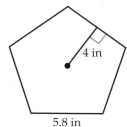

5.8 in
4 in

  A. 48 in²   C. 80 in²
  B. 58 in²   D. 106 in²

2. What is the area of a regular octagon with an apothem measuring 16 cm and a perimeter of 106 cm?

  A. 848 cm²   C. 1140 cm²
  B. 936 cm²   D. 1354 cm²

3. What is the approximate area of a regular polygon with 7 sides that are each 12.5 in long and an apothem measuring 13 in?

  A. 384 in²   C. 570 in²
  B. 436 in²   D. 827 in²

4. What is the area of a regular hexagon with a side length of 7 inches?

  A. 94 in²   C. 166 in²
  B. 127 in²   D. 210 in²

5. Provide a drawing of a regular polygon with central angle measures of 72°.

6. A regular polygon has an area of 3.6 cm² and a perimeter of 7 cm. What is the length of the apothem? Round to the nearest hundredth.

7. What is the area of a regular heptagon (7-sided polygon) with a side length of 4 cm and an apothem length of 4.1 cm?

8. Two rectangles are similar. The lengths of the corresponding sides are 8 cm and 6 cm. The rectangle with the length of 8 cm has an area of 40 cm². What is the area of the second rectangle?

9. Two polygons are similar. The lengths of the corresponding sides are 5 in and 7 in. The polygon with the length of 5 in has an area of 50 in². What is the area of the second polygon?

10. Two polygons are similar. The lengths of the corresponding sides are 12 in and 20 in. The polygon with the length of 20 in has an area of 421 in². What is the area of the first polygon? Round your answer to the nearest hundredth.

Exercises 11–15: Calculate the area of the regular polygon.

11.

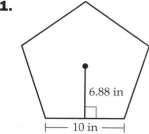

6.88 in
10 in

12.

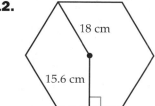

18 cm
15.6 cm

13.

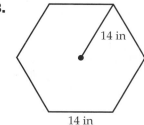

14 in
14 in

14.

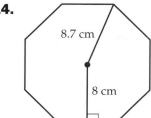

8.7 cm
8 cm

15.

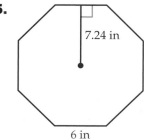

7.24 in
6 in

Practice Problems continue . . .

16. A regular pentagon has sides of length 8 cm and an apothem of approximately 5.6 cm. What is its area?

17. A regular pentagon has sides of length 10 cm and an apothem of approximately 7 cm. What is its area?

18. The regular polygon shown below has an area of approximately 127 cm². What is the length of its apothem?

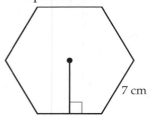

7 cm

19. The regular polygon below has an area of 387 cm². What is the length of the apothem? Round your answer to the nearest tenth of a centimeter.

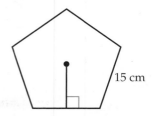

15 cm

20. If a regular polygon with 6 sides has a perimeter of 36 cm and an area of 93.6 cm², what is the length of the apothem? Round your area to the nearest tenth of a centimeter.

21. If a regular polygon with 6 sides has an apothem equal to 5 in and an area of 86.55 in², what is the perimeter of the polygon? Round your answer to the nearest tenth of an inch.

22. Explain how the measure of a central angle of a regular polygon can be determined.

23. Write a word problem that involves finding the area of a regular polygon in a real-world setting. Then solve for an unknown quantity.

24. Amy states, "The apothem of a regular polygon can also be described in terms of a radius." Elaborate on her statement. Hint: Consider sketching a circle inside the regular polygon.

25. **MP 3** Prove the area of a regular polygon is $\frac{1}{2} a \cdot s \cdot n$.

26. An architect creates a desk in the shape of a regular hexagon. The radius of the desk is 3 feet. What is the approximate area of the desk? Round to the nearest square foot.

27. **MP 3** A wall mirror has the shape of a regular hexagon. If the perimeter of the mirror is 30 cm, what is the area of the mirror? Round your area to the nearest square centimeter.

28. **MP 1, 5** The center of a regular polygon is connected to each of its vertices, forming n congruent isosceles triangles, each with a base angle measuring 70°. If the area of one of the triangles is 30 cm² what is the area of the polygon?

29. **MP 6** A regular hexagon is inscribed in a circle with a radius of r. What is the area of the hexagon, in terms of r?

9.8 Area and Trigonometry

Recall from previous lessons that trigonometry is the study of the relationships among the sides and angles of triangles. We can use trigonometric relationships to calculate the area of regular polygons, since all regular polygons are built out of triangles. If needed, you can review trigonometric ratios in chapter 7.

MODEL PROBLEMS

1. What is the area of the regular polygon shown to the right?

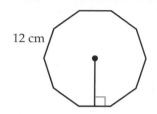

12 cm

SOLUTION

Draw diagram

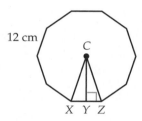

12 cm
C

X Y Z

We want to calculate the area of a regular decagon (10-sided polygon) given the length of its side. First, calculate the apothem using trigonometry.

Since it has 10 sides, the figure can be divided into 10 triangles. We show one of them. The angle XCZ is one of the triangle's angles.

Calculate measure of central angle	$m\angle XCZ = \dfrac{360°}{10} = 36°$	$360°$ is the measure of a complete revolution, so dividing that by 10 will give us the measure of the angle XCZ.
Calculate angle	$m\angle ZCY = \dfrac{1}{2}(m\angle XCZ) = 18°$	$m\angle ZCY$ is one-half $m\angle XCZ$, which means it equals $18°$.

Calculate apothem

$$\tan 18° = \frac{\text{opposite}}{\text{adjacent}} = \frac{6}{a}$$

$$a = \frac{6}{\tan 18°}$$

$$a \approx 18.5 \text{ cm}$$

Now move to trigonometry. The tangent equals the ratio of the opposite side to the adjacent. The opposite side is 6, one-half the length of a side of the figure. The adjacent side is a. Solve the equation for a, the apothem. Calculate 6 divided by the tangent of $18°$, which is about 18.5.

Equation for area of regular polygon

$$A = \frac{1}{2}a \cdot s \cdot n$$

Use the equation for the area of a regular polygon as a function of its apothem, side length, and number of sides.

Substitute, evaluate

$$A \approx \frac{1}{2}(18.5)(12)(10)$$

$$A \approx 1110 \text{ cm}^2$$

Substitute the apothem calculated above, the length of a side, and the number of sides. The area is about 1110 square centimeters.

Model Problems continue . . .

MODEL PROBLEMS *continued*

2. **MP 2, 4** Justin wants to design a table with six equal sides, and an apothem of 16 inches. To design the table, he needs to know its side length and area. What should these be?

SOLUTION

Draw diagram

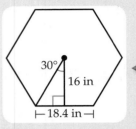

> The triangle is a 30-60-90 triangle. We use the ratio of the lengths of sides of this special triangle to solve the problem.

Calculate measure of central angle	measure of central angle = 60°	Since it has 6 sides, the figure can be divided into 6 triangles. 360° is the measure of a complete revolution, so dividing that by 6 will get us the measure of the central angle.
Calculate angle	half measure of central angle = 30°	Use one of the right triangles to find the side length. This means that we only need half of the central angle.
Calculate side length	$\tan 30° = \dfrac{\text{opposite}}{\text{adjacent}} = \dfrac{x}{16}$ $x = 16 \cdot \tan 30°$ $x \approx 9.2$ inches $s \approx 18.4$ inches	The tangent equals the ratio of the opposite side to the adjacent. The adjacent side is 16, the apothem given to us in the problem. The opposite side is half of the side length. Solve the equation for x, half of the side length, and evaluate to the nearest tenth. Since x is half the side length of the hexagon, multiply it by 2 to get s.
Equation for area of regular polygon	$A = \dfrac{1}{2} a \cdot s \cdot n$	Use the equation for the area of a regular polygon as a function of its apothem, side length, and number of sides.
Substitute and evaluate	$A \approx \dfrac{1}{2}(16)(18.4)(6)$ $A \approx 883.2$ square inches	Substitute the apothem given in the problem, the side length calculated above, and the number of sides in a hexagon. Multiply them to calculate the area of the table.

1. Which of the following best represents the area of a regular pentagon with side lengths of 38 cm?

   A. 2,484 cm²
   B. 2,644 cm²
   C. 3,096 cm²
   D. 3,482 cm²

2. Which of the following best represents the area of a regular hexagon with side lengths of 21 cm?

   A. 1,042 cm²
   B. 1,086 cm²
   C. 1,146 cm²
   D. 1,258 cm²

3. A piece of wall art is in the shape of a regular decagon. Each side length is 12 inches. If the area of the wall art is 1,108 square inches, which of the following best represents the distance from the center of the wall art to the midpoint of any side?

   A. 8.9 inches
   B. 13.6 inches
   C. 18.5 inches
   D. 22.0 inches

4. What is the area of a regular pentagon with side lengths of 39 cm?

5. What is the area of a regular pentagon with side lengths of 4 inches?

6. What is the area of a regular pentagon with side lengths of 28 cm?

7. What is the area of a regular hexagon with side lengths of 6 inches?

8. What is the area of a regular octagon that has side lengths of 10 cm?

9. What is the area of a regular octagon that has side lengths of 4 cm?

10. What is the area of a regular octagon that has side lengths of 15 cm?

11. What is the area of a regular heptagon with side lengths of 9 cm?

12. What is the area of a regular heptagon with side lengths of 14 inches?

13. What is the area of a regular octagon with side lengths of 49 cm?

14. What is the area of a regular octagon with side lengths of 18 cm?

15. What is the area of a regular octagon with side lengths of 9 inches?

16. What is the area of a regular octagon with side lengths of 22 cm?

17. What is the area of a regular nonagon (polygon with 9 sides) with side lengths of 8 inches?

18. What is the area of a regular nonagon with side lengths of 6 inches?

19. What is the area of a regular nonagon with side lengths of 29 cm?

20. What is the area of a regular decagon with side lengths of 25 inches?

21. What is the area of the regular polygon below?

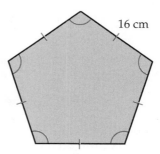

16 cm

22. What is the area of the regular polygon below?

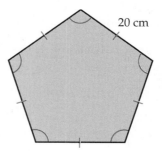

20 cm

Practice Problems continue . . .

23. What is the area of the regular polygon below?

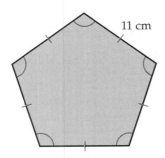

11 cm

24. MP 3 Kim states, "The area of a regular hexagon can also be determined by using the formula $\frac{3\sqrt{3}}{2}s^2$." Is she correct?

25. MP 4 A mirror, in the shape of a regular octagon, has an area of 477 square inches and an apothem measuring approximately 12 inches. What is the length of each side of the mirror?

26. MP 4 A sign, in the shape of a regular pentagon, has an area of 1,758 square inches and an apothem measuring approximately 22 inches. What is the length of each side of the sign? What is the radius of the sign?

27. Create a list of generic formulas that may be used to find the apothem of the following regular polygons, when only the side length is known: pentagon, hexagon, heptagon, octagon, nonagon, and decagon. Define the variables.

28. MP 3 Describe a regular polygon with n sides. Explain the process used to find the area of the polygon when only the side length is known.

• Multi-Part PROBLEM Practice •

MP 1, 2, 3, 4, 6

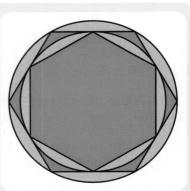

1. Art is designing a metal sculpture that will have circles and hexagons layered on top of one another, each figure inscribed in the figure below it. The first 4 figures are pictured in the diagram to the right.

a Write an expression for the exact area of each of the first 4 figures (2 circles, 2 hexagons) in terms of r, the radius of the largest circle.

b What is the ratio of the area of the small circle to the area of the large circle?

c What is the ratio of the area of the small hexagon to the area of the large hexagon?

2. Art wants his sculpture to be 4 feet across (that is, the diameter of the large circle will be 4 feet). He is budgeting $500 for materials. Aluminum will cost him about $9 per square foot, while steel will cost about $8 a square foot.

a Calculate the areas of each of the 4 figures to the nearest tenth of a square foot if the diameter of the large circle is 4 feet.

b Can he afford to make 2 circles out of aluminum and 2 hexagons out of steel?

c Using the ratios from the first 2 pairs of figures, argue whether Art can afford to make more figures and stay within his budget or not.

1. $\triangle ABC \sim \triangle DEF$. $AB = 8$ in, $DE = 10$ in, and the area of $\triangle ABC$ is 56 in². What is the area of $\triangle DEF$?

A. 44.8 in²
B. 70 in²
C. 87.5 in²
D. 90.5 in²

2. A parallelogram has congruent diagonals. This means it is also a

A. Square.
B. Rectangle.
C. Trapezoid.
D. None of the above figures.

3. Which answer indicates that a quadrilateral is a parallelogram?

A. Opposite angles are complementary.
B. Opposite angles are congruent.
C. Opposite angles are supplementary.

4. *TRAP* is a trapezoid. Which of the following expressions may represent the length of $\overline{SZ}$?

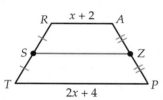

A. $3x + 6$
B. $x + 3$
C. $1.5x + 3$
D. $x^2 + 4x + 4$

5. A parallelogram is dilated by 124%, then rotated 46°, and dilated again by 117%. The final figure has

A. Diagonals that bisect one another.
B. Opposite angles that are congruent.
C. Opposite sides that are congruent.
D. All of the above.

6. What is the area of the parallelogram whose vertices are $(-2, 8)$, $(1, 4)$, $(1, -4)$, and $(-2, 0)$?

A. 10
B. 12
C. 16
D. 24

7. Select all that apply. If a figure is an isosceles trapezoid, then

A. Both pairs of opposite angles are congruent.
B. Each pair of base angles is congruent.
C. The bases are congruent.
D. The legs (not the bases) are congruent.

8. A polygon's interior angles sum to 1260°. How many sides does the polygon have?

A. 5
B. 7
C. 8
D. 9

9. Given rhombus $ABCD$, with diagonal $\overline{BD}$. If $m\angle ABD = 25°$, what is the $m\angle A$?

10. **MP 3** A parallelogram has vertices at $(1, 3)$, $(5, -9)$, $(8, 3)$, and $(-2, -9)$. Where do the parallelogram's diagonals intersect?

11. Find $m\angle A$ in the quadrilateral below, given that it is a parallelogram and that $m\angle A = 5x + 5$ and $m\angle D = 13x - 5$.

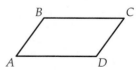

Chapter Review continues . . .

12. $\overline{NG}$ is the midsegment of trapezoid *PIYR*. What is the length of $\overline{NG}$?

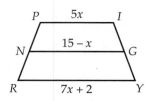

13. What is $m\angle ABC$ in the kite?

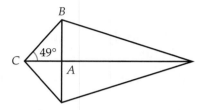

14. *AC* is 21 inches long, and *BD* is 17 inches long. What is the area of the kite?

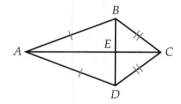

15. A trapezoid has a base of 5 inches, a height of 8 inches, and an area of 56 square inches. What is the length of its other base?

16. What is the area of a rectangle with vertices at (0, 5), (1, 3), (9, 7), and (8, 9)?

17. You want to build a kite with one diagonal twice as long as the other. You have a 6-foot-long pole from which to make the diagonals. What will be the area of the kite?

18. What is the area of the figure below?

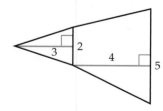

19. What is the area of a regular heptagon with side lengths of 34 cm? Round your answer to the nearest square centimeter.

20. Each side of an octagon is about 8 centimeters. Its apothem is about 9.7 centimeters. What is the octagon's area, to the nearest tenth of a square centimeter?

Exercises 21–23: Calculate the area of each of the regular polygons shown.

21.

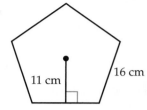

22.

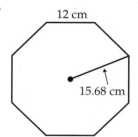

23.

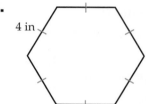

24. [MP 4] Mr. Allen creates a regular pentagon to symbolize a house on a wall map he is creating. The house should have side lengths of 8 centimeters. What should the distance from the center of the house to the midpoint of a side of the house be? Round your length to the nearest tenth of a centimeter.

25. [MP 4] Mr. Thompson is designing a board game for his math class. The board will be in the shape of a trapezoid. He wants the area of the board to be 162 square inches. If he makes the longer base 15 inches and the height 12 inches, what must be the length of the other base?

26. Create a rhombus on a coordinate grid. Provide the area of the rhombus.

Chapter Review continues . . .

27. What is the area of the figure in the graph?

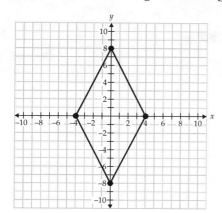

28. $\overline{AC}$ is 18 inches long, and $\overline{BD}$ is 9 inches long. What is the area of the shape below?

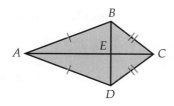

29. Find the area of the figure below.

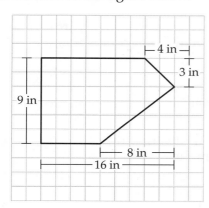

30. What is the sum of the interior angles in a regular 14-sided polygon?

31. In kite *ABCD*, *AB* = *BC* and *CD* = *DA*. Prove that diagonal $\overline{AC}$ of the kite is bisected by diagonal $\overline{BD}$.

32. **MP 3** Prove that a trapezoid is isosceles if and only if its diagonals are congruent. That is, prove both the theorem and its converse.

33. **MP 1, 3** A plastic triangle needs to be cut into exactly three pieces, each having a trapezoid shape. Show and explain how that could be done. The pieces don't have to be equal.

34. **MP 3** The points *E*, *F*, *G*, and *H* are the midpoints of the sides of a parallelogram *ABCD*. Prove that *EFGH* is also a parallelogram.

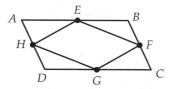

35. One pair of opposite angles in a convex quadrilateral are congruent, each of measure *n*, and one pair of consecutive angles is supplementary. Can we conclude this quadrilateral is a parallelogram? Why or why not?

1. In $\triangle JKL$, the $m\angle K = 40°$, and $m\angle L$ is 3 times $m\angle K$. What type of triangle is this? Choose all descriptions that apply.

A. Scalene   D. Acute

B. Isosceles   E. Right

C. Equilateral F. Obtuse

2. In the figure, "$\dfrac{JK}{JM} = \dfrac{LK}{LN}$, so $JL \parallel MN$" is an example of

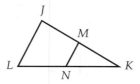

A. The triangle proportionality theorem.

B. The converse of the triangle proportionality theorem.

C. Neither of the above.

3. Choose the statement, or statements, that are true.

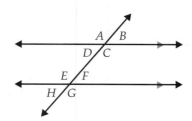

A. Angles A and B are corresponding angles.

B. Angles E and A are corresponding angles.

C. Angles C and F are consecutive interior angles.

D. Angles C and F are supplementary.

4. Triangle A's vertices are at $(0, 0)$, $(4, 0)$, and $(4, 3)$ and triangle B's vertices are at $(4, 4)$, $(9, 4)$, and $(9, 7)$. Are the triangles congruent? Hint: Sketch the triangles.

A. Yes

B. No

5. One side of a parallelogram lies along the line $y = 4x + 3$. The side opposite might lie along a line described by which equation below?

A. $y = 2x + 3$

B. $y = -\dfrac{1}{4}x + 3$

C. $y = 4x - 1$

D. $y = -4x + 1$

6. Select the statement(s) that must be true.

A. A rectangle has two pairs of parallel sides.

B. A rhombus has four right angles.

C. A rectangle has four right angles.

D. A rhombus has two obtuse angles and two acute angles.

7. A competent geometry instructor would agree with which of the following statements?

A. Constructions are like postulates because they must be accepted without proof.

B. All constructions are forms of rigid motion transformations.

C. Constructions are like theorems because it can be shown why they "work."

D. Answers B and C are true.

8. The sides of a triangle with a circle circumscribed about it are

A. Tangents.

B. Chords.

C. Secants.

D. Radii.

9. Which of the following are true statements? Select all that apply.

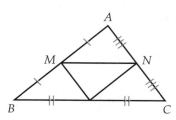

A. The length of $\overline{MN}$ is one-half that of $\overline{BC}$.
B. $MB = AM$
C. $AN = AM$
D. $\overline{MN}$ and $\overline{BC}$ are parallel.
E. $MB = NC$

10. A triangle has sides of $\sqrt{18}$, 3, and 3. What type of triangle is it?

A. Obtuse   C. Right
B. Acute

11. In the illustration below, $m\angle D < m\angle M$. This means:

A. $EF = NP$ C. $EF > NP$
B. $EF < NP$

12. What is the area of the triangle below?

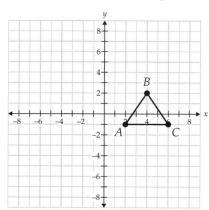

13. In the diagram, $IZ = 15$, and $SZ = 17$. What is DS?

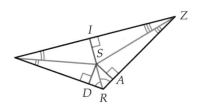

14. **MP 1, 3** Prove the similar polygons area theorem for rectangles given similar rectangles $ABCD$ and $EFGH$. Let $ABCD$ have length p and width q. Let $EFGH$ have length r and width s. Also, the ratio of $\frac{p}{r}$ and $\frac{q}{s}$ is k. Hint: Use substitution.

15. **MP 2, 6** In the diagram below, $\overline{DE}$ bisects angle ADF. Use the angle measures given on the diagram to find the angles of the triangle ADE.

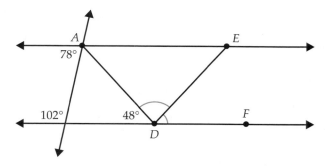

16. Provide a counterexample to the statement, "All quadrilaterals with two pairs of congruent sides have two pairs of congruent angles."

17. In the diagram shown below, is $\overline{TU} \parallel \overline{QS}$? Explain.

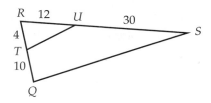

18. In a parallelogram, the adjacent angles formed by the diagonals and the sides are congruent. Show that the diagonals of the parallelogram are perpendicular to each other.

19. The hypotenuse of a 45-45-90 triangle measures $\sqrt{18}$ units. How long is one leg of the triangle?

20. A triangle has sides of length $c = 7$ and $a = 3.5$. If the measure of angle B is $73°$, what is the area of the triangle, to the nearest tenth?

21. A lawn mowing service provides estimates based on the area of the lawn. A new customer has a lawn in the shape of an isosceles trapezoid with side lengths 10, 10, 15, and 25 yards. If the service charges $0.25 per square yard, how much will it cost to have the lawn mowed? Round your answer to the nearest cent.

22. **MP 4, 8** Identical puzzle pieces in the shape of a rhombus with the obtuse angle of 150° are arranged to form a star design. The first three pieces have been placed to begin the design. How many pieces will be needed to complete the star in the diagram below?

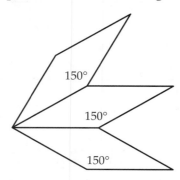

23. What is the length of a 317° arc in a circle with a 4.5-meter radius, to the nearest tenth of a meter?

24. A hexagonal game board has side lengths of 10 inches and a radius of 10 inches. What is its area, to the nearest square inch?

25. What is cos 60°?

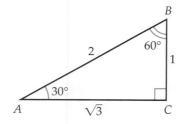

26. **MP 2, 6** Use the diagram below to calculate the altitude of $\triangle DEF$ given that $\triangle ABC \sim \triangle DEF$. Additionally, the length of $\overline{AB} = 5$, the length of $\overline{EF} = 21$, and the altitude of $\triangle ABC = 4$.

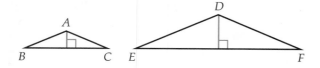

27. **MP 5, 6** The vertices of a quadrilateral are located at (4, 1), (−3, 2), (−5, −2), and (−1, −4). What is the area of this quadrilateral?

28. If you know the measures of two sides of a right triangle, is it necessary to use the Pythagorean theorem in order to find the length of the third side? Explain your reasoning.

Exercises 29–31: In each diagram, the labels refer to the length between the vertex and the center of the figure.

29. What is the area of the figure shown below?

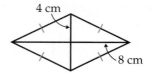

30. What is the area of the figure shown below?

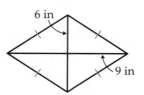

31. What is the area of the figure shown below?

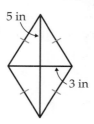

32. If $m\overset{\frown}{MP} = 160°$, what does $m\angle MPK$ equal?

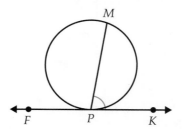

33. **MP 4, 5** Two boats left a port heading in different directions. Each continued in a straight line, and the angle formed between their paths measured 50 degrees. After 5 hours, the first boat was 30 miles from the port, while the second boat was 20 miles from the port.

a Make a sketch of the situation.

b How far apart were the boats 5 hours after they left port? Round your answer to the nearest tenth.

34. The area of a triangle is x square centimeters. All three midsegments of the triangle are constructed, forming a smaller triangle within the original triangle. What is the area of the new triangle, in terms of x?

35. **MP 2, 7** Given the diagram below, and the assumption that a, b, and c are all integer values, is it possible for the area of the four interior triangles to exactly match the area of the large square, causing the interior square to vanish completely? Explain your reasoning, and include a sketch with your explanation.

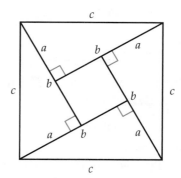

Chapter 10 Solids

Chapter Content

Chapter Vocabulary

Cavalieri's principle	lateral face	regular pyramid
cone	net	right solid
cross-section	oblique solid	solid
cube	perspective	sphere
cylinder	polyhedron	surface area
edge	prism	triangular prism
face	pyramid	vertex
isometric drawing	rectangular prism	volume

LESSON 10.1

10.1 Three-Dimensional Figures, Cross-Sections, and Drawings

Three-Dimensional Figures

You may be familiar with **cubes**, **cylinders**, **cones**, **pyramids**, and **spheres**, which are examples of three-dimensional shapes that occupy space, also known as **solids**.

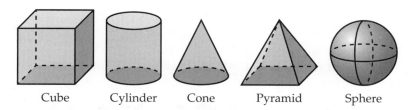

Cube Cylinder Cone Pyramid Sphere

A **polyhedron** is a solid whose surfaces are polygons. Prisms, boxes, and pyramids are polyhedrons, while spheres or cones are not, since they have curved surfaces. Each polyhedron's **face** is a region on the solid's exterior (outside), such as the top of a box. An **edge** is a line segment where two faces intersect. A **vertex** is a point where three or more edges meet. You may think of a vertex as a corner.

Three-dimensional solids can be formed by translating or rotating two-dimensional figures. Three-dimensional figures occupy space and have volume.

We show how a sphere, cylinder, and cone can be formed from rotating some familiar 2D shapes.

Circle	⃝	Sphere		If we rotate a circle about a diameter, it traces a sphere.
Square or rectangle	▭	Cylinder		If we rotate a square or rectangle about a side, we create a cylinder.
Right triangle	◺	Cone		If we rotate a right triangle about a leg, we form a cone.

MODEL PROBLEMS

1. Identify the number of faces, edges, and vertices in the polyhedron.

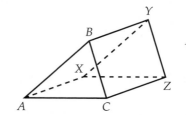

> This polyhedron is an example of a **triangular prism**.

SOLUTION

How many faces?	5 faces:	Faces are the polygons that make up the surface of a polyhedron. To count the number of faces, start with the triangles.
	△ABC, △XYZ, rectangles ABYX, BCZY, and ACZX	
How many edges?	9 edges:	Edges are segments formed by the intersection of two faces. There are 9 edges.
	$\overline{AB}, \overline{BC}, \overline{CA}, \overline{XY}, \overline{YZ}, \overline{ZX}, \overline{AX}, \overline{BY}, \overline{CZ}$	
How many vertices?	6 vertices:	There are 6 vertices.
	A, B, C, X, Y, Z	

2. The Swiss mathematician Leonhard Euler stated a formula that relates the number of faces, vertices, and edges in a simple polyhedron:

Euler-Descartes polyhedral formula

The sum of the number of a polyhedron's faces and its vertices minus the number of its edges equals 2.

F = number of faces
v = number of vertices
E = number of edges

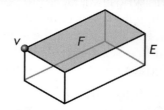

The numbers of a polyhedron's faces, vertices, and edges obey the relation $F + v - E = 2$.

Model Problems continue . . .

474 Chapter 10: Solids

Use Euler-Descartes polyhedral formula to determine the number of faces of a polyhedron with 12 edges and 6 vertices.

SOLUTION

Use Euler-Descartes polyhedral formula and substitute	$F + v = E + 2$ $F + 6 = 12 + 2$	Start with Euler-Descartes polyhedral formula. Substitute the values given in the problem.
Calculate the number of faces	$F + 6 = 14$ $F = 8$	Calculate F.

Cross-Sections

A **cross-section** is the intersection of a solid and a plane. Cross-sections form two-dimensional figures. Often, people refer to a cross-section as being a "slice" of a solid. The type of two-dimensional shape formed depends on how the plane intersects the solid.

> The result of slicing a sphere with a plane is a circle.

MODEL PROBLEM

MP 1, 7 Determine the figures that can be formed by the intersection of a cube and a plane.

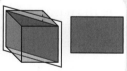

SOLUTION

Equilateral triangle

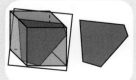

Non-equilateral triangle

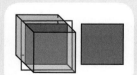

Hexagon

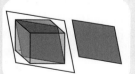

Rectangle

Pentagon

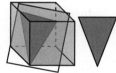

Square

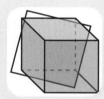

Parallelogram

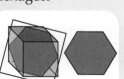

The Pythagorean Theorem in Three Dimensions

The Pythagorean theorem can be extended to three dimensions. On the right, we show an example of a diagonal that extends from one corner of a rectangular block to another.

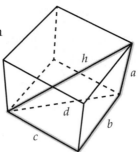

We want to compute h, the length from one corner to another. The formula below resembles that of the Pythagorean theorem, but includes another term for the third dimension:

$$h^2 = a^2 + b^2 + c^2$$

Paragraph Derivation

According to the Pythagorean theorem, $h^2 = a^2 + d^2$, with d being a diagonal along the surface of the box, and the hypotenuse of a right triangle. The same theorem tells us that $d^2 = b^2 + c^2$, since d is the hypotenuse of a right triangle formed by those two sides of the box. Substituting for d^2 in the first equation, we get $h^2 = a^2 + b^2 + c^2$.

MODEL PROBLEM

What is the value of h?

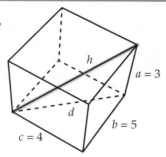

SOLUTION

Apply formula	$h^2 = a^2 + b^2 + c^2$ $h^2 = 3^2 + 5^2 + 4^2$	To calculate h, use the formula for the Pythagorean theorem in three dimensions. Substitute the lengths from the diagram.
Solve	$h^2 = 9 + 25 + 16$ $h^2 = 50$ $h = \sqrt{50}$ $h \approx 7.07$	Square and add the terms, take the square root of both sides, and determine that h approximately equals 7.07.

Optional: Isometric Drawing and Perspective

Isometric drawing is a method for representing a three-dimensional object in two dimensions. We show two examples of using isometric drawings to represent three-dimensional objects.

> Isometric drawings are useful for creating the illusion of three dimensions for objects that appear to be close.

Drawing a prism:

1. To draw a box in two dimensions that will appear like a three-dimensional object, we will create an isometric drawing using the background that has a grid, with lines drawn 30° from the horizontal.

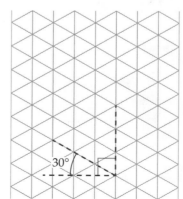

2. To draw a box that has a height of 3, a width of 4, and a depth of 2 (though you cannot see the depth yet), start with a face that is 3 by 4.

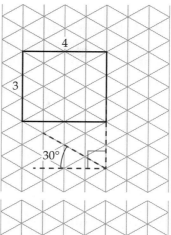

3. Take the side that is 4, and rotate the face so that it has a length of 4 along the 30° line.

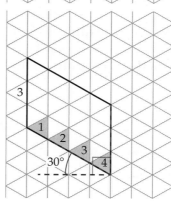

4. Next draw another face, the side of the box that has a depth of 2.

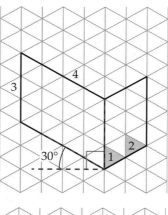

5. Then draw another face to connect the faces already drawn. We have drawn a figure that appears to be a three-dimensional prism.

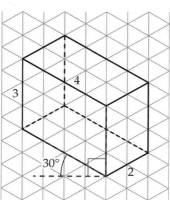

Drawing a cylinder:

1. To draw a cylinder with a diameter of 3, and height of 2, start with a square that has sides of length 3, and draw auxiliary lines to locate the square's center.

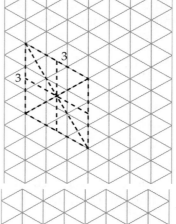

2. Draw an inscribed circle (in three dimensions), which is actually an ellipse, on the paper. The midpoints of each side of the square are points on the circle.

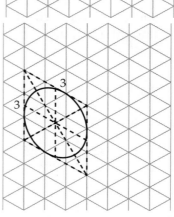

3. Next, for the depth, draw auxiliary lines of length 2, the height of the cylinder.

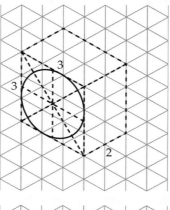

4. Then draw another pair of lines for the cylinder's depth, and a curve to connect them.

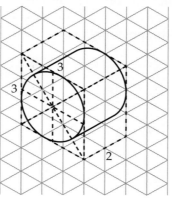

Perspective is used when an artist wants to create the impression that the viewer is at a particular location relative to the object. In perspective, for example, objects that appear far away will be drawn smaller, and objects that appear close will be drawn larger.

Using geometry to create perspective—the three-dimensional vision we all enjoy from a particular location—was one of the major accomplishments of the Renaissance. You can understand why people five hundred years ago were amazed by the first paintings that used perspective! It is not an easy feat.

We explain the basics of perspective:

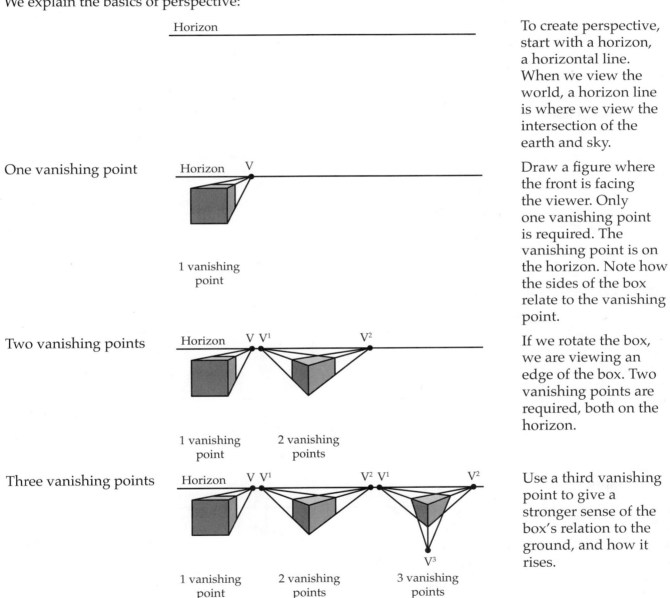

To create perspective, start with a horizon, a horizontal line. When we view the world, a horizon line is where we view the intersection of the earth and sky.

Draw a figure where the front is facing the viewer. Only one vanishing point is required. The vanishing point is on the horizon. Note how the sides of the box relate to the vanishing point.

If we rotate the box, we are viewing an edge of the box. Two vanishing points are required, both on the horizon.

Use a third vanishing point to give a stronger sense of the box's relation to the ground, and how it rises.

To draw a figure with perspective:

We explain in depth how to draw a figure with perspective. It is a fairly complicated set of steps. If you wonder why early paintings often appear flat, consider the insight required to create this system for creating perspective.

1. Start with view from above, location of viewer, picture plane.

We are looking down from above at the viewer and figure. The picture plane is the surface we are drawing on. Imagine this line as the top, horizontal 1D line of your piece of paper.

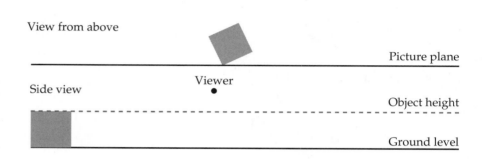

2. Draw object height and ground level.

Locate the height and ground level for the side view of our object.

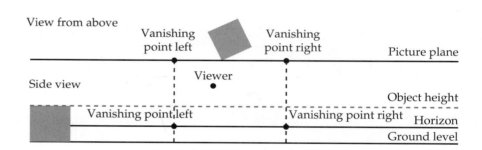

3. Draw vanishing points.

Draw two vanishing points. These will be the locations where our viewer will no longer see the building. The vanishing points define the horizon, our eye level.

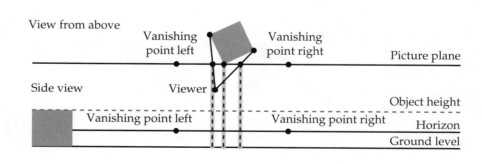

4. Draw additional lines and points.

Draw lines from the viewer to the visible vertices of the object on the view from above. Then draw lines from the intersection points on the picture plane to ground level. The line from the point of the object that is closest to the viewer intersects the object height line and the ground level line. Mark those two intersection points.

5. Find vanishing points.

Connect the marked intersection points to the vanishing points on the horizon. These lines define the edges of the third image.

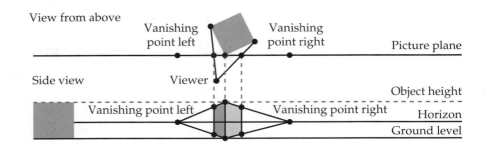

6. Remove points.

Remove the points to provide a better view of the final image.

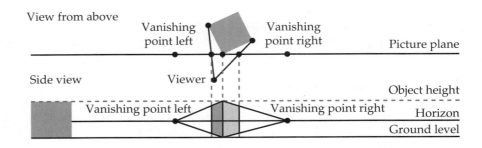

PRACTICE

1. Which of the following shapes cannot be created by slicing a cube?

  A. Hexagon   C. Parallelogram
  B. Octagon   D. Pentagon

2. Isometric drawing is used to represent

  A. A two-dimensional object in one dimension.
  B. An object which is far away from the viewer.
  C. A one-dimensional object in three dimensions.
  D. A three-dimensional object in two dimensions.

3. For which solid is it possible to slice a cross-section that is a circle?

  A. Cube
  B. Triangular prism
  C. Sphere

4. How many vertices does a cube have?

  A. 4   C. 8
  B. 6   D. 12

5. How many edges does a cube have?

  A. 4   C. 8
  B. 6   D. 12

6. A tetrahedron has 4 faces and 6 edges. How many vertices does this object have?

7. An octahedron has 8 faces and 12 edges. How many vertices does it have?

8. A dodecahedron has 12 faces and 20 vertices. How many edges does it have?

9. An icosahedron has 12 vertices and 20 faces. How many edges does this object have?

10. A cylinder has a height three times longer than its radius. Can a plane slice it in such a way as to form a square? Explain.

11. What three-dimensional solid is formed by rotating a rectangle around one of its sides?

12. What two-dimensional shape is formed when a cone standing on its base is sliced vertically and through the cone's vertex?

13. Name the two-dimensional shape that is rotated to form a cone.

Practice Problems continue . . .

14. State the number of edges, faces, and vertices of the solid below.

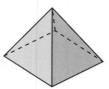

15. Sketch a triangular prism.

16. How many edges are found on a triangular prism?

17. What three-dimensional shape is formed by rotating a quarter of a circle about one of its straight sides?

18. Can a plane slice a sphere in such a way as to form a rectangle?

19. A cylinder has a height equal to its diameter. Can a plane slice it in such a way as to form a square? Explain.

20. An icosahedron has 12 vertices and 30 edges. How many faces does it have?

21. A soccer ball, like the one below, is a type of polyhedron sometimes called a *buckyball*. It has 32 faces, of which 20 are hexagons and 12 are pentagons. If a buckyball has 60 vertices, how many edges does it have?

22. Sketch a cube. Then, indicate how to slice the cube in order to form a rectangular slice that is not a square.

23. **MP 2, 7** What is the sum of the angles that meet at a single vertex of a regular octahedron? A regular octahedron is an eight-sided solid formed by congruent equilateral triangles. Explain how you found your answer.

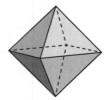

24. **MP 2, 7** The five Platonic solids are a tetrahedron, cube, octahedron, dodecahedron, and icosahedron. The faces of a Platonic solid are regular polygons of the same size and shape. For the five Platonic solids, there is a relationship between the number of faces, the number of sides of each face, and the number of edges found in the solid. Explain how to use the number of faces and the number of sides of each face to determine the total number of edges in the solid.

Tetrahedron Octahedron Cube

Icosahedron Dodecahedron

25. If the length of $\overline{AB}$ = 15 cm, $\overline{CB}$ = 9 cm, and $\overline{CD}$ = 12 cm, what is the length of $\overline{AD}$?

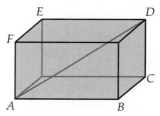

26. In the following figure, what is the length of $\overline{CE}$?

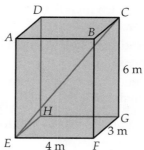

27. What is the length of $\overline{AF}$?

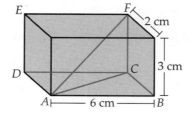

10.2 Surface Area

The **total surface area** of a solid is the measure of the total area that the surface of an object occupies. Because this is an area measurement, the units for surface area are properly expressed with square units.

Surface Area of Cubes and Boxes

A cube has edges of equal length. The length of an edge is s. When we are calculating one part of the surface area, such as the area of one face of a cube or the area of one side of a box, we use the variable A to represent its area. To calculate the area of a cube, we start with one face, which is a square. The area of a square equals the product of its sides.

$$A = s^2$$
$$A = \text{area}$$
$$s = \text{edge length}$$

A cube has six faces, so we can calculate its surface area by adding the sum of the areas of its faces. Since there are six faces on a cube, we multiply the area of one face by 6. We use S to represent the surface area of an entire solid. We flatten the cube to create a **net**.

$$S = 6s^2$$
$$S = \text{surface area}$$
$$s = \text{edge length}$$

MODEL PROBLEM

Calculate the surface area of the box. All the lengths are in inches.

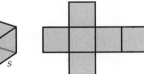

> With a box, we can think of the faces as the parts of the box. We calculate the area of each of the faces of the box. It is one way to calculate the surface area.

SOLUTION

Create net

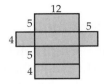

We want to calculate the surface area of this box, so we break the box apart.

Calculate areas

Top or bottom $= 12 \cdot 4 = 48$
Front or back $= 5 \cdot 4 = 20$
Either side $= 12 \cdot 5 = 60$

To calculate the surface area of the box, calculate the surface areas of its faces. Start with the top. It is a rectangle 12 by 4 inches. The bottom has the same area.

Sum areas

$S = 2 \cdot 48 + 2 \cdot 20 + 2 \cdot 60$
$S = 256 \text{ in}^2$

The surface area equals the sum of the areas. Multiply each area we calculated by two, since the box has a top and bottom, front and back, and two sides. For instance, the bottom and top each have an area of 48.

Surface Area of Prisms

A **prism** is a solid with two identical faces (called *bases*) in parallel planes. A prism's other surfaces are called **lateral faces**, or often simply just "faces."

We show two types of prisms:

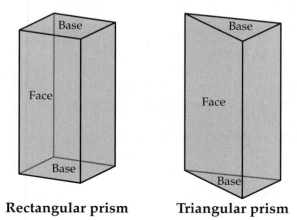

Rectangular prism   **Triangular prism**

The perimeter is the perimeter of a base. The height is the perpendicular distance between the bases.

To calculate the surface area of a prism, use the formula:

$S = 2B + Ph$
B = base area
P = perimeter
h = height

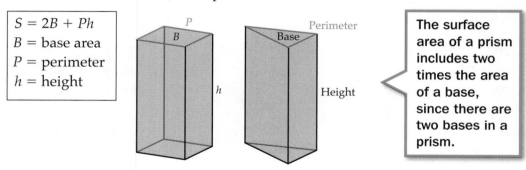

The surface area of a prism includes two times the area of a base, since there are two bases in a prism.

MODEL PROBLEM

What is the surface area of the prism?

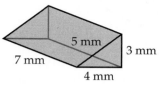

5 mm   3 mm   7 mm   4 mm

SOLUTION

Base area	$B = \dfrac{1}{2}b \cdot h$ $B = \dfrac{1}{2} \cdot 3 \cdot 4 = 6$	Start by calculating the area of a base. Each base is a 3, 4, 5 right triangle. Note that the height here is the height of the triangular base, not the height of the prism.
Perimeter	$P = 3 + 4 + 5$ $P = 12$	The perimeter equals 12, the sum of the sides of the triangle.
Surface area	$S = 2B + Ph$ $S = 2 \cdot 6 + 12 \cdot 7$ $S = 96 \text{ mm}^2$	Use the formula for the surface area. Substitute the values we calculated for the area of the base and the perimeter. Substitute the height from the diagram.

Surface Area of Cylinders

A cylinder is a solid with two congruent circular bases that lie in parallel planes. The surface area of a cylinder is the sum of the areas of its bases and the area of its curved surface. To state the formula for the surface area of a cylinder, we start with its bases. Each of these is a circle, so we use the formula for the area of a circle, πr^2, and multiply by 2.

$$S = 2\pi r^2 + 2\pi rh$$
$$r = \text{radius}$$
$$h = \text{height}$$

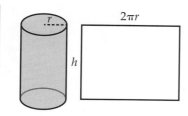

> We could roll a piece of paper to form the side. The side has a width equal to the circumference of the circle. The circumference of the circle is $2\pi r$.

MODEL PROBLEMS

1. What is the surface area of a cylinder with a radius of 3 and a height of 10?

SOLUTION

Area of base	$A = \pi r^2 = \pi(3)^2 = 9\pi$	We start with a cylinder that has bases with a radius of 3. Write the formula for the area of a circle.
Width of side	$2\pi r = 2\pi(3) = 6\pi$	Calculate the width of the side.
Area of side	$A = hw = 10 \cdot 6\pi = 60\pi$	The height is 10. Multiply the height by the width of the paper to calculate the area.
Sum areas	$S = 18\pi + 60\pi = 78\pi \text{ in}^2$	The surface area of the cylinder equals the sum of its faces. Start with its bases. We calculated the area of the top. Multiply that by 2 to include the area of the bottom as well.

2. What is the surface area of the cylinder?

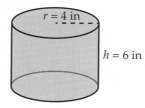

$r = 4$ in

$h = 6$ in

SOLUTION

Calculate area	$S = 2\pi r^2 + 2\pi rh$ $S \approx 2 \cdot 3.14 \cdot (4)^2 + 2 \cdot 3.14 \cdot 4 \cdot 6$	The cylinder has a radius of 4 inches, and height of 6 inches. Approximate π as 3.14. Substitute the values into the formula.
	$S \approx 251 \text{ in}^2$	Evaluate. To the nearest square inch, the surface area is 251 square inches.

Model Problems continue . . .

3. **MP 2, 4** A can of condensed soup is a right circular cylinder with height 9.5 cm and diameter 6.5 cm. Suppose the height of the can's label is the same as the can's height and the label runs all the way around the can. If the label were carefully peeled off the can and laid flat, what would be the area of the label?

SOLUTION

Express the formula for the area of a rectangle in terms of π	$A = lw$ but $l = 2\pi r$ and $w = h$, so the area of the label is $A = 2\pi rh$	The label is a rectangle, but we must express its area formula in terms of π because the rectangle's length is a result of the circle's diameter.
Determine the radius of the cylinder	$r = \dfrac{6.5}{2} = 3.25$ cm	The radius is half the length of the diameter.
Substitute the known information and solve	$A = 2\pi rh$ $A = 2\pi(3.25)(9.5)$ $A = 61.75\pi$ $A \approx 194$ cm^2	The radius is 3.25 cm and the height is 9.5 cm.

Surface Area of Pyramids

A pyramid is a polyhedron that has a polygonal base and three or more triangular faces that meet at a single point called the *apex*. **Regular pyramids** have a regular polygon as their base. For example, the Egyptian pyramids are regular pyramids with square bases.

Regular pyramids have a slant height. If you think of walking up a pyramid from the middle of a base edge to its peak, you understand slant height. It is the height of one of the lateral faces of the pyramid.

To calculate the surface area of a pyramid, use the formula:

$$S = B + \frac{1}{2}Pl$$
B = base area
P = perimeter
l = slant height

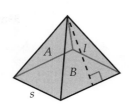

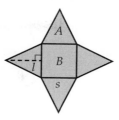

We explain the source of the formula for the surface area of a regular pyramid.

Determining the formula for the pyramid's surface area:

Four triangles $A = 4\left(\frac{1}{2}(sl)\right) = 2sl$ First calculate the area of one of the triangles. It equals one half the product of the base, s, and height, l.

Express in terms of perimeter $A = (2s)(l) = \frac{1}{2}Pl$ Group the multiplication. $2s$ is one-half the perimeter, since the perimeter is $4s$.

Add area of base $S = B + \frac{1}{2}Pl$ Add the area of the base B. This is an area formula for a regular pyramid.

MODEL PROBLEMS

1. What is the surface area?

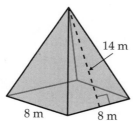

14 m

8 m   8 m

SOLUTION

Create net   Flatten the pyramid.

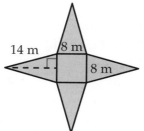

14 m   8 m

8 m

Substitute $S = B + \frac{1}{2}Pl$ Use the formula for the surface area of a pyramid. Start
by calculating the area of the base. It is the square of the
length of a side.

$S = 8^2 + \frac{1}{2}(4 \cdot 8)14$

Evaluate $S = 64 + \frac{1}{2}(32)14$ Evaluate expression. The surface area is 288 m^2.

$S = 288 \text{ m}^2$

Model Problems continue . . .

2. What is the surface area of the regular pyramid with a triangular base?

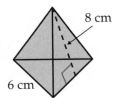

8 cm

6 cm

SOLUTION

Create net

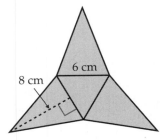

6 cm

8 cm

Flatten the pyramid.

Calculate B

$h = \sqrt{6^2 - 3^2} = \sqrt{27}$

$B = 2\left(\frac{1}{2}bh\right)$

$B = 2\left(\frac{1}{2} \cdot 3 \cdot \sqrt{27}\right) \approx 15.6$

To calculate the area of the base, calculate the height of the triangle. We do so by constructing its height, and calculating that height by using the Pythagorean theorem. One leg is 3 (half the base) and the hypotenuse is 6. Then use the area formula, multiplied by two, since our construction created two triangles.

Substitute

$S = B + \frac{1}{2}Pl$

$S = 15.6 + \frac{1}{2}(3 \cdot 6)8$

Start with the formula for the surface area of a pyramid and substitute.

Evaluate

$S = 15.6 + 72$
$S = 87.6 \text{ cm}^2$

Complete the calculation.

Surface Area of Cones

A cone is a solid with a circular base and a single vertex, which is the top of the cone. The slant height equals the distance to the vertex from any point on the edge of the base.

Like the other formulas for total surface area, a cone's total surface area is the sum of the area of the base and the lateral area of the cone. We show a few ways to calculate a cone's surface area, using factoring to create equivalent expressions:

$S = B + \pi r l$
$S = \pi r^2 + \pi r l$
$S = \pi r(r + 1)$
$B = \text{base area}$
$r = \text{base radius}$
$l = \text{slant height}$

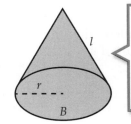

l

r

B

The lateral surface area of any solid is the sum of all the surface area of the figure excluding the bases.

MODEL PROBLEM

What is the surface area of the cone, to the nearest square foot?

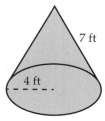

7 ft

4 ft

SOLUTION

Substitute

$S = \pi r^2 + \pi r l$
$S \approx 3.14(4)^2 + 3.14(4)(7)$

The diagram shows the radius and the slant height. Substitute those values, including 3.14 for π.

Evaluate

$S \approx 3.14 \cdot 16 + 3.14 \cdot 28$
$S \approx 138.16 \approx 138 \text{ ft}^2$

Evaluate and round.

Surface Area of Spheres

A sphere is a solid with all the points on its surface the same distance from its center. In other words, a sphere is a perfect ball with radius r.

$S = 4\pi r^2$
$r = \text{radius}$

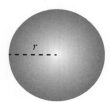

r

MODEL PROBLEMS

1. A sphere has a surface area of 64π square inches. What is its radius?

SOLUTION

Use formula for surface area of sphere

$S = 4\pi r^2$
$64\pi = 4\pi r^2$

Start with the formula for the surface area of a sphere and substitute.

Solve for r

$4\pi r^2 = 64\pi$

$r^2 = \dfrac{64\pi}{4\pi}$

$r^2 = 16$
$r = 4 \text{ in}$

We like to have the variable on the left, so we switch the sides of the terms. Cancel the coefficient of r^2 by dividing both sides of the equation by 4π.

Model Problems continue . . .

2. A hemisphere has a radius of r. What is the entire surface area of the hemisphere?

    A. $4\pi r^2$

    B. $3\pi r^2$

    C. $4\pi r^3$

    D. πr^3

SOLUTION

The answer is B. The surface area of a sphere is $4\pi r^2$, so half of that is $2\pi r^2$. The middle of the sphere, now exposed, is a circle, so its (surface) area is πr^2. Summing these, the result is $3\pi r^2$, so the answer is B.

3. **MP 1, 2, 4** The United Nations estimates the world will contain 10 billion people shortly. About 30% of Earth's surface is land. How many people per square mile of land will there be? The radius of Earth is about 3,950 miles.

SOLUTION

Surface area of Earth	$S = 4\pi r^2$ $S = 4\pi(3{,}950)^2$ $S \approx 1.96 \times 10^8$ square miles	Use the formula for surface area, substituting the radius of Earth in miles.
Amount of land on Earth	Land $\approx 0.3(1.96 \times 10^8)$ Land $\approx 5.88 \times 10^7$ square miles	The problem says that about 30% of Earth is land, so multiply by 0.3 to calculate the number of square miles of land.
People per square mile	density $\approx \dfrac{1.0 \times 10^{10}}{5.88 \times 10^7}$ density $\approx 1.70 \times 10^2$ density ≈ 170 people per square mile	To calculate the population density, divide the population of 10 billion (written in scientific notation) by the number of square miles.

Did you know? States such as Georgia and Michigan have about the population density calculated above. The District of Columbia has almost 10,000 people per square mile, while Alaska has about 1 person per square mile. It is worth noting Earth's land includes areas such as the Sahara (about 2 people per square mile) and Antarctica (about 0 permanent residents per square mile). This means higher population densities would be expected in more easily inhabited areas.

Surface Area Summary

Surface Area	Formula	
Cube 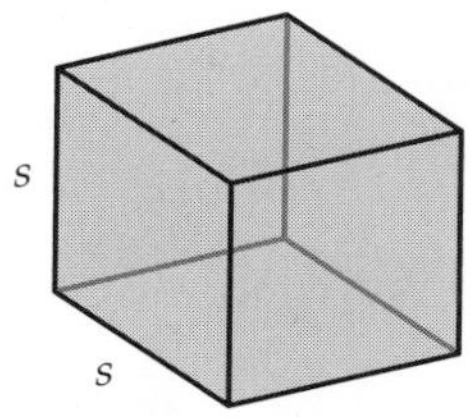	$S = 6s^2$	The surface area of a cube equals six times the square of the length of an edge.
Prism 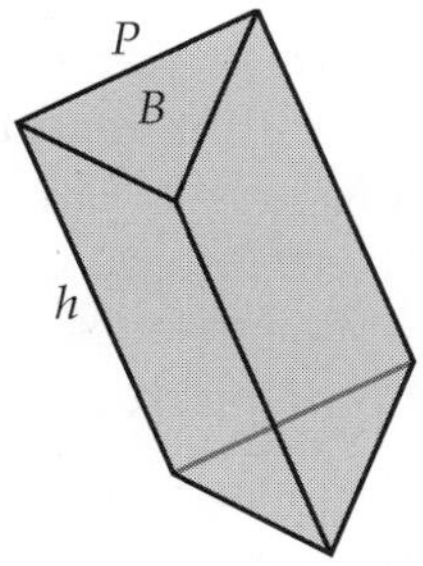	$S = 2B + Ph$	The surface area of a prism equals two times the area of its base plus the product of its base's perimeter and the prism's height.
Cylinder 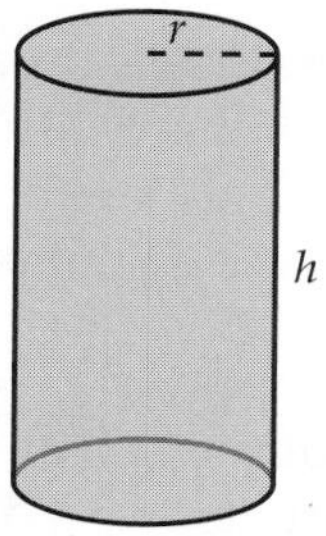	$S = 2\pi r^2 + 2\pi rh$	The surface area of a cylinder equals 2 times π times r squared, plus the product of $2\pi r$ and its height.
Regular pyramid 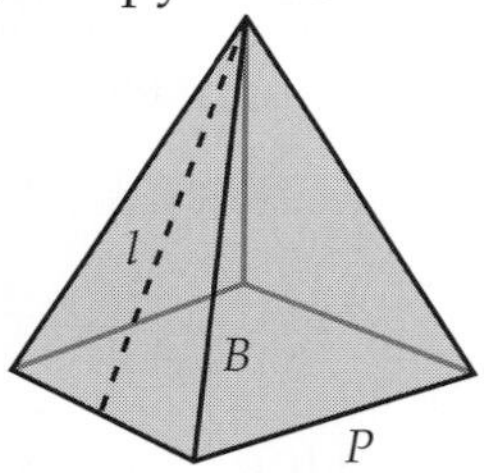	$S = B + \dfrac{1}{2}Pl$	The surface area of a pyramid equals the area of its base, plus one-half its perimeter times its slant height. The slant height is the height of a triangular face.
Cone 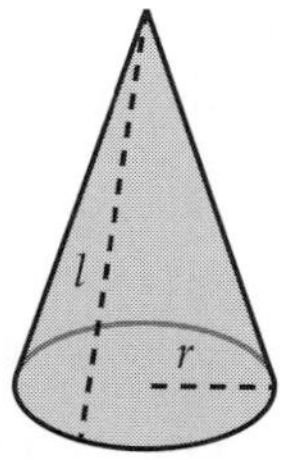	$S = \pi r^2 + \pi rl$	The surface area of a cone equals the area of its base, which is a circle, plus πrl.
Sphere 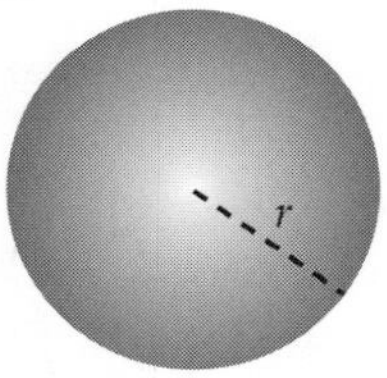	$S = 4\pi r^2$	The surface area of a sphere equals four times π times its radius squared.

A silo is used to store crops on a farm. What is the surface area of the silo to the nearest square foot? The upper part is a half of a sphere, a hemisphere. The hemisphere has a radius of 8 feet. Ignore the part of the silo surface on the ground.

SOLUTION

Draw diagram

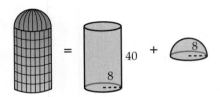

To calculate the surface area of the silo, which we might need to do if we wanted to know how much paint it would take to cover it, divide it into two surfaces, a cylinder and a hemisphere.

Cylinder surface area

Cylinder lateral surface area $= 2\pi rh$
Cylinder lateral surface area $\approx (2)(3.14)(8)(40)$
Cylinder lateral surface area ≈ 2009.6

Calculate the lateral surface area of the cylinder. It has a radius of 8 feet and a height of 40 feet.

Hemisphere surface area

$$\text{Surface area hemisphere} = \frac{1}{2}(4\pi r^2)$$
$$\approx \frac{1}{2}(4 \cdot 3.14 \cdot 8^2)$$
$$\approx 401.9$$

Now calculate the surface area of the top. It is half a sphere. Multiply the surface area of a sphere by one-half, since we are calculating one-half its area.

Total

The silo = cylinder + hemisphere

Silo surface area $\approx 2009.6 + 401.9 \approx 2412$ ft^2

The surface area of the silo equals the sum of the surface areas of the lateral part of the cylinder and the hemisphere. The silo has a surface area of about 2412 square feet.

PRACTICE

1. The slant height of a cone is twice the radius of its base. The radius is 3 cm. What is the surface area of the cone?

   A. 18π cm^2 C. 27π cm^2
   B. $27\pi^2$ cm^2 D. 36π cm^2

2. The formula $S = \pi r^2 + \pi rl$ can be used to find the surface area of a

   A. Cone.
   B. Cylinder.
   C. Regular pyramid.
   D. Sphere.

3. A spherical ball is glued on top of a box with dimensions of 10 feet by 5 feet by 8 feet. The total surface area of the ball and the box is 352.56 square feet. What is the radius of the ball?

   A. 1 in   C. π in
   B. 2 in   D. 3.14 in

4. What is the surface area of a cylinder whose circular base has a radius of 3 inches and whose height is $\frac{1}{3}$ inch?

   A. 11π in^2 C. 18π in^2
   B. $9\pi^2$ in^2 D. 20π in^2

Practice Problems continue . . .

5. The surface area of a cube is 294 in². How long is one edge of the cube?
   A. 5 in   C. 7 in
   B. 6 in   D. $\sqrt{294}$ in

6. What is the surface area of a cube with edges of length 1.5 inches?

7. What is the length of a side of a cube with a surface area of 150 square meters?

8. What is the surface area of the box below?

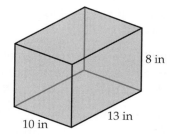

9. What is the surface area of the box below?

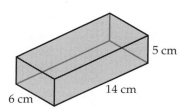

10. To find the surface area of a cube, you need only one piece of information: the length of one edge. Name another solid with a surface area that can be found with only one input, and give the input.

11. In the diagram below, what is the object's surface area?

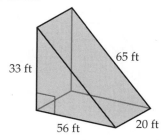

12. In the diagram below, what is the object's surface area?

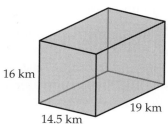

13. A mailing tube has a radius of 4 cm and a height of 17 cm. What is the surface area of the tube?

14. Can the surface area of a solid be smaller than the area of the solid's base? Why or why not? Explain.

15. If a silo has a radius of 12 feet and a height of 52 feet, what is its surface area?

16. What is the surface area of the solid below?

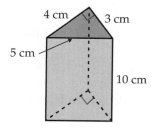

17. Find the surface area of a pyramid with a square base. The base has sides of length 6 centimeters, and the slant height of the pyramid is 14 centimeters. State your answer in square centimeters.

18. Find the surface area of a pyramid with a square base. The base has sides of length 4 centimeters, and the slant height of the pyramid is 10 centimeters. State your answer in square centimeters.

19. Find the surface area of a sphere with radius 7 centimeters.

20. The surface area of a sphere is 324π mm². What is its radius, in millimeters?

21. The surface area of a sphere is 196π mm². What is its radius, in millimeters?

22. What is the surface area of the object below? Its radius is 4 meters.

23. Paul needs to find the diameter of a steel ball bearing. If he knows the surface area of the ball bearing, how can he find the diameter?

Practice Problems continue . . .

24. Sketch a sphere with a surface area of 2826 square millimeters. Use 3.14 for π, and label the length of the radius in your sketch.

25. As a treat, Leo and his mother are making peanut butter balls dipped in chocolate. One peanut butter ball has a diameter of 24 millimeters. Leo dips it so that 70% of the surface of the ball is covered in chocolate. What is the surface area of the chocolate, to the nearest square millimeter?

26. What is the surface area of the gray shaded area below? The radius of the pumpkin is 14 centimeters. The mouth is half a circle and its radius is 3 centimeters. The eyes and nose are isosceles triangles with two sides of length 5 and a base of length 6.

27. A cone has a radius of 3 inches and a slant height of 7 inches.

  a Sketch the cone.
  b Find the surface area of the cone.

28. What is the surface area of the figure below? Its slant height is 7 inches. State your answer to the nearest tenth of a square inch.

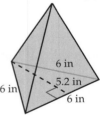

29. Find the surface area of a cone with a slant height of 5 centimeters. The radius of the base is 4 centimeters.

30. What is the surface area of the figure below in square meters? Its base is 4 meters by 4 meters.

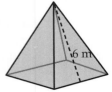

31. **MP 4** A vase has the shape of a prism with a height of 20 cm. Its base is a square with a side length of 8 cm. The opening in the top of the vase for flower stems is a rectangle with a width of 1.3 cm and a length of 5 cm. Find the total surface area of the vase in square centimeters.

32. **MP 3** Gregory says it is not possible to find the surface area of a cone if you are given its radius and vertical height, since the formula for the surface area of a cone uses slant height and radius. Do you agree with Gregory? Why or why not?

33. Is it possible to use the formula for the surface area of a pyramid on a non-regular pyramid? Why or why not?

34. Sketch a square pyramid with a base perimeter of 20 centimeters and a slant height of 8 centimeters. Then, find the surface area of the pyramid.

35. How much leather is needed to sew a ball with a diameter of 13.1 inches, if an extra 10% of the material is needed for the seams?

36. **MP 1, 5** The surface area of a cone is 245π inches and the slant height of the cone is four times its radius. What is the slant height of the cone?

37. **MP 1, 2** The surface area of a cube is 216 square centimeters. The cube is inscribed in a sphere (placed inside so that each vertex of the cube touches the surface of the sphere). What is the surface area of the sphere, in terms of π?

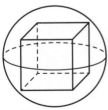

38. A cone and a sphere have the same surface area and radius. What is the slant height of the cone, in terms of its radius?

39. **MP 2, 7** A regular triangular pyramid and a regular square pyramid have the same slant height and the same base perimeter. Which solid will have a greater surface area? Explain your reasoning.

Practice Problems continue . . .

40. A local park has installed a climbing structure that is the shape of a pyramid with a square base, similar to the one shown below. The structure will support 20,000 pounds of weight, and each climber requires about 20 square feet of surface space while climbing.

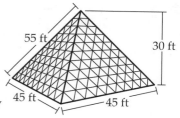

a Considering only the surface area of the climbing structure, how many people can use the equipment at the same time?

b One afternoon, a citizen counts 200 people using the climber at the same time. Will the structure support that number of people simultaneously? Why or why not?

c Suppose the average weight of a person using the climber is 75 pounds. What is the maximum number of people who can use the structure simultaneously? How do you know?

LESSON 10.3

10.3 Volume

Volume is the amount of three-dimensional space an object occupies. As with surface area, there are formulas for the volumes of common figures.

The units for volume are usually expressed as cubic units. This is because volume is a measure of capacity. We often use abbreviations such as in^3 or cm^3, but other units of volume include the gallon and liter.

Volume of Cubes and Rectangular Prisms

The general formula for the volume of any regular solid is $V = Bh$, where B is the area of the base and h is the height of the solid. Regular solids, such as rectangular prisms, cubes, cylinders, and more, have formulas specific to their properties, but they are all derived from the general formula given above. Below we see how the general formula is transformed into the specific formula for the volume of a rectangular prism.

$V = Bh$
$V = $ volume
$B = $ area of base
$h = $ height

$V = l \cdot w \cdot h$
$V = $ volume
$l = $ length
$w = $ width
$h = $ height

We can use the same general formula to determine the formula specific to the volume of a cube. Recall that the formula for the area of the base of a cube is s^2. As all the edges of a cube are the same length, multiplying s^2 by the height, s, yields s^3. Thus the volume of a cube is $V = s^3$.

$V = s^3$
$s = $ edge length

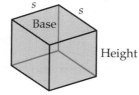

MODEL PROBLEMS

1. A cube with edges of length s centimeters can hold N marbles. The density of marbles in this box can be determined using the expression

   A. $(6s^2)N$

   C. $\dfrac{s^3}{N}$

   B. $\dfrac{6s^2}{N}$

   D. $\dfrac{N}{s^3}$

SOLUTION

The answer is D. Density is the amount divided by volume. The number of marbles is N, and the volume of a cube is s^3, so D reflects this division.

2. **MP 7** Determine the volume of the rectangular prism. Use two different formulas.

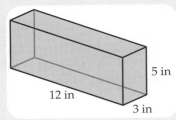

SOLUTION

Formula 1

$V = l \cdot w \cdot h$ $V = 12 \cdot 3 \cdot 5$ Substitute the values for the length,
                  $V = 180 \text{ in}^3$ width, and height and multiply. The
                                   volume is 180 cubic inches.

Formula 2

$V = Bh$ $B = 12 \cdot 3 = 36$ We could also calculate the area of its
         $V = 36 \cdot 5$ base first, and then multiply that area
         $V = 180 \text{ in}^3$ by the height. We get the same result.

3. What is the volume of the cube?

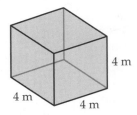

SOLUTION

Use formula $V = s^3$ To calculate the volume of this cube,
              $V = 4^3$ substitute the length of a side, which is 4 m.

Multiply $V = 64 \text{ m}^3$ Complete the calculation. The volume of
                                 the cube is 64 cubic meters.

Model Problems continue . . .

4. What is the volume? Each cube has a volume of 8 cubic centimeters.

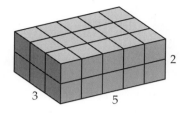

2

3   5

With a single cube, we multiply its length by its width by its height to calculate its volume. If we have many cubes, we can combine their volumes by multiplying.

SOLUTION

| Calculate the number of cubes | number of cubes = $5 \cdot 3 \cdot 2 = 30$ | To calculate the volume of this object, first calculate the number of cubes. There are 5 along the length of the object, 3 as we go back, and it is 2 high. Multiply these three values. |
| Multiply by volume of a single cube | $V = 30 \cdot 8 = 240 \text{ cm}^3$ | To calculate the volume of the object, multiply the number of cubes, 30, by the volume of a cube, 8 cm^3. |

Volume of Other Prisms and Cylinders

The volume of prisms and cylinders can be calculated as the product of the area of its base and its height.

$V = Bh$
B = area of base
h = height

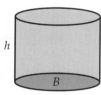

h

B

MODEL PROBLEMS

1. Calculate the volume of the cylinder.

5 ft

8 ft

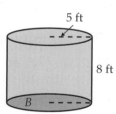

B

SOLUTION

| Calculate the base area | $B = \pi r^2$
 $B \approx 3.14 \cdot 5^2$ | To calculate the volume of the cylinder, first calculate the area of its base, using the formula for the area of a circle. Substitute the radius shown in the diagram. |
| Multiply by height | $V = Bh$
 $V \approx 3.14 \cdot 5^2 \cdot 8$
 $V \approx 628 \text{ ft}^3$ | The volume of a cylinder equals the product of its base area and height. |

Model Problems continue . . .

2. Calculate the volume of the triangular prism.

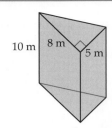

10 m   8 m   5 m

SOLUTION

Calculate the base area

B = area of triangle

$B = \dfrac{1}{2} \cdot 5 \cdot 8 = 20\ \text{m}^2$

Use the formula for the area of a triangle to calculate the area of the base of the triangular prism. The area of a triangle equals one-half the triangle's base times its height.

Multiply by height

$V = Bh$
$V = 20 \cdot 10$
$V = 200\ \text{m}^3$

The volume of a prism equals the product of the area of its base and the prism's height. The base area is 20 m². Multiply that by the height, 10 m, and get 200 m³.

3. Manufacturers package tennis balls in cylindrical cans. The cylinder is just wide enough to fit the ball and just large enough to hold 3 tennis balls stacked on top of each other. If each tennis ball has a diameter of 2.60 inches, what is the volume of air inside the cylindrical can?

SOLUTION

Determine the height of the cylinder

$h = 3 \cdot 2.6$
$h = 7.8$ inches

The height of the cylinder will be equal to the height of three tennis balls.

Find the volume of the cylinder

$V = \pi r^2 h$
$V = \pi (1.3)^2\,(7.8)$
$V \approx 41.4\ \text{in}^3$

Use the formula for the volume of a cylinder. Don't forget to calculate the radius of the tennis ball.

Find the volume of the tennis balls; there are 3 to a package

$V = 3\left(\dfrac{4}{3}\,\pi r^3\right)$
$V = 4\pi r^3$
$V = 4\pi (1.3)^3$
$V = 27.6\ \text{in}^3$

Multiply the formula for the volume of a sphere by 3 and simplify.

Subtract

$41.4 - 27.6 = 13.8\ \text{in}^3$ The volume of air in the cylinder is 13.8 in³.

Volume of Pyramids and Cones

For the first volumes we worked with—cubes, regular prisms, and cylinders—we could multiply the base area and height. Finding the volume of a pyramid or cone is not quite so simple. However, we can use the same formula to describe the volume of a pyramid or of a cone.

$$V = \dfrac{1}{3}Bh$$

B = area of base
h = height

With the surface area formulas we discussed earlier, the pyramids and cones had to have regular polygons, like a square, as a base. With the volume formulas, we can drop that requirement.

We explain the $\frac{1}{3}$ in the volume formula:

A pyramid inside a prism with the same base area and height

- Takes up $\frac{1}{3}$ the volume of the prism

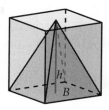

If we were to fit a pyramid into a prism with the same base area and height as the pyramid, the pyramid would only take up one-third of the space inside the prism.

A cone inside a cylinder with the same base area and height

- Takes up $\frac{1}{3}$ the volume of the cylinder

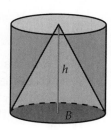

The same is true for a cone inside of a cylinder with the same base area and height.

Try it! One way to informally prove the relationship to yourself is to construct a pyramid and prism of the same base and height out of plastic or some other material that will hold water. Fill the pyramid with water and transfer the water to the prism. You should be able to do this exactly three times to completely fill the prism. The same works for a cone and a cylinder.

MODEL PROBLEMS

1. What is the cone's volume?

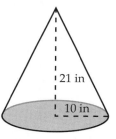

21 in

10 in

SOLUTION

Calculate the base area	$B = \pi r^2$ $B \approx 3.14 \cdot (10)^2 \approx 314 \text{ in}^2$	To calculate the volume of a cone, calculate the area of its base, using the formula for the area of a circle. Substitute the radius.
Multiply by height	$V = \frac{1}{3}Bh$ $V \approx \frac{1}{3}(314 \cdot 21) \approx 2198 \text{ in}^3$	The base area is 314 in², and the height is 21 in. Multiply and get 2198 in³.

Model Problems continue . . .

2. **MP 4** The Great Pyramid of Khufu is the last of the Seven Wonders of the Ancient World still standing. The pyramid is smaller now than when it was built due to erosion and other causes. It has a square base, and an estimate of its original dimensions appears in the diagram. What was its original volume?

147 m

230 m

SOLUTION

Draw diagram

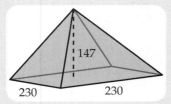

147

230   230

> Note that the height used for volume is not the slant height, but the vertical height from the base to the top.

Compute the base area

$B = s \cdot s$
$B = 230 \cdot 230$
$B = 52{,}900 \text{ m}^2$

Start by computing the area of the base. The problem says each side was about 230 meters, so substitute those values, and multiply.

Calculate the volume

$V = \frac{1}{3}Bh$

$V = \frac{1}{3}(52{,}900)(147)$

$V = 2{,}592{,}100 \text{ m}^2$

Apply the formula for the volume of a pyramid. Substitute the area of the base we just computed and the given vertical height. Notice that we do not need the slant height to calculate the pyramid's volume.

Volume of Spheres

We write the equation for the volume of a sphere:

$$V = \frac{4}{3}\pi r^3$$

$r = \text{radius}$

MODEL PROBLEM

Find the volume of the sphere.

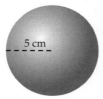

5 cm

SOLUTION

Formula

$V \approx \frac{4}{3}(3.14 \cdot 5^3)$

To calculate the volume of the sphere above, substitute the value of the radius.

Evaluate

$V \approx \frac{4}{3}(3.14 \cdot 125)$

$V \approx 523 \text{ cm}^3$

Then cube 5, and multiply. The volume of the sphere is about 523 cm³.

Volume Summary

Volume	Formula	
Cube 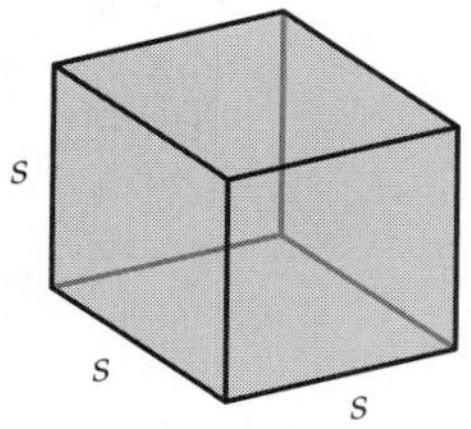	$V = s^3$	The volume of a cube equals the length of an edge, cubed.
Prism 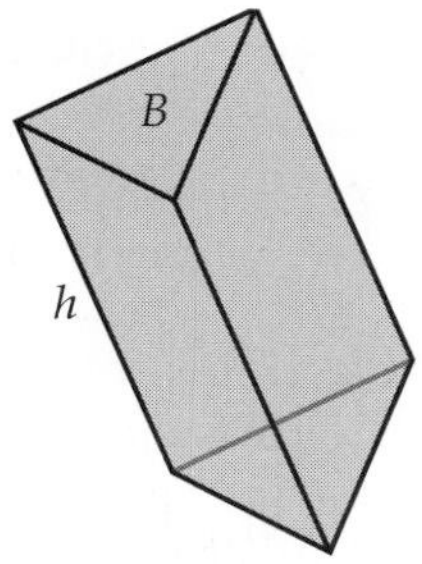	$V = Bh$	The volume of a prism can be calculated as the product of its base area and its height.
Cylinder 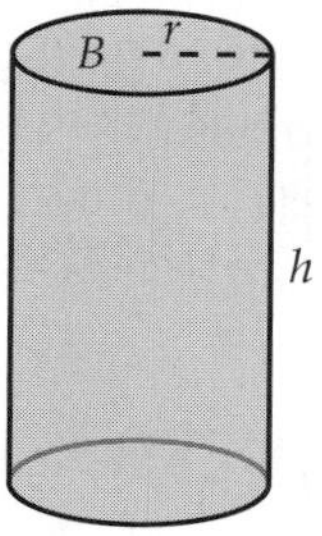	$V = Bh$ $V = \pi r^2 h$	The volume of a cylinder also equals the product of its base area and height. The area of the base, since it is a circle, is πr^2.
Pyramid and cone 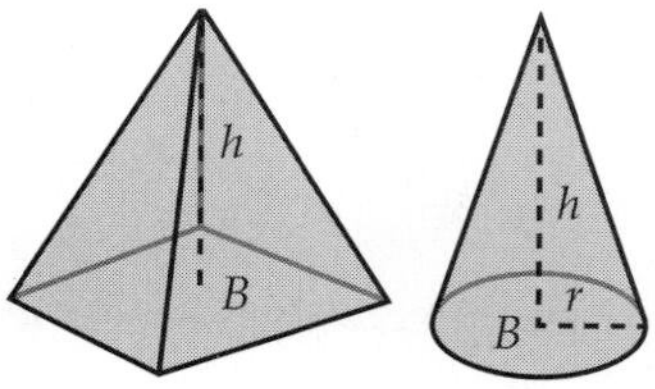	$V = \frac{1}{3}Bh$	The volume of a pyramid and cone can be calculated with this formula. The height is the distance from the center of the base to the top, not the slant height.
Sphere 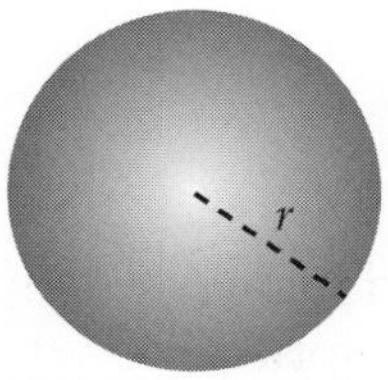	$V = \frac{4}{3}\pi r^3$	This is the formula for the volume of a sphere.

MODEL PROBLEMS

1. **MP 1, 7** Calculate the mass of the two identical children's blocks to the nearest hundredth of a pound. The density of the wood is $\dfrac{0.02 \text{ lbs}}{\text{in}^3}$.

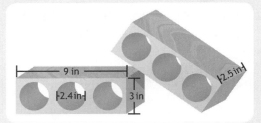

SOLUTION

Calculate volume of a block, ignoring holes	$V_{\text{one block}} = l \cdot w \cdot h$ $V_{\text{one block}} = 9 \cdot 2.5 \cdot 3$ $V_{\text{one block}} = 67.5 \text{ in}^3$	Start by calculating the volume of one block, ignoring the holes for now.
Calculate volume of holes	$B = \pi r^2$ $V_{\text{holes}} = 3 \cdot Bh$ $V_{\text{holes}} \approx 3 \cdot 3.14 \cdot 1.2^2 \cdot 2.5$ $V_{\text{holes}} \approx 33.9 \text{ in}^3$	Now calculate the volume of the holes in one block. They are cylinders.
Subtract holes	$V_{\text{one block}} - V_{\text{holes}} \approx 67.5 - 33.9$ $V_{\text{one block}} - V_{\text{holes}} \approx 33.6 \text{ in}^3$	Subtract the volume of the holes from the volume of the block if it were solid.
Two blocks	$V_{\text{two blocks}} \approx 2 \cdot 33.6$ $V_{\text{two blocks}} \approx 67.2 \text{ in}^3$	There are two blocks, so multiply by 2 the volume of one block with holes.
Weight	$\text{mass} = \text{volume} \cdot \text{density}$ $\text{mass} \approx 67.2 \text{ in}^3 \cdot 0.02 \dfrac{\text{lbs}}{\text{in}^3}$ $\text{mass} \approx 1.34 \text{ lbs}$	Mass equals the product of volume and density. We were told the density. Multiply to calculate the mass.

2. **MP 2, 4** How much ice cream does the cone hold? Assume the cone itself is very thin, the bottom scoop is a perfect hemisphere, and the top scoop is a perfect sphere. The cone itself is also packed. The cone has a radius of 3 cm on top and a height of 10 cm. Estimate the volume of the cone to the nearest tenth of a cubic centimeter.

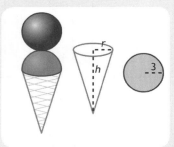

SOLUTION

Calculate the cone's base area	$B = \pi r^2$ $B \approx 3.14(3)^2$ $B \approx 28.3 \text{ cm}^2$	Calculate the area of the base, using the area formula for a circle.
Calculate cone's volume	$V = \dfrac{1}{3} Bh$ $V \approx \dfrac{1}{3}(28.3) \cdot 10$ $B = 94.3 \text{ cm}^3$	Use the formula for the volume of a cone.
Calculate volume of scoops	$V = 1.5\left(\dfrac{4}{3}\pi r^3\right)$ $V \approx 1.5\left(\dfrac{4}{3} \cdot 3.14 \cdot (3)^3\right)$ $V \approx 169.6 \text{ cm}^3$	Calculate the volume of the scoops. We have one whole sphere and one half sphere, so we multiply the expression for the volume of a sphere by 1.5.

Model Problems continue . . .

| Total | $V = \text{cone} + \text{scoops}$ $V \approx 94.3 + 169.6$ $V \approx 263.9 \text{ cm}^3$ | The entire ice cream volume equals the sum of the ice cream in the cone and the ice cream in the scoops. Add the two volumes. The volume of ice cream is approximately 263.9 cubic centimeters. The volume 263.9 cubic centimeters equals about 16 cubic inches. That is a cube with sides of approximately 2.5 inches. |

3. MP 2, 3 An artist is asked to design an ornament that is 10 grams of copper covered by gold leaf. She considers a cube and a sphere as her two possible shapes. She wants to minimize the surface area so that she uses as little gold as possible. Which shape should she choose?

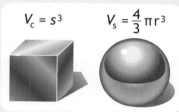
$V_c = s^3 \qquad V_s = \frac{4}{3}\pi r^3$

SOLUTION

Set volumes equal to each other	$V_s = \frac{4}{3}\pi r^3$ $V_c = s^3$ $V_c = V_s$ $s^3 = \frac{4}{3}\pi r^3$	We know that the volumes of the cube and sphere must be equal, so we use this fact to find the expression for the surface area of the cube in terms of r, the sphere's radius. The two volumes must be equal, since both shapes will contain 10 grams each.
Solve for s	$s = \sqrt[3]{\frac{4}{3}\pi r^3}$ $s = r\sqrt[3]{\frac{4}{3}\pi}$	Solve for s, the length of a side of the cube. Remove the r from the radical since the cube root of r^3 is r.
Surface area of cube	$S_{\text{cube}} = 6s^2$ $S_{\text{cube}} = 6\left(r\sqrt[3]{\frac{4}{3}\pi}\right)^2$ $S_{\text{cube}} = 6r^2\left(\sqrt[3]{\frac{4}{3}\pi}\right)^2$	Apply the formula for the surface area of a cube. Substitute the equation we just created for the length of a side.
Surface area of sphere	$S_{\text{sphere}} = 4\pi r^2$	This is the equation for the surface area of a sphere.
Ratio cube to sphere	$\dfrac{S_{\text{cube}}}{S_{\text{sphere}}} = \dfrac{6r^2\left(\sqrt[3]{\frac{4}{3}\pi}\right)^2}{4\pi r^2}$ $\dfrac{S_{\text{cube}}}{S_{\text{sphere}}} = \dfrac{3\left(\sqrt[3]{\frac{4}{3}\pi}\right)^2}{2\pi}$	State the ratio for the surface area of a cube to the surface area of a sphere.
Evaluate	$\dfrac{S_{\text{cube}}}{S_{\text{sphere}}} \approx 1.24$	Evaluate. Take the cube root of $\frac{4}{3}\pi$, square it, and multiply it by 3. Divide that by 2π. The ratio is 1.24 to 1, so the cube has a greater surface area, about 24% greater. The sphere will be the less expensive shape, since it will require less gold to cover it.

Model Problems continue . . .

4. **MP 1, 4** Estimate the volume of a hand using various solids.

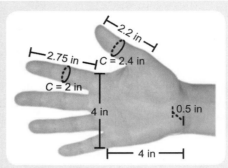

SOLUTION

Explain the diagram

We average the length of the four fingers as 2.75 inches and their circumference as 2 inches (it was easier to estimate circumference than radius). We estimate the thumb's length to be 2.2 inches with a circumference of 2.4 inches. The rest of the hand, which we will call the palm, is estimated to be 4 inches by 4 inches by 0.5 inches.

Calculate radius of finger

$$C = 2\pi r$$

$$r = \frac{C}{2\pi}$$

$$r \approx \frac{2}{2(3.14)} \approx 0.32 \text{ in}$$

We are given the circumference of a finger. Solve for the radius. Substitute 3.14 for π, and the value provided in the problem for the circumference of a finger.

Calculate finger volumes

$$V_{\text{fingers}} \approx 4(\pi r^2 h)$$

$$V_{\text{fingers}} \approx 4(3.14)(0.32)^2(2.75) \approx 3.5 \text{ in}^3$$

Now that we know the radius of a finger, use the formula for the volume of a cylinder multiplied by 4 for the 4 fingers. Substitute and evaluate. Our four fingers occupy about 3.5 cubic inches.

Thumb

$$r \approx \frac{2.4}{2\pi} \approx 0.38 \text{ in}$$

$$V_{\text{thumb}} \approx \pi r^2 h$$

$$V_{\text{thumb}} \approx (3.14)(0.38)^2(2.2) \approx 1.0 \text{ in}^3$$

Do similar steps for the thumb, solving and evaluating for its radius, and then using the radius to calculate its volume.

Palm

$$V_{\text{palm}} \approx l \cdot w \cdot h$$

$$V_{\text{palm}} \approx 4 \cdot 4 \cdot 0.5 \approx 8.0 \text{ in}^3$$

The palm can be calculated as the volume of a box or rectangular prism.

Sum volumes

$$V = V_{\text{fingers}} + V_{\text{thumb}} + V_{\text{palm}}$$

$$V \approx 3.5 + 1.0 \cdot 8.0 \approx 12.5 \text{ in}^3$$

The complete volume of the hand can be calculated by summing the volumes of the fingers, thumb, and palm.

Try it! You can do similar calculations with your own hand, and then perhaps test your answer by dipping your hand into a full container of water and seeing how much water you displace. Alternatively, you could completely submerge your hand in a partially full measuring cup and see how much the water level rises.

PRACTICE

1. What is the volume of the solid below?

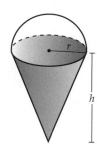

A. $\pi r^3 h$

B. $\frac{2}{3}\pi r^3 + \frac{1}{3}hr^2$

C. $\frac{\pi r^2}{3}(2r + h)$

D. $\pi r^3 h + \frac{4}{3}hr^2$

2. The surface area of a cube is 1.5 mm². What is the volume of the cube?

A. 2.25 mm³
B. 1.25 mm³
C. 0.125 mm³
D. 0.5625 mm³

3. The formula $V = \frac{1}{3}\pi r^2 h$ can be used to find the volume of a

A. Cone.
B. Cylinder.
C. Pyramid.
D. Sphere.

4. The base of a pyramid is a trapezoid with bases of 3.56 feet and 6.12 feet, and a distance between the bases of 5.27 feet. The pyramid's height is 6 feet and 6 inches. What is the volume of the pyramid rounded to the nearest cubic foot? Hint: Start with the formula for the area of a trapezoid.

A. 26 cubic feet
B. 166 cubic feet
C. 168 cubic feet
D. 160 cubic feet

5. Find the volume of a cube with sides of length 3 centimeters. State your answer in cubic centimeters.

6. Calculate the volume of the object below in in cubic feet. The length of each side is 3 feet.

7. What is the volume of the object below, in cubic inches? The box is 8 inches high by 7 inches wide by 3 inches deep (or high). The figure is not drawn to scale.

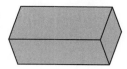

8. The top face of a rectangular prism is 9 by 6 inches, and the height of the prism is 6 inches. There is a triangular hole in the top face that cuts all the way through the prism and through the bottom face. The triangle has a base of 2 inches and a height of 3 inches. What is the net volume of the prism, without the volume of the hole?

9. Sketch a figure whose volume could be found by subtracting the volume of a rectangular prism from the volume of a triangular prism.

10. Find the volume of a cone with a height of 5 centimeters. The radius of the base is 6 centimeters.

11. What is the volume of the object below? Its height is 7 inches.

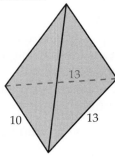

12. Find the volume of a cylinder with height 3 centimeters and radius 7 centimeters.

13. Find the volume of a cylinder with height 4 centimeters and radius 9 centimeters.

14. Find the volume of a prism with a triangular base. The base is a right triangle with sides of length 6 centimeters, 8 centimeters, and 10 centimeters, and the height of the prism is 7 centimeters.

Practice Problems continue . . .

15. Calculate the volume of the cylindrical portion of the hat below. State your answer to the nearest cubic centimeter. Its radius is 17 centimeters and its height is 30 centimeters.

16. What is the volume of the object shown in the figure, in cubic decimeters? Its base is 4 decimeters by 4 decimeters.

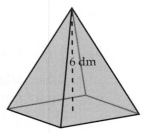

6 dm

17. Paulina says it is not possible for a cone and a pyramid that have the same height to have the same volume, since their bases are different shapes. Do you agree with Paulina? Why or why not?

18. If you triple the radius of a cone without changing its height, what happens to its volume? Why?

19. Felix made a paperweight out of clay. The paperweight was in the shape of a square pyramid with a base of 3 inches on a side and a height of 2 inches. Sketch Felix's pyramid and find its volume.

20. You need to make the volume of a pyramid k times bigger without changing the dimensions of its base. What must you do to the height to cause the volume to increase?

21. Find the volume of a sphere with radius 8 centimeters.

22. What is the volume of the object below in the figure? Its radius is 4 millimeters.

23. What is the volume of the sculpture below? Assume the waffle cone is 4 feet tall, with a radius of 1.2 feet. Assume the ice cream is in the shape of a cone with a radius of 1.4 feet, and a height of 3 feet.

24. Sketch a building whose volume could be found by treating it as a rectangular prism topped by a rectangular pyramid.

25. Isabel is senior class president and is in charge of purchasing the class time capsule. The model she prefers is cylindrical with a hemisphere on each end. The entire capsule is 6 feet long, with the cylinder composing 5 feet of the length. The diameter of the capsule is 12 inches.

   a What is the radius of the capsule and each of the hemispheres?

   b Make a sketch of the capsule. Label all the dimensions.

   c Calculate the capsule's volume.

26. A box has a volume of 48 cubic units. Make a table listing integer combinations of length, width, and height that would produce this volume. Include at least five distinct combinations in the table.

27. The radius of the base of the cone below is 3 inches. The volume of the cone is 37.68 cubic inches. Find the slant height of the cone. Hint: Use the Pythagorean theorem.

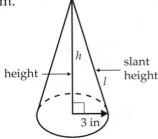

height — h — slant height — l

3 in

Practice Problems continue . . .

28. The base of the regular pyramid below is a square with a side length of 10 inches. The volume of the pyramid is 400 cubic inches. Find the slant height *l* of the pyramid.

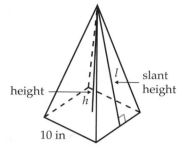

29. The radius of the base of a cone is 6 meters. The lateral surface area of the cone is 188.4 square meters. What is the cone's volume?

30. Anthony ordered a truck of decorative bark to be delivered to his house. The truck dumped the bark on Anthony's driveway. The heap has the shape of a cone with a base radius of 15 feet and a slant height of 17 feet. How many cubic feet of bark did Anthony order? Disregard the space between individual bark pieces.

31. Caroline pours her soda from the cone-shaped glass to the cylinder-shaped one, as in the diagram below. The cone has a base radius of 2.1 inches, and a height of 3.2 inches. The base radius of the cylindrical glass is 1.8 inches. How many inches high will the soda be in the cylindrical glass?

32. How do you need to change the radius of a cone to increase its volume 49 times, if the height of the cone stays the same?

33. **MP 2, 3** If the radius of a sphere is doubled, how does the volume of the sphere change? Explain your reasoning.

34. A spherical capsule, like the one below, has an outer diameter of 18 meters and the thickness of its walls is 3 meters. What is the volume of the material used for the capsule?

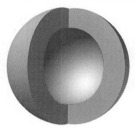

35. A tower has the shape of a cylinder with a height of 13 yards, with a hemisphere on top of the cylinder. The lateral surface area of the cylinder part is 530.66 square yards. What is the volume of the tower?

36. Select a complicated object. Make a sketch of the object, reducing it to four or more solids that have known formulas for volume.

37. Can you state a length of a cube where, when you compute its volume, the number for the volume is less than its surface area? Ignore the fact that the units (and quantities measured) differ.

38. **MP 5, 6** The density of a material is its mass per unit volume. For example, the density of gold is 19.32 grams per cubic centimeter. That means a gold cube with a side of 1 centimeter will have a mass of 19.32 grams. The density of lead is 11.4 grams per cubic centimeter. A lead pipe has an outer diameter of 7.9 cm, and an inner diameter of 3.3 cm. What is the mass, in grams, of a section of pipe that is 7 centimeters long? Use 3.14 for π and round your answer to the nearest whole gram.

39. The volume of a sphere is 179.5 mm^3. What is its radius to the nearest tenth of a micrometer?

Practice Problems continue . . .

40. **MP 4, 6** Three tennis balls fit exactly into a cylindrical can, shown below. The length of the can is 11.4 inches. Find the volume of the part of the can that is not filled by the balls.

41. **MP 2** A cube has an edge of k inches. If the length of each edge of the cube is tripled, what is the ratio of the volume of the larger cube to the volume of the original cube?

LESSON 10.4

10.4 Cavalieri's Principle

Up to this point in the chapter, we've focused on **right solids**, where the solid's base is at a right angle to the lateral surfaces or where a line drawn from the apex to the base of the figure creates a right angle. There are also **oblique solids**, where the base(s) are not at right angles to the lateral surfaces. Some examples of oblique solids are pictured to the right. We can determine the volumes of oblique solids by equating them to right solids using **Cavalieri's Principle**, which was formalized by the Italian mathematician Bonaventura Cavalieri. The principle states that solids of equal height will have equal volumes if cross-sections parallel to and equidistant from their bases have equal areas.

Cavalieri's principle

Two solids with the same height and same cross-sectional area at each height from their base have the same volume.

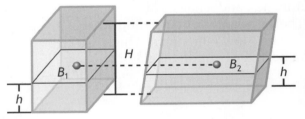

If $B_1 = B_2$ at every h, then $V_1 = V_2$.

> The volume of the figure on the left can be calculated with $V = BH$. The slanted figure on the right can *also* be calculated with the equation $V = BH$, because their cross-sections at height h are equal.

Derive the volume for two figures: a hemisphere and a sphere.

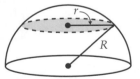

Derivation Strategy We can use Cavalieri's principle and a hemisphere, or half of a sphere, and simply double the result at the end. In Part 1, we calculate the area of a general cross-section of the hemisphere. In Part 2, we do the same for a cylinder and a cone. If we can find a relationship between these cross-sectional areas, then we can use Cavalieri's principle to deduce the volume of the hemisphere in Part 3.

Derivation continues . . .

Part 1:

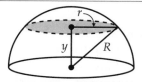

Statement	Reason	
$A = \pi r^2$	Area of circle	The figure above shows the area of a cross-section of the hemisphere. r is the radius of the circle. y denotes the height of the circle from the base of the hemisphere. R is the radius of the hemisphere. Any point on the hemisphere's surface is R away from the center of the base.
$R^2 = r^2 + y^2$ $r^2 = R^2 - y^2$	Use Pythagorean theorem	We want to eliminate r^2 from our equation. We note that the triangle formed by R, r, and y is a right triangle. Write an equation using the Pythagorean theorem.
$A = \pi r^2$ $A = \pi(R^2 - y^2)$	Substitute into equation for area	Substitute the equation for the square of the circle's radius into the equation for the area of the circle.

Part 2:

Cavalieri's principle says that if cross-sections are always equal, solids have the same volume. So we now move to two solids that we know the volumes of: a cone and a cylinder.

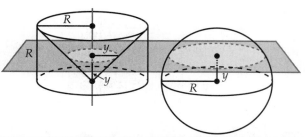

Statement	Reason	
radius = R	Equal radii of these solids	Within the cylinder is a cone whose vertex is at the center of the cylinder's lower base, and whose base is the cylinder's upper base. The radii of these solids are equal. The height of the cylinder and cone equals their radius, R.
Distance y is equal in all figures Bases and cross-sections are in same planes	Cross-sections in same plane	y is also the height of the cone's cross-sectional circle from the base of the cylinder. The radius of that circle is y as well, since the cylinder's radius and height are equal.
$A_{\text{cone}} = \pi y^2$	Area of cross-section of cone	The cross-section of the cone is a circle with radius y. We calculate its area.
$A_{\text{cylinder}} = \pi R^2$	Area of cross-section of cylinder	The cross-section of the cylinder is constant. It is a circle with radius R, the radius of the hemisphere. We calculate its area.
$A_{\text{difference}} = \pi R^2 - \pi y^2$ $A_{\text{difference}} = \pi(R^2 - y^2)$	Area of cylinder minus cone	To calculate the area of the cylinder minus that of the cone, we subtract the expressions and then simplify. We have shown what we needed to show: The area we calculated in Part 1 of a cross-section of the hemisphere equals the area of the difference of the cone and cylinder's cross-sectional areas.

Derivation continues . . .

Part 3:

Now we use basic algebra to substitute and simplify. Again, we rely on Cavalieri's principle. Since the expression for a hemisphere's cross-sectional area is equal to the expression for the difference of the cone and cylinder's cross-sectional areas, the difference in the volumes of the cylinder and cone is equal to the volume of a hemisphere.

Statement	Reason	
$V_{\text{cylinder}} = \pi r^2 h$ $V_{\text{cylinder}} = \pi R^3$	Equation for cylinder	This is the equation for the volume of a cylinder. Both the radius and the height of the cylinder in this case are equal to the radius of the hemisphere.
$V_{\text{cone}} = \dfrac{1}{3}\pi r^2 h$ $V_{\text{cone}} = \dfrac{1}{3}\pi R^3$	Equation for cone	Use the equation for the volume of a cone, and again, the two variables are equal to the radius of the hemisphere.
$V_{\text{difference}} = \pi R^3 - \left(\dfrac{1}{3}\pi R^3\right)$ $V_{\text{difference}} = \dfrac{2}{3}\pi R^3$	Subtract	Above, we said the cross-sectional area of the hemisphere equals the difference of those areas. We subtract to get the volume of the hemisphere.
$V_{\text{hemisphere}} = \dfrac{2}{3}\pi R^3$ $V_{\text{sphere}} = 2 \cdot \dfrac{2}{3}\pi R^3 = \dfrac{4}{3}\pi R^3$	Double for sphere	Since a sphere is made up of two hemispheres, we double the equation for hemisphere volume to get the equation for a sphere's volume.

MODEL PROBLEMS

1. Do the coins in the left and right piles have the same volume?

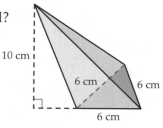

SOLUTION

The coins on the right have the same volume, since there are 9 coins in each stack, and each coin has the same area and volume. The two stacks of coins have the same volume because the cross-sectional area at every level is the same (that of a coin).

2. What is the volume of the oblique pyramid?

10 cm

6 cm   6 cm

6 cm

SOLUTION

Use formula for pyramid

$$V = \frac{1}{3}Bh$$

$$V = \frac{1}{3}\left(\frac{1}{2} \cdot 6 \cdot 3\sqrt{3}\right) \cdot 10$$

$$V \approx 52 \text{ cm}^2$$

Although the pyramid is oblique, Cavalieri's principle says its volume will be the same as that of a right pyramid. Use the formula for volume.

1. Which dimension is not used directly to find the volume of an oblique rectangular prism?

   A. Length
   B. Slant height
   C. Width
   D. Vertical height

2. What is the volume of the solid below? The base is rectangular.

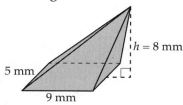

   A. 68 cubic millimeters
   B. 90 cubic millimeters
   C. 120 cubic millimeters
   D. 240 cubic millimeters

3. The volume of a cylinder is 180 ft³. What is the volume of a right cone which could fit exactly inside the cylinder?

   A. 60 ft³
   B. 90 ft³
   C. 180 ft³
   D. 450 ft³

4. A cone has a base with an area of 20 ft² and a height of 6 ft. What other solid will have the same volume as this cone?

   A. Cone with a base of 20 ft² and a slant height of 6 ft
   B. Cylinder with a base of 20 ft² and a height of 3 ft
   C. Pyramid with a base of 10 ft² and a height of 9 ft
   D. Pyramid with a base of 10 ft² and a height of 12 ft

5. For which solids is the area of a cross-section parallel to the base of the solid the same at all heights? Select all that apply.

   A. Cone
   B. Cylinder
   C. Prism
   D. Pyramid
   E. Sphere

6. The area of the base of an oblique prism is 37 square units and its height is 17 units. Find the volume of the prism, in cubic units.

7. The area of the base of an oblique prism is 67 square units and its height is 23 units. Find the volume of the prism, in cubic units.

8. The area of the base of an oblique prism is 37 square units and its height is 21 units. Find the volume of the prism, in cubic units.

9. The base of a rectangular prism measures 4 cm by 6 cm. The slant height of the prism is 10 cm, and its vertical height is 8 cm. What is the volume of the prism, in cubic centimeters?

10. The sketch below shows an oblique cylinder. The radius of the cylinder is 7 inches, and the height is 10 inches. What is the volume of the cylinder?

11. Harry says the volume of the rectangular prism below is 3900 cubic inches. Do you agree with Harry? Why or why not?

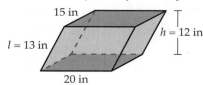

12. A lamp sits on a table that is an oblique cylinder. What is the volume of the table, in cubic inches?

13. Sketch an oblique cylinder with a radius of 3 cm and a height of 6 cm.

14. Ally stacked up 10 round crackers, forming a right cylinder. She then pushed the stack so the top slid to the left, forming an oblique cylinder. Do the two stacks of crackers occupy the same volume? Why or why not?

Practice Problems continue . . .

15. Sketch a sphere. Then, sketch two cross sections of the sphere that will have the same area.

16. **MP 3** A cylinder, a cone, and a sphere all share a radius of 6 meters. The height of the cylinder and the cone is also 6 meters. Express all values for parts **a–d** in terms of π.

   a Find the volume of the cone in cubic meters.

   b Find the volume of the cylinder in cubic meters.

   c Use your two prior answers to find the volume of the sphere. Show all steps required to find your answer.

   d Find the volume of the sphere using the formula $V = \dfrac{4}{3}\pi r^3$.

   e Should your answers to the two previous questions be the same? Why or why not?

17. The dimensions of a box are 18 inches wide by 11 inches long by 6 inches high. If a pyramid is placed within the box so its base and height have the same dimensions as those of the box, what is the volume of the pyramid?

18. The dimensions of a box are 15 inches wide by 15 inches long by 8 inches high. If a pyramid is placed within the box so its base and height have the same dimensions as those of the box, what is the volume of the pyramid?

19. The dimensions of a box are 12 inches wide by 13 inches long by 5 inches high. If a pyramid is placed within the box so its base and height have the same dimensions as those of the box, what is the volume of the pyramid?

20. The volume of a cone is 75 cubic centimeters. What is the volume of a cylinder that could exactly hold the cone?

21. The volume of a cone is 55 cubic centimeters. What is the volume of a cylinder that could exactly hold the cone?

22. You have a cylindrical glass filled to the brim with water. If you pour the water into cone-shaped glasses of the same base and height as the cylindrical glass, how many cone-shaped glasses can you fill before you run out of water?

23. For a project, a woodcarver cuts a pyramid from a solid rectangular block of wood. The pyramid has the same base and height as the block of wood. If the volume of the pyramid is 240 cubic inches, what was the volume of the original piece of wood?

24. An oblique triangular prism has a volume of 240 cubic inches. The slant height of the prism is 12 inches, and its vertical height is 10 inches. What is the area of the base of the prism?

25. When finding the volume of an oblique rectangular prism, you can use the formula for a right rectangular prism, $V = Bh$. Can you use also use the surface area formula for a right rectangular prism, $S = 2B + Ph$, to find the surface area of an oblique rectangular prism? Why or why not?

26. Sketch two oblique prisms that have the same base area and volume but different slant heights. Provide all information needed to calculate the volume of each prism.

27. A cylinder with a diameter of 18 units and a height of 9 units is topped by a cone of the same diameter and height. A sphere has the same volume as the sum of the volumes of the cylinder and the cone. What is the length of the radius of the sphere?

28. A ceramicist has 8 cylindrical blocks of clay that have a diameter of 10 inches and a height of 5 inches. How many spheres with a radius of 5 inches could be formed from all the clay?

29. Sketch a right cylinder that will have the same volume as six cones which each have a radius of 2 feet and a height of 6 feet.

30. **MP 5, 6** What is the volume of the solid below? The solid is an oblique cylinder with two holes that are in the shape of oblique prisms.

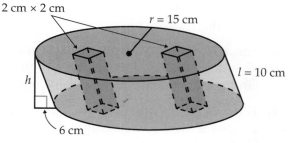

Practice Problems continue . . .

31. **MP 3** A right rectangular prism and an oblique rectangular prism have congruent bases and equal volumes. Which prism will have the greater surface area and why?

32. **MP 2, 6** A metal sphere with a radius of 15 inches is melted down and recast into a cone, which also has a radius of 15 inches. What is the height of the cone?

33. **MP 2, 8** It is possible to divide a cube into congruent regular pyramids that share a vertex at the exact center of the cube and whose bases form the faces of the cube. If an edge of the cube is called b and the height of each pyramid is called h, use the volume of the cube to show that the formula for the volume of each of the six congruent pyramids is $V = \dfrac{1}{3}b^2h$.

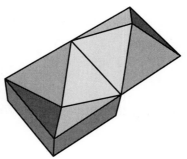

• Multi-Part PROBLEM Practice •

MP 2, 3, 7 An artist is planning to make a sculpture consisting of four oblique cylinders stacked atop one another at different angles. The diameter of each cylinder will be 16 inches and the height of each cylinder will be 20 inches.

a Make a sketch of the sculpture.

b What is the planned volume of the sculpture, in cubic inches? Use 3.14 for π and round your answer to the nearest cubic inch.

c The artist has a total of 9 cubic feet of aluminum for the sculpture. Does he have enough material to make it? Why or why not?

LESSON 10.5

10.5 Similar Solids

Congruent Solids

Like two-dimensional figures, solids can also be congruent. All their dimensions will be identical. For example, any two spheres with the same radius are congruent, as are any two cubes with sides of the same length.

Pyramids A and B are congruent. Pyramid A has a base area of 25 in² and a volume of 75 in³. What is the height of pyramid B?

SOLUTION

Calculate height of pyramid A	$V = \dfrac{1}{3} Bh$ $h = 3\dfrac{V}{B}$ $h = 3 \cdot \dfrac{75}{25} = 9$ in	The solids are congruent, so they must have the same heights. Calculate the height of pyramid A. To do so, solve the equation for a pyramid's volume for its height.
Pyramids are congruent	Height of pyramid $B = 9$ in	Since the solids are congruent, the height of B is also 9 inches.

Similar Solids

Solids can be similar. Any two spheres or two cubes will be similar since they have only one linear measurement, either the radius or the length of a side. Other shapes such as prisms or cylinders must have multiple lengths that have the same proportionate relationship in order to be similar.

We state a relationship for the surface areas and volumes of similar solids:

Similar solids theorem

If two figures are similar with a scale factor $x : y$, then their surface areas have the ratio $x^2 : y^2$, and their volumes have the ratio $x^3 : y^3$.

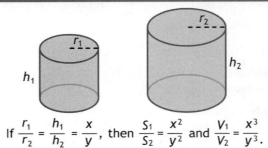

If $\dfrac{r_1}{r_2} = \dfrac{h_1}{h_2} = \dfrac{x}{y}$, then $\dfrac{S_1}{S_2} = \dfrac{x^2}{y^2}$ and $\dfrac{V_1}{V_2} = \dfrac{x^3}{y^3}$.

MODEL PROBLEMS

1. Given the surface area of the cylinders' tops, are the cylinders similar?

$A = 24$

24

$A = 3$

3

SOLUTION

Ratio of heights	$\dfrac{24}{3} = \dfrac{8}{1}$	If the cylinders are similar, then the ratios of measurements of their lengths will be proportionate. Start by calculating the ratio of their heights.

Model Problems continue . . .

Calculate radii

left cylinder area $= \pi r^2$

$$\text{left } r = \sqrt{24/\pi}$$

$$\text{right } r = \sqrt{3/\pi}$$

See if their radii form a proportion. Calculate the radius of the left cylinder's circular base. Calculate r for the right circle.

Ratio of radii

$$\frac{\text{left } r}{\text{right } r} = \frac{\sqrt{24/\pi}}{\sqrt{3/\pi}} = \sqrt{\frac{24/\pi}{3/\pi}} = \sqrt{8}$$

$$8 \neq \sqrt{8}$$

Divide the radii. The ratio of the heights is not equal to the ratio of the radii. The cylinders are not similar.

2. The right pyramid has a scale factor of 3 : 1 to the left pyramid. What is the volume of the right pyramid?

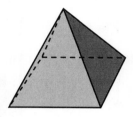

$V = 5 \text{ m}^3$

SOLUTION

Use the formula

$$\frac{V_{\text{right}}}{V_{\text{left}}} = \frac{x^3}{y^3} = \frac{3^3}{1^3}$$

Use the fact that the figures' volumes will follow this formula. We substitute a scale factor of 3 : 1 into the equation.

$$\frac{V_{\text{right}}}{5} = \frac{27}{1}$$

Solve for the right volume

$$V_{\text{right}} = 5\left(\frac{27}{1}\right)$$

$$V_{\text{right}} = 135 \text{ m}^3$$

Solve for the right volume by multiplying both sides by 5. The right pyramid has a volume of 135 cubic meters.

3. What is the scale factor of the two similar cylinders?

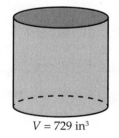

$V = 729 \text{ in}^3$ $V = 64 \text{ in}^3$

SOLUTION

Use the formula

$$\frac{x^3}{y^3} = \frac{V_{\text{left}}}{V_{\text{right}}}$$

Use the fact that the figures' volumes will follow this formula. Substitute the volumes.

$$\frac{x^3}{y^3} = \frac{729}{64}$$

Take cube roots

$$\frac{x}{y} = \frac{\sqrt[3]{729}}{\sqrt[3]{64}} = \frac{9}{4}$$

scale factor $= 2.25 : 1$

Take the cube root of each volume, which gives a ratio of 9 : 4. We can also write this scale factor as 2.25 : 1, as we divide 9 by 4.

Model Problems continue . . .

4. **MP 2, 4** Which sphere has the greater density? The mass of the lead sphere is 10,200 grams, and the mass of the uranium sphere is 5,094 grams.

Lead
6 cm
Uranium
4 cm

SOLUTION

Use equation for volume and dimension

$$\frac{V_{\text{left}}}{V_{\text{right}}} = \frac{x^3}{y^3}$$

$$\frac{V_{\text{left}}}{V_{\text{right}}} = \frac{6^3}{4^3}$$

Use the equation for volumes of similar solids. The ratio of volumes equals the ratio of the cubes of the radii. Substitute the values we were given.

Evaluate

$$\frac{V_{\text{left}}}{V_{\text{right}}} = \frac{216}{64} = \frac{27}{8}$$

scale factor = 3.375 : 1

Evaluate the cubes of the two numbers, and then simplify it to a scale factor. The larger sphere has a volume 3.375 times greater than the smaller one.

Compute ratio of masses

$$\frac{\text{mass}_{\text{left}}}{\text{mass}_{\text{right}}} = \frac{10,200}{5,094} \approx 2 : 1$$

Compute the ratio of the masses provided in the problem. It is about 2 : 1.

Sphere on right has greater density

Sphere on left has 3.375 times the volume, only about twice as massive

The sphere on the left has 3.375 times the volume but is only about twice as massive. That means its density is less. The sphere on the right has greater density. Another way to answer the question would be to compute the two densities: Calculate the volumes and divide the masses by those volumes.

PRACTICE

1. Rectangular prism *A* is congruent to rectangular prism *B*. Select all attributes of the prisms that will be the same.

   A   Height
   B. Length
   C. Surface area
   D. Volume
   E. Width

2. Two pyramids are congruent. If the volume of the first is 45 cubic yards, what is the volume of the second pyramid?

   A. 9 cubic yards
   B. 15 cubic yards
   C. 45 cubic yards
   D. 75 cubic yards

3. Two boxes are similar. The depth of box *A* is 6 meters and its height is 8 meters. The depth of box *B* is 12 meters. What is the height of box *B*?

   A. 4 meters
   B. 8 meters
   C. 12 meters
   D. 16 meters

4. The ratio of the edge of one cube to the edge of a second cube is 5 : 1. What is the ratio of the surface areas of the two cubes?

   A. 5 : 1
   B. 10 : 1
   C. 20 : 1
   D. 25 : 1

Practice Problems continue . . .

5. Sphere X has a radius of 15 and a mass of 27 grams. Sphere Y has a radius of 20 and a mass of 64 grams. Which sphere has the greater average density?

   A. Sphere X
   B. Sphere Y
   C. They have the same density.
   D. There is too little information to tell.

6. Which of the following solids are always similar to all other solids of the same type? Select all that apply.

   A. Cube
   B. Cylinder
   C. Prism
   D. Pyramid
   E. Sphere

7. The surface area of a sphere is 576π units^2. What is the volume of a congruent sphere, in terms of π?

8. Five congruent cones are attached end-to-end along the same axis. The total length of the cones is 50 cm. The total volume of the cone is 150π cm^3.

   a What is the volume of one of the cones, in terms of π?
   b What is the radius of each cone?

9. Cone D has a diameter of 12 inches and a height of 7 inches. Sketch a cone that is congruent to cone D.

10. Two pyramids are similar. The first pyramid is 20 meters high and has a base that measures 40 meters long by 50 meters wide. The height of the second pyramid is 30 meters.

   a What is the length of the base of the second pyramid?
   b What is the width of the base of the second pyramid?
   c What is the ratio of the height of the second pyramid to the height of the first pyramid? Express your answer as a ratio of integers and simplify.

11. The two cones below are similar.

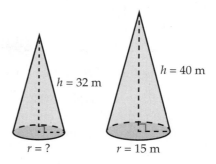

   a What is the scale factor relating the dimensions of the larger cone to those of the smaller cone? Express your answer as a ratio of integers and simplify.
   b What is the radius of the smaller cone?

12. The radius of sphere Q is 5 meters. The radius of sphere R is twice the length of the radius of sphere Q.

   a What is the radius of sphere R?
   b What is the ratio of the surface area of sphere Q to the surface area of sphere R?
   c What is the ratio of the volume of sphere Q to the volume of sphere R?
   d How many spheres with the volume of sphere Q could be formed from the material in sphere R?

13. The ratio of the volumes of two similar boxes is $27 : 1$. What is the ratio of the length of the larger box to the length of the smaller box?

14. Icosahedron H is congruent to icosahedron K. Icosahedron H has a mass of 400 grams, while icosahedron K's mass is 500 grams. Which icosahedron has a greater density?

15. When comparing the densities of two solids, does the actual shape of each solid matter? Why or why not?

16. The ratio of the volumes of two spheres is 27. William says that one sphere could be obtained from the other by increasing its radius 27 times. Do you agree? Why or why not?

17. If two polyhedrons are similar, will the ratio of the lengths of two corresponding edges be the same as the ratio of the areas of two corresponding faces? Why or why not?

Practice Problems continue . . .

18. The area of the base of a right rectangular prism is 30 square feet. The area of the base of a similar prism is 90 square feet. If the area of a lateral face of the first prism is 40 square feet, what is the area of the corresponding face of the second prism?

19. Ian drew a triangular right prism with a base that is a right triangle. The base has legs that measure 6 cm and 8 cm, and the height of the prism is 20 cm. A similar prism has a height of 10 cm. What is the ratio of the area of the larger prism's base to the area of the smaller prism's base?

20. Make a table showing the relationship between radius and surface area of a sphere for radius values of 1 to 6. State surface area in terms of π.

21. The volume of a cube is 64 cubic yards. Sketch a rectangular prism that has the same volume, has a square base, but does not have the same dimensions as a cube.

22. If two solids are congruent and have the same mass, what can you conclude about their average densities? Why?

23. A cylinder and a cone have the same radius and height. The mass of the cylinder is twice the mass of the cone. Which solid is denser?

24. **MP 2, 7** A sphere is shrunk so its volume is 343 times smaller than it was originally. How does the surface area of the sphere change when it is shrunk?

25. If the ratio of the surface areas of two spheres is $n^2 : m^2$, what is the ratio of their volumes?

26. **MP 2, 4** In a rectangular prism, the length is twice the width and the height is three times the width. The mass of the prism is 2550 grams, and the density of the prism is 3.4 grams per cubic centimeter. Sketch the prism and label its dimensions.

27. **MP 3** Prove the similar solids theorem for cylinders given similar cylinders C_1 and C_2 with heights h_1 and h_2, and radii r_1 and r_2, respectively. The ratio of $\dfrac{h_1}{h_2}$ and $\dfrac{r_1}{r_2}$ is k. Hint: Use substitution.

28. **MP 2** A piece of metal with a density of 7.4 grams per cubic centimeter has a mass of 90 grams. How many balls with a radius of 1 centimeter could be made out of this metal piece?

• Multi-Part PROBLEM Practice •

MP 1, 2, 3, 4, 5 After a snowstorm, Raul built a snowman using three balls of snow. The snowman's head measured 1 foot across, his middle measured 2 feet across, and his base measured 3 feet across.

a Sketch the snowman.

b Treating the snowman as three spheres, find his total surface area, to the nearest square foot. Use 3.14 for π.

c Would the surface area you calculated be accurate for a real snowman? Why or why not?

d Calculate the total volume of snow used to make the snowman, to the nearest tenth of a cubic foot. Use 3.14 for π.

e Raul's sister, Rose, wants to build a snowman too, but there is not much snow left in their yard. If Rose can build a snowman with half the volume of snow that her brother used, what is the scale factor of her snowman to her brother's? What would be the dimensions of her snowman? Give your answers to the nearest hundredth.

CHAPTER 10 REVIEW

1. **MP 2** A cube with edges of length S has a drill pass perpendicularly through it, removing the shape of a cylinder, which has a radius of R. What is the best estimate of the remaining volume of the cube, once the drill has passed through?

   A. $6S^2 - 2\pi R^2$
   B. $6S^2 - 2\pi R^2 - 2\pi RS$
   C. $2(3S^2 - \pi rR^2 - \pi RS)$
   D. $S^3 - \pi R^2 S$

2. How do you make a cube from a square?
   A. Rotate the square around an edge.
   B. Rotate the square around a line passing through two diagonals.
   C. Move the square in a direction perpendicular to its face.
   D. Rotate the square around a line passing through the center, parallel to an edge.

3. Prism A has a height of 5.0 and a mass of 1000. Similar prism B has a height of 7.0 and a mass of 2744. Which prism has the greater density?

   A. Prism A
   B. Prism B
   C. They have the same density.

4. What is the volume of the prism below?

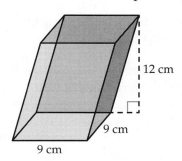

   A. 60 cubic cm
   B. 108 cubic cm
   C. 486 cubic cm
   D. 972 cubic cm

5. You want to know if the volumes of two stacks of playing cards are equal. What has to be true about the two stacks? Check all that apply.

   A. The height of both stacks is the same.
   B. The cards in both stacks have the same area.
   C. The weight of each card in both stacks has to be equal.
   D. Both stacks have to contain an equal number of cards.

6. Which of the following are polyhedrons? Select all that apply.

   A. Cone
   B. Cylinder
   C. Prism
   D. Pyramid
   E. Sphere

7. For which of the following solids is it possible to slice a cross-section that is a circle? Select all that apply.

   A. Cone
   B. Cube
   C. Cylinder
   D. Pyramid
   E. Sphere

8. What three-dimensional shape is formed by rotating a circle about a diameter?

   A. Cone
   B. Cylinder
   C. Pyramid
   D. Sphere

9. Which of the following names best describes the solid shown below?

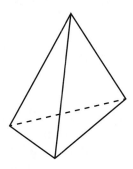

   A. Triangular prism
   B. Triangular pyramid
   C. Rectangular prism

Chapter Review continues . . .

10. Which of the following is a possible cross-section for a triangular prism?

    A.   Circle

    B.   Rectangle

    C.   Hexagon

11. A building is drawn in perspective. The front face of the building is parallel to the picture plane. How many vanishing point(s) are required?

    A.   0

    B.   1

    C.   2

    D.   3

12. What is the height of the pyramid shown in the figure?

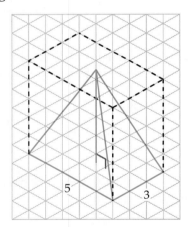

    A.   3

    B.   4

    C.   5

    D.   6

13. **MP 7** Pyramids X and Y each have a square base. Pyramid X has a height of 2 and a base area of 9. Pyramid Y has a height of 6 and base area of 81. Are they similar solids?

14. Cylinders X and Y are similar. Cylinder X has a radius of 8 inches and height of 32 inches. If the radius of cylinder Y is 6 inches, what is the height of cylinder Y?

15. The area of the base of an oblique prism is 35 square units and its height is 25 units. Find the volume of the prism.

16. **MP 2, 5** A rectangular prism made of lead has dimensions of 4 m by 3 m by 5 m and has a mass of 680,400 kg. What is the mass density of lead in kilograms per cubic meter?

17. **MP 4, 5** A cylinder made of gel has a mass of 20,410 kilograms. The cylinder has a radius of 5 meters and a height of 20 meters. What is the average mass density of the cylinder in kilograms per cubic meter?

18. What is the volume of the oblique solid below?

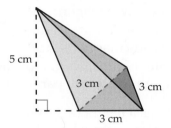

19. A cylinder has a lateral surface area of 100 square feet and a height of 14 feet. What is the volume of the cylinder?

20. **MP 3** A right rectangular prism with a base of 4 meters by 9 meters has the same volume as an oblique rectangular prism with a base of 6 meters by 6 meters. What can you conclude about the heights of the two prisms and why?

21. **MP 4** A biologist studying ape hands averaged the length of an ape's four fingers as 5.15 inches and the circumference of each finger as 4.3 inches (it was easier to estimate circumference than radius). What is the total volume of the ape's four fingers, in cubic inches?

22. A giant alien space cube is moving toward Earth! Not again! It has sides that are 1 kilometer long and growing! If the edges double in length, which increases by the larger factor: the volume or the surface area?

Chapter Review continues . . .

23. What is the surface area of the solid below?

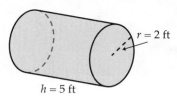

$r = 2$ ft

$h = 5$ ft

24. What is the volume of the object shown below? Its radius is 2 miles.

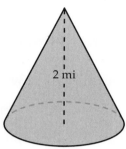

2 mi

25. What is the surface area of a cone if the radius is 2 meters and the slant height is 5 meters?

26. On an isometric grid, no lines actually meet at right angles. What angle measures on the grid can be used to indicate a 90° angle between two adjacent sides of the base of a rectangular prism? List both possibilities.

27. A rectangle has a base of 10 meters and a height of 18 meters. What is the diameter of the cylinder formed by rotating the rectangle about its height?

28. The doors in the town of Antigua, Guatemala, were designed to be tall enough to allow a person on a horse to pass through. The bottom part of the door below would be opened for people on foot and the entire door for people on horseback. Calculate the area of the doorway, approximating the top part of the door as half a circle.

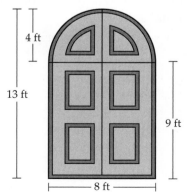

4 ft

13 ft

9 ft

8 ft

29. What is the area of the figure below in square feet? The center square has sides that are 5 feet long. The triangles on the top and bottom are 2 feet high. The rectangles on the left and right have a width of 1.5 feet.

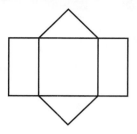

30. Mrs. Beasley's first-grade class is making decorative planters out of 3-pound coffee cans, which they will then fill with soil and plant with flowers for Mother's Day gifts. The students are covering the sides and bottoms of the cans with colorful construction paper that they have decorated. The coffee cans are cylinders with a diameter of 6 inches and a height of 7 inches.

a How much construction paper is needed for each can? Round to the nearest square inch.

b How much soil is needed to fill each can? Round to the nearest cubic inch.

c Mrs. Beasley bought two 1.5-cubic-foot bags of soil. If each student fills their can $\frac{3}{4}$ full with soil, will this be enough for her class of 30 students? Justify your answer.

1. A circle is rotated about its diameter. The resulting three-dimensional figure is

   A. A cylinder.
   B. A pyramid.
   C. A sphere.
   D. A cube.

2. What is the most precise description of a quadrilateral with at least one pair of parallel sides?

   A. A rhombus
   B. A trapezoid
   C. A square
   D. A rectangle

3. Two bikers start riding from their houses, located at points B and C, respectively. They leave at exactly the same time and ride toward each other at the same speed. If they plan to meet at the coffee shop located at point O, at what coordinates will they meet?

   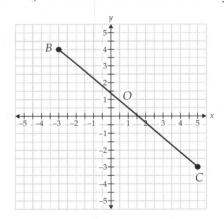

   A. $(1, 0.5)$
   B. $(0.5, 1)$
   C. $\left(\dfrac{5}{8}, \dfrac{7}{8}\right)$
   D. $\left(\dfrac{7}{8}, \dfrac{5}{8}\right)$

4. As the number of sides of a regular polygon increases, the measure of each interior angle

   A. Increases.
   B. Decreases.
   C. Increases then decreases.
   D. Decreases then increases.
   E. It is impossible to know.

5. Which statement is true?

   A. Theorems are used to prove postulates.
   B. Postulates are used to prove theorems.
   C. Constructions are used to prove postulates.
   D. Only postulates can be used to prove theorems.

6. Choose all that apply. A point rotates from $(53, 22)$ to $(-53, 2)$. It rotated

   A. 90° counterclockwise.
   B. 90° clockwise.
   C. 180° counterclockwise.
   D. 180° clockwise.

7. A solid is rotated 90° and then translated up 14.2 units. The statement that best describes the resulting solid states that it is

   A. Congruent but not similar to the original solid.
   B. Similar to but not congruent to the original solid.
   C. Both similar to and congruent with the original solid.
   D. A cross-section of the original solid.

8. Which of the following statements is correct about parallelograms?

   A. A quadrilateral is a parallelogram if and only if two of its opposite angles are congruent.

   B. The diagonals of a parallelogram bisect its angles.

   C. A quadrilateral is a parallelogram if its diagonals are perpendicular to each other.

   D. A quadrilateral is a parallelogram if and only if its diagonals bisect each other.

9. Which triangle is not similar to the other two?

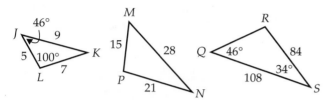

   A. △JKL

   B. △MNP

   C. △QSR

   D. They are all similar.

10. Which line segments are parallel in the figure below? Choose all that apply.

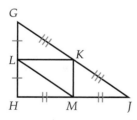

   A. $\overline{LK}$ and $\overline{KM}$

   B. $\overline{LM}$ and $\overline{GJ}$

   C. $\overline{GH}$ and $\overline{KM}$

   D. $\overline{HM}$ and $\overline{GK}$

11. What geometric shape forms the basis of an isometric grid?

12. Find the midpoint between $(-17, 6)$ and $(3, 10)$.

13. A regular polyhedron has 10 edges and 6 vertices. How many faces should it have? Sketch a possible view of this solid.

14. Sketch a cone. Then, sketch a slice of the cone which will produce an oval (ellipse).

15. **MP 4** If the distance along Oak Street from 1st Avenue to 2nd Avenue is 120 yards, what is the distance along Maple Street from 1st Avenue to 2nd Avenue? The map is not drawn to scale. Assume that 1st, 2nd, and 3rd Avenues are all parallel.

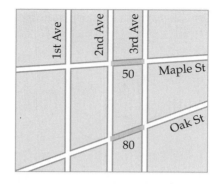

16. Draw and label a scalene right triangle whose side lengths are all integer values.

17. **MP 2** To create the design shown below, four squares are constructed on the sides of the central square. Then the vertices of the squares are connected to obtain an octagon. Is this octagon regular? Find the measure of each angle of this octagon.

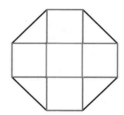

18. **MP 7** △ABC ~ △DEF. AB = 5 inches and BC = 12 inches. The angle formed by $\overline{AB}$ and $\overline{BC}$ measures 45°. DE = 15 inches. What is EF? What is the measure of the angle formed by $\overline{DE}$ and $\overline{EF}$?

19. **MP 5** The area of the circle below is 9 cm². What is the measure of the larger central angle ACB? Hints: Solve the equation for sector area for the angle, and remember what the formula πr^2 represents.

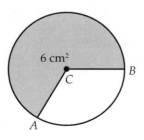

20. A dodecahedron has 20 vertices and 30 edges. How many faces does this object have?

21. Find the surface area of a cone with a slant height of 9 centimeters. The radius of the base is 6 centimeters.

22. What is the surface area of the object below?

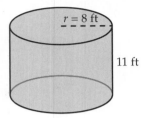

23. MP 3 In the parallelogram $ABCD$, the points Q and M are the midpoints of the sides $\overline{AD}$ and $\overline{BC}$, respectively. Also $LB = PD = \frac{1}{3}DC$. Is quadrilateral $LMPQ$ a parallelogram? Justify your answer.

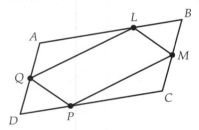

24. In the diagram below, if $m\overset{\frown}{MP} = 162°$, what does $m\angle MPK$ equal?

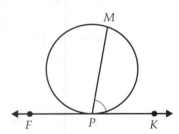

25. MP 2 Three squares are constructed on the sides of an equilateral triangle. The vertices of the squares are then connected to obtain a hexagon. Is this hexagon regular? Make a sketch, and find the measure of the interior angles of this hexagon.

26. What is the length of $\overline{AD}$?

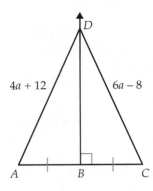

27. The cylindrical checker piece below is 5 mm tall and 22 mm in diameter. Find the volume of the piece in cubic millimeters. Use 3.14 for π. Round your answer to the nearest tenth.

28. What is the area of the figure below?

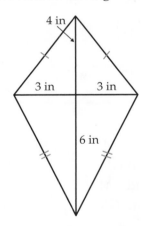

29. The side of length 4 is tangent to the circle. What is the value of r below?

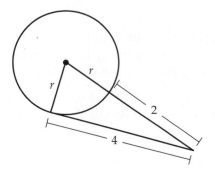

30. MP 3, 4 An adventure course has a zip line that connects two platforms together. The first platform is 90 feet above the ground and the second platform is 70 feet above the ground. The zip line connecting the two platforms is 164 feet long. The owner of the adventure course is concerned that people build up too much speed along the zip line, so he wants to change the height of the second platform to make the angle of depression between the two platforms smaller. Suggest a new height for the second platform, and justify your answer.

31. Sketch an acute triangle. Then, sketch all three midsegments, which divide the original triangle into four smaller triangles. Explain how you know the four smaller triangles are all congruent to one another.

32. Lines a, b, and c are coplanar. Two lines a and b are parallel. The line c intersects the line a. Show that the line c also intersects the line b. Make a sketch, label D the point of intersection of the lines c and a, and use the parallel postulate.

Chapter Content

Lessons	Standards

Chapter Vocabulary

asymptote	focus of an ellipse	standard form of the equation for a circle
axis	focus of a hyperbola	standard form of the equation for a circle centered at the origin
conic section	focus of a parabola	standard form of the equation for an ellipse centered at the origin
co-vertices	hyperbola	standard form of the equation for a hyperbola centered at the origin
directrix	major axis	standard form of the equation for a parabola
ellipse	minor axis	standard form of the equation for a parabola centered at the origin
focal radii	quadratic equation	vertices of an ellipse
		vertices of a hyperbola

LESSON 11.1

11.1 Circles at the Origin

Conic Sections

The circle, parabola, ellipse, and hyperbola are all **conic sections**. A conic section, or simply a *conic*, is an intersection of a plane and a cone. The intersection can be an ellipse, a circle, a parabola, or a curve with two parts called a **hyperbola**. Other sections, such as intersecting lines or even a single point, can be created with the plane as well.

A Greek mathematician, Apollonius of Perga, wrote a series of books on conics around 200 BCE. He started with a hollow double cone, as shown in the diagram to the right. He then used a plane that intersects the double cone to create an ellipse, a circle, and so on. The line through the center of the cone is called its **axis**. The curve formed where the plane intersects the cone is drawn in orange, and it is also drawn on a coordinate plane on the right side. In this case, the conic is an ellipse.

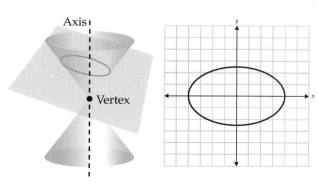

Circles Centered at the Origin

As we have mentioned, a circle is the set of all points in the plane that are equidistant from the circle's center, which is also a point in the plane. That distance is the circle's *radius*, denoted r. Note that a circle is a conic section created by passing a plane horizontally through the vertical double cone, as shown below.

The quadratic equation $x^2 + y^2 = r^2$ is the **standard form of the equation for a circle centered at the origin**.

> A **quadratic equation** is one with one or more variables squared but raised to no greater power.

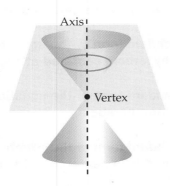

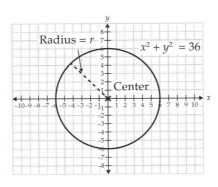

The graph of the quadratic equation $x^2 + y^2 = r^2$ is a circle with the center at the origin, $(0, 0)$, and radius r. The radius of the circle is r, the square root of the constant on the right side of the equation. In the example graph, $x^2 + y^2 = 36$, so the radius of the circle is equal to 6, since $r = \sqrt{36} = 6$.

Paragraph Proof

Let P be any point on the circle, and let the coordinates of P be (x, y). Let C be the center of the circle $(0, 0)$. Points P and C are connected by line r. Now we can draw a horizontal line through point C and a vertical line through point P. The lines will intersect at point A as shown. Because the intersection of a horizontal with a vertical line forms a right angle, the triangle PAC is a right triangle. The lengths of its sides are related by the Pythagorean theorem, giving $x^2 + y^2 = r^2$, which is the general equation for a circle centered at the origin.

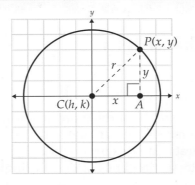

MODEL PROBLEMS

1. Rearrange the equation $6y^2 = 48 - 6x^2$ so it is in standard form.

SOLUTION

Move terms
with variable to
left

$$6y^2 = 48 - 6x^2$$
$$6x^2 + 6y^2 = 48 - 6x^2 + 6x^2$$
$$6x^2 + 6y^2 = 48$$

We want the terms with variables
to be on the left. To do this, add
$6x^2$ to both sides.

> An equation with
> x^2 and y^2 added
> together, and
> with the same
> coefficient,
> defines a circle.

Change
coefficients to 1

$$x^2 + y^2 = 8$$

In the standard form for the
equation of a circle, the coefficient
of the squared terms is 1. Divide
both sides of the equation by 6.

2. The point (2, 5) is on a circle centered at the origin. State the equation for the circle in standard form.

SOLUTION

Point on circle
$(x, y) = (2, 5)$

$$x^2 + y^2 = r^2$$
$$2^2 + 5^2 = r^2$$
$$29 = r^2$$

Substitute the coordinates of the point into the equation for a
circle. The sum of their squares equals r^2.

Substitute r^2
into standard
equation

$$x^2 + y^2 = r^2$$
$$x^2 + y^2 = 29$$

The equation for this circle is $x^2 + y^2 = 29$. With the equation
stated in standard form, describing the circle becomes easier. It is
centered at the origin and has a radius of $\sqrt{29}$.

3. **MP 2, 4** Avalanche beacons are used to find mountaineers buried under snow. The beacons both
send and receive signals. When a mountaineer is lost, others in the party turn their beacons on to
receive. A typical beacon might have a range of 50 meters. You are 38 meters north and 29 meters
east of a lost mountaineer—will you receive her signal?

SOLUTION

Draw
diagram

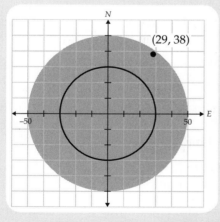

The signal will travel the same distance in all
directions, so its range can be described as a circle.

State as
inequality

$$x^2 + y^2 \leq r^2$$
$$x^2 + y^2 \leq 50^2$$
$$x^2 + y^2 \leq 2500$$

The signal travels the same distance in all directions. That
describes a circle. Its range is less than or equal to that distance.

Substitute
position

$$29^2 + 38^2 \overset{?}{\leq} 2500$$
$$841 + 1444 \overset{?}{\leq} 2500$$
$$2285 \leq 2500$$

Locate your position on the graph. It is 29 m east and 38 m north
of the origin. The lost mountaineer is at the origin. Substitute that
for the x- and y-coordinates into the inequality. You are just in
range of the other mountaineer's beacon.

PRACTICE

Exercises 1–2: Assume the circles in the diagram below are centered at the origin.

1. State the equation for the inner circle.

2. State the equation for the outer circle.

Exercises 3–4: State the center and radius of the circles described by the equations below.

3. $x^2 + y^2 = 144$

4. $x^2 + y^2 = 289$

Exercises 5–7: Write the equation for the circle based on each description.

5. Center at origin and radius of 9.

6. Center at origin and radius of 25.

7. Center at origin and radius of 7.

Exercises 8–12: Graph each equation.

8. $x^2 + y^2 = 16$

9. $x^2 + y^2 = 81$

10. $x^2 + y^2 = 13$

11. $x^2 + y^2 = 9$

12. $x^2 + y^2 = 25$

Exercises 13–14: Based on the graphs, state the equation of the circle.

13.

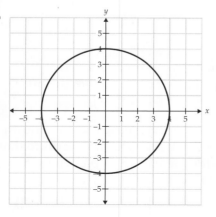

14.

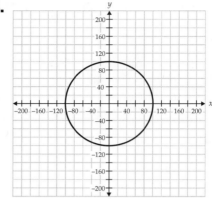

Exercises 15–18: The coordinates are from a circle centered at the origin. Write the equation for the circle.

15. $(4, -3)$

16. $(-1, -1)$

17. $(\sqrt{5}, -\sqrt{2})$

18. $(\sqrt{3}, 4)$

Exercises 19–22: State in standard form.

19. $11x^2 + 11y^2 = 44$

20. $2x^2 + 2y^2 - 28 = 0$

21. $-5x^2 = -30 + 5y^2$

22. $\dfrac{x^2}{4} + \dfrac{y^2}{4} = 1$

23. What is the center of the circle described by the equation $x^2 + y^2 = 49$?

24. What is the radius of the circle described by the equation $x^2 + y^2 = 49$?

25. The point $(-7, 3)$ is on a circle centered at the origin. State the equation for the circle in standard form.

26. State $7x^2 = 35 - 7y^2$ in the standard form for the equation of a circle.

27. What is the radius of the circle described by the equation $x^2 + y^2 = 9$?

28. What is the radius of the circle described by the equation $x^2 + y^2 = 100$?

29. What is the radius of the circle described by the equation $x^2 + y^2 = 81$?

Practice Problems continue . . .

30. The point $(-8, -2)$ is on a circle centered at the origin. State the equation for the circle in standard form.

31. The point $(2, 12)$ is on a circle centered at the origin. State the equation for the circle in standard form.

32. A circle centered at the origin contains the point $(3, 4)$. What is the radius of the circle?

33. A circle centered at the origin contains the point $(-5, -7)$. What is the radius of the circle?

LESSON 11.2

11.2 Parabolas at the Origin

Geometric Definition of a Parabola

A parabola can be described by a quadratic equation of the form $y = ax^2$, with the y-axis as its axis of symmetry. A parabola is also a conic section that is formed by passing a plane through a cone so the plane is perfectly parallel to the cone's side. You can see this below.

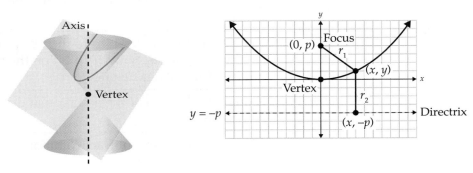

A parabola can also be described geometrically using a line and a point:

Set of points equidistant from point and line	$r_1 = r_2$	A parabola is the set of all points in a plane where each point is the same distance from a point as it is from a line. We call these two distances r_1 and r_2. See diagram above.
Point is focus	$(0, p)$	The point the distance is measured from is called the **focus of the parabola**. With a parabola that opens up and with its vertex at the origin, the focus is at $(0, p)$.
Line is directrix	$y = -p$	The line is called the **directrix**. With a parabola that opens up and with its vertex at the origin, it is the line $y = -p$.

We derive an equation for a parabola from its geometric definition. We start with a parabola that opens up with its vertex at the origin.

Derive: $y = \dfrac{1}{4p}x^2$

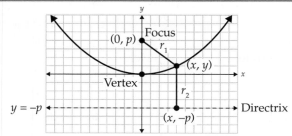

Definition of parabola	$r_1 = r_2$	The definition of a parabola says that the distance from any point on it to the directrix equals the distance from the point to the focus.
Distances from point (x, y) on parabola	Directrix: $r_1 = y - (-p) = y + p$ Focus: $r_2 = \sqrt{(0 - x)^2 + (p - y)^2}$	Find the distances from the point (x, y) on the parabola. The directrix is the line $y = -p$. The distance to the directrix is the difference in the y-coordinate of the point on the parabola, and the point directly below it on the line.
Substitute expressions for r_1 and r_2	$y + p = \sqrt{x^2 + (p - y)^2}$	Substitute the expressions found above for the two distances. Simplify a bit on the right, since adding 0 has no effect.
Square both sides	$y^2 + 2py + p^2 = x^2 + p^2 - 2py + y^2$	Square both sides of the equation and expand the expressions.
Simplify	$2py = x^2 - 2py$ $4py = x^2$ $y = \dfrac{1}{4p}x^2$	Simplify. To do so, subtract common terms from each side of the equation.

The activity shows the focus and directrix, which define the parabola. The parabola can open up, down, left, or right.

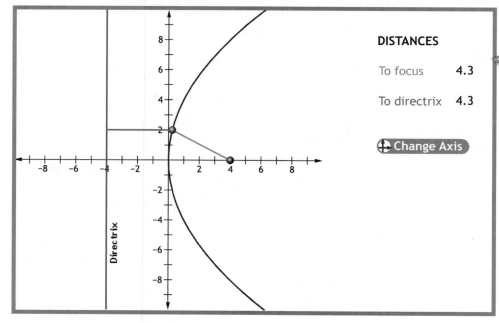

DISTANCES

To focus   4.3

To directrix   4.3

⊕ Change Axis

The distances to the focus and to the directrix are always equal for any point on the parabola.

Graphing a Parabola at the Origin

The equation for a parabola, $y = \frac{1}{4p}x^2$, can be used to determine some of its important properties. The constant p can be positive or negative. Its sign determines whether the parabola opens up or down $\left(\text{for } y = \frac{1}{4p}x^2 \right)$ or right or left $\left(\text{for } x = \frac{1}{4p}y^2 \right)$. These equations are in the **standard form of the equation for a parabola centered at the origin**.

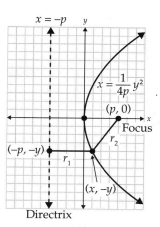

 In this activity, you will move the focus, and you will see the equation and the value of p change.

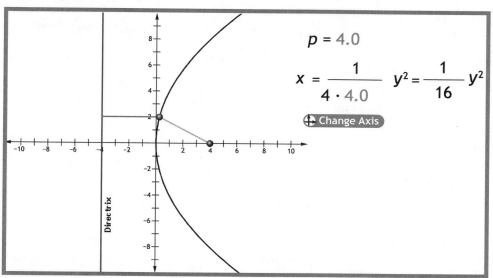

$$p = 4.0$$

$$x = \frac{1}{4 \cdot 4.0} \, y^2 = \frac{1}{16} \, y^2$$

Change Axis

 In this activity, enter the coordinates of the focus and the equation of the directrix and see how they affect the parabola's graph.

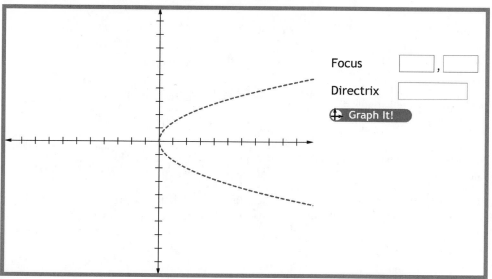

Focus ☐ , ☐

Directrix ☐

Graph It!

We summarize some key properties of parabolas located at the origin:

Equation	Vertex	Axis of Symmetry	Orientation
$y = \dfrac{1}{4p}x^2, p > 0$	(0, 0)	Vertical	Up
$y = \dfrac{1}{4p}x^2, p < 0$	(0, 0)	Vertical	Down
$x = \dfrac{1}{4p}y^2, p > 0$	(0, 0)	Horizontal	Right
$x = \dfrac{1}{4p}y^2, p < 0$	(0, 0)	Horizontal	Left

MODEL PROBLEMS

1. Parabola E is defined by the equation $y = \dfrac{1}{24}x^2$, and parabola F is defined by the equation $x = -2y^2$. Select the true statement.

   A. Parabola E would have a vertical axis of symmetry, and parabola F would have a horizontal axis of symmetry.
   B. Parabola E would be steeper than parabola F if they were both viewed with their axes vertical.
   C. Both choice A and choice B are true.
   D. Neither choice A nor choice B is true.

SOLUTION

The answer is A. With y equal to an expression with a squared x-term, it is a vertical parabola, and its axis of symmetry is vertical, which makes the first half of answer A true. With x equal to a squared y-term, parabola F would be a horizontal parabola (opening to the left due to the negative sign). Its axis of symmetry would be horizontal. Parabola E is not steeper than parabola F, since its coefficient has a lesser absolute value, so statement B is false. That makes answer C false, and D is false since statement A is true.

2. **MP 2, 5, 7** Graph $x = -\dfrac{1}{4}y^2$ using the properties determined from its equation.

SOLUTION

Calculate p	$4p = -4, p = -1$	The squared term is multiplied by $-\dfrac{1}{4}$. This means $4p = -4$, so $p = -1$.
Determine the axis of symmetry	x-axis since it is the y-term that is squared	The y-term is squared so this will be a horizontal parabola.
Calculate the directrix and the focus	directrix: $x = -p = -(-1) = 1$ focus: $(p, 0) = (-1, 0)$	The vertex is at the origin. The directrix is a vertical line since the parabola is horizontal.

Model Problems continue . . .

Graph

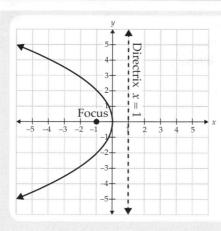

x	y
0	0
-1	2
-2.25	3
-1	-2
-2.25	-3

Plot points and then draw the curve. Note that we can use the symmetry of the parabola to help us. The x-values are the same for $y = 3$ and $y = -3$.

3. State the equation of the graph below.

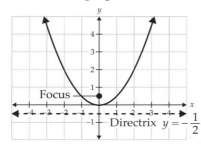

With this problem, we can see where the focus and directrix are. We use that information to calculate p and then state the parabola's equation.

SOLUTION

Focus $\quad (0, p)$

$p = \dfrac{1}{2}$

The focus is at $(0, p)$ for a vertical parabola.

Since the focus of the parabola is at $\left(0, \dfrac{1}{2}\right)$, $p = \dfrac{1}{2}$.

Substitute into the equation

$y = \dfrac{1}{4p}x^2$

$y = \dfrac{1}{4\left(\dfrac{1}{2}\right)}x^2$

$y = \dfrac{1}{2}x^2$

Since the parabola is vertical, the x-term is squares. Substitute the value of p. Then simplify by multiplying.

Model Problems continue . . .

4. [MP 3, 7] In previous math classes, you learned that an equation with the general form $y = ax^2 + bx + c$ is a parabola. We expanded that definition in this lesson to include alternative forms of the equation, where the value of p determined the axis of symmetry and the direction the curve opens. Recall that when we use the form $y = ax^2 + bx + c$, the axis of symmetry and the orientation of the parabola are determined by the value of a. This is because $a = \dfrac{1}{4}p$. Thusly, in the general form, $y = ax^2 + bx + c$, the value of a also determines the distance between the focus and the directrix.

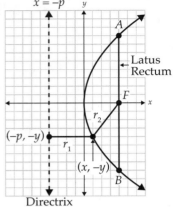

Examine the graph on the right. A vertical line has been drawn through the parabola's focus, perpendicular to the axis of symmetry, with endpoints on the curve. This line segment is called the *latus rectum*. Show that the length of the latus rectum for any parabola is $4p$.

SOLUTION

We use the definitions of a parabola, focus, vertex, directrix, and the segment addition postulate to create a short paragraph proof.

Paragraph Proof

Let point F be the focus of a parabola. Then the length $AF = 2p$, since the latus rectum is parallel to the directrix and the distance between the directrix and F is $2p$. This flows from the geometric definition of a parabola as a set of all points equidistant from a point and a line. From this, we know the distance BF is $2p$. Using the segment addition postulate, $AF + FB = AB$, and by substitution, $2p + 2p = AB$, and the length of the latus rectum, $\overline{AB}$ is $4p$.

PRACTICE

1. The parabola defined by the equation $y = \dfrac{1}{12}x^2$ opens in which direction?

   A. Up   C. Left

   B. Down   D. Right

2. Which of the following is the equation for the axis of symmetry for the parabola $x = \dfrac{1}{2}y^2$?

   A. $x = y$

   B. $y = 0$

   C. $x = 0$

   D. $y = x$

3. Given the parabolic equation $y = -\dfrac{1}{8}x^2$, which of the given coordinates correctly defines the focus?

   A. $(-2, 0)$ C. $(0, 0)$

   B. $(0, 2)$ D. $(0, -2)$

4. Find the equation for the directrix of the parabola $x = -y^2$.

   A. $y = 1$ C. $x = \dfrac{1}{4}$

   B. $x = -\dfrac{1}{4}$ D. $y = \dfrac{1}{2}$

Practice Problems continue . . .

5. Determine the equation of the parabola given that the focus is located at (0, 5).

    A. $y = \dfrac{1}{20}x^2$

    B. $x = \dfrac{1}{5}y^2$

    C. $y = 20x^2$

    D. $x = 5y^2$

6. If the equation for a parabola's directrix is $y = 4$, which of the following could be the location of the parabola's focus?

    A. $(-4, 0)$ C. $(0, -4)$

    B. $(0, 4)$ D. $(4, 0)$

7. The receiver of a parabolic television dish antenna is located at the focus. The cross section of the reflector is modeled by the equation $y = \dfrac{1}{18}x^2$ feet. What is the distance from the lowest point on the reflector to the receiver?

    A. 7 feet   C. 18 feet

    B. 4.5 feet   D. 36 feet

8. A parabola's focus is located at $\left(0, -\dfrac{7}{4}\right)$ and its directrix is at $y = \dfrac{7}{4}$. What is the equation for this parabola? State your answer in the standard form of an equation for a parabola at the origin.

9. A parabola is determined by the equation $y = \dfrac{5}{8}x^2$. What are the coordinates of the parabola's focus?

10. A parabola is determined by the equation $x = \dfrac{7}{4}y^2$. What are the coordinates of the parabola's focus?

11. A parabola is determined by the equation $y = \dfrac{3}{16}x^2$. What are the coordinates of the parabola's focus?

12. A parabola's focus is located at $(0, -1)$ and the equation for its directrix is $y = 1$. What is the equation of the parabola?

13. A parabola's focus is located at $\left(0, -\dfrac{1}{28}\right)$ and the equation for its directrix is $y = \dfrac{1}{28}$. What is the equation for the parabola?

14. A parabola has an equation $x = 2y^2$. At what coordinates is its focus located?

15. **MP 4** A parabolic trough collects solar energy. The mirrored trough has a parabolic cross-section. Its focus is shown on the graph. Write an equation for the trough with its vertex at the origin.

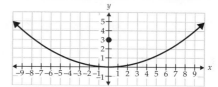

16. **MP 4, 5** A person is located as shown below on the grid. The radio tower can broadcast 8 miles. Will the person receive a signal?

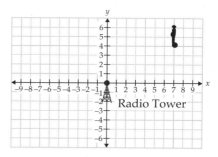

17. What are the coordinates of the focus of the parabola described by the equation $y = -ax^2$?

Exercises 18–21: Find the equations of the axis of symmetry and the directrix for each of the given parabolas.

18. $x = -2y^2$

19. $y = 4x^2$

Practice Problems continue . . .

20. $x = 3y^2$

21. $y = 3x^2$

Exercises 22–23: Graph each of the equations. Draw and label the focus and the directrix for each parabola.

22. $x = -y^2$

23. $y = \dfrac{1}{4}x^2$

Exercises 24–25: State the equation for each parabola.

24. Focus at $(0, 9)$ and directrix is $y = -9$.

25. Focus at $(-8, 0)$ and directrix is $x = 8$.

Exercises 26–28: Each parabola described has its vertex at the origin. State the equation of each parabola in standard form and graph it.

26. The focus of the parabola is $(-3, 0)$.

27. The directrix of the parabola is $y = \dfrac{3}{4}$.

28. The focus of the parabola is $\left(0, \dfrac{5}{4}\right)$.

29. Is it possible for a parabola to intersect its directrix? Why or why not? Support your argument with examples.

30. Dina wants to find the equation of the directrix for a parabola that has its vertex at the origin and its focus along the vertical axis. She writes the equation for the directrix in the form $x = a$. Will this be the correct equation for the directrix?

31. **MP 3** Prove that the equation for a horizontal parabola can be written $x = \dfrac{1}{4p}y^2$, where $(p, 0)$ is the focus and $x = -p$ is the directrix.

LESSON 11.3

11.3 Circles Translated from the Origin

The Standard Form of the Equation for a Circle

The equation $(x - h)^2 + (y - k)^2 = r^2$ is the **standard form of the equation for a circle**. The center of the circle is the point (h, k) and the radius is r, the square root of the constant on the right side of the equation. The constant h translates the graph left and right, while k translates it up and down. When $h = k = 0$, the equation is equivalent to $x^2 + y^2 = r^2$ and the center of the circle is at the origin, $(0, 0)$.

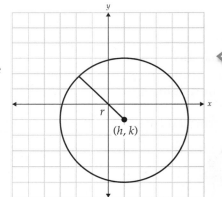

> In the standard form of a circle, the circle's center is at (h, k), where h and k are the constants subtracted from x and y. The radius is r.

MODEL PROBLEMS

1. Where is the center of the circle $(x + 3)^2 + (y - 2)^2 = 25$? What is the length of the radius?

SOLUTION

Standard form:
$(x - h)^2 + (y - k)^2 = r^2$

$[x - (-3)]^2 + (y - 2)^2 = 25$

To write the equation in standard form, change the addition $x + 3$ to the subtraction $x - (-3)$. We do this to make sure we state h correctly.

Center: (h, k)

Center: $(-3, 2)$

The center of the circle is at the point (h, k). In this case, the center is at $(-3, 2)$.

Model Problems continue . . .

Radius: r $\qquad$ $r = 5$ $\qquad$ The radius of a circle is found by taking the positive square root of the constant on the right side of the standard equation. In this case, the radius is 5.

2. A circle is defined by the equation $(x + 4)^2 + (y - 3)^2 = 36$. Select the true statement.

A. The circle's center is at $(4, -3)$ and its radius is 36.
B. The circle's center is at $(-4, 3)$ and its radius is 36.
C. The circle's center is at $(4, -3)$ and its radius is 6.
D. The circle's center is at $(-4, 3)$ and its radius is 6.

SOLUTION

The answer is D. The equation for a circle is $(x - h)^2 + (y - k)^2 = r^2$. The point (h, k) is the center and r is its radius.

3. Use the center and radius of $(x - 3)^2 + (y + 2)^2 = 16$ to create a graph of the circle.

SOLUTION

Locate center (h, k) $\qquad$ $(x - 3)^2 + [y - (-2)]^2 = 16$ $\qquad$ First locate the center, (h, k). In the standard form, the constants h and k are subtracted from x and y, but in this equation, 2 is added to y. Rewrite this addition as a subtraction, $y - (-2)$, to see that k is -2. The center is the point $(3, -2)$.

Center: $(3, -2)$

Calculate radius r $\qquad$ $r = \sqrt{16} = 4$ $\qquad$ For an equation in this form, the radius is the square root of the constant on the right side.

Plot points r to right, left of center $\qquad$ $(3 + 4, -2) = (7, -2)$
$(3 - 4, -2) = (-1, -2)$ $\qquad$ All the points on the circle are distance r from the center. Calculate two points directly to the right and left of the center. Calculate these points by adding the radius, 4, to the x-coordinate to find one point, and subtracting it from the x-coordinate to find another point.

Plot points r above, below center $\qquad$ $(3, -2 + 4) = (3, 2)$
$(3, -2 - 4) = (3, -6)$ $\qquad$ Similarly, calculate the points directly above and below the center by adding the radius to the y-coordinate for one point, and subtracting it from the y-coordinate for another point. This provides four points on the circle.

Create graph

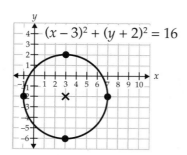

To graph a circle, locate the center, calculate the radius r, and plot points at distance r from the center. Convenient points are the ones at distance r directly to the right, left, above, and below the center. Then draw a circle through the points.

Model Problems continue . . .

4. **MP 2, 5** Calculate the center and radius of $3(x - 2)^2 + 3(y + 1)^2 + 5 = 17$. Use the standard form to graph it.

> The graph of $3(x - 2)^2 + 3(y + 1)^2 + 5 = 17$ is a circle, even though the equation is not written in the standard form for a circle.

SOLUTION

Given	$3(x - 2)^2 + 3(y + 1)^2 + 5 = 17$	The graph of this equation is a circle because the squared terms are on the same side of the equation and have the same coefficient, 3. Change this equation into standard form to simplify graphing it.
Move the constant to the right	$3(x - 2)^2 + 3(y + 1)^2 = 12$	In standard form, the constant term is on the right side of the equation. Subtract 5, the constant term on the left, from each side of the equation.
Set the coefficients of the squared terms to 1	$(x - 2)^2 + (y + 1)^2 = 4$	In standard form, the squared terms have a coefficient of 1. Divide each side of the equation by 3, the common factor on the left side.
Identify center and radius	Center: $(2, -1)$ Radius: 2	The equation is now in standard form. The coordinates of the center are the constants subtracted from x and y, which are 2 and -1. The radius is 2, the square root of 4, the right side of the equation.
Create graph	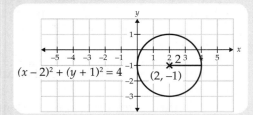	

Circles: Completing the Square

The equation $2x^2 + 2y^2 + 4x - 8y - 22 = 0$ is the equation for a circle, which can be determined because the coefficients of the x^2 and y^2 terms are equal. However, the equation is not stated in standard form. We want to transform it so we can determine its center and radius.

We complete the square for both variables to transform the equation:

State the equation as given	$2x^2 + 2y^2 + 4x - 8y - 22 = 0$	We state the equation as it is given.
Move constant to right	$2x^2 + 2y^2 + 4x - 8y = 22$	Add 22 to both sides so the constant is on the right.
Simplify	$x^2 + y^2 + 2x - 4y = 11$	Simplify by dividing both sides by 2.
Collect x and y terms	$(x^2 + 2x) + (y^2 - 4y) = 11$	Collect the x and y terms.
Complete the square for x by adding 1 to both sides	$(x^2 + 2x + 1) + (y^2 - 4y) = 11 + 1$	Add 1 to create a perfect square trinomial involving x. Remember to add it to both sides.
Factor x trinomial	$(x + 1)^2 + (y^2 - 4y) = 12$	Factor the perfect square trinomial on the left side and write it as $(x + 1)^2$. On the right, add the constants 11 and 1.
Complete the square for y	$(x + 1)^2 + (y^2 - 4y + 4) = 12 + 4$	Add 4 to create a perfect square trinomial involving y.
Factor y trinomial	$(x + 1)^2 + (y - 2)^2 = 16$	Factor the other perfect square trinomial on the left side and write it as $(y - 2)^2$. On the right, add the constants 12 and 4. The result is an equation for a circle in standard form. The center of the circle is $(-1, 2)$ and the radius is 4, the square root of 16.

One way to check this equation would be to find any point on the circle and check that the equation holds for that point. We do this below:

Add radius to x-coordinate of center	$(-1 + 4, 2) = (3, 2)$	As one check that the equation we created is correct, check to see if a point that should be on the circle is a solution to the original equation. Add the radius, 4, to the x-coordinate of the center to find a point on the circle.
Substitute point $(3, 2)$ and evaluate	$2x^2 + 2y^2 + 4x - 8y - 22 \stackrel{?}{=} 0$ $2 \cdot 3^2 + 2 \cdot 2^2 + 4 \cdot 3 - 8 \cdot 2 - 22 \stackrel{?}{=} 0$ $18 + 8 + 12 - 16 - 22 \stackrel{?}{=} 0$ $0 = 0$	Substitute the point into the original equation. Do the calculations. The two sides of the equation are equal, so we have confirmed the equation.

Circles Are Similar

In chapter 2, we stated that all circles are similar figures. We now show this to be true using dilation and rigid motion. We dilate the black circle on the right by a scale factor of 4. This produces the orange circle, which is a similar figure. We then use translation as our example of rigid motion to create the gray figure. The proof is below.

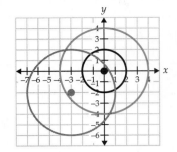

No matter how we change a circle's size or position, it remains a similar circle.

Dilation	$x^2 + y^2 = 4$ $x^2 + y^2 = 16$	Dilate the black circle by doubling its radius. We can still describe it with the equation of a circle. Each point on the dilated circle is now twice as far from the center—the scale factor is constant for all points. The dilated circle is orange.
Translation	$(x + 3)^2 + (y + 2)^2 = 16$	We also can perform a rigid motion transformation of the orange circle, and it remains a circle. For instance, translate the figure down 2, left 3. We can describe the circle with the equation to the left, and you can see that each point still remains the same distance from the circle's center as before. The translated circle is gray. Dilation and rigid motions create similar figures.

We chose translation, but a reflection or rotation would also provide a congruent figure that we could describe with an equation in the same form above. All the circles obey the definition of a circle: Points are the same distance from the center. This is another way to conclude they are similar: The radius can be changed, but it is changed by the same scale factor for all points.

PRACTICE

1. Which of the following represents the standard form of the equation of a circle with center $(-7, 2)$ and radius 3?

   A. $(x + 49)^2 + (y - 4)^2 = 9$
   B. $(x + 7)^2 + (y - 2)^2 = 9$
   C. $(x - 7)^2 + (y - 2)^2 = 3$
   D. $(x - 7)^2 + (y - 2)^2 = 9$

Exercises 2–3: State the center and radius of the circles described by the equation.

2. $(x - 2)^2 + (y - 2)^2 = 16$

3. $(x - 9)^2 + (-3 + y)^2 = 9$

4. **MP 3** The picture shows one of a series of sculptures by the artist Robert Indiana. Its shape is close to circular. Use the outer edge of the sculpture to answer the questions.

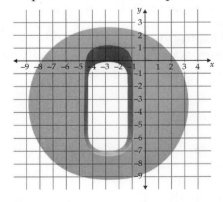

   a Approximate the center of the circle to the nearest half an integer.

   b Write the equation for the circle. Approximate its radius by calculating the distance from its center to its rightmost point.

Practice Problems continue . . .

5. Use the diagram to answer the questions. The center of the gray circle is (0, 4).

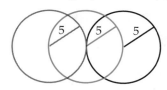

  a State the equation for the orange ring.
  b State the equation for the black ring.

6. What is the center of the circle described by the equation $(x - 6)^2 + (y + 7)^2 = 9$?

7. What is the radius of the circle described by the equation $(x - 6)^2 + (y + 7)^2 = 9$?

8. What is the center of the circle described by the equation $(x + 16)^2 + (y + 29)^2 = 100$?

9. What is the center of the circle described by the equation $(x - 65)^2 + (y + 72)^2 = 64$?

10. What is the radius of the circle described by the equation $(x - 65)^2 + (y + 72)^2 = 64$?

11. What is the radius of the circle described by the equation $(x + 81)^2 + (y - 26)^2 = 16$?

12. What are the center and radius of the circle defined by the equation below?

$$\frac{1}{2}(x + 11)^2 - 51 = 21 - \frac{1}{2}(y - 17)^2$$

13. What are the center and radius of the circle defined by the equation below?

$$\frac{1}{4}(x - 9)^2 + 61 = 70 - \frac{1}{4}(y + 20)^2$$

14. The graph of $2x^2 + 2y^2 + 16x - 24y + 54 = 0$ is a circle. Write the equation in standard form.

15. The graph of $10x^2 + 10y^2 + 40x + 140y + 40 = 0$ is a circle. Write the equation in standard form.

Exercises 16–18: State the equations below in standard form for a circle.

16. $5x^2 + 10x + 5y^2 - 40y = 0$

17. $x^2 - 8x + y^2 + 4y - 101 = 0$

18. $-6x + x^2 + y^2 + 10y = -32$

Exercises 19–20: State in standard form the equation for a circle that has the following properties.

19. Its center is at (2, 3) and it has a radius of 7.

20. Its center is at (4, 7) and it has a radius of 2.

Exercises 21–22: Graph each circle and state its center and radius.

21. $(x - 3)^2 + (y + 2)^2 = 16$

22. $(x - 5)^2 + (y - 8)^2 = 25$

23. Write the equation for the circle shown below in standard form.

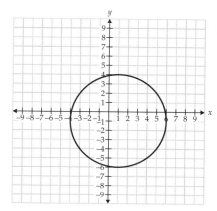

24. Give an equation of a circle that intersects both coordinate axes a units from the origin.

25. Give an equation of a circle with radius 3 that is touching the x-axis at the point $(-5, 0)$. Graph the circle.

26. Write the equation for the circle with a center at $(2, -3)$ and passing through the point (5, 1). Graph the circle.

27. **MP 2, 5** Write the equation for the circle with diameter endpoints at (3, 9) and (7, 3).

28. **MP 2, 3** A line and a point (that doesn't lie on the line) are given. Consider a family of circles all passing through this point and having the line be tangent. What shape will the centers of these circles form? Explain your answer.

29. **MP 1, 3** Prove that $x^2 - ax + y^2 - by = c$ is the equation for a circle whose center has been translated from the origin to the point $\left(\dfrac{a}{2}, \dfrac{b}{2}\right)$.

11.4 Optional: Parabolas Translated from the Origin

In Lesson 11.2, we wrote the equations for parabolas in their standard form $y = \dfrac{1}{4p}x^2$.

But parabolas written in this form are not easy to graph by hand because the vertex must be the origin. In this lesson, we allow the parabola's vertex to take on values other than (0, 0); generally, we define the parabola's vertex to be (h, k).

If the parabola's vertex is (h, k) and it has a vertical axis of symmetry, then the

standard form of the equation for a parabola becomes $y - k = \dfrac{1}{4p}(x - h)^2$.

For parabolas with a horizontal axis of symmetry, the equation is slightly different: $x - h = \dfrac{1}{4p}(y - k)^2$. Because the vertex can be any (h, k), the value of p must be

added and subtracted from the vertex to locate the focus and directrix. As always, the sign of p determines which way the parabola opens. This information is summarized below.

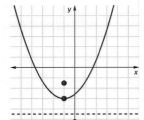

Equation	Vertex	Orientation	Focus	Directrix
$y - k = \dfrac{1}{4p}(x - h)^2$	(h, k)	Vertical	$(h, k + p)$	$y = k - p$

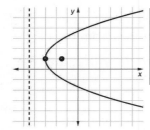

Equation	Vertex	Orientation	Focus	Directrix
$x - h = \dfrac{1}{4p}(y - k)^2$	(h, k)	Horizontal	$(h + p, k)$	$x = h - p$

 In this activity, see how changing *p*, *h*, and *k* change and translate the graph. You can think of *k* as translating the parabola up and down, and *h* as translating the parabola left and right. As these values change, they move the vertex, which translates the parabola.

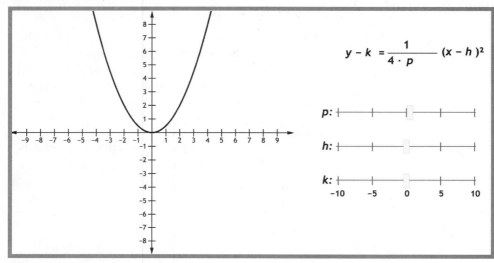

$$y - k = \frac{1}{4 \cdot p}(x - h)^2$$

In this activity, use the graph to identify properties of the parabola.

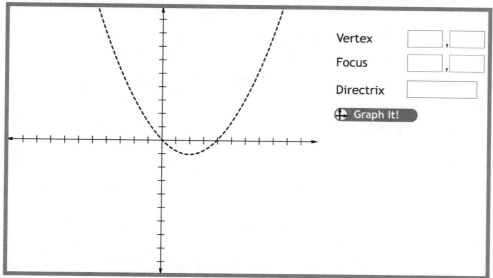

Vertex [   ] , [   ]

Focus [   ] , [   ]

Directrix [   ]

⊕ Graph It!

MODEL PROBLEMS

1. Graph $y - 1 = -\dfrac{1}{8}(x - 2)^2$.

SOLUTION

Standard form for parabola	$y - k = \dfrac{1}{4p}(x - h)^2$ $y - 1 = -\dfrac{1}{8}(x - 2)^2$	The standard form of the equation for a vertical parabola is $y - k = \dfrac{1}{4p}(x - h)^2$. The standard form has a constant k subtracted from y and a constant h subtracted from x.
Vertex: (h, k)	Vertex is $(2, 1)$	The vertex of the parabola is determined by the constants h and k, subtracted from x and y. In this case, $h = 2$ and $k = 1$.
Axis of symmetry: $x = h$	Axis is $x = 2$	The parabola is symmetric around a vertical line that passes through the vertex. It is vertical because the squared term includes x, not y. The equation of the axis of symmetry is $x = h$, which is $x = 2$ in this particular case.
Calculate p	$-\dfrac{1}{8} = \dfrac{1}{4p}$ $p = -2$	The coefficient of the squared term is $-\dfrac{1}{8}$. This means p equals -2.
Focus	$(2, (1 + -2)) = (2, -1)$	Since the squared term includes x, this parabola opens up or down. This means the focus is above or below the vertex. Add p to the y-coordinate of the vertex.
Directrix	$y = 1 - (-2) = 3$	Subtract p from the y-coordinate of the vertex to calculate the directrix.
Create graph	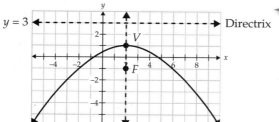	

> The standard form of the equation for a parabola is $y - k = \dfrac{1}{4p}(x - h)^2$. The vertex of the parabola is located at (h, k). You add and subtract p to calculate the focus and directrix.

Model Problems continue . . .

2. Graph $x + 3 = -\frac{1}{4}(y - 1)^2$.

> To graph a parabola in standard form, we first plot the vertex (h, k). Remember that h and k are the values subtracted from x and y. In the equation, h is -3, since this equation in standard form would be stated as $x - (-3)$.

SOLUTION

Standard form of equation for parabola	$x - h = \frac{1}{4p}(y - k)^2$ $x - (-3) = -\frac{1}{4}(y - 1)^2$	The standard form of the equation for a parabola is $x - h = \frac{1}{4p}(y - k)^2$. The standard form has a constant h subtracted from x and a constant k subtracted from y. Write $x + 3$ as $x - (-3)$.
Vertex: (h, k)	$h = -3, k = 1$ Vertex is $(-3, 1)$	The vertex of the parabola is determined by the constants h and k subtracted from x and y. In this case, $h = -3$ (since -3 is subtracted from x to get $+3$) and $k = 1$.
Axis of symmetry: $y = k$	Axis is $y = 1$	The parabola is symmetric around a horizontal line that passes through the vertex. It is horizontal because the squared term includes y, not x. The equation of the axis of symmetry is $y = k$, which is $y = 1$ in this particular case.
Calculate p	$-\frac{1}{4} = \frac{1}{4p}$ $p = -1$	The coefficient of the squared term is $-\frac{1}{4}$. Set this equal to p and solve. p equals -1.
Focus	$(-3 + (-1), 1) = (-4, -1)$	Since the squared term includes y, this parabola opens left or right. This means the focus is to the right or left of the vertex.
Directrix	$x = -3 - (-1) = -2$	Subtract the p from the x-coordinate of the vertex to calculate the directrix.
Create graph	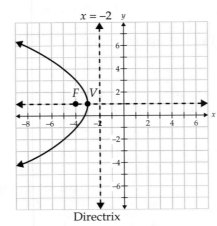	

Model Problems continue . . .

3. Write an equation for the parabola.

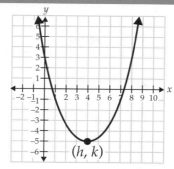

SOLUTION

Vertex: (h, k)	Vertex is $(4, -5)$	From the graph, we note the location of the vertex.
Substitute h and k in standard form equation	$y - k = a(x - h)^2$ $y - (-5) = a(x - 4)^2$ $y + 5 = a(x - 4)^2$	Start with the standard form of the equation for a parabola and substitute the values h and k from the coordinates of the vertex, $(4, -5)$. Note that in this version of the standard form, an a precedes the parentheses on the right-hand side. Recall from earlier in this lesson that $a = \dfrac{1}{4p}$
Substitute coordinates of another point on the parabola for x and y	$y + 5 = a(x - 4)^2$ $3 + 5 = a(0 - 4)^2$	Calculate the coefficient of the square term. We will call it a. There is no need to calculate p. We choose the y-intercept, $(0, 3)$, and substitute these coordinates into the equation. The y-intercept $(0, 3)$ is an easy one to read on the graph, and use it to determine the equation.
Solve for coefficient	$8 = 16a$ $a = \dfrac{1}{2}$	Simplify the equation and then solve for a.
Write equation using coefficient	$y + 5 = \dfrac{1}{2}(x - 4)^2$	Finish writing the equation in standard form by substituting the value of the coefficient.

 In this activity, use your knowledge of parabolas to design a roller coaster.

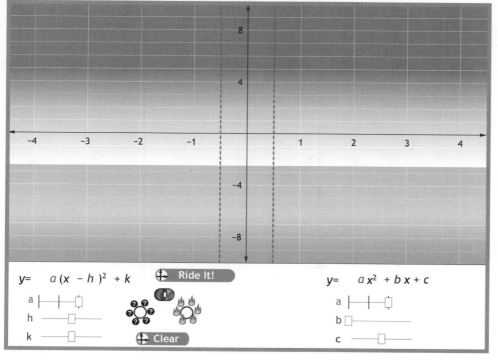

PRACTICE

1. The equation $x^2 + 2x - y + 36 = 0$ represents which type of conic section?

    A. Ellipse
    B. Circle
    C. Hyperbola
    D. Parabola

Exercises 2–5: Find the vertex, axis of symmetry, and directrix of these parabolas.

2. $y - 6 = 2(x - 1)^2$

3. $y - 1 = 3(x + 4)^2$

4. $x - 4 = 2(y - 5)^2$

5. $x + 3 = 3(y - 1)^2$

6. **MP 3** Use the inside edge of the water to define the parabola.

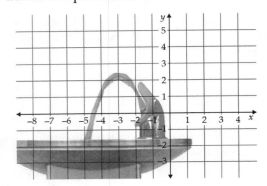

  a State the vertex of the water parabola.
  b Write the equation for the parabola. Approximate the position of the water to the nearest half an integer.

Exercises 7–10: State the equations below in standard form for a parabola.

7. $y = 3x^2 - 18x + 27$

8. $y = \dfrac{1}{2}x^2 - 4x + 27$

9. $x = -3y^2 + 6y - 13$

10. $x = \dfrac{1}{4}y^2 + 2y + 13$

Exercises 11–18: Find the vertex, axis of symmetry, and directrix of these parabolas.

11. $x = y^2 - 8y$

12. $y = 2x^2 + 12x - 5$

13. $y = x^2 - 14x + 37$

14. $x = 2y^2 + 16y - 11$

15. $0 = -3x^2 + 12x - y$

16. $0 = 5x^2 + 20x + 7 - y$

17. $y = x^2 + x + 2$

18. $y = -x^2 + 5x + 6$

Exercises 19–28: State in standard form the equation for a parabola with the following properties.

19. A focus at $(8, 0)$ and a directrix at $x = -8$.

20. A vertex at $(0, 0)$ and a directrix at $x = -3$.

21. A focus at $(3, 0)$ and a directrix at $x = -3$.

22. A focus at $(0, -6)$ and a directrix at $y = 6$.

23. A vertex at $(0, 0)$ and a directrix at $x = 5$.

24. A vertex at $(6, -2)$ and a directrix at $y = 2$.

25. A vertex at $(4, -3)$ and a directrix at $x = -5$.

26. A focus at $(-2, 3)$ and a directrix at $x = 2$.

27. A vertex at $(5, 2)$ and a focus at $(3, 2)$

28. A vertex at $(-3, 3)$ and a focus at $(0, 3)$

Exercises 29–36: Graph each quadratic and state its vertex, focus, and directrix.

29. $x = y^2 + 2y + 1$

30. $y = -x^2 - 6x - 9$

31. $y = -x^2 + 6x - 1$

32. $x = 4y^2 - 16y + 9$

33. $y = \dfrac{1}{2}x^2 + 5x + 8$

34. $y = -\dfrac{3}{2}x^2 + 2$

35. $y = 3x^2 + 6x - 4$

36. $y = 2x - x^2 - 4$

Practice Problems continue . . .

Exercises 37–40: Write the equation for the parabola shown in standard form.

37.

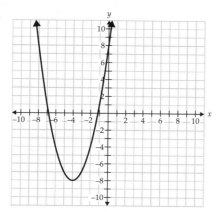

38.

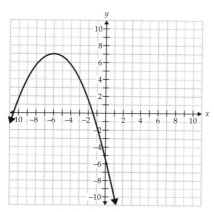

39.

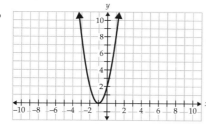

40.

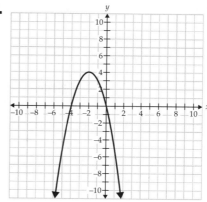

41. MP 1, 2 The segment that has endpoints on a parabola passes through the focus of the parabola and is perpendicular to its axis of symmetry is called the *latus rectum*. Find the length of the latus rectum of the parabola $x - 3 = \frac{1}{4}(y + 2)^2$.

42. MP 1, 5 A parabola passes through the points $(1, 9)$, $(2, 3)$, and $(5, 9)$. Write an equation for the parabola in standard form.

43. MP 1, 5 A parabola passes through the points $(5, -4)$, $(5, -2)$, and $(13, 0)$. Write an equation for the parabola in standard form.

• Multi-Part PROBLEM Practice •

MP 1, 2, 4 The height of an object thrown vertically into the air and left to free-fall back to earth can be described by the equation $y = -5t^2 + v_i t + y_i$, where y is the object's height at any time t seconds after the ball has been thrown, y_i is the object's initial height, and v_i is the velocity with which the object was thrown into the air. A ball is thrown with an initial velocity of 30 meters per second from a height of 10 meters. Give all answers to the nearest integer.

a When does the ball reach its highest point? Hint: What is the highest point of a parabola?

b How high does it travel?

c When does the ball hit the ground? Hint: What is the height when the ball is on the ground?

11.5 **Optional: Ellipses at the Origin**

Geometric Definition of an Ellipse

An **ellipse** is a conic section that can be defined with two foci. The diagram of an ellipse shows two points, each called a **focus of the ellipse**. We label the foci F_1 and F_2. An ellipse is the set of all points in a plane such that the sum of the distances between any point on the ellipse and the two foci is a constant. As shown below, we can create an ellipse by passing a plane through one cone of the double cone at an angle between the perpendicular to the axis and the parallel to the side of the cone.

> The plural of focus is *foci*, pronounced "foe-sigh."

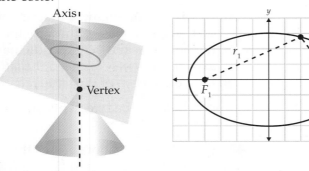

The geometric definition of an ellipse that is stated below involves the distances from the foci to a point on the ellipse:

Sum of distances to foci is constant $r_1 + r_2 = a$ constant   An ellipse is defined by two foci. The sum of the distances from the foci to any point on the ellipse is constant for the ellipse.

Try it! You may have drawn an ellipse using this geometric principle. If you put two pins in a board, and tie a string between them, you can draw an ellipse by using a pencil to pull the string taut as you move it around. The pins are at the foci of the ellipse, and the string ensures the pencil is always at the same total distance to the foci.

 In this activity, experiment with moving the point on the ellipse to any location on it, and moving either of the foci along the axis.

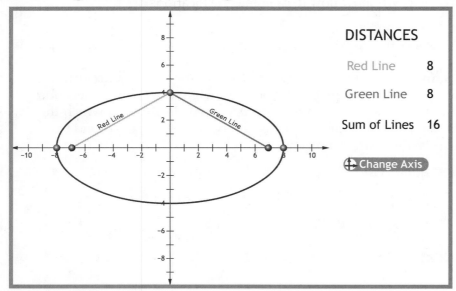

Ellipses Centered at the Origin

The equation $\dfrac{x^2}{a^2} + \dfrac{y^2}{b^2} = 1$ is the **standard form of the equation for an ellipse centered at the origin**. Both a and b must be positive.

> Like a circle, an ellipse has x^2 and y^2 in its equation, but the coefficients of the variables are not equal with an ellipse.

When $a > b$:

If $a > b$, then the ellipse is horizontal because the length of the ellipse along the x-axis is greater than it is along the y-axis.

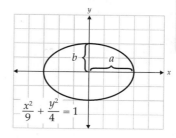

$$\frac{x^2}{9} + \frac{y^2}{4} = 1$$

Equation of a horizontal ellipse	$\dfrac{x^2}{9} + \dfrac{y^2}{4} = 1$ $\dfrac{x^2}{3^2} + \dfrac{y^2}{2^2} = 1$	When $a > b$, the ellipse is horizontal, and its foci are on the horizontal axis. In this case, $a = 3$ and $b = 2$. Both a and b must be positive.
a, b determine intercepts	x-intercepts: $(3, 0)$ and $(-3, 0)$ y-intercepts: $(0, 2)$ and $(0, -2)$	a and b determine the intercepts on the axes for the ellipse.

When $b > a$:

If $b > a$, then the ellipse is vertical because the length of the ellipse along the y-axis is greater than it is along the x-axis.

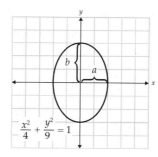

$$\frac{x^2}{4} + \frac{y^2}{9} = 1$$

Equation of a vertical ellipse	$\dfrac{x^2}{4} + \dfrac{y^2}{9} = 1$	When $b > a$, the ellipse is vertical, and its foci are on the vertical axis.

As you have seen, the foci define an ellipse. We show how to calculate the locations of the foci:

Standard form	$\dfrac{x^2}{a^2} + \dfrac{y^2}{b^2} = 1$	
Compute c	$c^2 = a^2 - b^2$ if the ellipse is horizontal $c^2 = b^2 - a^2$ if the ellipse is vertical	The value of c can be calculated using these equations.
Horizontal ellipse	At $(-c, 0)$ and $(c, 0)$	If the ellipse is horizontal, which occurs when $a > b$, then the foci are at $(-c, 0)$ and $(c, 0)$.
Vertical ellipse	At $(0, c)$ and $(0, -c)$	If the ellipse is vertical, then the foci are at $(0, c)$ and $(0, -c)$.

Graphing an Ellipse at the Origin

To graph an ellipse, you plot the four points where the ellipse crosses the coordinate axes, using the values of a and b, and draw an oval through them:

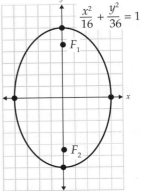

Given equation:
$$\frac{x^2}{16} + \frac{y^2}{36} = 1$$

The graph of an equation in this form will be an ellipse. Its center will be at the origin.

1. Calculate a and b

$a = \sqrt{16} = 4, b = \sqrt{36} = 6$

Take the square roots of the denominators to determine a and b.

2. Plot four points

$(a, 0)$ and $(-a, 0) = (4, 0)$ and $(-4, 0)$
$(0, b)$ and $(0, -b) = (0, 6)$ and $(0, -6)$

Two points on the ellipse are a to the right and left of the center. Since a equals 4, this means $(4, 0)$, which is 4 to the right of the center, and $(-4, 0)$, which is 4 to the left of the center, are on the ellipse.

3. Calculate c

$c^2 = b^2 - a^2$
$c^2 = 36 - 16 = 2\sqrt{5}$

We use the equation for the foci. Since the ellipse is vertical, we subtract a^2 from b^2.

4. Plot foci

$(0, 2\sqrt{5})$ and $(0, -2\sqrt{5})$

The foci are on the vertical axis at $(0, c)$ and $(0, -c)$.

 In this activity, use the graph to describe the properties of the ellipse.

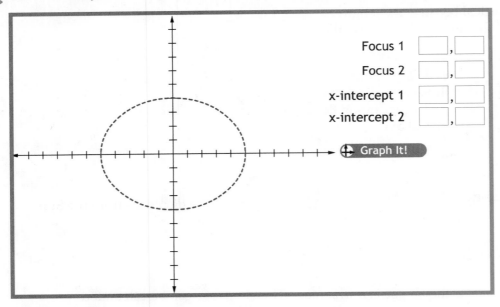

Focus 1 [ ] , [ ]
Focus 2 [ ] , [ ]
x-intercept 1 [ ] , [ ]
x-intercept 2 [ ] , [ ]

Graph It!

The Vertices, Axes, and Center of an Ellipse

The **vertices of an ellipse** ("vertices" is the plural of "vertex") are the points farthest from each other. On a horizontal ellipse, the vertices are the leftmost and rightmost points. On a vertical ellipse, they are the highest and lowest points. The line segment connecting the vertices is called the **major axis** of the ellipse. The **minor axis** passes through the center and is perpendicular to the major axis. Its endpoints are called the **co-vertices**.

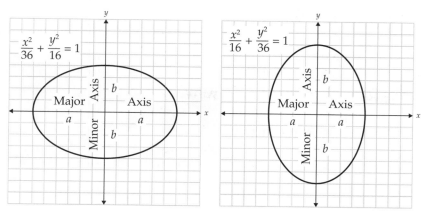

$$\frac{x^2}{36} + \frac{y^2}{16} = 1$$

$$\frac{x^2}{16} + \frac{y^2}{36} = 1$$

An ellipse with an equation in the form $\frac{x^2}{a^2} + \frac{y^2}{b^2} = 1$ has its center at the origin.

For a horizontal ellipse $(a > b)$, the length of the major axis is $2a$ because its endpoints are $(-a, 0)$ and $(a, 0)$. For a vertical ellipse $(b > a)$, the length of the major axis is $2b$. In general, the length of the major axis is the larger of $2a$ and $2b$. If $a = b$, then the equation describes a circle.

MODEL PROBLEMS

 1. **MP 4** Mars, like all the planets of the Solar System, has an elliptical orbit. Its distance from the Sun ranges from 205 million kilometers to 249 million kilometers along the major axis. With the center of the Sun as a focus of the orbit, write an equation for the orbit of Mars.

SOLUTION

Create diagram

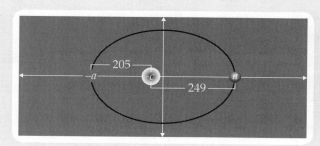

We put the center of the orbit at the origin. The Sun is at a focus of the ellipse. The Sun's distance from the center is c, the distance from the center to a focus. The distance from the origin to Mars at a vertex is a.

Add equations and solve for a	$2a = 205 + 249$ $a = 227$	$2a$ equals the sum of the distances from the Sun to the vertices. Solve for a.
Use relationship of a and c	$227 + c = 249$ $c = 22$	Solve for c.
Use equation for foci	$c^2 = a^2 - b^2$ $22^2 = 227^2 - b^2$ $484 = 51{,}529 - b^2$	Substitute the values for a and c into the equation that relates the focal length and the intercepts.
Solve for b	$b^2 = 51{,}045$ $b \approx 226$	Subtract 484 from 51,529 and add b^2 to both sides. Then take the square root of 51,045 to solve for b.
Substitute a and b into standard equation for ellipse	$\dfrac{x^2}{227^2} + \dfrac{y^2}{226^2} = 1$	Substitute the values for a and b into the standard ellipse equation to find the equation of Mars' orbit. x and y are in millions of kilometers.

Model Problems continue . . .

2. **MP 2, 4** The Roman Colosseum, built nearly 2000 years ago, stands today as one of the world's greatest historical landmarks. It has an elliptical shape, approximately 616 feet long and 512 feet wide.

  a Given these dimensions, write an equation for the Roman Colosseum.

  b Calculate its area. The area of an ellipse can be calculated using the formula, $A = \pi ab$.

SOLUTION

a Solve for a and b

$$a = \frac{length}{2} = \frac{616}{2} = 308$$

$$b = \frac{width}{2} = \frac{512}{2} = 256$$

Since the Roman Colosseum's length is greater than its width, its length defines the major axis. The length is equal to $2a$, while the width is equal to $2b$. To then solve for the intercepts, we divide both the length and width by 2.

Ellipse equation

$$\frac{x^2}{a^2} + \frac{y^2}{b^2} = 1$$

Given the standard ellipse equation, substitute for a and b.

$$\frac{x^2}{308^2} + \frac{y^2}{256^2} = 1$$

b Substitute values for a and b

$$A = \pi \cdot 308 \cdot 256$$

Substitute the values for a and b, half the length and half the width, in the formula for the area of an ellipse.

Multiply to solve for area

$$A \approx 248{,}000 \text{ ft}^2$$

Multiply the three values to solve for the area, rounding to the nearest thousand.

Derivations: Ellipse Equations

We derive the equation for the foci of the ellipse, $c^2 = a^2 - b^2$. We use the sum of the focal radii, the sum of the distances from the foci to a point on an ellipse, in the derivation:

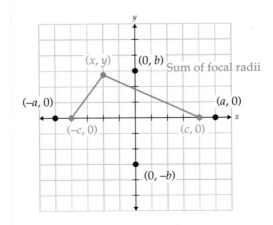

Derive: $c^2 = a^2 - b^2$

Sum of distances from foci to any point on ellipse is constant	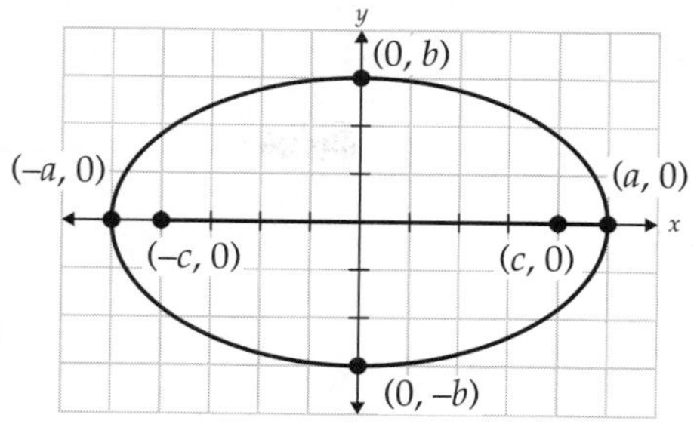	The definition of an ellipse states that the sum of the distances from the foci to any point on the ellipse is constant. We call this distance the *sum of the focal radii*. Since the sum of the focal radii is a constant for any point on the ellipse, we choose the right x-intercept (vertex), $(a, 0)$, as our point.
$2a$ equals sum of focal radii	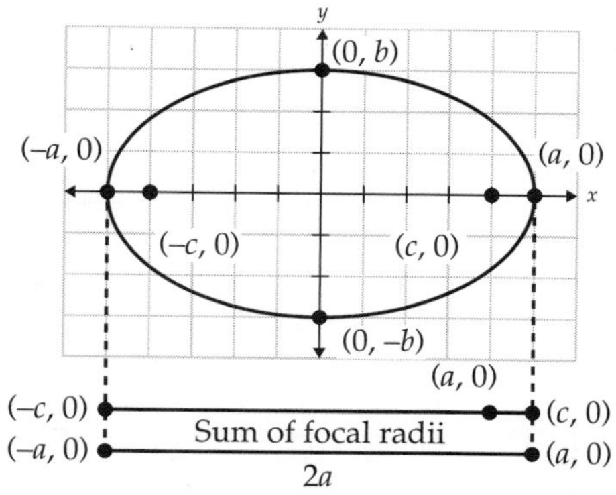	We want to show the relationship between the sum of the focal radii and $2a$, twice the value of the x-intercept. To do this, we drop down the line segments of the focal radii of $(a, 0)$, repositioned to be next to each other, so the total segment shows the sum of the focal radii. In the ellipse, the segment from $(-c, 0)$ to $(a, 0)$ overlaps the segment from $(c, 0)$ to $(a, 0)$. For comparison, we also show the line segment of length $2a$ between the two x-intercepts (vertices).
Expression for distance between intercepts	$2a$ = distance between intercepts	The distance $2a$ is the distance between the x-intercepts. It also equals the sum of the focal radii. This is the key insight for the derivation.
Use Pythagorean theorem	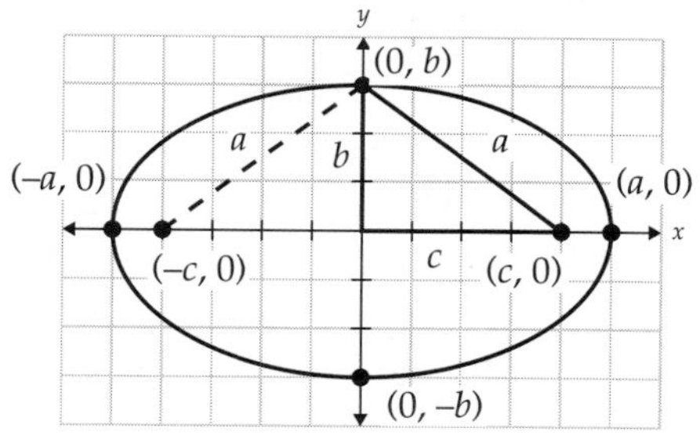	Use the Pythagorean theorem to show the relationship between c, a, and b. As the diagram shows, the point $(0, b)$ on the ellipse, $(c, 0)$, and the origin form a triangle. To finish the derivation, we now switch to using the y-intercept $(0, b)$. The sum of the distances from the foci to the y-intercept must equal $2a$, since we just showed that this is true for every point on the ellipse. Each distance to the y-intercept equals a, since it is the same distance from each focus.
Form a right triangle	Legs are y-intercept and x-coordinate of focus	Form a right triangle. Its height is b, the y-coordinate of the y-intercept. The length of the other leg is c, the x-coordinate of that focus, since that is the distance from the origin to a focus.
Solve for c	$a^2 = b^2 + c^2$ $c^2 = a^2 - b^2$	Use the Pythagorean theorem. Then solve for c. We have shown the relationship between the foci and the intercepts.

Now, we derive the equation for an ellipse, $\dfrac{x^2}{a^2} + \dfrac{y^2}{b^2} = 1$, from its geometric definition, the set of points with a constant sum of distances from the two foci. We derive the equation for a horizontal ellipse centered at the origin, but the derivation for other ellipses is similar.

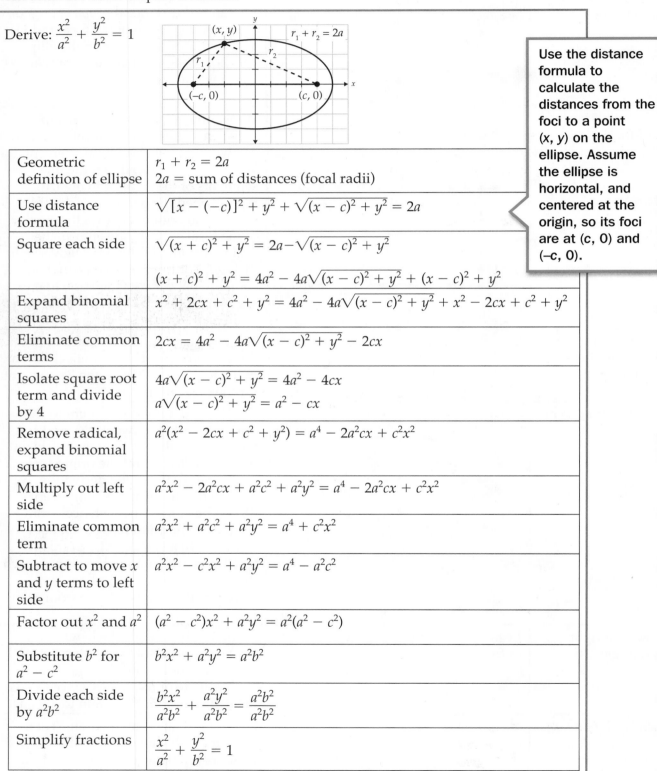

Derive: $\dfrac{x^2}{a^2} + \dfrac{y^2}{b^2} = 1$

Use the distance formula to calculate the distances from the foci to a point (x, y) on the ellipse. Assume the ellipse is horizontal, and centered at the origin, so its foci are at $(c, 0)$ and $(-c, 0)$.

Geometric definition of ellipse	$r_1 + r_2 = 2a$ $2a = $ sum of distances (focal radii)
Use distance formula	$\sqrt{[x - (-c)]^2 + y^2} + \sqrt{(x - c)^2 + y^2} = 2a$
Square each side	$\sqrt{(x + c)^2 + y^2} = 2a - \sqrt{(x - c)^2 + y^2}$ $(x + c)^2 + y^2 = 4a^2 - 4a\sqrt{(x - c)^2 + y^2} + (x - c)^2 + y^2$
Expand binomial squares	$x^2 + 2cx + c^2 + y^2 = 4a^2 - 4a\sqrt{(x - c)^2 + y^2} + x^2 - 2cx + c^2 + y^2$
Eliminate common terms	$2cx = 4a^2 - 4a\sqrt{(x - c)^2 + y^2} - 2cx$
Isolate square root term and divide by 4	$4a\sqrt{(x - c)^2 + y^2} = 4a^2 - 4cx$ $a\sqrt{(x - c)^2 + y^2} = a^2 - cx$
Remove radical, expand binomial squares	$a^2(x^2 - 2cx + c^2 + y^2) = a^4 - 2a^2cx + c^2x^2$
Multiply out left side	$a^2x^2 - 2a^2cx + a^2c^2 + a^2y^2 = a^4 - 2a^2cx + c^2x^2$
Eliminate common term	$a^2x^2 + a^2c^2 + a^2y^2 = a^4 + c^2x^2$
Subtract to move x and y terms to left side	$a^2x^2 - c^2x^2 + a^2y^2 = a^4 - a^2c^2$
Factor out x^2 and a^2	$(a^2 - c^2)x^2 + a^2y^2 = a^2(a^2 - c^2)$
Substitute b^2 for $a^2 - c^2$	$b^2x^2 + a^2y^2 = a^2b^2$
Divide each side by a^2b^2	$\dfrac{b^2x^2}{a^2b^2} + \dfrac{a^2y^2}{a^2b^2} = \dfrac{a^2b^2}{a^2b^2}$
Simplify fractions	$\dfrac{x^2}{a^2} + \dfrac{y^2}{b^2} = 1$

PRACTICE

Exercises 1–3: State the location of the foci, x-intercepts, and y-intercepts for each ellipse.

1. $\dfrac{x^2}{169} + \dfrac{y^2}{144} = 1$

2. $\dfrac{x^2}{16} + \dfrac{y^2}{25} = 1$

3. $\dfrac{x^2}{36} + \dfrac{y^2}{100} = 1$

4. **MP 3** Lithotripsy breaks kidney stones into small particles using a high-intensity acoustic pulse. The acoustic generator is at one focus of a reflecting ellipse and the kidney stone is at the other. The pulse reflects off the ellipse, concentrating at the other focus.

 a How far must the generator be from the stone?

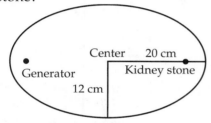

 b State the equation for the ellipse, assuming it is centered at the origin.

5. Find some circular or elliptical shapes in your town or on the Internet. Photograph them, print them on graph paper, and then write equations for them.

6. Sara says: "I can describe the elliptical shape with the formula $\dfrac{x^2}{4} + \dfrac{y^2}{4} = 1$." Elaine says: "That is the formula for a circle." Who is right? Why?

7. Does the graph of an ellipse represent the graph of a function? How do you know? Hint: Use the vertical line test.

8. Find another real-world elliptical object similar to the Colosseum and compute its area.

Exercises 9–12: State the equations in the standard form for an ellipse.

9. $3x^2 + 9y^2 = 36$

10. $25x^2 + 10y^2 = 100$

11. $2x^2 - 24 = -8y^2$

12. $2x^2 + 3y^2 - 6 = 0$

Exercises 13–14: State the location of the center, the foci, and the endpoints of the major axis for the ellipses described by the equations.

13. $25x^2 + 16y^2 - 400 = 0$

14. $16x^2 + 25y^2 - 400 = 0$

Exercises 15–18: Use the properties to state the equation for the ellipse in standard form.

15. Foci at $(3, 0)$ and $(-3, 0)$ and x-intercepts $(5, 0)$ and $(-5, 0)$.

16. The x-intercepts are $(4, 0)$ and $(-4, 0)$. The y-intercepts are $(0, 2)$ and $(0, -2)$.

17. The x-intercepts are $(5, 0)$ and $(-5, 0)$. The foci have the coordinates $(0, 10)$ and $(0, -10)$.

18. The foci are $(-7, 0)$ and $(7, 0)$. The y-intercepts are $(0, 3)$ and $(0, -3)$.

Exercises 19–22: Graph each ellipse, locating each of the foci in your graph.

19. $\dfrac{x^2}{36} + \dfrac{y^2}{25} = 1$

20. $\dfrac{x^2}{100} + \dfrac{y^2}{676} = 1$

21. $\dfrac{x^2}{15} + \dfrac{y^2}{3} = 1$

22. $\dfrac{x^2}{25} + \dfrac{y^2}{8} = 1$

23. Graph the ellipse given by the equation $4x^2 + 9y^2 - 576 = 0$. Label the foci and vertices.

24. Graph the ellipse given by the equation $y^2 = 25 - 4x^2$. Label the foci and vertices.

25. **MP 2** A circle of radius 11 is inscribed into an ellipse $\dfrac{x^2}{a^2} + \dfrac{y^2}{121} = 1$. The area of the circle is one-half the area of the ellipse. Find the length of the ellipse's major axis.

26. **MP 2** An ellipse is inscribed into a rectangle with an area of 17 square inches. Find the area of the part of the rectangle that is not covered by the ellipse. Leave your answer in terms of π.

MP 2, 4 All planets in the solar system have elliptical orbits, with the Sun at one focus point of the ellipse. To the right is a table for the planets' closest and farthest positions from the Sun, in millions of kilometers.

a Find the equation for the orbit of Jupiter.

b Find the equation for the orbit of Earth.

c Which planet's orbit, Earth's or Jupiter's, is better approximated by a circle? Justify your answer.

d Using your answer to part **c**, what is the equation for a circular orbit for that planet? What is the orbit's radius?

Planet	Closest	Farthest
Mercury	46	70
Venus	107.5	109
Earth	147	153
Mars	207	249
Jupiter	740	817
Saturn	1348	1503
Uranus	2739	3003
Neptune	4456	4546

LESSON 11.6

11.6 Optional: Hyperbolas at the Origin

Geometric Definition of a Hyperbola

A hyperbola is another conic section that can be defined with two foci. The hyperbola is the set of all points in a plane where the difference of the distance between any point on the hyperbola and the foci is constant.

For a hyperbola, it is the *difference* of the distances between two fixed points to any point on the curve that is a constant. Each of these two fixed points is called a **focus of the hyperbola**. The distances shown are called **focal radii**. The **vertices of a hyperbola** are the two of its points, one on each part (or branch), that are closest together. As shown in the conic illustration below, when the plane cuts the double cone at an angle closer to the axis than the side of the cone, a hyperbola is formed.

> The *sum* of the distances is a constant for an ellipse. The *difference* of the distances is a constant for a hyperbola.

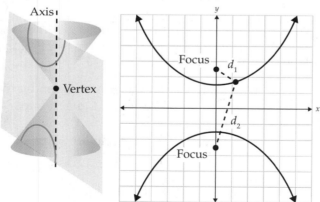

We state the geometric definition of a hyperbola:

Difference of distances to foci is constant $|d_2 - d_1|$ = constant

A hyperbola is defined by two foci. The absolute value of the difference of the distances from any point on the hyperbola to the foci is constant.

In this activity, no matter where you place the point on either branch of the hyperbola, the difference of these two distances is 8, unless you move the vertices or foci.

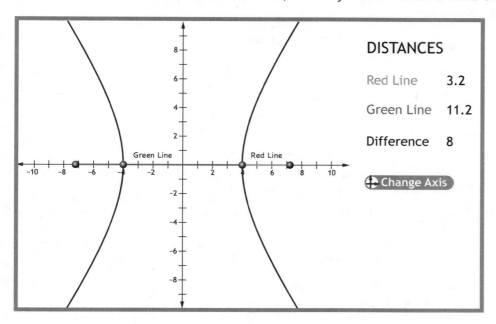

DISTANCES

Red Line   3.2

Green Line   11.2

Difference   8

⊕ Change Axis

Hyperbolas Centered at the Origin

The equations below are in **standard form of the equation for a hyperbola centered at the origin**. We discuss a hyperbola with the y^2 term subtracted and a hyperbola with the x^2 term subtracted.

For a hyperbola centered at the origin:

$$\frac{x^2}{a^2} - \frac{y^2}{b^2} = 1$$

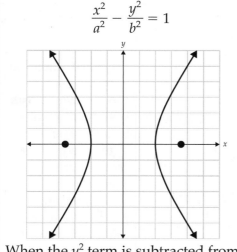

When the y^2 term is subtracted from the x^2 term, the foci are on the x-axis.

$$\frac{y^2}{b^2} - \frac{x^2}{a^2} = 1$$

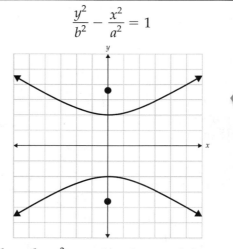

When the x^2 term is subtracted from the y^2 term, the foci are on the y-axis. Note that a^2 is still below x^2, even though this term is now the term that is being subtracted.

The foci are *c* units from the origin. The foci can be calculated using $c^2 = a^2 + b^2$. It applies to both horizontal and vertical hyperbolas.

We describe the main parts of a hyperbola and where they are located when the foci are on the x-axis (the y^2 term is subtracted):

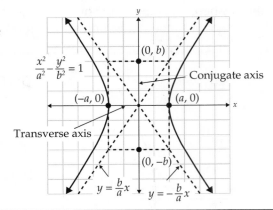

Branches	The branches are the two parts of the hyperbola.
Vertices	The vertices are the closest points on the hyperbola. The vertices are at $(-a, 0)$ and $(a, 0)$.
Transverse axis	The transverse axis is the line segment that connects the vertices.
Conjugate axis	The conjugate axis is a line segment perpendicular to the transverse axis, passing through its midpoint. It starts at $(0, b)$ and stops at $(0, -b)$.
Center	The center is at the intersection of the axes. It is at the midpoint of the vertices, and also of the foci. We drew a rectangular box defined by a and b.
Branches approach asymptotes as $|x|$ increases	The branches of the hyperbola approach two lines called **asymptotes**. When the hyperbola has a center at the origin, the two lines are the graphs of $y = \dfrac{b}{a}x$ and $y = -\dfrac{b}{a}x$. The branches approach but never reach the lines. The larger the absolute value of x, the closer they are. You can see that the lines pass through the center (here the origin), and through the corners of the rectangular box.

We describe the main parts of a hyperbola and where they are located when the foci are on the y-axis (the x^2 term is subtracted). You can see the branches of the hyperbola open up and down. The vertices of the hyperbola are on the y-axis.
For an equation in this form, it is the value of b (not a) that determines the vertices, which are where the hyperbola crosses the y-axis. The center is still the origin.

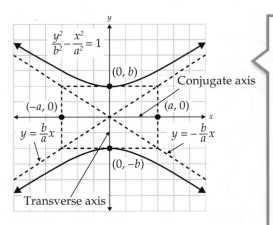

Note that when the y^2 term is positive, the transverse axis is vertical, parallel to the y-axis. If the x^2 term is positive, then the transverse axis is horizontal. In both cases, the square root of the denominator of the first term determines the coordinates of the vertices.

Vertices	When the x^2 term is subtracted, the vertices are on the y-axis, at $(0, b)$ and $(0, -b)$. Note that b^2 is still below y^2, even though the term is now the first term.
Transverse axis	With the x^2 term subtracted, the transverse axis is vertical. As always, the conjugate axis is perpendicular to the transverse axis, passing through its midpoint.

Graphing a Hyperbola at the Origin

To graph the hyperbola, start by sketching a rectangle whose sides have midpoints at $(-a, 0)$, $(a, 0)$, $(0, -b)$, and $(0, b)$. Then draw the asymptotes of the hyperbola through the corners of the rectangle. Plot the foci and draw the hyperbola.

We summarize how to graph a hyperbola at the origin:

Equation	Direction	Vertices	Asymptotes	Foci
$\dfrac{x^2}{a^2} - \dfrac{y^2}{b^2} = 1$	Horizontal	$(a, 0)$ and $(-a, 0)$	$y = \dfrac{b}{a}x$ and $y = -\dfrac{b}{a}x$	$(c, 0)$ and $(-c, 0)$
$\dfrac{y^2}{b^2} - \dfrac{x^2}{a^2} = 1$	Vertical	$(0, b)$ and $(0, -b)$	$y = \dfrac{b}{a}x$ and $y = -\dfrac{b}{a}x$	$(0, c)$ and $(0, -c)$

 In this activity, calculate various properties of the hyperbola.

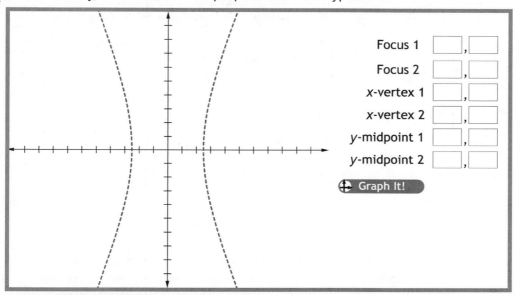

Focus 1 [ ] , [ ]
Focus 2 [ ] , [ ]
x-vertex 1 [ ] , [ ]
x-vertex 2 [ ] , [ ]
y-midpoint 1 [ ] , [ ]
y-midpoint 2 [ ] , [ ]

Graph It!

MODEL PROBLEMS

1. Graph the hyperbola $9x^2 - 16y^2 = 144$.

SOLUTION

State in standard form

$$\frac{9x^2}{144} - \frac{16y^2}{144} = \frac{144}{144}$$

$$\frac{x^2}{16} - \frac{y^2}{9} = 1$$

First, divide each term in both sides of the equation by 144 so the constant on the right equals 1. The y^2 term is subtracted, so this will be a horizontal hyperbola.

Sketch the rectangle

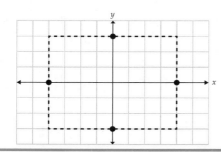

We want to sketch the rectangular box. First, locate the vertices, since they are midpoints of two sides of the box. They are $(-a, 0)$ and $(a, 0)$, which in this case are the points $(-4, 0)$ and $(4, 0)$. The other rectangle midpoints are at $(0, 3)$ and $(0, -3)$

Model Problems continue . . .

Calculate foci
$$c^2 = 4^2 + 3^2 = 25$$
$(-5, 0)$ and $(5, 0)$

Calculate c. The foci are at $(-c, 0)$ and $(c, 0)$ when the vertices are on the horizontal axis.

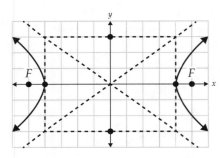

Draw asymptotes then draw the hyperbola

Calculate and draw the asymptotes using the equations $y = \frac{3}{4}x$ and $y = -\frac{3}{4}x$. Note they pass through the corners of the rectangle. Then draw the hyperbola.

2. Graph $\dfrac{y^2}{4} - \dfrac{x^2}{25} = 1$

SOLUTION

Sketch the rectangle

Vertices at $(0, 2)$ and $(0, -2)$
Midpoints of other rectangle sides $(5, 0)$ and $(-5, 0)$

We want to sketch the rectangular box. First, locate the vertices, since they are midpoints of two sides of the box. They are $(0, b)$ and $(0, -b)$, since the x^2 term is being subtracted and the hyperbola is vertical.

Calculate foci
$$c^2 = 2^2 + 5^2 = 29$$
$(0, \sqrt{29})$ and $(0, -\sqrt{29})$

Calculate c. The foci are at $(0, c)$ and $(0, -c)$ when the vertices are on the vertical axis.

Draw asymptotes then draw the hyperbola

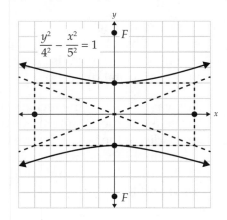

Calculate and draw the asymptotes using the equations $y = \frac{2}{5}x$ and $y = -\frac{2}{5}x$. Note they pass through the corners of the rectangle. Then draw the hyperbola.

Model Problems continue . . .

3. A hyperbola has its foci at $(5, 0)$ and $(-5, 0)$, and the absolute value of the difference between the distances from the foci to any point on the hyperbola is 8. Write an equation for the hyperbola in the correct form, $\dfrac{x^2}{a^2} - \dfrac{y^2}{b^2} = 1$ or $\dfrac{y^2}{b^2} - \dfrac{x^2}{a^2} = 1$.

> From any point on the hyperbola, the difference of the distances from the two foci is the constant $2a$.

SOLUTION

Calculate a	$2a = 8$ $a = 4$	The problem says the difference of distance to foci equals 8.
Calculate b^2	$c^2 = a^2 + b^2$ $5^2 = 4^2 + b^2$ $b^2 = 9$	With a hyperbola, c^2 equals the sum of a^2 and b^2. The value of c equals the positive x-coordinate of the right focus of the hyperbola, which is stated in the problem.
State equation	$\dfrac{x^2}{16} - \dfrac{y^2}{9} = 1$	Use the values of a^2 and b^2. Since the hyperbola has foci on the x-axis, the y^2 term is subtracted.

4. **MP 2, 4** The hyperbola has many practical applications. For example, nuclear reactor cooling towers are built in the shape of hyperboloids, a solid obtained by rotating a hyperbola about its conjugate axis. This shape provides stability against high winds and can be built with as little material as possible. Some of the largest nuclear cooling towers can be found in Europe. One such tower in France is 170 meters tall and 150 meters across (diameter) at the base. If the narrowest part of the tower has a diameter of 80 meters and is 100 meters above the ground, find

  a An equation for the hyperbola cross-section of the tower.
  b The diameter of the tower at the top.

SOLUTION

a
Narrowest part is $2a$	$2a = 80$ $a = 40$	The narrowest part of the hyperbola is between the vertices of the hyperbola. Solve for a.
Substitute point to find b	$\dfrac{75^2}{40^2} - \dfrac{100^2}{b^2} = 1$	The base is 100 m below the vertices and 150 m across. We have 2 choices, $(75, -100)$ or $(-75, -100)$.
Solve for b	$b^2 = 3975$ $b = 63$	Combining constant terms, multiplying by b^2, dividing by 100^2, and taking the square root gives us b.
Write equation	$\dfrac{x^2}{40^2} - \dfrac{y^2}{63^2} = 1$	Write the equation with the center at the origin.

b
Identify point	$y = 70, x = ?$	The tower is 170 m high, or 70 m above its narrowest part.
Substitute to find x	$\dfrac{x^2}{40^2} - \dfrac{70^2}{63^2} = 1$	Substitute the known value for y into the equation we derived.
Solve for x	$x^2 = 3573.3$ $x \approx 60$	Combining constant terms, multiplying by 40 squared, then taking the square root gives $x = 59.794$, which we round to 60.
Double to find diameter	$60 \cdot 2 = 120$ m	The hyperbola is centered about the y-axis, so to find the diameter, we double the x-coordinate.

Derivation: Hyperbola Equation

One method of finding an equation for a hyperbola is to use the fact that the difference in distances from the foci to any point on the hyperbola equals the length of the transverse axis ($2a$ for horizontal hyperbolas and $2b$ for vertical hyperbolas). The derivation of this relationship is similar to that for ellipses.

Derive: $\dfrac{x^2}{a^2} - \dfrac{y^2}{b^2} = 1$

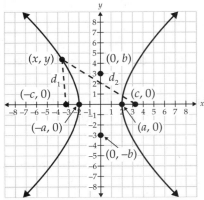

The process is the same for a vertical hyperbola except we use $2b$ instead of $2a$ for the difference of the distances from the foci to a point on the hyperbola. We skip many of the algebraic steps, since the process is very similar to deriving the equation for an ellipse.

Geometric definition of hyperbola	$|d_1 - d_2| = 2a$	Start with an equation stating that the difference in distances from the foci to any point on the hyperbola is constant. d_1 is the distance from one focus and d_2 is the distance from the other focus.
Use the distance formula	$\sqrt{(x + c)^2 + (y - 0)^2} - \sqrt{(x - c)^2 + (y - 0)^2} = 2a$	Use the distance formula to calculate the distances to a point (x, y) on the hyperbola. Assume the ellipse is horizontal, and centered at the origin, so its foci are at $(-c, 0)$ and $(c, 0)$.
Perform lengthy algebra similar to that on page 556	$\dfrac{x^2}{a^2} - \dfrac{y^2}{c^2 - a^2} = 1$	After many steps similar to those in our derivation of the equation for an ellipse, we are close to having our hyperbola equation.
Substitute	$\dfrac{x^2}{a^2} - \dfrac{y^2}{b^2} = 1$	From our work with ellipses, we know that since $b^2 = c^2 - a^2$, we can replace the $c^2 - a^2$ with b^2 to finish our derivation.

PRACTICE

1. Which of the following equations best describes the figure shown below?

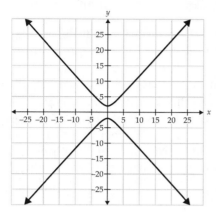

A. $\dfrac{y^2}{4} + \dfrac{x^2}{4} = 1$

B. $\dfrac{y^2}{4} - \dfrac{x^2}{3} = 1$

C. $\dfrac{x^2}{100} - \dfrac{y^2}{4} = 1$

D. $\dfrac{y^2}{4} + \dfrac{x^2}{3} = 1$

2. Which of the following represents the foci of the hyperbola $\dfrac{y^2}{9} - \dfrac{x^2}{25} = 1$?

A. $(0, \pm 2\sqrt{2})$ C. $(\pm 2\sqrt{2}, 0)$

B. $(0, \pm \sqrt{34})$ D. $(\pm \sqrt{34}, 0)$

3. Which is the conic section that could be described by the equation $y^2 = 5x^2 + 15$?

A. Parabola   C. Circle

B. Ellipse   D. Hyperbola

Exercises 4–9: State the location of the foci, the slope of the asymptotes, and the x- or y-intercepts for the hyperbolas described by the equations below.

4. $\dfrac{x^2}{144} - \dfrac{y^2}{25} = 1$

5. $\dfrac{x^2}{49} - \dfrac{y^2}{36} = 1$

6. $\dfrac{y^2}{144} - \dfrac{x^2}{25} = 1$

7. $\dfrac{y^2}{16} - \dfrac{x^2}{9} = 1$

8. $\dfrac{x^2}{16} - \dfrac{y^2}{13} = 1$

9. $\dfrac{y^2}{25} - \dfrac{x^2}{5} = 1$

Exercises 10–13: Graph, showing the foci and stating the equations for the asymptotes.

10. $\dfrac{x^2}{25} - \dfrac{y^2}{144} = 1$

11. $\dfrac{y^2}{36} - \dfrac{x^2}{64} = 1$

12. $\dfrac{y^2}{9} - \dfrac{x^2}{36} = 1$

13. $\dfrac{x^2}{25} - \dfrac{y^2}{9} = 1$

Exercises 14–19: State the equation for a hyperbola that has the following properties.

14. Foci at $(5, 0)$ and $(-5, 0)$ and x-intercepts at $(4, 0)$ and $(-4, 0)$.

15. Slopes of the asymptotes are $\dfrac{4}{3}$ and $-\dfrac{4}{3}$ and foci at $(0, 5)$ and $(0, -5)$.

16. Foci at $(0, -5)$ and $(0, 5)$ and y-intercepts at $(0, 4)$ and $(0, -4)$.

17. Foci at $(0, -25)$ and $(0, 25)$ and y-intercepts at $(0, 20)$ and $(0, -20)$.

18. Vertices at $(0, 8)$ and $(0, -8)$ and asymptotes are $y = \dfrac{3}{4}x$ and $y = -\dfrac{3}{4}x$.

19. Vertices at $(0, 4)$ and $(0, -4)$ and passes through the point $(6, 6)$.

Exercises 20–21: State in standard form.

20. $2x^2 - 6y^2 - 12 = 0$

21. $11y^2 - 66 = 33x^2$

Practice Problems continue . . . .

Exercises 22–23: Write the equation for each graph.

22.

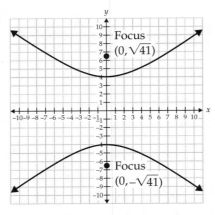

23.

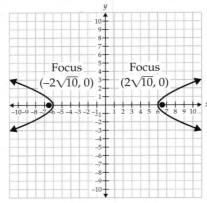

24. Explain how to use the central rectangle of a hyperbola to draw its asymptotes.

25. **MP 2** How many times can a hyperbola with its center at the origin intersect an ellipse with the same center? Draw a sketch of possible options to explain your answer. Hint: Consider more than one case.

26. **MP 3** Two reporters 6 miles apart hear the sound of an explosion. One reporter hears it 2 seconds later than the other. Write an equation of a hyperbola on which the point of the explosion must be located. Assume that sound travels at 1100 feet per second, and there are 5280 feet in a mile. Use units of feet in your equation. The positions of the reporters are at the foci of the hyperbola.

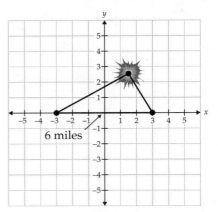

1. The graph of a conic section is shown. Which of the following statements is true?

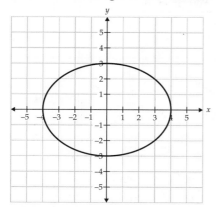

I.   The intercepts are $(0, \pm 3)$ and $(\pm 4, 0)$.

II. The equation of the graph is
$$\frac{x^2}{9} + \frac{y^2}{16} = 1.$$

III. The foci are on the x-axis.

A.   I only

B.   I and II

C.   I and III

D.   I, II, and III

2. Which of the following represents the equation of an ellipse with foci at the points $(\pm 2, 0)$ and vertices at the points $(\pm 6, 0)$?

A. $\dfrac{x^2}{36} + \dfrac{y^2}{32} = 1$

B. $\dfrac{x^2}{32} + \dfrac{y^2}{36} = 1$

C. $\dfrac{x^2}{6} + \dfrac{y^2}{4\sqrt{2}} = 1$

D. $\dfrac{x^2}{36} + \dfrac{y^2}{4} = 1$

3. The boundary of a lawn of elliptical shape is described by the equation $\dfrac{x^2}{196} + \dfrac{y^2}{324} = 1$, measured in feet. What is the longest distance across the lawn?

A.   14 ft

B.   18 ft

C.   28 ft

D.   36 ft

4. Two parabolas have the same vertex. The equation $y = \dfrac{4}{3}x^2$ represents one parabola. Which of the following could be the equation of the other parabola?

A. $y = \dfrac{4}{3}x^2 + 1$

B. $y = x^2$

C. $y = x^2 - \dfrac{4}{3}$

D. $y = 3x^2 + 4$

5. Which equation could represent a parabola with a focus that is 2.5 units above its vertex?

A. $y = 10x^2$

B. $x = \dfrac{1}{10}y^2$

C. $y = -\dfrac{5}{2}x^2$

D. $y = \dfrac{1}{10}x^2$

6. The graph shows the path of a satellite around the planet. Which of the following could *not* be a position of the satellite at any time?

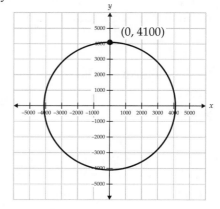

A. $(0, 4100)$

B. $(-4000, -900)$

C. $(20{,}000, -20{,}000)$

D. $(-4100, 0)$

Chapter Review continues . . .

7. A circle is initially defined by the equation $x^2 + y^2 = 2$. It is dilated by a factor of 5 and then translated up 2 and 3 to the right. The resulting circle is defined by the equation:

    A. $(x + 3)^2 + (y + 2)^2 = 10$
    B. $(x + 3)^2 + (y - 2)^2 = 10$
    C. $(x + 3)^2 + (y + 2)^2 = 50$
    D. $(x - 3)^2 + (y - 2)^2 = 50$

8. A parabola can be defined as

    A. The set of points the same distance from a point V and a point F.
    B. The set of points the same distance from a line a and a line b.
    C. The set of points twice the distance from point A on a circle and half the distance from point B on a circle.
    D. The set of points the same distance from a point F and a line d.

9. What is a way to rotate the parabola $y = 2x^2$ by $90°$ while retaining its shape?

    A. Add a negative sign to expression on the right so the equation becomes $y = -2x^2$.
    B. Swap the x- and y-variables so the equation becomes $x = 2y^2$.
    C. Take the reciprocal of the coefficient of the squared term, $y = \frac{1}{2}x^2$.
    D. Take the negative reciprocal of the coefficient of the squared term, $y = -\frac{1}{2}x^2$.

Exercises 10–11: Determine the center and radius of the circle.

10. $x^2 + y^2 = 22$

11. $x^2 + y^2 = 17$

12. Graph $x^2 + y^2 = 6$.

Exercises 13–14: How many points of intersection could the graphs of the given functions have? State all possible numbers and explain your answer.

13. $3x^2 + 3y^2 = 75$ and $y = mx + b$

14. $y = mx + b$ and $y^2 = 4x$

Exercises 15–16: State the equation for each parabola below.

15.

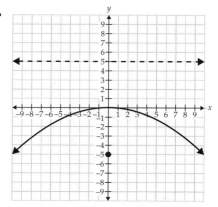

16.

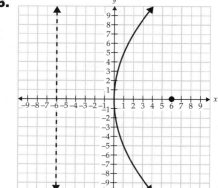

Exercises 17–19: Each parabola described below has its vertex at the origin. State the equation of each parabola in standard form and graph it.

17. The directrix of the parabola is $x = -\frac{1}{2}$.

18. The parabola passes through the point $(6, 4)$ and the directrix is vertical.

19. The parabola passes through the point $(-4, -4)$ and the directrix is horizontal.

20. How many points of intersection could the graphs of $y^2 = r^2 - x^2$ and $x^2 = ay$ have? State all possible numbers and explain your answer.

21. Give an example of parabola or parabolic shape in real life.

22. The lamp of a flashlight light is located 2 inches from the parabolic reflector. What is the equation of the cross-section of the reflector through its axis? Introduce the coordinate grid so the focus lies on the negative horizontal axis and the vertex is at the origin.

Chapter Review continues . . .

Exercises 23–25: State the center and radius of each circle described by the equations below.

23. $(y - 3)^2 + (x + 1)^2 = 23$

24. $(3 + x)^2 + (4 + y)^2 = 34$

25. $(x - 56)^2 + y^2 = 169$

Exercises 26–27: Graph each circle. State its center and radius.

26. $(x + 15)^2 + (y - 15)^2 = 81$

27. $(x - 2)^2 + (y - 1)^2 = 9$

28. Write the equation for the circle below in standard form.

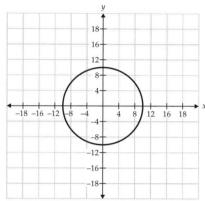

29. **MP 6** A circle passes through the points $(-8, 3)$, $(-1, 10)$, and $(6, 3)$. Write an equation for the circle in standard form.

30. **MP 3** When a satellite following a circular path around its planet, like the one in the diagram below, increased its speed, it escaped the circular orbit and followed a parabolic path with the center of the planet as the focus of the parabola. Assuming that the radius of the planet is 3500 miles and the orbit is 150 miles above the surface at its closest point, find the equation for the satellite's parabolic path.

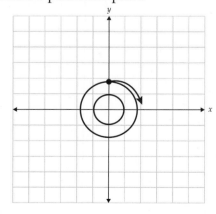

31. **MP 7** The revenue R from producing x units of some product is described by the equation $R = 320x - \dfrac{5}{4}x^2$. What is the maximum revenue?

32. Rewrite the expression by completing the square: $4y^2 - 40y + 24$

33. **MP 7** Write the equation for the parabola below in standard form, $y - k = a(x - h)^2$.

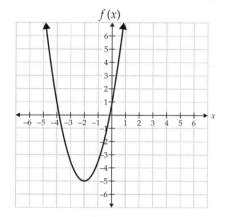

34. The graph of the equation $y = 2x^2 - 16x + 12$ is a parabola. What is the equation for this parabola in standard form, $y - k = a(x - h)^2$?

Exercises 35–37: State the location of the foci, x-intercepts, and y-intercepts for the ellipses described by the equations.

35. $\dfrac{x^2}{4} + \dfrac{y^2}{2.5^2} = 1$

36. $\dfrac{x^2}{169} + \dfrac{y^2}{25} = 1$

37. $\dfrac{x^2}{14} + \dfrac{y^2}{6} = 1$

Exercises 38–40: Graph, showing the foci and stating the equations for the asymptotes.

38. $4x^2 - 16y^2 = 1$

39. $y^2 = x^2 - 25$

40. $x^2 = 4(y^2 - 4)$

Chapter Review continues . . .

41. **MP 3** Two stations, *A* and *B*, are located 400 miles apart on an east-west line, with *B* east of *A*, as in the diagram below. Both stations receive a signal from a boat located in an area to the south and 50 miles east of station *A*. The signal arrived at station *A* about 0.0009 seconds earlier than at station *B*. Given that the signal is transmitted at the speed of light (186,000 miles per second), find how far south the boat is from the line connecting the stations. Round your answer to the nearest mile.

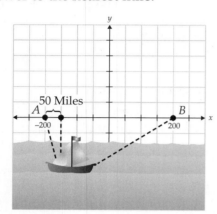

42. **MP 2** For which values of *k* will the hyperbola $\dfrac{x^2}{a^2} - \dfrac{y^2}{b^2} = 1$ intersect the line $y = kx$? Justify your answer.

43. Identify the conic section represented by each of the following equations. Sketch the graph, write the equation in standard form, and then for the proper conic section identify:

Circle	center and radius
Parabola	focal point, equations for directrix and axis of symmetry
Ellipse	foci, vertices, co-vertices
Hyperbola	foci, vertices, equations of asymptotes

  a $x^2 = 2y$
  b $9x^2 = 16y^2 + 144$
  c $4x^2 = 100 - 4y^2$
  d $2x^2 = 12x - 2y^2 + 4y + 8$

Cumulative Review
for Chapters 1–11

1. What is the height of the cylinder below?

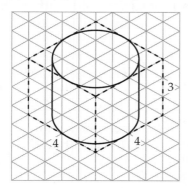

   A. 1   C. 3
   B. 2   D. 4

2. In a parallelogram $ABCD$, the diagonals $\overline{AC}$ and $\overline{BD}$ intersect at point O. Which of the following must be true? Select all that apply.

   A. $AO = OC$ C. $BO = OD$
   B. $AC = BD$ D. $AB = CD$

3. Two of a triangle's interior angles measure 45° and 55°. If the triangle's side lengths are represented by a, b, and c and $a < b < c$, which of the following statements is true for this triangle?

   A. $a^2 + b^2 > c^2$
   B. $a^2 + b^2 < c^2$
   C. $a^2 + b^2 = c^2$
   D. Not enough information to determine

4. Which line segments are parallel in the figure below? Choose all that apply.

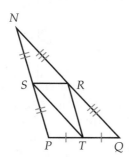

   A. $\overline{NP}$ and $\overline{RT}$ C. $\overline{NS}$ and $\overline{NR}$
   B. $\overline{ST}$ and $\overline{NQ}$ D. $\overline{SR}$ and $\overline{PQ}$

5. A figure has 12 faces and 20 vertices. How many edges does it have?

   A. 8   C. 24
   B. 16   D. 30

6. A triangle has sides of lengths 8, 10, and 7. What type of triangle is it?

   A. Obtuse   C. Right
   B. Acute   D. Cannot tell

7. A triangle has sides of lengths 84, 187, and 207. What kind of triangle is it?

   A. Acute   C. Right
   B. Obtuse   D. Cannot tell

8. The lengths of the sides of a triangle are 12 inches, 1 foot, and $\frac{1}{3}$ of a yard. The triangle is

   A. Scalene.
   B. Isosceles.
   C. Equilateral.

9. Cylinders X and Y are similar. Cylinder X has a height of 5 inches and radius of 15 inches. If the height of cylinder Y is 7 inches, what is the radius of cylinder Y?

   A. 19 inches   C. 21 inches
   B. 20 inches   D. 22 inches

10. A circle is defined by the equation $x^2 + y^2 = k$, with k being a real number such as 12. To dilate the circle with a scale factor of 9, you should

   A. Multiply k by 9.
   B. Multiply k by 3.
   C. Multiply k by 81.
   D. Divide k by 9.

11. A circle is defined by the equation $x^2 + y^2 = 34$. The circle is translated up 4 units vertically, then rotated 27°, and dilated by a factor of 1.89. The resulting circle is

   A. Congruent to the original circle.

   B. Similar to the original circle.

   C. A figure that is no longer a circle.

   D. No statement above is true.

12. **MP 2, 3** In the triangle below, show that the midpoint of the hypotenuse of a right triangle is equidistant from the three vertices.

Prove: $MA = MB = MC$

Given: ABC is a right triangle with vertices $A(0, 0)$, $B(0, b)$, and $C(c, 0)$.

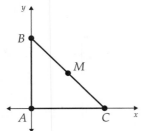

13. Find an example of an oblique solid in real life. Make a sketch of the solid and estimate its volume.

14. **MP 3** In the parallelogram *BODY* below, the segments $\overline{BH}$ and $\overline{DK}$ are the heights. Is the quadrilateral *BKDH* a parallelogram? Justify your reasoning.

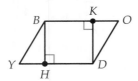

15. Carl says the point (a, b) must be the midpoint of the line segment from $(2, 3)$ and $(8, -5)$ because he proved (a, b) is equidistant from these two points. Show that Carl's reasoning is wrong by giving an example of a point that is equidistant from the endpoints of the line segment but is not the midpoint.

16. What is the volume of the spherical nuclear power plant below? Assume its radius is 160 m.

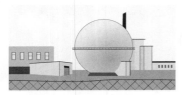

17. **MP 2, 8** Consider the two points $A = (1, 2)$ and $B = (3, 4)$. Using each of the numbers 1, 2, 3, and 4 as coordinates exactly once, write as many other pairs of points as you can where the distance between them is the same as the distance between A and B.

18. Fred buys stones to use as part of his landscaping project. Each stone comes in the shape of a trapezoid, with bases of 8 in and 12 in. The distance from one base of the stone to the other base is 6 in. He plans to put together two trapezoidal stones, along their longer bases, to make one large six-sided stepping stone. What is the area of one large six-sided stepping stone?

19. **MP 2, 3** A cone and a pyramid have the same volume. The height of the cone is four times the height of the pyramid. What is the relationship between the areas of the bases of these two solids? Why?

20. The area of the circle below is 36 cm². What is the measure of the central angle *ACB*? Hints: Solve the equation for sector area for the angle, and remember what the formula πr^2 represents.

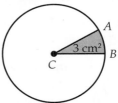

21. Find the equation for the ellipse with the foci $(5, 0)$ and $(-5, 0)$ and the major axis of length 12. Graph the ellipse.

22. Find the surface area of a cone with a base radius of 4 cm and a slant height of 15 cm.

23. If $m\angle MPK = 78°$, what does $m\overarc{MP}$ equal?

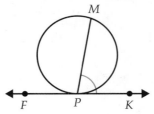

24. **MP 4, 5** A semielliptical opening leads into a cave where the famous Captain Flint hides his treasures. The opening is 5 ft high and 8 ft wide. Will Captain Flint be able to push a treasure chest 4 ft high, 4 ft wide, and 6 ft deep into the cave through this opening? Why or why not? Include a diagram to explain your reasoning.

25. Rajiv found the vertices of an ellipse to be at the points (4, 0) and (−4, 0) and the foci at the points (−4.5, 0) and (4.5, 0). What should you conclude about Rajiv's calculations?

26. Explain why the area of an ellipse is never greater than the area of a circle with a diameter equal to the ellipse's major axis.

27. The graph of $4x^2 + 4y^2 + 40x + 24y + 120 = 0$ is a circle. Write the equation in standard form.

28. A parabola's focus is at $\left(0, -\dfrac{7}{2}\right)$ and its directrix is at $y = \dfrac{7}{2}$. What is the equation for the parabola? State your answer in the standard form of an equation for a parabola at the origin.

Exercises 29–30: Graph the equations below. Draw and label the focus and directrix of each parabola.

29. $x = \dfrac{1}{8}y^2$

30. $y = 5x^2$

31. What is $m\overparen{YW}$?

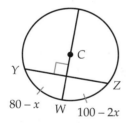

32. $\triangle ABC$ is isosceles, with the vertex angle at B. $\overline{BD}$ is a perpendicular bisector. If $m\angle ABD = 51°$, what is $m\angle C$?

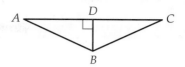

33. In the diagram below, a is parallel to b, c is parallel to d, and $\angle 4 = 40°$. Find the measures of the angles 1, 2, and 3.

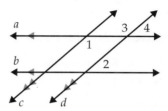

34. Use the following biconditional statement to answer each question: "The side lengths are equal in a quadrilateral if and only if the measures of the interior angles are equal."

  a Write the two conditional statements for the biconditional.

  b Write the two converse statements for the two conditionals.

  c What do you notice about the two conditional statements and the two converse statements in a biconditional?

35. Suppose figure L is dilated by a scale factor of a to produce figure L'. What scale factor would you need in order to dilate figure L' back to figure L?

---

36. **MP 3** Prove the angle bisector theorem converse.

Angle bisector theorem converse

If a point of an angle is the same distance from that angle's sides, then it is on the bisector.

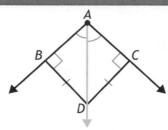

If $\overline{DB} \perp \overrightarrow{AB}$ and $\overline{DC} \perp \overrightarrow{AC}$ and $\overline{DB} \cong \overline{DC}$, then $\overrightarrow{AD}$ bisects $\angle BAC$.

Chapter Content

Chapter Vocabulary

addition rule	experimental probability	observation
circular permutation	false negative	outcome
combination	false positive	permutation
complement	fundamental counting principle	probability
compound event	independent event	sample space
conditional probability	independently combined probability model	subtraction rule
event	multiplication rule	theoretical probability
expected value	mutually exclusive	tree diagram

LESSON 12.1

12.1 Introduction to Probability

Experimental Probability

Probability is the study of how likely it is that some event will occur. There are two ways to determine the probability of an event. We first focus on **experimental probability**, which is based on observation. *Theoretical probability* is based on reasoning.

To determine the experimental probability that a coin will come up heads, you might toss a coin 100 times. Each time, you make an **observation**, noting the outcome. An **outcome** is a possible result of the observation, like "heads" or "tails" for a coin toss. If you were to toss a pair of coins such as a quarter and a dime, one possible outcome is heads for the quarter and tails for the dime.

Based on observations, you can calculate an experimental probability that an event occurs. An **event** is a set of outcomes that are of interest.

$$P(A) = \frac{\text{\# of times event } A \text{ occurs}}{\text{\# of observations}}$$

The experimental probability of an event A, $P(A)$, equals the number of times A occurs, divided by the total number of observations.

> Experimental probability varies. The experimental probability might be 0.4 after five coin tosses, 0.6 after ten tosses, and 0.48 after 100 tosses.

Let's say that out of 100 tosses, the coin lands heads up 48 times. The experimental probability of heads from this series of observations is $P(\text{heads}) = \frac{48}{100} = 0.48$, or 48%.

MODEL PROBLEMS

1. Surveyors counted the number of trees in a popular city park. There were 62 spruce trees, 44 firs, 12 oaks, and 2 maples. What is the experimental probability that a randomly selected tree is an oak?

SOLUTION

Formula for experimental probability

$$P(A) = \frac{\text{\# of times event } A \text{ occurs}}{\text{\# of observations}}$$

$$P(\text{oak}) = \frac{\text{\# of oaks}}{\text{Total \# of trees}}$$

Begin with the formula for experimental probability.

Substitute

$$P(\text{oak}) = \frac{12}{62 + 44 + 12 + 2}$$

$$P(\text{oak}) = \frac{12}{120}$$

$$P(\text{oak}) = \frac{1}{10}$$

The numerator is the number of trees that are oaks. The denominator is the number of observations, or in this case, the total number of trees. Add the numbers of different types of trees together to get the total number. Add 62, 44, 12, and 2. Simplify the fraction.

2. **MP 2** What is the probability a person prefers candidate Jones, based on the data of a survey of people about their preferences for candidates in an election?

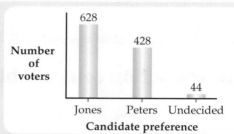

SOLUTION

Formula for experimental probability

$$P(A) = \frac{\text{\# of times event } A \text{ occurs}}{\text{\# of observations}}$$

$$P(\text{Jones}) = \frac{\text{\# of people who prefer Jones}}{\text{\# of people surveyed}}$$

The probability a person prefers Jones equals the number of people who prefer Jones divided by the number of people surveyed.

Substitute

$$P(\text{Jones}) = \frac{628}{628 + 428 + 44} = \frac{628}{1100} = 0.57$$

The chart says 628 people prefer Jones, so put that in the numerator and divide.

Theoretical Probability and Sample Spaces

Unlike experimental probability, which is determined from observations, **theoretical probability** is determined using reasoning and analysis.

In theoretical probability, we assume that outcomes are equally likely. For example, if you toss a coin, heads is as likely to come up as tails. From a well-shuffled deck of cards, any one of the cards is equally likely to be drawn.

> A **sample space** is the set of all possible outcomes of some action. This is a sample space for tossing a coin twice.

Assuming each outcome is equally likely, the theoretical probability of an event can be calculated using the formula:

$$P(A) = \frac{\text{\# of outcomes of event } A}{\text{\# of outcomes in the sample space}}$$

Theoretical probability equals the number of ways an event can occur divided by the number of possible outcomes.

In this activity, and the ones that follow, you can simulate hundreds or even thousands of coin tosses. Use it to determine the theoretical probability of various outcomes.

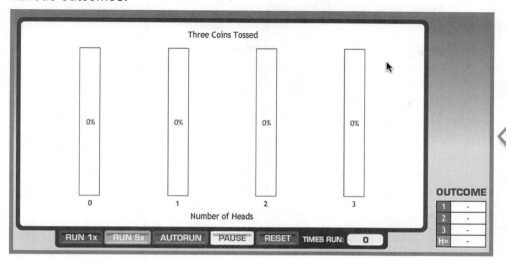

This activity simulates tossing three coins, with outcomes of 0, 1, 2, or 3 heads. The graph shows the percent of each outcome. How does that percentage compare to the experimental probability when you toss the coins 5 times? 500 times? Use data to estimate the theoretical probability of 1 head as an outcome, as well as 2 heads.

 In this activity, four coins are tossed. Compare conclusions drawn about probability of outcomes after 5, 50, and 500 tosses.

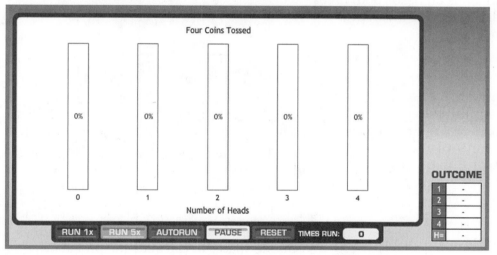

 In this activity, six coins are tossed. Use the data to answer various questions posed in the activity.

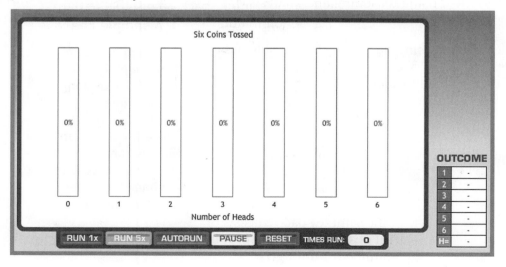

In this activity, sixteen coins are tossed. Compare and contrast the outcomes when tossing three, four, six, and sixteen coins.

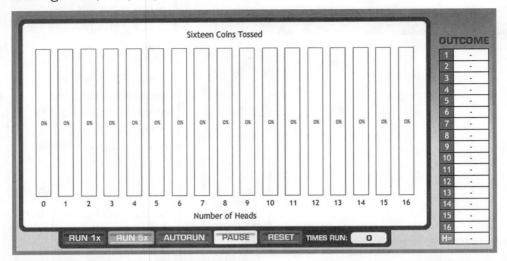

MODEL PROBLEMS

1. A coin is flipped twice and lands on heads both times. Use the sample space to determine the theoretical probability of this outcome.

Sample space for a coin flipped twice

SOLUTION

Formula for theoretical probability

$$P(A) = \frac{\text{\# of outcomes of event } A}{\text{\# of outcomes in the sample space}}$$

The theoretical probability of an event A is the number of outcomes of event A divided by the number of outcomes in the sample space. This definition assumes that all outcomes in the sample space are equally likely.

Use data $P(\text{heads twice}) = \dfrac{1}{4}$

The event "heads twice" occurs once in the sample space. To calculate the probability of getting heads twice, start by putting 1 in the numerator. There are four outcomes in the sample space, so put that in the denominator.

2. There are six sides to a die (die is the singular of dice). Each side has a certain number of dots on it: 1, 2, 3, 4, 5, or 6. Assume the die is fair, so that the six outcomes are equally likely. Calculate the probability that the die comes up with an odd number.

> **Although we started this chapter with a brief discussion of experimental probability, as we move ahead, when we say "probability" we mean "theoretical probability" unless we say otherwise.**

SOLUTION

Create sample space

Use the sample space to determine the theoretical probability of getting an odd number when rolling a die. The sample space consists of all possible outcomes of rolling a die: the numbers 1 through 6.

Model Problems continue . . .

Number of ways odd occurs $P(\text{odd number}) = \dfrac{3}{?}$ The event "the die is odd" occurs three times in the sample space, which are circled in the sample space.

Total outcomes $P(\text{odd number}) = \dfrac{3}{6} = \dfrac{1}{2}$ There are 6 outcomes in the sample space. The probability of rolling an odd number equals $\dfrac{3}{6}$ or $\dfrac{1}{2}$.

3. **MP 1, 5, 7** **a** If you roll a pair of dice, what is the probability that the *total* on the two dice will be 7?
b Graph the outcomes—the sums of the two dice—based on their frequency of occurring.

SOLUTION

a Create sample space

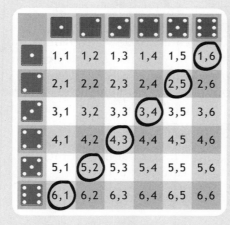

The sample space represents all the possible outcomes when two dice are rolled. To make it easier to see all the outcomes in the sample space, we use one orange die and one black die. For instance, the outcome on the upper right, 1, 6, means the orange die came up 1 and the black die came up 6.

Count number of times event occurs   Number of times dice total 7 is 6   All the outcomes where the dice total 7 are circled. There are 6 such outcomes.

Count total number of outcomes   36 outcomes   There are 36 outcomes in the sample space.

Compute probability $P(7) = \dfrac{6}{36} = \dfrac{1}{6}$ The probability of the dice totaling 7 is $\dfrac{6}{36}$, or $\dfrac{1}{6}$, because there are 6 outcomes where the dice total 7 and 36 outcomes in the sample space.

b Sample space distribution

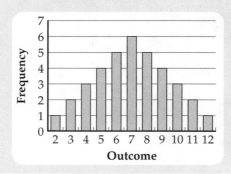

Use the sample space to graph the frequencies of various outcomes. For instance, there is one cell in the table with an outcome of a sum of 2, so put up a bar of height one. Continue for each outcome.

Model Problems continue . . .

4. **MP 2, 4** 78% of the students in a town go to one school, and the rest go to another. The City Council wants to decide which school will get a new football field based on the probability of some chance outcome, where the probability matches the student percents.

    a How might they do this by flipping a coin?

    b How about using a deck of playing cards?

SOLUTION

a Coin

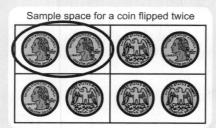

Sample space for a coin flipped twice

Create a sample space for a coin flipped twice. The probability of two heads is one out of four outcomes or 25%. The probability of any of the other 3 outcomes is 3 out of 4, or 75%. That is not exactly 78%, but close.

If anything but heads twice, then the 78% school gets it.

Two heads has 25% probability, not 22%. Are there better ways to use a coin? Yes. For instance, the probability of tossing 8 coins and obtaining any outcome other than 3 heads and 5 tails is extremely close to 78%. You're welcome to show this by counting in the sample space.

b Cards

Remove 2 cards (leaving 50)
Write "78% school" on 39 of the cards
Pick a card, any card

$$\frac{39}{50} = 78\%$$

The probability of picking a "78% school" card is exactly 78%.

 In this activity, solve various probability problems. With each question, you risk money each time. If you are correct, you win it. If not, you lose.

PRACTICE

1. A jar contains jelly beans, 5 of which are white, 14 blue, 18 yellow, and 7 red. What is the probability of grabbing a blue jelly bean?

   A. $\dfrac{5}{44}$

   B. $\dfrac{7}{44}$

   C. $\dfrac{7}{22}$

   D. $\dfrac{14}{22}$

2. Hanson randomly draws a card from a 52-card deck. Which of the following statements is true?

   I.   The probability of drawing a jack of spades is $\dfrac{1}{52}$.

   II. The probability of drawing a queen is $\dfrac{1}{13}$.

   III. The probability of drawing a diamond is $\dfrac{1}{4}$.

   A. I only
   B. II only
   C. I and II only
   D. I, II, and III

3. What is the probability that two six-sided dice numbered from 1 to 6 will sum to 4?

   A. $\dfrac{1}{6}$

   B. $\dfrac{1}{9}$

   C. $\dfrac{1}{12}$

   D. $\dfrac{1}{18}$

4. This tally below shows the number of times that Jim and Rob won games of checkers. What is the experimental probability that Rob beats Jim in future games?

   Jim: I I I I I I I I I
   Rob: I I I I I

5. What is the theoretical probability of getting one tail and one head when you flip a coin twice?

6. What is the theoretical probability of drawing an ace from a deck of cards? There are 52 total cards and 4 aces in a standard deck.

7. What is the theoretical probability of drawing a teal marble from a bag filled with 5 teal marbles and 7 pink marbles?

8. What is the theoretical probability of rolling a prime number with a single die?

9. What is the probability that when you roll two dice, they total 10?

10. Suppose you have two four-sided dice, numbered from 1 to 4.

    a What is the most likely sum of the dice?
    b What is the probability that the dice will total 7?

11. What is the probability that when you roll two six-sided dice, they total 5?

12. Last year in November it rained 18 days, snowed 2 days, and there was no precipitation on the other 10 days. Based on those observations, what is the experimental probability that it will rain on a random day in November of this year?

13. A group of boys is on a hike. You take a random sample of ten of them and find that, of those ten boys, six of them wear shorts. What is the experimental probability of a boy in the whole group wearing shorts?

14. You pour out half a bag of jelly beans, and 17 of the 25 are red. Then you return them to the bag. What is the experimental probability of randomly pulling out a red jelly bean from the bag?

15. Of the people you survey, 14 of the 56 say they want Rodriguez for president. What is the experimental probability of a person in the general population saying they want Rodriguez for president?

16. Two out of every 250 phone calls are "dropped." State the experimental probability of a phone call being dropped.

17. A bag contains two kinds of fruit, peaches and apples. The probability of picking a peach is 0.4, and there are 60 peaches. How many apples are in the bag?

Practice Problems continue . . .

18. A bag contains two kinds of fruit, oranges and pears. The probability of picking an orange is 0.3, and there are 24 oranges. How many pears are in the bag?

19. Consider rolling two three-sided dice.

    a Fill in the sample space for the two three-sided dice.

    b What is the probability of an even total, stated as a percent?

    c What is the probability of an odd total, stated as a percent?

    d What is the probability of the dice totaling 5, stated as a fraction?

    e What is the probability the total will be prime?

20. Create a sample space to answer the questions below. There are two five-sided dice. The numbers on each die go from one to five.

    a What is the probability that the dice sum to 4?

    b What is the probability that the dice sum to an even number?

    c What is the probability that the dice sum to an odd number?

    d What is the probability that the dice sum to a number 8 or larger?

21. The draft in a professional sports association wants to determine a random method for awarding the first pick to one of the bottom two teams. If they want the team with the worst record to have a two-thirds chance of getting the first draft pick, how would you use a die to determine which team gets the first draft?

Exercises 22–24: There are two six-sided dice. The numbers on each die go from one to six.

22. What is the probability that the sum and product of the dice are the same?

23. What is the probability that the sum is greater than the product of the dice?

24. What is the probability that the product is at least 5 greater than the sum of the dice?

25. **MP 2** Ten balls numbered from 0 to 9 are placed in a bingo wheel. A person rolls the wheel and draws a ball, places it back in the wheel, and then draws again.

    a How many possible ways can two balls that sum to 10 be drawn?

    b Based on part **a**, determine the probability that the sum is 10.

    c A person rolls the wheel and draws two balls without replacement. How many possible ways can the sum be 10?

    d Based on part **c**, determine the probability that the sum is 10.

    e Explain how the results of the scenarios in parts **a–b** differ from parts **c–d**.

26. Kim was given a fair six-sided die. She did an experiment by rolling the die exactly 30 times, resulting in each number appearing 5 times each, confirming the theoretical probabilities. She then states that for any $6n$ rolls, the number 2 will appear exactly n times. Is her statement correct? Explain.

27. What are some of the uses of finding probabilities through experiments?

28. What are some of the disadvantages of using experimental probabilities?

29. **MP 3** How might you use probability to your advantage in board games involving dice?

30. Explain how you might perform experiments and use probabilities to predict the weather on a given day.

Practice Problems continue . . .

31. **MP 4** At a party, one of the 18 guests will be given a special prize. To choose the winner, each guest has an envelope, and one envelope contains a card saying "You are the winner!" The guests open the envelopes one at a time. Seven guests have opened their envelopes with no winners before Christy's turn. What is the probability that out of the remaining envelopes, Christy's has the winning paper?

32. **MP 2** Lucky you. You have acquired two fake quarters, one that has heads on both sides and one that has tails on both sides. You put them in your pocket with a genuine quarter, draw out one coin at random, and place it on a table. The face you can see is heads. What is the probability the other face is also heads?

Expected Value

An **expected value** is the predicted value of a variable. To calculate the expected value, multiply the value of each outcome by the probability of it occurring, and sum the products.

> Expected value = Sum of (Each outcome · Its probability)

MODEL PROBLEMS

1. Calculate the expected value of a lottery ticket when there is a $10 million prize and a 1 in 40 million chance of winning.

SOLUTION

Calculate expected value

$$\text{Expected value} = \text{Sum of (Each outcome · Its probability)}$$

$$\text{Expected value} = \frac{1}{40,000,000} \cdot 10,000,000 + \frac{39,999,999}{40,000,000} \cdot 0$$

$$\text{Expected value} = \frac{1}{4} + 0 = \$0.25$$

There are two possible outcomes in this case: the prize or nothing. We sum the expected value of both outcomes.

This problem illustrates the fact that the expected value is not necessarily a possible outcome. The expected value is $0.25, but the only possible outcomes are winning $0 or $10,000,000. It is akin to saying that an average household with children has 1.86 children—that doesn't mean each household includes 0.86 of a child, just that it is the expected value of the number of children.

2. In a game, a child lands on a space. She can simply choose to receive 20 points or she can spin a spinner, with two possible outcomes. There is a 30% chance it lands on red, and the child earns 10 points. There is a 70% chance it lands on purple, which is worth 25 points. What choice will likely earn the child more points?

SOLUTION

Calculate expected value

$$\text{Expected value} = \text{Sum of (Each outcome · Its probability)}$$
$$\text{Expected value} = 0.3 \cdot 10 + 0.7 \cdot 25$$
$$\text{Expected value} = 20.5$$

The expected value of a spin is 20.5 points, so choosing to spin is the better option. You can again note that 20.5 is not a possible outcome; it is the expected value of possible outcomes.

Model Problems continue . . .

3. Ted is playing a game where how far his piece moves is determined by the number on a die he rolls. How far should he expect to move?

SOLUTION

Calculate expected value

Expected value = Sum of (Each outcome · Its probability)

$$\text{Expected value} = \frac{1}{6} \cdot 1 + \frac{1}{6} \cdot 2 + \frac{1}{6} \cdot 3 + \frac{1}{6} \cdot 4 + \frac{1}{6} \cdot 5 + \frac{1}{6} \cdot 6$$

Expected value = 3.5

Again, 3.5 is not a possible outcome, but it represents the average distance Ted's piece will move.

4. A football team earns one point for kicking the ball through the uprights or two points if it passes or runs the ball into the end zone after a touchdown. Assume that 99% of points after touchdowns (PAT) are "good"—the kicker succeeds. What percent of two-point conversions would a team have to make for it to consider doing a two-point conversion instead of a kick?

SOLUTION

Set expressions equal to one another

$$0.99 \cdot 1 = x \cdot 2$$

A team successfully kicks 99% of its points after touchdowns. That means the expected value for this strategy is the product of 0.99 and 1. The other outcome, missing the kick, contributes zero to the expected value.

Solve equation

$$x = \frac{0.99 \cdot 1}{2}$$

$$x = 0.495$$

$$x > 49.5\%$$

Solve the equation for x and divide. A team would have to make more than 49.5% of its two-point conversions in order for it to consider that the better strategy.

In this activity, you flip an aardvark. There are various outcomes. You are told the probability of an outcome, and how many points each outcome is worth. Using expected value, you can select your strategy, and see how when a correct strategy is selected and played multiple times, it will win.

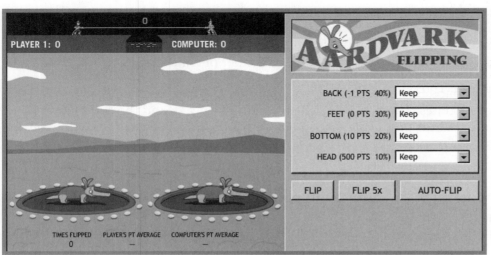

PRACTICE

1. A raffle ticket has a one in 700 chance of winning a $1000 gift card. What is the approximate expected value of the ticket?

   A. $0.82
   B. $0.21
   C. $1.43
   D. $1.64

2. After two years in the professional leagues, a baseball player has a 1% chance of playing in the major leagues, a 60% probability of playing in the minor leagues, and a 39% chance of leaving professional sports. If professional players earn $500,000 at this point in their careers and minor league players earn $20,000, what is the expected value of a player's earnings from professional baseball?

3. **MP 4** In American football, a team earns three points for making a field goal (kicking the ball through the uprights). A team earns seven points for a touchdown (assuming they always attempt and make the point after touchdown). For a particular high school team, 98% of the field goals from a distance of 9 yards are "good"—the kicker completes his task successfully. What percent of touchdowns from 9 yards would this team have to make for them to consider going for a touchdown instead of kicking a field goal?

4. **MP 3** SAT exams contain a large portion of multiple-choice questions. Each multiple-choice question has five choices. For every multiple-choice question answered correctly, the student is awarded 1 point, while a student is penalized one-fourth of a point for each incorrect answer. Explain using expected value why this method of assessment is fair.

5. **MP 3** A man on the street offers to play a game with you. He opens a brand-new deck of 52 playing cards, shuffles it, and says if you select a king, he will give you $100. However, if you do not select a king from the deck, you will have to pay him $10. Should you play this game? Explain using expected value.

6. Explain how expected values and probabilities are related.

7. A report states that approximately 5.3 people live in a single dwelling in India. If you randomly survey 1000 homes, how many people do you expect to find?

8. A study finds that each household in the United States owns an estimated 2.28 cars. If you randomly survey 5000 households, how many cars should you expect to find?

• Multi-Part PROBLEM Practice •

MP 3 A person accused of a crime has two options. One is that he can accept an offer to plead guilty and get a two-year sentence. The other option is that he can go to trial. In that case, his lawyer says there is a 70% chance he will be found guilty of a lesser crime and serve one year, and a 30% chance he will be found guilty of a more severe crime and serve six years.

a Which choice will result in the least expected amount of time served?

b At what percent probability of being found guilty of the more severe crime will the person be facing the same probable prison sentence with either choice he makes?

12.2 Permutations and Combinations

Tree Diagrams and the Fundamental Counting Principle

A **tree diagram**, shown to the right, shows all the possible outcomes of an event. It is a good way to count and keep track of the outcomes that result in a large sample space. We use a tree diagram to determine the number of outcomes that result from choosing one of two pairs of shoes and one of four sweaters.

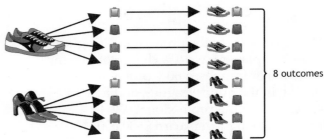

8 outcomes

Suppose that you have 2 pairs of shoes and 4 sweaters. How many ways can you match a pair of shoes with a sweater? First, count the number of outcomes. Start the tree with sneakers and high heels, your two shoe options. There are four options for the sweater.

There are 8 combinations, which equals 2 times 4. You might note there are 2 options for the first choice in the tree diagram above, choosing your shoes. Each of those options then branches into 4 options for the second choice, choosing your sweater.

Generally, with two or more choices, you can calculate the number of outcomes in the sample space by multiplying the number of options for the first choice by the number of options for the second choice by the number of options for the third choice, and so on.

This pattern is formalized by the **fundamental counting principle**. Let m_1 = the number of options for the first choice, m_2 = the number of options for the second choice, all the way up to m_k, the number of options for the kth choice. Then the total number of outcomes in the sample space will be equal to $m_1 \cdot m_2 \cdot \ldots \cdot m_k$.

> Number of outcomes = $m \cdot n$
> m = options for first choice
> n = options for second

MODEL PROBLEMS

1. The Select Ice Creamery sells 8 flavors of ice cream and 3 types of cones. How many single-scoop combinations can you buy?

SOLUTION

Apply the fundamental counting principle

Number of outcomes = $m \cdot n$
m = 8 (flavors)
n = 3 (types of cones)
Number of outcomes = $8 \cdot 3 = 24$

To apply the fundamental counting principle, consider the choices for the ice cream cones. There are two choices here: a flavor and a cone. There are 8 flavors and 3 types of cones. Substitute and multiply.

Model Problems continue . . .

2. Victory Shoes sells red, blue, green, and yellow sneakers. They come in low-top, high-top, and extra high-top. If you order a random pair of shoes, what is the probability you get your desired red or blue, low- or extra high-top sneaker?

SOLUTION

Number of types of sneakers	Number of outcomes = $m \cdot n$ $m = 4$ (colors) $n = 3$ (heights) Total number of outcomes = $4 \cdot 3 = 12$	Multiply the number of colors by the number of heights to calculate the numbers of styles of sneakers they sell.
Number of colors and styles	Number of outcomes = $m \cdot n$ $m = 2$ (red or blue) $n = 2$ (low or extra high) Number of desired outcomes = $2 \cdot 2 = 4$	You want a pair of red or blue sneakers, in either low-top or extra high-top. Again, apply the fundamental counting principle. There are 4 combinations you would like.
Calculate probability	$P(A) = \dfrac{\# \text{ of ways event occurs}}{\# \text{ of possible outcomes}}$ $P(\text{desired style}) = \dfrac{4}{12} = \dfrac{1}{3}$	Use the formula for calculating probability. Divide 4, the number of styles you like, by 12, the total number of shoe styles that Victory Shoes makes. The probability is $\dfrac{1}{3}$ that you get your desired pair of sneakers.

3. You are making an ice cream sundae. You have 5 flavors of ice cream, and 4 toppings like hot fudge and caramel. You can serve the sundae in a waffle cone or a dish. How many types of sundaes can you make?

SOLUTION

Fundamental counting principle	Number of outcomes = $m_1 \cdot m_2 \cdot \ldots \cdot m_k$ $m_1 = 5$ (flavors) $m_2 = 4$ (toppings) $m_3 = 2$ (cone or dish)	The fundamental counting principle can be extended to more than two choices. The number of outcomes is the product of the number of options for all of the choices. There are 5 ice cream flavors, 4 toppings, and 2 options for serving, either a dish or a cone.
Number of sundaes	Number of outcomes = $5 \cdot 4 \cdot 2 = 40$	To answer the question, apply the fundamental counting principle. Multiply 5 times 4 times 2 to get 40 outcomes.

Factorials

The factorial, denoted $n!$, is the product of all positive integers less than or equal to n. This notation is an efficient way to express products of a sequence of consecutive integers from 1 to n. Formally, $n! = n \cdot (n - 1) \cdot (n - 2) \cdot \ldots \cdot 2 \cdot 1$. For example, $3! = 3 \cdot 2 \cdot 1 = 6$.

> The factorial of 0 is defined as 1 so $0! = 1$.

MODEL PROBLEM

Compute 7!

SOLUTION

$7! = 7 \cdot 6 \cdot 5 \cdot 4 \cdot 3 \cdot 2 \cdot 1$
$7! = 5040$

Permutations

A **permutation** is an ordered arrangement of a set of objects. The order of the objects <u>matters</u> in a permutation. XYZ is a permutation of the last three letters of the alphabet using all three letters, and ZYX is another.

Permutations of $\{X, Y, Z\}$

$$X \longrightarrow \begin{matrix} Y \longrightarrow Z = XYZ \\ Z \longrightarrow Y = XZY \end{matrix}$$
$$Y \longrightarrow \begin{matrix} X \longrightarrow Z = YXZ \\ Z \longrightarrow X = YZX \end{matrix}$$
$$Z \longrightarrow \begin{matrix} X \longrightarrow Y = ZXY \\ Y \longrightarrow X = ZYX \end{matrix}$$

6 permutations

3 options 2 options 1 option

> Each time we make a choice with a permutation, there is one less option. For instance, with the first letter with our example to the left, we have 3 options, all three letters. If we choose X, then we have two options, Y and Z, and for the final letter, we have only one option. This leads to the conclusion that the number of permutations of n objects equals $n!$, the factorial of n.

Number of permutations of XYZ:

Count options for each choice	3 options for first choice 2 options for second choice 1 option for third choice	Calculate the number of permutations using the fundamental counting principle. There are three choices: the first letter in the permutation, the second letter, and the third letter. For the first letter, there are three options.
Fundamental counting principle	Number of outcomes $= 3 \cdot 2 \cdot 1 = 6$	Use the fundamental counting principle and multiply the number of options for each choice. There are six permutations of three letters.
Number of permutations of n objects	$n!$	In general, for n objects, there are n options for the first choice, $n - 1$ for the second choice, and so on. The product of these numbers is $n!$. This is the number of permutations of n objects. A permutation is an arrangement of the objects in a set where the order of the elements matters. When all the elements in a set are used in permutations, such as all three letters in $\{X, Y, Z\}$, the number of permutations is $n!$.

> The number of permutations of all the objects in a set of n objects is $n!$.

MODEL PROBLEMS

1. **MP 5** How many permutations are there of the ten digits 0 through 9? When doing calculations like this, a calculator comes in handy.

SOLUTION

| Number of permutations of n objects | $n! = 10! = 3,628,800$ | The number of permutations of n objects is $n!$. There are 10 digits, so n is 10. Using a calculator, calculate that 10! is 3,628,800. |

2. **MP 1** Suppose you have 2 quarters, 1 nickel, and 3 pennies. Assuming the coins of the same type are indistinguishable, how many permutations are there of all the coins?

SOLUTION

| Permutations with identical objects | Number of permutations $= \dfrac{n!}{n_1! \cdot n_2! \, ...}$

 n = total number
 n_1 = number of objects of 1st kind
 n_2 = number of objects of 2nd kind | We show the formula for finding the number of permutations of n objects where some of them are identical. There are n_1 identical objects of the first kind, n_2 identical objects of the second kind, and so on. |
| Number of permutations | $n = 6$ coins, $n_1 = 2$ quarters
 $n_2 = 1$ nickel, $n_3 = 3$ pennies

 $\dfrac{6 \cdot 5 \cdot 4 \cdot 3 \cdot 2 \cdot 1}{2 \cdot 1 \cdot 1 \cdot 3 \cdot 2 \cdot 1} = \dfrac{6 \cdot 5 \cdot 4}{2} = 60$ | There are 6 coins, so n is 6. The coins of each type are identical, so $n_1 = 2$, $n_2 = 1$, and $n_3 = 3$. Substitute the values into the formula and evaluate. |

3. Negotiators for Argentina, Bangladesh, Chad, and Denmark are seated at a circular table. Find the number of circular permutations of the negotiators. Use $\{A, B, C, D\}$ to represent the countries.

> Another kind of permutation is a circular permutation. In a **circular permutation**, the objects are arranged in a circle, and for the permutations to be different, an object must appear in a different order as you go around the circle. For example, *ABCD* and *DABC* are different permutations of *A*, *B*, *C*, and *D*, but they are equivalent circular permutations.

SOLUTION

A permutation of objects in a circle	ABCD ABDC ACBD ACDB ADBC ADCB	A circular permutation is a permutation of objects arranged in a circle. We show circular permutations of the set $\{A, B, C, D\}$.
Number of circular permutations of n objects	$(n - 1)!$	The number of circular permutations of a set of n objects is $(n - 1)!$.
Permutations of the negotiators	$(n - 1)! = (4 - 1)! = 3! = 6$	There are 4 negotiators so n is 4. Substitute 4 into the formula and calculate that there are 6 circular permutations.

Permutations of *n* Objects Taken *r* at a Time

The fundamental counting principle explains why the formula below is true. When choosing *r* objects from a set of *n* objects, there are *n* options for the first choice, $n - 1$ for the second choice, and so on until *r* choices have been made. The number of outcomes from the choices is the product $n(n - 1)(n - 2) \ldots (n - r + 1)$, which is the same as $n! \div (n - r)!$.

$$_nP_r = \frac{n!}{(n - r)!}$$

The number of permutations of *n* objects chosen *r* at a time is found by dividing *n*! by the product of $(n - r)!$.

MODEL PROBLEMS

1. How many permutations are there of 2 letters from the 26 letters of the alphabet? Each letter can only be used once.

SOLUTION

$_nP_r$ is the number of permutations of *n* objects *r* at a time	$_nP_r = \dfrac{n!}{(n - r)!}$	In this case, *n* is 26 and *r* is 2. To represent choosing 2 elements out of a set of 26, use the notation $_{26}P_2$. To calculate the number of permutations of *n* objects taken *r* at a time, divide *n*! by $(n - r)!$.
Permutation of 2 letters from 26 letters of alphabet	$_{26}P_2 = \dfrac{26!}{(26 - 2)!}$	Apply the formula to calculate the number of permutations of 2 letters chosen from the alphabet. *n* is 26 and *r* is 2.
Cancel common factorials	$_{26}P_2 = \dfrac{26 \cdot 25 \cdot \cancel{24!}}{\cancel{24!}}$	The expression simplifies to $26 \cdot 25$.
	$_{26}P_2 = 26 \cdot 25$	
Evaluate	$_{26}P_2 = 650$	There are 650 two-letter permutations of the 26 letters in the alphabet.

2. How many different ways are there to order 5 cards from a 52-card deck?

SOLUTION

Identify *n* and *r*	$_nP_r = \dfrac{n!}{(n - r)!}$ $n = 52$ $r = 5$	Find the number of different ways to order 5 cards from a 52-card deck. *n* is equal to 52 and *r* is equal to 5.
Substitute in *n* and *r*	$_{52}P_5 = \dfrac{52!}{(52 - 5)!}$	Substitute the values for *n* and *r* into the expression for the permutation.
Calculate	$_{52}P_5 = \dfrac{52!}{47!}$	Cancel 47! from the numerator and denominator. Multiply the remaining factors in the numerator to get the result.
	$_{52}P_5 = \dfrac{52 \cdot 51 \cdot 50 \cdot 49 \cdot 48 \cdot \cancel{47!}}{\cancel{47!}}$	
	$_{52}P_2 = 52 \cdot 51 \cdot 50 \cdot 49 \cdot 48$	
	$_{52}P_2 = 311{,}875{,}200$	

Model Problems continue . . .

3. 100 people enter a contest where there is a first, second, and third prize. How many different ways are there for the prizes to be awarded? Assume that a person is not allowed to win more than once.

SOLUTION

Identify n and r

$$_nP_r = \frac{n!}{(n-r)!}$$

$$n = 100$$

$$r = 3$$

n is equal to 100 and r is equal to 3.

Substitute in n and r

$$_{100}P_3 = \frac{100!}{(100-3)!}$$

Substitute the values for n and r into the permutation.

Calculate

$$_{100}P_3 = \frac{100!}{97!}$$

$$_{100}P_3 = \frac{100 \cdot 99 \cdot 98 \cdot \cancel{97!}}{\cancel{97!}}$$

$$_{100}P_3 = 100 \cdot 99 \cdot 98$$

$$_{100}P_3 = 970,200$$

Cancel 97! from the numerator and denominator. Multiply the remaining factors in the numerator to get the result.

4. In how many ways can a 30-member math and computer science club select a president, vice-president, secretary, treasurer, and club liaison? Assume that each position is held by a unique individual.

SOLUTION

Identify n and r

$$_nP_r = \frac{n!}{(n-r)!}$$

$$n = 30$$

$$r = 5$$

n is equal to 30 and r is equal to 5.

Substitute in n and r

$$_{30}P_5 = \frac{30!}{(30-5)!}$$

Substitute the values for n and r into the formula.

Calculate

$$_{30}P_5 = \frac{30!}{25!}$$

$$_{30}P_5 = \frac{30 \cdot 29 \cdot 28 \cdot 27 \cdot 26 \cdot \cancel{25!}}{\cancel{25!}}$$

$$_{30}P_5 = 30 \cdot 29 \cdot 28 \cdot 27 \cdot 26$$

$$_{30}P_5 = 17,100,720$$

Cancel 25! from the numerator and denominator. Multiply the remaining factors in the numerator to get the result.

Combinations

With permutations, the order matters. It is like spelling a word: RAT is different than TAR, even though both include the same letters. With a combination, order does not matter. A **combination** is a selection of the elements of a set where the order does not matter.

$$_nC_r = \frac{n!}{r!(n-r)!}$$

The number of combinations of n objects chosen r at a time is found by dividing $n!$ by the product of $(n-r)!$ and $r!$.

MODEL PROBLEMS

1. How many combinations of 2 cards can be formed from 4?

SOLUTION

Equation to calculate a combination

$$_nC_r = \frac{n!}{r!(n-r)!}$$

To calculate the number of combinations of n objects taken r at a time, divide $n!$ by the product of $r!$ and $(n-r)!$.

Substitute and evaluate

$$_4C_2 = \frac{4!}{2!(4-2)!}$$

$$_4C_2 = \frac{4 \cdot 3 \cdot 2!}{2! \cdot 2!} = 6$$

Apply the formula to the example. In this example, n is 4 and r is 2. Substitute and evaluate.

2. You have 3 extra tickets to a concert by your favorite band. You have 10 friends who would like to go. How many different groups can you choose?

> The question asks for the number of ways to choose 3 friends from a set of 10. The order in which you choose does not matter, so this problem deals with combinations.

SOLUTION

Formula for combinations

$$_nC_r = \frac{n!}{r!(n-r)!}$$
$$n = 10$$
$$r = 3$$

Start with the formula for the number of combinations of r objects chosen from a set of n objects.

Substitute and evaluate

$$_{10}C_3 = \frac{10!}{3!(10-3)!}$$

$$_{10}C_3 = \frac{10 \cdot 9 \cdot 8 \cdot 7!}{3! \, 7!}$$

$$_{10}C_3 = \frac{10 \cdot 9 \cdot 8}{6}$$

$$_{10}C_3 = 120$$

Substitute the number of friends, 10, and the number of available tickets, 3. Evaluate.

Permutation or Combination?

For each of the model problems in this section, the first step is to determine if the problem involves a permutation or a combination.

MODEL PROBLEMS

1. A set has 14 elements. How many subsets with 5 elements are there?

SOLUTION

Order does not matter: Combination

$$_nC_r = \frac{n!}{r!(n-r)!}$$

$n = 14$
$r = 5$

Start with the formula for the number of combinations of n objects chosen r at a time.

Substitute and evaluate

$$_{14}C_5 = \frac{14!}{5!(14-5)!}$$

$$_{14}C_5 = \frac{14 \cdot 13 \cdot 12 \cdot 11 \cdot 10 \cdot \cancel{9!}}{5! \, \cancel{9!}}$$

$$_{14}C_5 = \frac{14 \cdot 13 \cdot 12 \cdot 11 \cdot 10}{120}$$

$$_{14}C_5 = 2002$$

Calculate the number of ways to choose 5 elements from a set of 14. There are 2002 combinations.

2. A Little League baseball team has 15 players. How many different 9-player teams, without designated positions, can the coach create?

SOLUTION

Order does not matter: Combination

$$_nC_r = \frac{n!}{r!(n-r)!}$$

$n = 15$
$r = 9$

$$_{15}C_9 = \frac{15!}{9!(15-9)!}$$

$$_{15}C_9 = 5005$$

Start with the formula for combinations and enter 15 for n and 9 for r. The number of combinations is 5005. The coach chooses 9 players from a team of 15. This problem is a combination, since the order does not matter. It does not matter whether a player is chosen first or last, as long as the player is one of the nine players chosen.

3. During a game, the players come to bat in a particular order determined by the coach. This is called the *batting order*. How many different batting orders can a coach make for 9 players out of a team of 15?

SOLUTION

Order matters: Permutation

$$_nP_r = \frac{n!}{(n-r)!}$$

$n = 15$
$r = 9$

The order the players come to bat matters, so calculate the number of permutations of 9 players chosen from 15.

Substitute and evaluate

$$_{15}P_9 = \frac{15!}{(15-9)!}$$

$$_{15}P_9 = \frac{15!}{6!}$$

$$_{15}P_9 = 1,816,214,400$$

Apply the formula to calculate the number of batting orders. n is 15 and r is 9. There are over a billion batting orders possible.

The number of permutations of 15 objects taken 9 at a time is much larger than the number of combinations. This is true in general. Why? Consider a simpler case, the permutations and combination of the letters A and B, when both letters are used. There are two permutations, BA and AB, but only one combination $\{A, B\}$. Considering order means there are more selections.

Complex Counting Problems

The model problems in this section require that you combine ideas that have been presented for calculating permutations and combinations and also use the fundamental counting principle.

MODEL PROBLEMS

1. A 6-person team is chosen from 7 girls and 4 boys. It must have an equal number of each gender. How many ways can the team be created?

SOLUTION

Calculate girl combinations	$_nC_r = \dfrac{n!}{r!(n-r)!}$	The team must have 6 members and an equal number of boys and girls, so there are 3 girls and 3 boys on the team. First calculate the number of ways to choose the girls and the boys. Since the order does not matter, these selections are combinations.
Substitute and evaluate	$_7C_3 = \dfrac{7!}{3!(7-3)!} = 35$	There are 7 girls, and 3 of them will be on the team. Substitute in the values.
Calculate boy combinations	$_4C_3 = \dfrac{n!}{r!(n-r)!}$ $_4C_3 = \dfrac{4!}{3!(4-3)!} = 4$	Use the formula for combinations again. There are 4 boys, and again 3 of them on the team. Substitute and evaluate. There are 4 combinations for the boys.
Fundamental counting principle	# of outcomes = $m \cdot n$ # of outcomes = $35 \cdot 4 = 140$	Apply the fundamental counting principle. The number of ways to choose the team is the number of ways to choose the girls times the number of ways to choose the boys.

2. Drawing cards from a full deck, how many ways can you form a hand of 5 cards, 4 of which are the same suit, and the fifth an ace of another suit?

SOLUTION

Calculate combinations of four cards from a suit	$_nC_r = \dfrac{n!}{r!(n-r)!}$ $_{13}C_4 = \dfrac{13!}{4!(13-4)!} = 715$	A suit like spades is made up of 13 cards. We want 4 cards from the same suit, which is the number of combinations of 4 objects chosen from a set of 13. Use the formula for combinations, substitute in the values, and evaluate.
Fundamental counting principle	# of outcomes = $m \cdot n$ # of outcomes = $4 \cdot 715$ # of outcomes = 2860	There are four suits of cards. Apply the fundamental counting principle. Multiply 715 by 4 to get 2860, which is the number of ways you could get 4 cards of the same suit.
Fundamental counting principle again	# of outcomes = $m \cdot n$ # of outcomes = $3 \cdot 2860$ # of outcomes = 8580	There are three aces in other suits. Applying the counting principle, multiply the number of choices calculated above by 3 to get the number of ways to get 4 cards of one suit, and the fifth card an ace of another suit.

Model Problems continue . . .

3. A license plate of 6 symbols is made up of 2 different letters and 4 different digits, in any order. How many different license plates are possible?

SOLUTION

Position of letters: Combination

$$_6C_2 = \frac{6!}{2!(6 - 2)!}$$

$$_6C_2 = \frac{6 \cdot 5 \cdot \cancel{4!}}{2! \, \cancel{4!}} = 15$$

Calculate the number of positions where the two letters can go. We could choose any 2 of the 6 positions, which is a combination. There are 15 ways to make this choice.

Choice of letters: Permutation

$$_{26}P_2 = \frac{26!}{(26 - 2)!}$$

$$_{26}P_2 = \frac{26 \cdot 25 \cdot \cancel{24!}}{\cancel{24!}} = 650$$

The 2 letters must be different, so this is a permutation of 26 objects chosen 2 at a time. There are 650 such permutations.

Choice of digits: Permutation

$$_{10}P_4 = \frac{10!}{(10 - 4)!}$$

$$_{10}P_4 = \frac{10 \cdot 9 \cdot 8 \cdot 7 \cdot \cancel{6!}}{\cancel{6!}} = 5040$$

The 4 digits must be different, so this is a permutation of 10 objects chosen 4 at a time. There are 5040 such permutations.

Fundamental counting principle

$15 \cdot 650 \cdot 5040 = 49{,}140{,}000$ license plates

The number of license plates is the product of the number of positions for the letters, the letter possibilities, and the digit possibilities. There are almost 50 million license plates possible.

4. **MP 1, 8** If you toss a coin 10 times, what is the probability that you get a head exactly 3 times?

SOLUTION

Formula for combinations

$$_nC_r = \frac{n!}{r!(n - r)!}$$

$$_{10}C_3 = \frac{10!}{3!(10 - 3)!}$$

Getting heads 3 of 10 times is the same as choosing 3 of the 10 tosses to be heads. This is the number of combinations of 3 objects chosen from a set of 10. Use the formula for combinations, with n equal to 10 and r equal to 3.

Evaluate

$$_{10}C_3 = \frac{10 \cdot 9 \cdot 8 \cdot \cancel{7!}}{3! \, \cancel{7!}}$$

$$_{10}C_3 = \frac{720}{6}$$

$$_{10}C_3 = 120$$

Cancel out the 7! and do the remaining calculations. There are 120 ways for heads to appear 3 times in 10 coin tosses.

Formula for probability

$$P(A) = \frac{\text{\# of outcomes of event}}{\text{\# of possible outcomes}}$$

$$P(3 \text{ heads}) = \frac{120}{\text{\# of possible outcomes}}$$

To find the probability to get heads 3 times when tossing a coin 10 times, divide the number of ways to get heads 3 times by the number of outcomes in the sample space. We calculate the number of ways to get 3 heads as 120.

Total outcomes

\# of outcomes $= 2 \cdot 2 \cdot 2 \dots$

\# of outcomes $= 2^{10}$

\# of outcomes $= 1024$

To determine the number of outcomes in the sample space, use the fundamental counting principle. There are 10 tosses, and each toss has 2 possible results (heads or tails).

Calculate probability

$$P(3 \text{ heads}) = \frac{120}{1024}$$

$$P(3 \text{ heads}) = \frac{15}{128}$$

Substitute in the number of ways to get heads 3 times and the number of possible outcomes. The probability of getting heads three times is 15 in 128.

1. A local restaurant offers a lunch buffet with 5 meats, 8 vegetables, 3 breads, and 12 desserts. If a complete meal consists of one of each, how many possible complete meals does the restaurant offer?

   A. 28 meals
   B. 120 meals
   C. 1,010 meals
   D. 1,440 meals

2. How many different 7-card hands are possible in a 52-card deck?

   A. $\dfrac{52!}{7!}$

   B. $\dfrac{52!}{45!}$

   C. $\dfrac{52!}{7!45!}$

   D. None of the above

3. During the school year, there are 10 scheduled football games. You would like to attend at least 6 of the games. How many different combinations of games can you attend?

   A. 210
   B. 386
   C. 638
   D. 5,040

4. Jan's book club is choosing one book to read in each of the months December, January, and February. If there are 14 books to choose from, how many permutations are there?

5. How many kinds of jelly sandwiches can you make? You use one type of bread and one type of jelly in a sandwich.

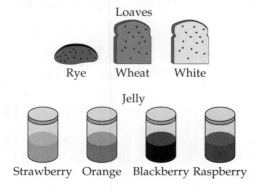

Loaves

Rye   Wheat   White

Jelly

Strawberry   Orange   Blackberry   Raspberry

6. You will give your friend one of three colors of T-shirts and one of five colors of sweatshirts. How many choices do you have?

7. A company only makes three types of flashlights, each of which must use one of seven types of light bulbs. How many types of products does the company sell?

8. You choose from one of five types of pizza and from one of eight types of drinks for dinner. How many choices do you have?

9. Pizzas can be made in three sizes, with four types of cheese, and with seven kinds of topping. Assume all pizzas have one type of cheese and one topping. How many kinds of pizzas are there?

10. A candy factory makes five types of candy, each in four colors, and each candy can be made with or without nuts. How many types of candies does the factory make?

11. A rock star owns five tops, three bottoms, six kinds of shoes, and four colors of socks. She wears one of each article of clothing when performing. How many outfits can she choose from? (And yes, she wears a matching pair of shoes and a matching pair of socks, even though she is a rock star.)

12. A factory makes four types of cars, each of which comes in seven colors. Each car also has the option to come with or without a satellite radio. How many types of cars can the factory make?

13. A safe has a lock with the numbers 1 through 36 arranged in a circle. It takes 3 numbers to open it, and any number must be at least 2 away from the prior number. For example, if the first number is 20, the second number can't be 19, 20, or 21. How many possible combinations are there?

Practice Problems continue . . .

14. DNA is formed from four base units, represented by the letters A, T, C, and G. DNA encodes information using these letters. Assume a short strand of DNA has 10 base units. How many possible sequences are there in the strand? (To give you a sense of how much information can be encoded: A human chromosome can be over 200 million base pairs long.)

15. How many ways can you arrange the first half of the letters in the alphabet? State your answer using factorial notation.

16. How many ways can you arrange the letters in the word COMPUTER? State your answer using factorial notation.

17. How many ways can you arrange two of the first three letters of the alphabet?

18. How many ways can you arrange three of the first six letters of the alphabet?

19. A company makes seven colors of dresses. How many ways can you dress three mannequins in a window with three of the dresses, using as many colors as possible.

20. How many ways can you arrange three-letter sets from the letters A, B, C, and D, with no repeated letter?

21. In how many distinguishable ways can the letters in BANANA be written?

22. In how many distinguishable ways can the letters in MISSISSIPPI be written?

23. A cookie jar contains 7 chocolate chip cookies, 5 oatmeal cookies, and 3 others that are different from each other. How many ways can you stack the 15 cookies? Assume two cookies of the same type are indistinguishable.

24. A bracelet has four charms, each with a different gemstone. How many ways can the charms be arranged on the bracelet?

25. Six friends are performing a Maypole dance, forming a circle. How many ways can the friends arrange the circle?

26. Five countries have each sent a representative to peace talks. The talks are being held at a circular table so no country will sit at the table's head. As the person organizing the talks, you are very concerned about which representative is seated next to another representative. How many choices will you have?

27. A coach has a 12-person basketball team that is not getting along. At meals, he puts them at one circular table, hoping they "bond." He wants them to sit together in every possible fashion. How many ways can he seat them? Hint: They better have a very, very long season.

28. You need to choose three of your five friends for a trip. How many combinations can you choose from?

29. You have to choose three people from a group of eight. How many choices will you have?

30. You are making lunch by choosing any three items from a group of seven. How many different lunches can you make?

31. You get to choose two rabbits from nine to bring home as pets. How many choices do you have?

32. How many two-letter groups can you form from the word MOUSE if you don't care about the order?

33. If you do not care about order, how many ways can you arrange any three of the prime numbers from 6 to 20?

34. How many ways can you pick out half the letters from the word COMPUTER?

35. How many ways can you choose three-letter sets from the word CHEMISTRY?

36. You are making omelets by mixing in any four out of six types of ingredients. How many types of omelets can you make?

37. A group of 30 people are invited into a courtroom for jury selection in a trial. How many choices are possible on the jury panel if only twelve people are selected?

Practice Problems continue . . .

38. In the game of Hearts, a full 52-card deck is dealt evenly to four players. Then each player passes 3 of their cards to a specified player. How many ways can you choose the cards to pass along?

39. You are painting your living room and putting up new curtains. You have narrowed it down to 6 different colors of paint and 4 different kinds of curtains. How many combinations of paint colors and curtains do you have to choose from?

40. Denise is picking out an outfit by randomly selecting one item of clothing from each drawer in her dresser. The first drawer has a pair of red socks and a pair of white socks. The second drawer has a blue shirt, a green shirt, and a red shirt. The third drawer has jeans and a skirt.

  a Create a tree diagram of her choices.
  b What is the probability that Denise will get both a red shirt and red socks?
  c Denise is picking an outfit again, in the same way as in parts **a**–**b**. What is the probability that Denise will not get the red shirt?

41. Jim randomly selects an outfit for an interview. He has a checked shirt, a striped shirt, and a solid shirt. He also has four ties: striped, solid, dotted, and a novelty light-up tie. His two jackets are gray and black. What is the probability that he picks out a combination where the shirt and tie do not have the same pattern?

42. On Friday night, you and your friends are going to a mall where you will eat at the food court and then go to a movie. To get there you can either take the bus, drive, or ride your bike. There are 8 different movies you could see, and 5 different places to get food at the food court. How many different combinations of transportation, movies, and food are available to you for this Friday night?

43. Every day Sandra chooses whether to wear green or brown flip-flops. How many possible ways could she choose her shoes over the course of 5 days?

44. **MP 3** Michael thought for a moment about the following problem, "A teacher of a 30-student classroom asks her students to introduce themselves to each other by shaking each other's hand. If each student shakes hands with another student exactly once, how many handshakes are taking place?" Michael says that since there are 30 students, each student must shake hands with 29 other students. Hence, there must be exactly 30 times 29 handshakes. Did Michael count correctly? If yes, explain. Otherwise, find the number of handshakes.

45. Choose four different random letters in the alphabet. Then list all the distinct arrangements containing the four letters. How many of them are actual words? Refer to a dictionary if necessary.

46. **MP 1, 2** How many even 3-digit numbers can be written using the digits 1, 2, 4, 6, and 8, if any digit can only appear once?

47. **MP 7** Six beads are arranged on a circular ring to make a bracelet. Two of the beads are the same color. How many different permutations of colors are there?

48. There are six airmail planes that take off from an airport each morning. Only one plane takes off at a time. Two of the planes fly to Dallas, two fly to Chicago, and two fly to New York. The planes going to the same city must depart one after another. How many different permutations are there for flight departures?

49. Each face of a cube is painted with one of two colors. How many different ways are there to paint the cube with one or both colors? Assume two cubes are painted the same if one can be arranged to match the other one exactly.

50. There are n soccer teams playing in a tournament. A team is eliminated when it loses two games. What is the maximum number of games, in terms of n, that must be played to determine the winning team? Assume there are no ties.

Practice Problems continue . . .

51. At Ruthie's Roadside Chili Parlor, the
regulars hang their coffee mugs on a rack.
Each peg on the rack has a customer's name
on it. A new dishwasher decides to take
all the mugs down and wash them, but
then returns them to the pegs at random.

a If there are 7 regulars at Ruthie's, what is
the probability that the dishwasher put
exactly 6 of the mugs back on the right
pegs?

b What is the probability that exactly 5 of
the mugs are on the correct pegs?

LESSON 12.3

12.3 Independent Events and the Multiplication Rule

Independent events are events in which the outcome of one has no effect on
the probability of another occurring. The fact that one occurs does *not* affect the
probability of the other occurring.

In probability, one way to discuss multiple events is with the word *and*. For
example, you might want to determine the probability of drawing a red king
from a deck of cards. This is the probability that two events both occur: the card
is red and the card is a king.

The probability of two events both occurring is stated
with an "and." The expression $P(A \text{ and } B)$ is the
probability of both events A and B occurring.

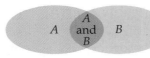

The set of outcomes for the event "A and B" is the intersection of the set of
outcomes for event A and the set of outcomes for event B. This set is the area in
the diagram where A and B overlap. The intersection of A and B is written $A \cap B$,
so $P(A \cap B)$ is the probability that both A and B occur.

The probability that two independent events both occur can be calculated using
the **multiplication rule**: The probability that both events occur equals the product
of the probabilities of the two events. In fact, this is the definition of independent
events: the events A and B are independent if and only if $P(A \text{ and } B) = P(A) \cdot P(B)$.

> Multiplication rule:
> With two independent events A and B, $P(A \text{ and } B) = P(A) \cdot P(B)$.

One can recognize if two events are independent using this rule. For instance,
let us say the probability of "rain" is 0.3 and "carrying an umbrella" is 0.1. If the
probability of both is 0.05, the events are not independent. If they were, the product
would be $0.3 \cdot 0.1 = 0.03$.

On the other hand, let's assume the probability of taking a green marble from the
bag is 0.4 and the probability of drawing a diamond card is 0.25. If the probability
of doing both is 0.1, the events are independent, since $0.4 \cdot 0.25 = 0.1$. These two
events occurring together would be considered an **independently combined
probability model**.

> Two consecutive
> coin tosses are a
> classic example
> of independent
> events since the
> outcome of one
> does not change
> the probability of
> the next toss. The
> probability of heads
> is 0.5 for each
> toss.

> If this
> relationship
> holds, two
> events are
> independent. If
> it does not, they
> are dependent.

In this activity, solve various probability problems that get harder and harder! With each question, you risk money each time. If you are correct, you win it. If not, you lose.

MODEL PROBLEMS

1. What is the probability of a coin coming up heads twice?

SOLUTION

| Multiplication rule | $P(A \text{ and } B) = P(A) \cdot P(B)$
$A =$ heads first toss
$B =$ heads second toss | Getting heads on the first toss and getting heads on the second toss are independent events. This means use the multiplication rule to calculate the probability of getting heads twice. A represents getting heads on the first toss and B getting heads on the second toss. Calculate the probability of the event "A and B," which means the coin comes up heads both times. |
| Apply the rule | $P(\text{heads}) = \dfrac{1}{2}$
$P(A \text{ and } B) = \dfrac{1}{2} \cdot \dfrac{1}{2}$
$P(A \text{ and } B) = \dfrac{1}{4}$ | The probability of getting heads on either of the tosses is $\dfrac{1}{2}$. Multiply. The probability of heads coming up both times is $\dfrac{1}{4}$. |

2. A bag contains 11 marbles where 3 are red, 2 green, and 6 blue. You choose a marble from the bag, replace it, then draw again. What is the probability of drawing a red marble followed by a green one?

SOLUTION

| Multiplication rule | $P(A \text{ and } B) = P(A) \cdot P(B)$
$A =$ red first
$B =$ green second | A chosen marble is replaced in the bag before the second marble is drawn. This means the events are independent and we can use the multiplication rule to calculate the probability that both events occur. |

Model Problems continue . . .

600 Chapter 12: Probability

Substitute and evaluate

$$P(A) = \frac{3}{11}, P(B) = \frac{2}{11}$$

$$P(A \text{ and } B) = \frac{3}{11} \cdot \frac{2}{11}$$

$$P(A \text{ and } B) = \frac{6}{121}$$

The probability of red then green is $\frac{6}{121}$.

3. There is a 30% chance Julie will work on Saturday and a 70% chance of rain. There is a 50% chance her favorite hockey team will win that evening. If the events are independent, what is the probability that on Saturday Julie works in the rain and her hockey team wins?

> The multiplication rule can apply to 3, 4, or however many independent events there are. Their probabilities can be multiplied as long as they are independent.

SOLUTION

Multiplication rule

$P(A \text{ and } B \text{ and } C)$
A = Julie works
B = It rains
C = Team wins

A represents the event that Julie works, B the event that it rains, and C the event that her hockey team wins. Calculate the probability that all three occur. Since the events are independent, use the multiplication rule.

Substitute and evaluate

$P(A) = 30\% = 0.3$
$P(B) = 70\% = 0.7$
$P(C) = 50\% = 0.5$
$P(A \text{ and } B \text{ and } C) = 0.3 \cdot 0.7 \cdot 0.5$
$P(A \text{ and } B \text{ and } C) = 0.105$
$P(A \text{ and } B \text{ and } C) = 10.5\%$

Write the probabilities and multiply. The probability of Julie working in the rain and her hockey team winning is 10.5%.

4. What is the probability that you draw two queens in a row from a deck of cards? You do not replace cards that you draw.

SOLUTION

Probability of dependent events

$P(A \text{ then } B) = P(A) \cdot P(B \text{ after } A)$

We can use the multiplication rule in the problem even though the two events were not initially independent. Once we know the first card is a queen, we can calculate the probability of choosing a second queen from the remaining 51 cards. The two events are dependent since you do not replace the cards. The probability of one event affects the probability of the second. The probability of the events A and B occurring sequentially equals the probability of A times the probability of B occurring after A.

Probabilities

$$P(\text{first card is queen}) = \frac{4}{52}$$

$$P(\text{queen after queen}) = \frac{3}{51}$$

For the first card you draw, there are 4 queens and 52 cards. The probability of a queen is $\frac{4}{52}$.

Multiply

$$P(\text{two queens}) = \frac{4}{52} \cdot \frac{3}{51} = \frac{1}{221}$$

Multiply the individual probabilities to calculate the probability of drawing two queens in a row without replacement. The probability is $\frac{1}{221}$.

Compound Events

Let's say that you want to calculate the probability that if you draw 5 cards one after the other, at least one of them will be both a club and a numbered club, such as the three of clubs. We assume each time you draw a card, you return it to the deck.

In other words, the probability that if you draw 5 cards with replacement, you will get the two of clubs, the three of clubs, the four of clubs, or any other card that is both a numbered card and a club. This is a **compound event** (club and numbered card).

Try it! One way to answer this question is simply a simulation using real cards and hands of 5 cards. You can take a deck of cards, draw 5 cards repeatedly, and see how often at least one numbered club appears.

MODEL PROBLEMS

 1. **MP 2, 4** A breed of dog can be white, black, or chocolate-colored. 25% of the breed will be chocolate-colored, and that is the color we want. What is the probability that if we visit a breeder who has a litter of 6 puppies, we will find a puppy that is chocolate-colored that we will take home and love?

SOLUTION

Use simulation

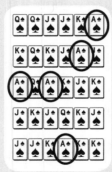

Use cards as a simulation system. We use 4 cards (the jack, queen, king, and ace of spades), with the ace representing the 25% probability of a chocolate-colored puppy. Draw the cards with replacement—once a card is drawn, it is replaced back to the four cards. This means for each draw of the cards, there is always a 25% possibility of the ace, which represents a 25% probability of chocolate-colored. Six draws simulate the six-puppy litter. Perform five simulations to get a reasonable amount of data. Our results are on the left.

Calculate probability

$$P(\text{chocolate puppy in the litter}) = \frac{4}{5} = 0.8$$

Four of the five times, there were one or more chocolate-colored puppies. Again, this is a small experimental sample space, so it should not be used to draw any conclusion.

Model Problems continue . . .

2. What is the probability of drawing at least one card that is both a club and numbered card, if you draw 5 cards?

SOLUTION

Use a simulation	Draw sets of cards four times	If you draw 5 cards, at least one will be both a club, and a card with a number. We assume each time you draw a card, you return it to the deck.	Is the theoretical probability of this occurring equal to 0.5? No! This is an experimental simulation. If we did several hundred draws, the empirical result would become close to the theoretical probability.
Calculate probability	$P(\text{club and numbered card}) = \dfrac{2}{4} = 0.5$	Repeat this three more times. This very simple simulation shows that of the four times, twice there was at least one card that was both a club and a numbered card. The experiment showed an experimental probability of 0.5 that if you draw 5 cards at a time with replacement, you will get at least one numbered club card.	

3. The events A, B, C, D, and E are all independent. The probability of event A is a, the probability of B occurring is b, the probability of C occurring is c, and so on. The probability of all these events occurring is

A. $a + b + c + d + e$

B. $1 - (a + b + c + d + e)$

C. The product of a, b, c, d, and e.

D. $\dfrac{1}{a \cdot b \cdot c \cdot d \cdot e}$

SOLUTION

The answer is C. Since the probability of each event is independent, their probabilities can be multiplied.

PRACTICE

1. Patrick rolls a die and flips a coin. What is the probability he will roll a 6 and get heads?

A. $\dfrac{1}{12}$

B. $\dfrac{1}{6}$

C. $\dfrac{1}{2}$

D. $\dfrac{2}{3}$

2. A jar contains a ratio of 2 green to 3 blue to 5 white marbles. What is the probability of selecting a green marble first, a blue marble second, and a white marble last?

A. $\dfrac{1}{24}$

B. $\dfrac{2}{57}$

C. $\dfrac{3}{100}$

D. Not enough information

Practice Problems continue . . .

3. What is the probability of rolling a die, getting an even number, then rolling again and getting a six?

4. If the probability that it is a windy day is 65% and the probability that Jim took a shower today is $\frac{1}{4}$, what is the probability that it is both windy and Jim took a shower? The events are independent.

Exercises 5–8: Find the probabilities. The die is a typical die with six sides.

5. What is the probability of rolling a die and getting the number 6 three times in a row?

6. What is the probability of rolling a die and getting the number 2 four times in a row?

7. What is the probability of getting a black card if you draw one card from a deck?

8. You simultaneously flip a coin and roll a six-sided die. What is the probability that the coin turns up heads and you roll a prime number? Remember that 1 is not prime.

9. There are 5 green marbles, 3 blue marbles, and 2 red marbles in a bag. If you pick 1 marble and then pick a second without replacing the first, what is the probability you will pick 2 blue marbles?

10. A batter is taking batting practice. The probability she hits a ball is 0.4, that she swings and misses is 0.3, that she does not swing is 0.25, and that she is hit by the ball is 0.05. Each swing is an independent event.

  a What is the probability that she hits the ball two times in a row?

  b What is the probability that she swings and misses three times in a row?

  c What is the probability she hits the ball, and then swings and misses two times in a row?

  d What is the probability that she does not swing twice in a row, and then gets hit by a ball?

11. The probability that someone wants to vote for Nguyen is $\frac{1}{2}$, for Smith is $\frac{1}{3}$, and for Norton is $\frac{1}{6}$. A computer randomly dials phone numbers to ask voters whom they prefer.

  a What is the probability of hearing Nguyen followed by Smith?

  b What is the probability of hearing Smith three times in a row?

  c What is the probability of hearing Norton, Norton, and then Smith?

  d What is the probability of hearing Smith, Smith, and then Nguyen?

12. You are playing a game with a die where you only move if the die comes up as an even number. How many times must you roll the die so that the probability of rolling even numbers every time is less than 0.1?

13. You are playing a game with a die where you get a bonus every time you roll a 5 or a 6. How many times must you roll the die so that the probability of getting a bonus every time is less than 0.05?

14. There are 25 jelly beans; 16 blue, 5 green, and 4 red. You take jelly beans from a bag and give them to a friend who eats them.

  a What is the probability of first drawing a green bean then a red?

  b What is the probability of first drawing a green bean followed by a blue?

  c What is the probability of first drawing a red bean then a green?

  d What is the probability of first drawing a blue bean followed by a green?

  e What is the probability of the first two jelly beans being green?

  f What is the probability of the first two jelly beans being red?

15. Estimate the probability of obtaining an odd prime from the roll of a single die by rolling the die 30 times. Remember that 1 is not a prime number. How close is your experimental probability compared to the theoretical probability? Is your experimental probability a good indicator of future outcomes? Explain.

Practice Problems continue . . .

Practice Problems continued . . .

16. The probability of an arrow hitting a region on the target below is proportional to the area of that region of the target. All triangles in the image are equilateral. Each shot is independent and all shots hit the target.

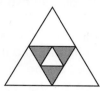

   a What is the probability that three consecutive shots fired will hit the shaded region? State your answer in decimal form.

   b What is the probability that three consecutive shots fired will hit the white region? State your answer in decimal form.

17. Suppose you draw four cards in succession from a deck, putting each card back after you draw it. Make a prediction of the probability of drawing a diamond as one of the four cards. Repeat this experiment 20 times and record the number of times you draw a diamond as one of the 4 drawn cards. Are you surprised by your experimental probability?

18. Sketch a Venn diagram that represents the probability of events A, B, and C.

19. Suppose that events A, B, and C are independent. Then, by extension of the multiplication rule, $P(A \cap B \cap C) = P(A \cap B) \cdot P(C)$. Since $0 \le P(C) \le 1$, what can we conclude about the relationship between $P(A \cap B \cap C)$ and $P(A \cap B)$? How do you know?

20. Give an example of 3 events, A, B, and C, in which A and B are dependent and B and C are independent.

21. MP 2, 5 Stu has five pairs of matching socks in his drawer, each pair a different color. He picks two socks at random from the drawer. What is the probability he picked a matching pair?

22. MP 2, 5 Given an eight-sided die numbered from 3 to 10, find the probability that a prime smaller than 6 will appear at least once in five rolls.

LESSON 12.4

12.4 Addition and Subtraction Rules

The Addition Rule

In probability, the word "or" means at least one of a set of events occurs. Probabilities that use the word "or" are written $P(A \text{ or } B)$. It is the probability of A or B occurring.

> An example is the probability that a card you draw from a deck is a queen or a club.

The probability that at least one of two events occurs is stated with an "or."

A or B

A B

The set of outcomes for the event "A or B" is the union of the set of outcomes for event A and the set of outcomes for event B. This set is represented by the total area of the diagram, consisting of the area occupied by A alone, the area occupied by B alone, and the overlap area occupied by both A and B. The union of A and B is written $A \cup B$, so $P(A \cup B)$ is the probability that A or B occurs.

The **addition rule** is used to calculate the probability $P(A \text{ or } B)$, which is the probability of either A or B, or both, occurring. The probability of A or B equals the probability of A plus the probability of B, minus the probability that A and B both occur.

> Addition rule:
> $$P(A \text{ or } B) = P(A) + P(B) - P(A \text{ and } B)$$

> You can relate this to the Venn diagam. If you add two shapes that overlap, you will notice the overlapping section was added twice. As a result, the intersection (represented by the "and" probability) needs to be subtracted.

MODEL PROBLEMS

1. What is the probability that you roll a 6 on at least one of two dice?

> The outcome of each die is independent, and each number is equally likely to appear. The addition rule enables us to compute the probability that a certain outcome appears on the dice.

SOLUTION

Addition rule

$P(A \text{ or } B) = P(A) + P(B) - P(A \text{ and } B)$
$A = 6$ on red die
$B = 6$ on blue die

For ease in referring to the dice, we use a red die and a blue die. Calculate the probability that the number 6 appears when we roll two dice. A represents getting 6 on the red die and B represents getting 6 on the blue die. Calculate the probability of "A or B". Use the addition rule to do the calculation.

Probability of a 6 on a die

$$P(6) = \frac{1}{6}$$

The probability that you roll a 6 on the red die is $\frac{1}{6}$ because it is one of 6 possible outcomes of rolling a die.

Use multiplication rule

$$P(A \text{ and } B) = \frac{1}{6} \cdot \frac{1}{6} = \frac{1}{36}$$

Use the multiplication rule to find the probability that both dice come up 6. We use this rule because the outcomes are independent. Multiply the two probabilities together and find that the probability of red and blue both being 6 is $\frac{1}{36}$.

Substitute computed values into equation and evaluate

$$P(A \text{ or } B) = P(A) + P(B) - P(A \text{ and } B)$$
$$P(A \text{ or } B) = \frac{1}{6} + \frac{1}{6} - \frac{1}{36}$$
$$P(A \text{ or } B) = \frac{6}{36} + \frac{6}{36} - \frac{1}{36} = \frac{11}{36}$$

Substitute the probabilities into the formula for the addition rule. The probability of one die or the other (or both) equaling 6 is $\frac{11}{36}$. Dice are a convenient item to use as a model since their probabilities are well understood. But we could model other situations—such as the possibility that two unrelated items fail in the same car—using the same approach.

Model Problems continue . . .

2. Of 100 students surveyed, 95 like chocolates or raisins, 35 like both chocolate and raisins, and 40 like raisins. How many students like chocolate?

> If you know the probability $P(A \text{ or } B)$ you can use the addition rule to find other probabilities. A corporation might be modeling student food preferences using this survey.

SOLUTION

State probabilities	C = likes chocolate R = likes raisins $P(C \text{ or } R) = \dfrac{95}{100} = 0.95$ $P(C \text{ and } R) = \dfrac{35}{100} = 0.35$ $P(R) = \dfrac{40}{100} = 0.4$	Calculate the probability that a student likes certain foods by dividing the number of students who like those foods by the total number of students.
Addition rule	$P(C \text{ or } R) = P(C) + P(R) - P(C \text{ and } R)$	State the addition rule, substituting in C and R.
Substitute probabilities	$0.95 = P(C) + 0.4 - 0.35$	Substitute the probabilities.
Solve for $P(C)$	$P(C) = 0.9$	Solve for the probability that a student likes chocolate.
Find number of students who like chocolate	$P(C) = \dfrac{\text{chocolate likers}}{\text{total students}}$ $0.9 = \dfrac{\text{chocolate likers}}{100}$ chocolate likers = 90	Use the definition of probability, substituting in chocolate likers and total students. Using this survey, the corporation would conclude there are a lot of chocolate fans out there because the probability that a student likes chocolate is 0.9.

Mutually Exclusive Events and the Addition Rule

If two events are **mutually exclusive**, it is impossible for both events to occur. For instance, if you draw a card from a standard deck, it is impossible for the card to be both a spade and a heart. The events "draw a heart" and "draw a spade" are mutually exclusive.

If A and B are mutually exclusive events, the probability of the event "A and B" is 0. For instance, the events that a die comes up 3 and that it comes up 5 are mutually exclusive. A die cannot come up both 3 and 5. The probability of events that are mutually exclusive both occurring is 0. If events are mutually exclusive, the addition rule can be simplified, since $P(A \cap B) = 0$. We state the addition rule for mutually exclusive outcomes below.

> Mutually exclusive:
> $P(A \text{ and } B) = 0$

What is the probability of a 3 or a 5 on a single die?

SOLUTION

> When the events A and B are mutually exclusive, the addition rule simplifies to adding the probabilities of the events.

Addition rule	$P(A \text{ or } B) = P(A) + P(B) - P(A \text{ and } B)$ $P(A \text{ and } B) = 0$ $P(A \text{ or } B) = P(A) + P(B) - 0$ $P(A \text{ or } B) = P(A) + P(B)$ $A = \text{roll a } 3$ $B = \text{roll a } 5$	Use the fact that the events of rolling a 3 and rolling a 5 are mutually exclusive to calculate the probability of rolling a 3 or a 5. We state the addition rule for mutually exclusive events A and B. The probability of the event "A and B" is 0, so drop the last term in the addition rule. The probability that A or B occurs is just the sum of their probabilities.
Substitute and evaluate	$P(A \text{ or } B) = \dfrac{1}{6} + \dfrac{1}{6}$ $P(A \text{ or } B) = \dfrac{1}{3}$	Since the events of rolling a 3 and a 5 are mutually exclusive, the probability that a 3 or a 5 is rolled equals the probability that a 3 is rolled plus the probability that a 5 is rolled.

The Subtraction Rule

Not is another word used in probability. If you are considering the roll of the die, you might ask: What is the probability the number will *not* be 6? The probability $P(\text{not } A)$ is the probability that the event A does not occur. "Not A" is the **complement** of A: A complement consists of all outcomes that are *not* the event. The probability of the complement of A occuring is $P(\text{not } A)$.

The **subtraction rule** says the probability of an event *not* occurring is 1 minus the probability that it does occur. The subtraction rule follows from the fact that the probabilities of all possible outcomes must sum to 1. For instance, the probability of heads on a coin toss is 0.5, the probability of tails (the only other possible outcome) is 0.5, and $0.5 + 0.5 = 1$.

> Subtraction rule:
> $P(\text{not } A) = 1 - P(A)$

MODEL PROBLEMS

1. The probability that Charlie catches a fish tomorrow is 0.3. The probability that Charlie doesn't catch a fish is

  A. Unknowable from this information.
  B. 0.3
  C. The reciprocal of 0.3.
  D. 0.7

SOLUTION

The answer is D. It is 0.7 from using the subtraction rule: $1 - 0.3 = 0.7$

Model Problems continue . . .

2. The probability the toast lands butter side down is 0.85. What is the probability it lands butter side up?

SOLUTION

Probabilities of all outcomes sum to 1

$$P(up) + P(down) = 1$$
$$P(down) = 0.85$$
$$P(up) + 0.85 = 1$$
$$P(up) = 1 - 0.85 = 0.15$$

The sum of the probabilities of all the outcomes of an event is 1. Assume the toast must land with one of the two sides up. The probability of "butter side up" and the probability of "butter side down" sum to 1. The probability of toast landing butter down is 0.85. Substitute and solve the equation for the probability of the butter side landing up. The probability is 0.15.

3. What is the probability a U.S. college student will not be drafted by the NBA if the probability of being drafted is 0.000004?

SOLUTION

Subtraction rule

$$P(\text{not } A) = 1 - P(A)$$
$$P(A) = \text{probability drafted by NBA}$$
$$P(A) = 0.000004$$
$$P(\text{not } A) = 1 - 0.000004$$
$$P(\text{not } A) = 0.999996$$

Use the subtraction rule. $P(A)$ represents the probability that a student is drafted by the NBA. The probability of a US college student being drafted by the NBA is 0.000004. Substitute that value in the equation and solve.

4. If you toss a coin four times, what is the probability that it comes up heads at least once?

SOLUTION

Subtraction rule

$$P(\text{not } A) = 1 - P(A)$$
$$A = \text{all tails}$$
$$\text{not } A = \text{heads at least once}$$

One way to solve the problem is to realize you can compute the probability of the opposite event. The opposite of "at least one heads" is "all tails." If the coin comes up tails every time, then it never comes up heads. The probability of getting heads at least once equals the probability that you will not get tails four times. The subtraction rule is used to calculate the probability of the event "not A" from the probability of A. Let A be the event that the coin comes up tails each time. If the event of getting tails all four times does not occur, that means heads came up at least once. The event "not A" is the one we are interested in.

Use multiplication rule to calculate $P(A)$

$$P(A) = \frac{1}{2} \cdot \frac{1}{2} \cdot \frac{1}{2} \cdot \frac{1}{2} = \frac{1}{16}$$

To calculate the probability of getting tails all four times, apply the multiplication rule because the coin tosses are independent events. The probability of four tails in a row is $\frac{1}{16}$.

Substitute and evaluate

$$P(\text{not } A) = 1 - \frac{1}{16}$$
$$P(\text{not } A) = \frac{15}{16}$$

In the subtraction rule, substitute in the probability of all tails, which is $\frac{1}{16}$. The probability of heads in at least one of the four tosses is $\frac{15}{16}$.

The Origin of Probability Studies

The study of probability began in the 17th century with the French nobleman and gambler Antoine Gombaud, Chevalier de Méré. The Chevalier de Méré noticed that an even bet that a 6 would appear at least once in four rolls of one die was a good bet to make, while an even bet that a pair of sixes would appear at least once in 24 rolls of two dice was not a good bet.

> On an *even bet*, you win the same amount that you wager.

In other words, it seemed to the Chevalier that the probability of rolling a 6 in 4 tries was greater than 0.5, while the probability of rolling a pair of sixes in 24 tries was less than 0.5. The Chevalier was seeking a model to explain the probabilities he observed.

This was puzzling to him, because he reasoned that the ratio of the number of dice rolls to the number of possible outcomes was the same for both games, namely $\frac{4}{6} = \frac{2}{3}$ and $\frac{24}{36} = \frac{2}{3}$. He wrote to the mathematician Blaise Pascal asking for an explanation. This resulted in a correspondence between Pascal and another mathematician, Pierre Fermat, who together established the basic ideas of probability.

MODEL PROBLEM

Was the Chevalier correct? Is it more likely that a 6 will appear in 4 rolls of a single die than a pair of 6's in 24 rolls of two dice?

SOLUTION

Probability of at least one 6 in 4 rolls	A = at least one 6 $P(\text{not } A)$ easier to calculate	Calculate the probability that a 6 will occur at least once in 4 rolls of a single die. Start by letting A be the event that at least one 6 appears in 4 rolls. It is easier to calculate the probability that A does not occur. That is, the probability that a 6 never occurs in the 4 rolls of the dice.
Use multiplication rule	$P(\text{not } A) = [P(\text{not } 6)]^4$ $P(\text{not } A) = \left(\frac{5}{6}\right)^4$ $P(\text{not } A) = \frac{625}{1296}$ $P(\text{not } A) \approx 0.482$	Write an expression for the probability of "not A." Using the multiplication rule, multiply the probability of "not 6" in a single roll by itself, four times. This is the equivalent of the probability of "not 6" to the fourth power.
Subtraction rule	$P(A) = 1 - P(\text{not } A)$ $P(A) = 1 - 0.482$ $P(A) \approx 0.518$	By the subtraction rule, the probability of A equals 1 minus the probability that A does not occur. The probability that a 6 appears in at least one of 4 rolls is 0.518.
Probability of at least one double 6 in 24 rolls	B = at least one pair of sixes $P(\text{not } B)$ easier to calculate	Start by letting B be the event that a pair of 6's appears at least once in 24 rolls. It is easier to calculate the probability that B does not occur. That is, the probability that a pair of sixes never occurs.

Model Problem continues . . .

| Use multiplication rule | $P(\text{not } B) = [P(\text{not 6s})]^{24}$ | Write an expression for the probability of "not B." By the multiplication rule, write this as the probability that a pair of sixes does not occur in any roll, raised to the 24th power, since the Chevalier was curious about the probability after 24 rolls. |

$$P(\text{not } B) = \left(\frac{35}{36}\right)^{24}$$

$$P(\text{not } B) = (0.97222\ldots)^{24}$$
$$P(\text{not } B) \approx 0.509$$

Subtraction rule

$$P(B) = 1 - P(\text{not } B)$$
$$P(B) = 1 - 0.509$$
$$P(B) \approx 0.491$$

By the subtraction rule, the probability of B is 1 minus the probability that B does not occur. The probability that a pair of sixes appears at least once in 24 rolls is 0.491.

> The Chevalier de Méré was right. The probability of rolling at least one 6 in four rolls of a single die is 0.518, better than 50/50, while the probability of rolling at least one pair of sixes in 24 rolls is only 0.491.

PRACTICE

1. Find the probability of drawing a face card or a spade in a 52-card deck.

   A. $\dfrac{1}{13}$ C. $\dfrac{11}{26}$

   B. $\dfrac{4}{13}$ D. $\dfrac{25}{52}$

2. The probability that a house in the Hidden Hills subdivision has a hot tub is 0.2, that it has a pool is 0.1, and that it has both is 0.02. What is the probability a house has a hot tub or a pool?

3. The probability that a student likes ice cream is 0.8, that a student likes french fries is 0.7, and that a student likes both is 0.6. What is the probability that a student likes ice cream or french fries?

4. There are 20 climbing ropes. Five are thicker than 8 mm, four are waterproof, and one is both thicker than 8 mm and waterproof. What is the probability of a rope being thicker than 8 mm or waterproof?

5. The probability that a dog at a certain animal shelter is black is 0.4. The probability that it is yellow is 0.2. What is the probability that a dog at the shelter is black or yellow?

6. The probability a Labrador weighs more than 60 lb is 0.5. The probability a Labrador weighs less than 40 lb is 0.05. What is the probability a Labrador weighs more than 60 lb or less than 40 lb?

7. The probability that a student's favorite sport is soccer is 0.3. The probability that a student's favorite sport is basketball is 0.2. What is the probability that a student's favorite sport is soccer or basketball?

8. A promotional giveaway offers three types of vacations: beach trip, skiing, or hiking. Each customer is allowed to take one type of vacation. The probability that a customer chooses the beach is 0.7 and skiing is 0.2. What is the probability that a customer chooses hiking?

Practice Problems continue . . .

9. If you roll two dice, there is a $\frac{1}{6}$ probability that they will sum to 7. What is the probability that the two dice do not sum to 7?

10. There are two species of mushrooms in a forest, and one species is poisonous. On average, if you pick 50 mushrooms, you will find that 47 mushrooms are fine to eat. What is the probability of picking a poisonous mushroom?

11. With a particular coin, the probability of the coin coming up heads is 0.49. What is the probability of the coin coming up tails twice in a row? Round your answer to the nearest hundredth.

12. You hold 10 cards in a card game. Five cards are clubs, three cards are face cards, and one card is both a club and a face card. If an opponent takes one of your cards, what is the probability she draws a club or a face card? State your answer as a decimal.

13. What is the probability if you roll two dice that they will total 11 or greater?

14. The probability that Ignacio has his ice cream in a waffle cone is 0.4 and in a sugar cone is 0.5. What is the probability that his ice cream is in a waffle cone or a sugar cone?

15. The probability of a warm day is 0.6, of a sunny day is 0.4, and of a warm and sunny day is 0.2. What is the probability of a warm or sunny day?

16. What is the probability of rolling an even number on a die four times in a row?

17. **MP 1, 2** On a television game show, there are three curtains, *A*, *B*, and *C*. Behind one curtain is a brand-new car, and behind the other two are a live goat and a fruitcake from the previous holiday season. You are a contestant on the show and have won the right to pick a curtain and get the prize behind it. You pick curtain *B*. Before it is opened, the host opens curtain *A*, revealing the goat, and gives you the opportunity to switch to curtain *C*. Before curtain *A* was opened, the probability you would win the car was $\frac{1}{3}$. After the curtain was opened, what is the probability if you don't switch? and if you do switch? Note: This problem has created much debate and discussion, which can be found on the Internet.

18. **MP 7** Show algebraically that the probability of the complement of not *A* equals the probability of *A*. That is, $P(\text{not}(\text{not } A)) = P(A)$.

19. **MP 3** Are independent events mutually exclusive? Explain.

20. **MP 2** Determine if:
$P((A \text{ or } B) \text{ and } C) = P(A \text{ or } (B \text{ and } C))$

• Multi-Part PROBLEM Practice •

MP 1, 8

a Make an educated guess on the probability that out of *n* randomly selected people, two or more people will have the same birthday (month and date). Assume no leap years exist.

b Find the probability that two randomly selected people will have different birthdays. Use your result to determine the probability they will have the same birthday.

c Find the probability that *n* randomly selected people will have different birthdays.

d Determine the probability that out of 30 randomly selected people, two or more people will have the same birthday.

e How many randomly selected people are needed to ensure that the probability of two or more people having the same birthday is at least 0.5?

f How many randomly selected people are needed to ensure that the probability of two or more people having the same birthday is at least 90%?

12.5 Conditional Probability

We have discussed independent events, but many events are dependent. For instance, the probability of "carrying an umbrella" is dependent on the weather since more people carry an umbrella when it is raining than when it is sunny. We can say it is a **conditional probability**—if it is raining, then the probability of carrying is increased. The probabilities of the two events are related.

> A conditional probability is the probability of a second event occurring, given that a first event has already occurred.

We use a Venn diagram to illustrate conditional probability. Outcome A has X events, and outcome B has Y events. Z is the number of events common to both.

Another example of conditional probability: What is the probability you will sink a second free throw in a basketball game, if you have already sunk the first? You might feel more confident if you sank the first, and be more likely to sink the second. Formally, the conditional probability that A occurs given that B already occurred is written as $P(A|B)$. Using our basketball example, it would be $P(\text{Sink second shot}|\text{Sank first shot})$. The formula below can be used to calculate conditional probability.

Conditional probability:

$$P(A \mid B) = \frac{P(A \text{ and } B)}{P(B)}$$

> This is a formula for calculating the probability that A occurs, given B has occurred. It equals the probability that both A *and* B occur, divided by the probability that B occurs.

We can use conditional probability to describe independent events as well. If two events are independent, then the conditional probability of A given B is equal to the probability of A, and the conditional probability of B given A is the probability of B.

Conditional probability for independent events

If A and B are independent events, then:

$$P(A|B) = P(A)$$
$$P(B|A) = P(B)$$

Note that for dependent events, $P(A|B)$ is not necessarily equal to $P(B|A)$. To show why, we will use the Venn diagram first presented on page 613 and duplicated here.

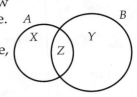

If we calculate $P(A|B)$ using the diagram, we find $P(A|B) = \dfrac{P(A \cap B)}{P(B)} = \dfrac{Z}{Y}$. Likewise,

if we calculate $P(B|A)$, we see that $P(B|A) = \dfrac{P(A \cap B)}{P(A)} = \dfrac{Z}{X}$. Since $\dfrac{Z}{Y}$ will only be

equivalent to $\dfrac{Z}{X}$ if $Y = X$, $P(A|B)$ may or may not be equal to $P(B|A)$.

MODEL PROBLEMS

1. In the diagram, the numbers represent the number of events. The conditional probability of A occurring given that B has occurred is

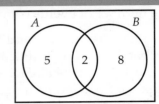

   A. 0.4   C. 0.25

   B. 0.2   D. 0.625

SOLUTION

The answer is B. A total of $5 + 2 + 8 = 15$ events form our sample space. The probability of A and B occurring is $P(A \text{ and } B) = \dfrac{2}{15}$. The probability of B occurring (with or without A) is $P(B) = \dfrac{10}{15}$.

The conditional probability of A occurring given B is then, according to the formula,

$$P(A|B) = \frac{2/15}{10/15} = \frac{2}{10} = 0.2.$$

2. You roll two dice, a blue die and a red die. What is the probability that the red die comes up 3 if you roll an 8?

SOLUTION

Use equation for conditional probability	$P(A \mid B) = \dfrac{P(A \text{ and } B)}{P(B)}$ $A = $ red die 3 $B = $ dice total 8	We calculate the probability that the red die comes up 3, given that the total of the dice is 8. In other words, given that B, a total of dice totaling 8 has occurred, what is the probability A, that the red die is 3? We model possible rolls of the dice for a game. There are five ways two dice can total 8. There is only one way two dice can total 8 if a specific die is 3 (the other die must be 5). We define A as the event that the red die comes up 3, and B as the event that the total of the dice is 8.
Calculate the probability of both events occurring	$P(A \text{ and } B) = \dfrac{1}{36}$	The probability that the red die comes up 3 and the total of the dice is 8 is $\dfrac{1}{36}$. We could calculate this probability from a sample space.
Calculate the probability of event B (dice totaling 8) occuring	$P(B) = \dfrac{5}{36}$	There are five ways to roll an eight with a pair of dice. Since there are 36 outcomes in the sample space, the probability of rolling an eight is $\dfrac{5}{36}$.
Substitute and evaluate	$P(A \mid B) = \dfrac{1/36}{5/36}$ $P(A \mid B) = \dfrac{1}{5}$	Substitute the probabilities into the equation for conditional probability. We find that the probability that the red die comes up 3 if the total of the dice is 8 is $\dfrac{1}{5}$.

Model Problems continue . . .

3. If a player is a pitcher, the probability he is left-handed is 40%. Thirty-two percent of players on a team are pitchers. What percent are left-handed pitchers?

SOLUTION

Solve conditional probability for "and"	$P(A \mid B) = \dfrac{P(A \text{ and } B)}{P(B)}$	Use the equation for conditional probability, and solve it for the "and" case.
	$P(A \text{ and } B) = P(B) \cdot P(A \mid B)$ $A = $ left-handed $B = $ being a pitcher	
Substitute	$P(B) = 0.32$ $P(A \mid B) = 0.4$ $P(A \text{ and } B) = 0.32 \cdot 0.4$ $P(A \text{ and } B) = 0.128$	Substitute the probabilities and multiply. The probability of both occurring is 0.128. The result is that 12.8% of players on a team are left-handed pitchers.

Did you know? Professional baseball teams have 25 players, so that means about 3.2 players. There is no "0.2" of a person, so it means most teams probably have 3 left-handed pitchers, while some have more. Of course, some teams might have fewer than 3—the 12.8% is an average across teams.

4. A certain clinic is testing the effects of a new wonder drug on a certain disease. Of the patients being treated at the clinic, 20% of the patients are taking the wonder drug, while 5% are both recovering from the disease and taking the wonder drug. What is the probability that if a patient with the disease takes the wonder drug, they will recover?

SOLUTION

Formula for calculating conditional probability	$P(A \mid B) = \dfrac{P(A \text{ and } B)}{P(B)}$ $A = $ recovering $B = $ taking drug	We want to calculate the probability that a patient is recovering, given that they are taking the drug. Let A be the event they are recovering and B the event they are taking the drug.
Substitute and evaluate	$P(A \text{ and } B) = 0.05$ $P(B) = 0.2$ $P(A \mid B) = \dfrac{0.05}{0.2}$ $P(A \mid B) = 0.25 = 25\%$	The probability that a patient is taking the drug *and* recovering is 5%, which we state as 0.05. The probability a patient is taking the drug is 20%, which we state as 0.2.

Note that both independent and conditional events are given in this problem. The probability of recovering and being on the new wonder drug is 5%. The conditional probability is whether they are on the wonder drug and recovering. The question creates a simple model for analyzing the success of drugs, which is a complex topic. For instance, patients might recover without taking the drug–the data does not prove the drug cures patients. Also, if patients know they are taking the drug, that might have an impact on their recovery rate. But the simple model forecasts that 25% of the patients with the disease are cured by the wonder drug.

Conditional Probability and Two-Way Tables

In the two-way table to the right, we surveyed 50 people, and asked if they like cats or dogs better, and then what flavor they prefer in ice cream, chocolate, or strawberry. The percent in each row is calculated by dividing the value in a cell by the total of the row—it is a *conditional probability*, "if someone prefers dogs, then what is the probability of chocolate," for instance.

	Chocolate	Strawberry	Total
Cats	4	6	10
Dogs	16	24	40

	Chocolate	Strawberry
Cats	40%	60%
Dogs	40%	60%

As we have discussed earlier, if conditional probabilities have a certain property, then two events are independent. Specifically, if $P(A|B) = P(A)$ and $P(B|A) = P(B)$, then A and B are independent. One event occurring has no impact on the other. You can see whatever pet someone owns, the probability they like chocolate is always 40%. To show that pet and ice cream preferences are independent, we would reverse columns and rows, putting ice cream flavors on the left. We leave that as an exercise for you–when you do the calculations, you will see the probability of cat is always 20%, and dog is always 80%, whatever ice cream is preferred. Since we have $P(\text{pet}|\text{ice cream}) = P(\text{pet})$ and $P(\text{ice cream}|\text{pet}) = P(\text{ice cream})$, the two events are independent.

To the right, we provide an example where the probabilities are not independent. We surveyed coffee and tea preferences, and then asked about cracker versus cookie preferences. The table shows that the conditional probabilities differ. If a person prefers cookies, she is more likely to prefer coffee than if the person prefers crackers. Since the conditional probabilities are not equal, the probabilities are not independent.

	Coffee	Tea	Total
Crackers	6	4	10
Cookies	28	12	40

	Coffee	Tea
Crackers	60%	40%
Cookies	70%	30%

Optional: Bayes' Theorem

In most sections of this book, we show a formula and then provide examples of how to apply it. In this section, we will reverse the order by first discussing a situation that requires Bayes' theorem and then explaining the theorem. The theorem is used to model conditional probabilities.

Example Situation

Let's say you know a friend who just tested positive for the dreaded Bolagong disease, a condition that causes victims to write math textbooks. Could there be anything worse? (Answer: No.)

The manufacturer of the test says that 97% of the people who have Bolagong disease will test positive when they use the test. Testing positive means the test indicates they have the disease. The test is not perfect; some people with the disease will test negative. Testing negative means the test says they do not have the disease.

What is the probability that your friend, who has tested positive, has the disease?

The conveniently *wrong* answer is: 97%. That is wrong because it is the probability that if you have the disease, you test positive. Your poor friend wants to know the opposite: If he tests positive, what is the probability he has the disease? If he tests positive but does not have the disease, then we have what is called a **false positive**.

This is a common problem: People test positive for a disease but do not have it; geologists drill test wells and conclude there is oil even though there is none; a piece of manufacturing test equipment says a product is faulty, but it is not. All of these are false positives.

Tests also give **false negatives**. They indicate negative when the underlying condition really does exist but is not detected by the test. Tests report a false negative when they indicate that someone is healthy when she is sick, or report a dry location where there is water, and so on.

> Bayes' theorem lets you reverse a conditional probability. If you know the probability of A given that B has occurred, what is the probability of B occurring, if A has occurred?

To calculate the probability of having the disease given a positive test result, we will use a formula called *Bayes' theorem*. Bayes' theorem deals with conditional probabilities. It assumes you know one conditional probability. For instance, you know the probability that if you have a certain disease, the test will come back positive.

We state the situation again, using probability notation. We let A represent the event that the test is positive, and B represent the event that you have the disease:

One conditional probability known	A = test positive B = have disease $P(A \mid B)$	It is assumed you know the probability that A occurs, given that B occurs. In our example above, this is the probability that if you have the disease, you will test positive.
The "reversed" conditional you want to know	$P(B \mid A)$	Bayes' theorem lets you calculate the reverse: the probability of B occurring, given that A occurs. In our example, the probability that if you test positive, you have the disease.

Let's return to your friend, who has tested positive. He wants to know if he truly has the disease, given the positive test result. To answer his question, you need two more pieces of information. First, what percent of people in general have the disease? Let's say that 5% of the people on the planet have the disease. Second, what is the probability of a false positive? The company that supplies the test says that 4% of the time there is a false positive. The probability of a false positive is stated as $P(A \mid \text{not } B)$, that is, the probability that the test is positive given that you do not have the disease.

We state these additional facts that are required using probability notation:

Probability of having the disease	$P(B)$	You have to know some other facts to use Bayes' theorem. What is the probability that anyone in the general population will have the disease? This is $P(B)$.
Probability of not having the disease	$P(\text{not } B)$ $P(\text{not } B) = 1 - P(B)$	You also need to know the probability of not having the disease.
Probability of false positive	$P(A \mid \text{not } B)$	We also need to know how often in general the test gives a false positive.

> Using probability notation, Bayes' theorem starts with one conditional probability, $P(A \mid B)$, the probability of A given B. It enables you to calculate another conditional probability, $P(B \mid A)$, the probability of B given A.

Does the false positive rate of 4% mean the probability that your friend has the Bolagong is 96%? No. You have to factor in the probabilities mentioned above, including the probability that anyone has the disease and the probability of a false positive.

We state the formula.

Bayes' Theorem:

$$P(B \mid A) = \frac{P(A \mid B) \cdot P(B)}{P(A \mid B) \cdot P(B) + P(A \mid \text{not } B) \cdot P(\text{not } B)}$$

> If you know the conditional probability $P(A \mid B)$ and three other probabilities, $P(B)$, $P(\text{not } B)$, and $P(A \mid \text{not } B)$, you can calculate $P(B \mid A)$. Sort of a mouthful, but it turns out to be highly useful.

Having stated the formula, we apply it to the situation at hand and calculate the probability that if your friend tests positive, he has the disease.

$P(A \mid B) = 0.97$ $P(B) = 0.05$ $P(A \mid \text{not } B) = 0.04$ $P(\text{not } B) = 0.95$	$P(B \mid A) = \dfrac{P(A \mid B) \cdot P(B)}{P(A \mid B) \cdot P(B) + P(A \mid \text{not } B) \cdot P(\text{not } B)}$ $P(B \mid A) = \dfrac{0.97 \cdot 0.05}{0.97 \cdot 0.05 + 0.04 \cdot 0.95}$ $P(B \mid A) \approx 56\%$	Substitute the probabilities into the equation and simplify. The probability that your friend has the dreaded Bolagong disease is about 56%.

To give you a sense of how the theorem works, let's change two factors that cause your friend to feel even more nervous. Let's say the test gives false positives only 1% of the time and that 10% of people have the disease. With those two changes, the probability he has the disease increases to about 91%.

MODEL PROBLEM

MP 2, 4 You run a credit card company. You know that 5% of your customers turn out to be bad risks, because if their account becomes overdue, they will never pay. The other 95% you consider good risks. Of the "bad-risk" customers, 75% allow their account to become overdue. Only 7% of "good-risk" customers allow their account to become overdue. A customer of yours named Charlie has an account that is overdue. What is the probability that he is a bad risk?

SOLUTION

Event A = customer is overdue Event B = customer is a bad risk	$P(B) = 0.05$	Define A as the event that the customer is overdue. Define B as the event that the customer is a bad risk.
Use subtraction rule	$P(\text{not } B) = 1 - P(B)$ $P(\text{not } B) = 0.95$	Use the subtraction rule to find the probability that a customer is a good risk, which is to say that he is not a bad risk.

Model Problem continues . . .

State conditional probability	$P(A \mid B) = 0.75$	The probability that a bad-risk customer lets his account become overdue is 75%. Another way to say this is that the probability that a customer lets his account become overdue given that he is a bad risk is 0.75.
State another conditional probability again	$P(A \mid \text{not } B) = 0.07$	The probability that a good-risk customer lets his account become overdue is 7%. Another way to put this is that the probability that a customer lets his account become overdue given that he is not a bad risk is 0.07.
Use Bayes' theorem	$P(B \mid A) = \dfrac{P(A \mid B) \cdot P(B)}{P(A \mid B) \cdot P(B) + P(A \mid \text{not } B) \cdot P(\text{not } B)}$	Calculate the probability that Charlie, who is overdue, is a bad credit risk.
Substitute	$P(B \mid A) = \dfrac{(0.75)(0.05)}{(0.75)(0.05) + (0.07)(0.95)}$	Fill in the probabilities found.
Evaluate	$P(B \mid A) \approx 36\%$	Do the necessary calculation. The probability that Charlie is a bad risk is 0.36. Now it's up to you to decide what to do with that information!

PRACTICE

1. A large number of students took a math and an English test. If 60% passed both tests and 75% passed the math, what percent of the students who passed the math also passed the English?

   A. 15%   C. 80%

   B. 45%   D. 90%

2. A black and a white die are rolled. What is the probability that the black die comes up 2, if the sum of the two dice is 5?

   A. $\dfrac{1}{4}$ C. $\dfrac{1}{12}$

   B. $\dfrac{1}{6}$ D. $\dfrac{1}{36}$

Practice Problems continue . . .

3. What is the probability that the sum of 3 dice is 10, given the first roll is a 3?

   A. $\dfrac{1}{2}$ C. $\dfrac{1}{12}$

   B. $\dfrac{1}{6}$ D. $\dfrac{1}{36}$

4. The ovals in the diagram represent sets of event occurrences, denoted *A*, *B*, *X*, and *Y*. Shaded areas show the event occurrences of interest for calculating probabilities. Which statement correctly describes what the shaded areas represent in the two diagrams?

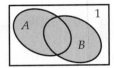 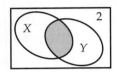

   A. In diagram 1, *A* and *B* occur; in diagram 2, *X* or *Y* occurs.

   B. In diagram 1, *A* or *B* occurs; in diagram 2, *X* and *Y* occur.

   C. In diagram 1, *A* or *B* occurs; in diagram 2, *X* occurs but *Y* does not occur.

   D. In diagram 1, *A* and *B* occur; in diagram 2, *X* does not occur but *Y* occurs.

Exercises 5–7: Use the sample space below for rolling a pair of dice to answer the following.

1,1	1,2	1,3	1,4	1,5	1,6
2,1	2,2	2,3	2,4	2,5	2,6
3,1	3,2	3,3	3,4	3,5	3,6
4,1	4,2	4,3	4,4	4,5	4,6
5,1	5,2	5,3	5,4	5,5	5,6
6,1	6,2	6,3	6,4	6,5	6,6

5. What is the probability of rolling a sum of 5, 6, or 7, given both dice show a value of 3 or greater?

6. What is the probability of rolling a sum of 5, 6, or 7, given exactly one die shows a value of 4 or greater?

7. What is the probability of both dice showing the same value, given at least one die shows a value of 3 or greater?

8. Out of 100 cars on a used car lot, 20 cars have manual transmissions, 50 cars have air conditioning, and 8 cars have both.

   a What is the percentage of cars that have air conditioning given they have manual transmissions?

   b What is the percentage of cars that have manual transmissions given they have air conditioning?

9. In an aquarium containing 120 fish, there are 55 yellow fish, 71 fish with stripes, and 23 fish that are yellow and have stripes.

   a If you catch a fish that is yellow, what is the probability that it has stripes?

   b If you catch a fish that has stripes, what is the probability that it is yellow?

10. The probability that is it raining on a given day is 40%. The probability that it is raining and you will be late to work is 25%. If it is raining, what is the probability that you will be late to work?

11. 5% of circuit boards made by a factory are defective. 98% of defective circuit boards will be detected by the factory's quality control methods. However, 3% of non-defective circuit boards will also be labeled as defective.

   a What is the probability that a circuit board labeled as defective is truly defective?

   b What is the probability that a circuit board labeled as good is not defective?

12. 10% of the population has a certain genetic trait. A test to detect this trait has a false positive rate of 4% and a false negative rate of 7%.

   a What is the probability that a person has this genetic trait if the test results are positive?

   b What is the probability that a person does not have this genetic trait if the test results are negative?

Practice Problems continue . . .

13. A company manufactures 500 televisions each day. The company states that its test of defective products is 95% accurate. When consumers purchased the TVs, they found 20 out of 100 of them were defective.

   a Indicate the conditional probabilities on the branches of the given tree diagram.

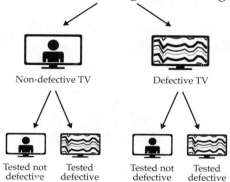

   b What is the probability that a randomly selected TV that tested positive (not defective) will not be defective?

   c What is the probability that a randomly selected TV that tested negative (defective) will in fact be defective?

14. The probability that it is below freezing in Lake Ashley is one fifth, and the probability that it is snowing and below freezing is 15%. What is the probability that it will snow if it is below freezing?

15. The probability that it is below freezing in Rushtown is 24%, and the probability that it is snowing and below freezing is one tenth. What is the probability that it will snow if it is below freezing?

16. The probability that it is below freezing in Fellowville is 5%, and the probability that it is snowing and below freezing is 0.01. What is the probability that it will snow if it is below freezing?

17. You draw two cards from a well-shuffled, standard deck. What is the probability that the second card is an ace given that the first card was an ace?

18. You draw two cards from a well-shuffled, standard deck. What is the probability that the second card is a spade given that the first card is a spade?

19. You draw two cards from a well-shuffled, standard deck. What is the probability that the second card is a face card given that the first card drawn was a face card? (Face cards include jacks, queens, and kings.)

20. A medical research lab proposes a screening test for an infection. Out of 100 randomly selected people, the test indicated that 5 out of 70 infected people tested negative, while 3 out of the 30 non-infected people tested positive.

   a Which of the false test results is more serious? Explain.

   b Indicate the conditional probabilities on the branches of the given tree diagram.

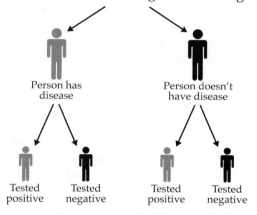

   c What is the probability that a randomly selected person who tested positive will have the disease? Round to the nearest hundredth.

   d What is the probability that a randomly selected person who tested negative will not have the disease? Round to the nearest hundredth.

21. Searching for underground water sources, Xue uses a device that has a 90% chance of beeping if there is water beneath it. The device has a false positive rate of 12%. In the particular location Xue is searching, there is water underground 30% of the time. What is the probability that there is water beneath her if the device goes off?

Practice Problems continue . . .

22. A small village in Nevada contains a population of snakes, some of which are poisonous and some of which are not. Snakes that are poisonous have a $\frac{3}{4}$ chance of having a red stripe. Researchers also found that 1 of every 10 snakes that were not poisonous had a red stripe. If 9% of the total snake population is poisonous, what is the probability that you need to get some antidote if you've been bitten by a snake with a red stripe?

23. Elwood has a bad knee that he says is sore in the morning if it is going to rain that day. His daughter Tanya watches and finds that it is indeed true that 98% of the time it rains, her father's knee is sore. However, the probability of a false positive (the knee being sore when it does not rain) is 40%. If it rains 20% of the time, what is the probability that it will rain if Elwood's bad knee is sore?

24. There are 5000 students at a new university. 30% are chemistry majors, and 1350 students are both chemistry majors and pre-med. What is the probability that a student is pre-med given that he is a chemistry major?

25. If a cell phone call is disconnected, there is a 10% chance it was due to a phone company switch error as opposed to lack of reception and other causes. Of all calls placed, 1 in 250 is disconnected because of a phone company error. What is the probability that a call will be disconnected?

26. Determine the incorrect reasoning in Todd's statement: "The probability of A is the number of outcomes in A divided by the total number of outcomes in the sample space S. The probability of A given B is the number of outcomes in A divided by the number of outcomes in B. Thus, $P(A)$ must be less than $P(A \mid B)$."

27. Create an analogy of conditional probability by writing a conditional statement containing the word "if" or "given." For example, "Tony will receive allowance money from his parents if (given that) he completes his daily chores." Describe how your conditional statement relates to conditional probability.

28. The diagrams of $P(A \cap B)$ and $P(A \mid B)$ are shown below. Which of them is $P(A \mid B)$? Explain.

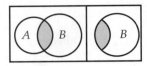

29. Give an example of a true statement in which the converse is not true.

30. **MP 2, 5** Jar A contains x green marbles and y black marbles. Jar B contains all black marbles. If one jar is randomly chosen and a marble is then picked out, what is the probability the marble is green, given it is taken from Jar A? What is the probability the marble is black?

31. **MP 7** What is the probability that the sum of two 6-sided dice will be at least 3 greater than the value of the higher die of the pair, given the difference of the value of the two dice is one?

32. **MP 1, 2** If Rachel studies for her test, she has a 90% chance of passing the test. If she does not study, she has a 60% chance of passing the test. The probability that she studied, given she passes the test, is 65%. What is the probability she studied for the test? Round your answer to the nearest tenth of a percent.

1. In the graph of the sample space below, the height of the bar for the outcome "6" is

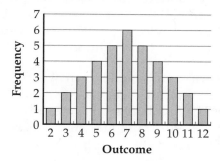

A. 4
B. 5
C. 6
D. 7

2. There are 49 possible candidates for leadership positions in a new company. What is the difference between n, the number of ways that three co-presidents can be chosen, and m, the number of ways that a president, vice president, and secretary can be chosen?

A. n and m are the same.
B. n is twice as large as m.
C. m is three times as large as n.
D. m is six times as large as n.

3. Is it possible that the probability of A or B occurring is greater than the probability of A alone occurring, or B alone occurring?

A. Yes
B. No

4. A pizza place has a different toppings, and b different sizes. How many different ways are there to order a pizza with one topping?

A. $a + b$
B. $a - b$
C. $a \cdot b$
D. $\dfrac{a}{b}$

5. Which of the pairs of events below are independent? Check all that apply.

A. A coin coming up heads and then the same coin coming up tails.
B. The weather being sunny and people carrying umbrellas.
C. Drawing a 5 from a deck of cards, replacing it in the deck and then drawing a queen.
D. Drawing a red gumdrop from a bag, eating it, and then drawing a blue gumdrop.

6. The probability that event Z occurs is 0.4; the probability that event K occurs is 0.5; and the probability that events Z and K both occur is 0.2. This means

A. The probability of Z is conditional on the probability of K.
B. The probability of K is conditional on the probability of Z.
C. The two events are independent.
D. The event Z is the complement of the event K.

7. Laetitia is relating probability and sets. She states: "In probability, we can compute the probability that A and B may occur. We might also compute the probability that X or Y may occur." To relate this to sets, Laetitia should say

A. The probability of A and B occurring is a union of two sets, and the probability of X or Y occurring is an intersection of two sets.
B. The probability of A and B occurring is an intersection of two sets, and the probability of X or Y occurring is the union of two sets.
C. The probability of A and B occurring is a complement of two sets, and the probability of X or Y occurring is the intersection of two sets.
D. The probability of A and B occurring is a union of two sets, and the probability of X or Y occurring is the complement of two sets.

Chapter Review continues . . .

8. Robert is finding the probability of randomly drawing a queen or diamond from a deck of 52 cards. His solution steps are stated below.

Step 1: $P(A \text{ or } B) = P(A) + P(B) - P(A \text{ and } B)$

Step 2: $P(A \text{ or } B) = \dfrac{4}{52} + \dfrac{13}{52} - \dfrac{1}{52}$

Step 3: $P(A \text{ or } B) = \dfrac{4}{13}$

Which is the first incorrect step shown above, if there are any errors at all?

A. Step 1
B. Step 2
C. Step 3
D. All of the steps are correct.

9. How many ways can you arrange the numbers 14, 11, 23, and 105?

10. A flag is made up of stripes of the colors brown, purple, black, fuchsia, and orange. Each color appears once. How many flags are possible?

11. MP 4, 5 Customers order one or two scoops of ice cream at the corner store. The probability that the store serves a chocolate scoop is 0.4, the probability that a customer orders two scoops is 0.3, and the probability that they order two chocolate scoops is 0.1. What is the probability they order some chocolate or two scoops?

12. MP 4, 7 There is a 70% chance that it will rain, and a 30% chance that the temperature will be above 80° F. There is a 20% chance that it will rain and the temperature will be above 80°. What is the probability that it will rain or the temperature will be above 80°?

13. What is the probability that you draw a diamond or a 3 from a standard deck of 52 cards?

14. There are 57 prairie dogs in a small colony. 32 have a black spot, 5 only have a gray spot, and 10 have both a gray and a black spot. A scientist traps the prairie dogs and examines the first one he catches with a black spot. What is the probability that it has a gray spot?

15. MP 4, 5 Searching for underground caves, Justin uses a device that has an 85% chance of beeping if there is a cave beneath it. The device has a false positive rate of 10%. In the particular location Justin is searching, there is a cave underground 5% of the time. What is the probability that there is a cave beneath him if the device goes off? Round your answer to the nearest hundredth.

16. Create a sample space to answer the questions below. There are two six-sided dice. The numbers on one die are even (2, 4, 6, 8, 10, 12) and the numbers on the other are odd (1, 3, 5, 7, 9, 11).

　a What is the probability that the dice sum to 7?
　b What is the probability that the dice sum to an even number?
　c What is the probability that the dice sum to an odd number?
　d What is the probability that the dice sum to a number 8 or larger?

Exercises 17–19: Sketch a graph to represent the sample space. Refer to Model Problem 3 on page 579 to assist you.

17. The sum of two 5-sided dice.

18. The sum of two 8-sided dice.

19. The number of heads when flipping 3 fair coins.

Exercises 20–24: Determine whether the events are dependent or independent. Justify your answer.

20. Randomly purchasing two dogs out of a group of 14 dogs and 6 cats.

21. The test scores of individuals on the AP exam.

22. Five players rolling the same two dice in a board game.

23. The number of pins a player can knock down on his first and second bowls in bowling.

24. The number of people eating out on a given day of the week.

Chapter Review continues . . .

25. **MP 4, 5** Searching for underground silver, Eric uses a device that has a 75% chance of beeping if there is silver beneath it. The device has a false positive rate of one-ninth. In the particular location Eric is searching, there is silver underground 10% of the time. What is the probability that there is silver beneath him if the device goes off? Round your answer to the nearest hundredth.

26. You draw a card from a standard 52-card deck three times, replacing the card after each draw. What is the probability that you draw a heart at least once?

27. Arnold's bowling alley holds a competition between the top four bowlers in the city. There are four prizes for first to fourth place. How many possible ways are there for the four bowlers to claim the four prizes?

28. What is the probability of drawing a jack from a full deck of cards, replacing it, and then drawing a spade?

29. What is the probability of getting an orange on the spinner below and then spinning again and getting a star? Note: All the wedges are the same size.

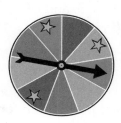

30. **MP 4, 5** A survey asked people which days of the week they usually go grocery shopping. 70% of those surveyed went grocery shopping on Saturday or Sunday, 50% of people went shopping on Saturday, and 30% of people went shopping on Sunday. What percentage of people went shopping on both Saturday and Sunday?

Cumulative Review
for Chapters 1–12

1. In $\triangle ABC$ and $\triangle EDF$, $\angle A \cong \angle E$, $\angle C \cong \angle F$, $AC = 30$, $DE = 15$, and $EF = 3$. What is the length of $\overline{AB}$?

   A. 1.5
   B. 6
   C. 150
   D. There is not enough information to calculate AB.

2. $\overline{ON}$ is a midsegment. Which of the following are true statements? Select all that apply.

   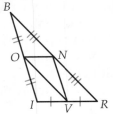

   A. The length of $\overline{ON}$ is twice that of $\overline{IR}$.
   B. $IV = VR$
   C. $OI = NR$
   D. $\overline{ON}$ and $\overline{IR}$ are parallel.
   E. $\overline{ON}$ and $\overline{VR}$ are parallel.

3. You want to model an event that has a probability of 15%. You draw a card from a 52-card deck and see if it is part of a special set of cards. To best model the 15% event, the special set should consist of

   A. Any heart.
   B. Any face card of any suit.
   C. The jack or queen of any suit.
   D. The three through the seven cards, inclusive, of any suit.

4. You want to model an event that has a probability of 27%. You draw a card from a 52-card deck and see if it is part of a special set of cards. To best model the 27% event, the special set should consist of

   A. Any spade and the ace of hearts.
   B. Any face card.
   C. The two through the nine cards, inclusive, of any suit.
   D. Any diamond and any club.

5. Where are the asymptotes of the hyperbola $\dfrac{y^2}{9} - \dfrac{x^2}{16} = 1$? Check all that apply.

   A. x-axis
   B. y-axis
   C. $y = \dfrac{3}{4}x$
   D. $y = -\dfrac{3}{4}x$
   E. $y = \dfrac{4}{3}x$
   F. $y = -\dfrac{4}{3}x$

6. The probability that Z will occur is 0.3, the probability that Y will occur is 0.5, and the probability that Z or Y will occur is 0.8. Sammy correctly can make the hypothesis that

   A. Z and Y are independent events.
   B. The probability of Z is conditional on the probability of Y.
   C. The probability of Y is conditional on the probability of Z.
   D. Z and Y are mutually exclusive events.

7. How would the congruent triangles below be described?

   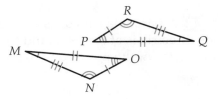

   A. $\triangle MNO \cong \triangle PQR$
   B. $\triangle MNO \cong \triangle QPR$
   C. $\triangle MNO \cong \triangle QRP$

8. The diagram below shows three quadrilaterals with congruent sides and angles marked. Which of these must be a rhombus?

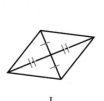  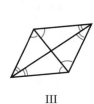

I   II   III

A. I
B. II
C. III
D. None of the above

9. How many ways can you arrange the first six letters in the alphabet?

Exercises 10–12: A diagonal is a segment connecting two non-adjacent vertices of a polygon. Determine the number of diagonals in each of the following polygons. Make a sketch of the polygon with its diagonals to verify your answer.

10. Pentagon

11. Hexagon

12. Octagon

13. Compute 100! using your calculator. Is your calculator able to make this computation? Why do you think you got the result you did?

14. **MP 5, 6** A parabola's focus is at $(0, 5)$ and its directrix is at $y = -5$. Find the y-coordinates of the points on the parabola with the x-coordinates 10 and -10.

15. A parabola's focus is at $\left(0, -\dfrac{3}{2}\right)$ and its directrix is at $y = \dfrac{3}{2}$. What is the equation for the parabola? State your answer in the standard form of an equation for a parabola at the origin.

16. **MP 3** On Sunday night, the weatherman forecasts a 20% chance of snow throughout the rest of the week. Torrey observed that there was not a single snowflake from Monday through Thursday. Suddenly, Torrey jumped in excitement, yelling out, "Tomorrow we'll definitely have no school because of snow!" Should Torrey be less enthusiastic? Why or why not?

17. **MP 3** There is a 99.9% chance that a randomly selected person does not have cancer. Sylvia interviewed almost a thousand people who were not related to her and found out that none of them have any type of cancer. Sylvia is worried that she has a high chance of having cancer since all these people did not have cancer. What can you say to Sylvia to ease her worries?

18. What is the focus of the parabola described by the equation $y - 6 = \dfrac{1}{20}(x - 7)^2$? What is the directrix?

19. Find the surface area of a sphere with radius 10 centimeters. Use 3.14 for π. State your answer to the nearest tenth of a square centimeter.

Exercises 20–22: State the equations below in standard form for a circle.

20. $x^2 + 16x + 8 + y^2 - 2y = 43$

21. $x^2 + 81 + y^2 - 18y = 1$

22. $18 + 2x^2 + 2y^2 + 4\sqrt{7}y = 36 + 12x$

23. What is the volume of the smokestack below? Assume it is 40 meters high and has a radius of 8 meters. Use 3.14 for π. Round your answer to the nearest cubic meter.

24. The measure of a major arc of a circle is 282°. What is the measure of the minor arc of the circle? What is the measure of the central angle enclosing the minor arc?

25. `MP 3, 5` *ABCD* is a parallelogram. Two equilateral triangles *ABX* and *BCY* are constructed outside of the parallelogram on its sides. Make a sketch and prove that triangle *XYD* is equilateral.

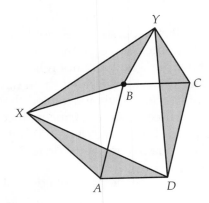

26. `MP 2, 3` The midpoints *K* and *L* of the opposite sides of the parallelogram *ABCD* below are connected with the vertices *B* and *D*. Prove that the segments $\overline{BL}$ and $\overline{DK}$ divide the diagonal $\overline{AC}$ of the parallelogram into three equal parts. In other words, prove that $AX = XY = YC$.

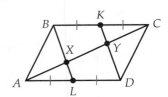

27. What is the area of a triangle with sides measuring 8 and 8 and the angle between them measuring 29°? Give your answer to the nearest whole number.

Exercises 28–29: Find the radius of each circle.

28. What is the value of *x* shown below?

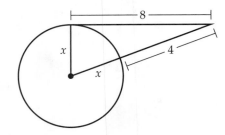

29. What is the value of *r* shown below?

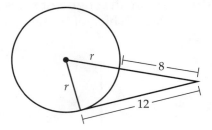

30. `MP 3` If you are given one trigonometric ratio for an acute angle in a right triangle, explain what steps are needed to find the other two trigonometric ratios.

31. `MP 3` Prove that the perpendicular bisectors of a triangle intersect at a concurrency point (the circumcenter). Hint: Use a coordinate proof.

32. Two parallel lines are intersected by a transversal. The sum of three angles—an interior angle, its consecutive angle, and an alternate interior angle to the first—is equal to 232°. Find the measure of the smallest angle.

33. Kendall wants to enclose part of her yard so she can plant a garden and keep out the deer. She has determined that she can afford 300 feet of the fencing that will work best for her. Using the side of the barn on her property as one side of the enclosed yard,

  a Write an expression for the area of a rectangle enclosed on one side by the barn and on three sides by the 300 feet of fencing.

  b Find the dimensions and the maximum area, to the nearest square foot, that can be enclosed this way.

  c Kendall realizes that because she is using chain link, she can make the yard any shape she wants as long as there is one straight side, the side of the barn. Determine the area, to the nearest square foot, of a semicircle that uses all 300 feet of fencing for the perimeter.

34. `MP 4, 6` Quinn has 1000 feet of fencing and wants to cordon off one acre (43,560 ft²) of his land in the shape of a rectangle for his dogs to run loose, but remain safe.

  a Write an equation to find the dimensions of a rectangular fence that uses 1000 ft of fencing and encloses one acre of land.

  b Is it possible to do what Quinn is hoping?

  c If so, find the dimensions of the rectangular plot, to the nearest tenth of a foot.

  d What is the largest rectangular plot of land that Quinn could enclose with his 1000 ft of fencing, to the nearest foot?

35. In circle O below, of radius 5 cm, $\triangle AOC$ is an equilateral triangle. Find exact values for

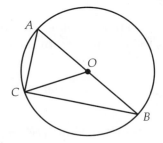

  a $m\angle ACB$
  b $m\angle COB$
  c AC
  d BC
  e The area of $\triangle ABC$

36. `MP 2` Consider the integers from 1 to 999. If one of those numbers is chosen at random, what is the probability that it is an even number or not a multiple of 3?

Glossary

acute angle (p. 39) An angle greater than 0° and less than 90°.

acute triangle (p. 195) A triangle with each of its three angles less than 90°.

addition rule (p. 606) In probability: $P(A \text{ or } B) = P(A) + P(B) - P(A \text{ and } B)$.

adjacent angle (p. 134) Angles that share a common side and vertex, but do not overlap.

adjacent arc (p. 364) Arcs that share a common endpoint, but do not overlap.

adjacent leg (p. 317) In a right triangle, the side of the angle that is not the hypotenuse. Also called an *adjacent side.*

alternate exterior angle (p. 151) Angles on the opposite sides of the transversal and outside the lines.

alternate interior angle (p. 151) Angles on the opposite sides of the transversal and inside the lines.

altitude (p. 258) A line segment from a vertex of a triangle that is perpendicular to the line containing the opposite side.

angle (p. 39) A shape formed by two rays or lines starting at a common point (the vertex).

angle-angle-side (AAS) theorem (p. 222) In trigonometry, the law of sines can be used to solve a triangle when two angles and a side not between the angles are known.

angle-angle (AA) similarity postulate (p. 283) If two angles of one triangle are congruent to two angles of another triangle, then the triangles are similar.

angle bisector (p. 243) A ray that bisects an angle, dividing it into two equal parts.

angle of depression (p. 331) The angle between a horizontal line and a line of sight to an object below the horizontal line.

angle of elevation (p. 322) The angle between a horizontal line and a line of sight to an object above the horizontal line.

angle of rotation (p. 62) In a rotational transformation, the measure of degrees that a figure is rotated about a fixed point.

angle-side-angle (ASA) postulate (p. 218) If two angles of a triangle and the side between them are congruent to those of another triangle, then the triangles are congruent.

apothem (p. 457) In a regular polygon, the apothem is the distance from the center to a side.

arc (p. 363) Part of a circle that is defined by two endpoints.

arc length (p. 388) The length of an arc can be calculated using the equation

$$\text{arc length} = \left(\frac{\text{central angle (in degrees)}}{360°} \right) \cdot 2\pi r =$$

central angle (in radians) $\cdot r$

area (p. 31) The measure of the interior region of an enclosed two-dimensional shape.

asymptote (p. 560) A line that a graph approaches but never reaches.

auxiliary line (p. 183) A line that is added to a diagram in order to help carry out a proof.

axis (conic sections) (p. 527) The line running along the center of a cone or cylinder.

base (p. 198) The side of a two-dimensional figure or the face of a solid that is perpendicular to the height of the figure.

base angle (p. 198) Either of the congruent angles of an isosceles triangle.

biconditional (p. 126) A statement that can be written in the "if and only if" form. Also a definition.

binomial (p. 19) A polynomial with two terms.

Cavalieri's principle (p. 508) Two solids with the same height and same cross-sectional area at each height from their base have the same volume.

center of dilation (p. 95) Point about which a figure is dilated.

central angle (p. 363) An angle with its vertex at the center of a circle.

centroid (p. 254) In a triangle, the three medians' point of concurrency.

chord (p. 355) A line segment with its endpoints on a circle. A chord that passes through the center of a circle is a diameter.

circle (p. 31) All the points in a plane that are the same distance from a point called the *center*.

circular permutation (p. 589) The different ordered arrangements of objects around a circle.

circumcenter (p. 250) Point of concurrency of the perpendicular bisectors of a triangle. The circumcenter of a triangle is at the center of a circle that circumscribes that triangle.

circumference (p. 31) The perimeter of a circle.

circumscribe (p. 250) To construct a circle around a polygon that passes through all of its vertices. For a triangle, the center of the circle is the triangle's circumcenter.

circumscribed angle (p. 360) An angle formed by two tangents to a circle, drawn from one common endpoint.

circumscribed circle (p. 373) A circle that contains an inscribed polygon's vertices.

combination (p. 592) A selection from among the elements of a set, in which the order does not matter.

common tangent (p. 355) A tangent shared by two circles.

complement (probability) (p. 608) The complement of event A is the set of all outcomes that are not A. It is denoted "not A." For a coin toss, heads is the complement of tails.

complementary angles (p. 134) Two angles that sum to 90°.

completing the square (p. 24) A technique for solving quadratic equations; to complete the square means to add a constant to a binomial to create a perfect square.

composition of transformations (p. 79) The application of a sequence of transformations to a figure.

compound event (p. 602) A combination of two or more simple events, such as drawing a club and then drawing a three when playing cards.

concave polygon (p. 433) A polygon with one or more interior angles greater than 180°.

conclusion (p. 119) A statement resulting from reasoning. In a conditional statement, the conclusion is part B of "If A, then B."

concurrent lines (p. 248) Three or more lines that intersect at the same point.

concurrent rays (p. 248) Three or more rays that intersect at the same point.

concurrent segments (p. 248) Three or more line segments that intersect at the same point.

conditional probability (p. 613) The probability that event A occurs, given that event B occurs.

conditional statement (p. 124) Statement in the form "If A, then B."

cone (p. 473) A solid with a circular base and a single vertex.

congruent (p. 40) Geometric shapes that are the same size and shape are congruent. That includes, but is not limited to, line segments, angles, circles, and three-dimensional shapes. Parts of figures can be congruent as well. If you can take a figure and flip, translate, and/or rotate it, but not resize it, and superimpose it on another figure, then the two figures are congruent.

conic section (p. 527) Intersection of a plane and a cone. Intersections include circles, parabolas, ellipses, and hyperbolas.

conjecture (p. 122) A conclusion that may be thought to be true but that is not proven.

consecutive interior angles (p. 153) Angles on the same side of the transversal and between the lines.

construction (p. 40) The use of tools, such as a compass, straightedge, piece of string, and so on, to accomplish a geometric task.

contrapositive (p. 126) A conditional statement that is the inverse of the converse. The contrapositive of "If *A*, then *B*" is "If not *B*, then not *A*."

converse (p. 126) A statement that reverses a hypothesis and its conclusion. The converse of "If *A*, then *B*" is "If *B*, then *A*."

convex polygon (p. 433) A polygon in which all diagonals are inside the polygon.

coordinate plane (p. 44) The coordinate plane consists of a horizontal number line, called the *x*-axis, and a vertical number line, called the *y*-axis, that intersect at the origin, (0, 0).

coordinate proof (p. 219) A proof that uses the coordinate system.

coplanar (p. 149) In the same plane; two lines are coplanar if they exist in the same plane.

corollary (p. 185) A theorem easily proven from another theorem.

corresponding angles (p. 52) Angles formed by a transversal and located at the same position relative to the transversal.

corresponding sides (p. 52) Congruent sides of congruent figures.

cosine (p. 317) In a right triangle, the cosine of an angle is the ratio of the length of the leg adjacent to the angle and the length of the hypotenuse.

counterexample (p. 122) An example that will prove a conjecture false.

co-vertices (p. 552) The endpoints of the minor axis of an ellipse.

cross-section (p. 475) The intersection of a solid and a plane.

cube (p. 473) A six-sided solid with all sides congruent squares.

cyclic quadrilateral (p. 373) A quadrilateral with each vertex on a circle.

cylinder (p. 473) A solid with two congruent circular bases that lie in parallel planes so that the line connecting the circles' centers is perpendicular to the planes.

deductive reasoning (p. 130) Reasoning that starts from known facts, definitions, and accepted properties, and proceeds logically to show that other statements must also be true.

definition (p. 126) The specific meaning of a term. In logic, a biconditional.

diagonal (p. 103) A line segment connecting two non-adjacent vertices of a polygon.

diameter (p. 31) A line segment that passes through the center of a circle, ending at two points on the circle.

difference of squares (p. 22) A term used to describe a polynomial in which one perfect square is subtracted from another. For example, $x^2 - 9$.

dilation (p. 89) The shrinking or expanding of a figure, with each side shrinking or expanding proportionally about the center of dilation. Dilation creates a similar figure.

directrix (p. 531) A line not through the focus of a parabola used to establish the locus of points of the parabola such that the distance to the focus equals the distance to the directrix.

edge (p. 473) A line segment where two faces of a solid meet.

ellipse (p. 550) A conic section that can be defined with two foci. The ellipse is the set of all points in a plane for which the sum of distances from the foci is the same.

endpoint (p. 37) A point at an end of a line segment or ray.

equilateral triangle (p. 195) A triangle with three congruent sides and three congruent angles (60°).

event (p. 575) A set of outcomes that are of interest in probability.

expected value (p. 583) A representative value of a variable. It equals the sum of all possible values for the variable, each multiplied by the probability of that value.

experimental probability (p. 575) Determining a probability based on observation.

exterior angle (polygon) (p. 182) Angle formed by a side of a polygon and the extension of its adjacent side.

face (p. 473) A flat surface of a polyhedron.

factoring (p. 21) The process of writing an equivalent expression that shows the factors of the original product.

false negative (p. 617) The result of a test for a condition that indicates negative (the condition does not exist) when the condition does exist but is not detected by the test.

false positive (p. 617) The result of a test for a condition that indicates positive (the condition exists) when the condition actually does not exist.

flow proof (p. 222) A way to format a proof using arrows to indicate that a statement follows from one or more other statements.

focal radii (hyperbola) (p. 558) The two line segments from the foci of a hyperbola to a point on the hyperbola. The difference of the two focal radii from any point on the hyperbola is the same for all points of the hyperbola.

focus of an ellipse (p. 550) An ellipse is the set of all points in a plane such that the sum of the distances between any point on the ellipse and two given points, called the *foci*, is a constant. Each of those two points is a focus of the ellipse.

focus of a hyperbola (p. 558) The hyperbola is the set of all points in a plane where the difference of the distance between any point on the hyperbola and two given points, called the *foci*, is constant. Each of those two points is a focus of the hyperbola. **focus of a parabola** (p. 531) A parabola is the set of all points in a plane that are the same distance from a point, called the *focus*, and a line, called the *directrix*.

FOIL (p. 20) A way to multiply two binomials; stands for First, Outer, Inner, Last.

fractal (p. 120) A pattern that is repeated at every scale, so that if you zoom in, you are seeing the same pattern you would at a distance.

fundamental counting principle (p. 586) A method of counting outcomes resulting from several choices among options given, such as finding the number of outfits given m pairs of pants and n shirts. Multiply: $m \cdot n$.

given (p. 130) Information that you are told is true, from either a diagram or a statement, that is used in a proof.

glide reflection (p. 80) A composition of a "glide" (translation) and a reflection across a line parallel to the path of the translation.

hyperbola (p. 527) A conic section that can be defined with two foci. A hyperbola is the set of all points in a plane where the difference of the distances between any point on the hyperbola and the foci is constant.

hypotenuse (p. 33) The side opposite the right angle in a right triangle.

hypothesis (p. 124) In a conditional "If A, then B," the A statement is the hypothesis. It is the statement one attempts to show to be true or false.

incenter (p. 262) Point of concurrency of angle bisectors of a triangle. The incenter is the same distance from all the sides of the triangle. It is at the center of a circle inscribed in the triangle.

independent events (p. 599) Two events are said to be independent when one event has no effect on the other. The probability of two independent events occurring is equal to the product of the probabilities of each of the two events.

independently combined probability models (p. 599) See *independent events*.

indirect reasoning (p. 271) Reaching a conclusion by proving that a hypothesized statement is false.

inductive reasoning (p. 119) Reaching conclusions based on a pattern of facts and data. A conclusion reached by inductive reasoning is not guaranteed to be true. Also called *induction*.

inscribed angle (p. 370) An inscribed angle is one with its vertex on a circle and sides that are chords of the circle.

inscribed polygon (p. 373) A polygon located within another closed figure, with all of its vertices located on that figure. For example, to inscribe a triangle in a circle, place the vertices of the triangle on the circle.

intercept (p. 13) The point at which a graph crosses either the *x*- or *y*-axis.

intercepted arc (p. 370) The part of a circle inside the rays of an inscribed angle.

interior angle (polygon) (p. 182) An angle formed by two adjacent sides of a figure (polygon).

inverse (p. 126) A statement that negates both the hypothesis and the conclusion. The inverse of "If *A*, then *B*" is "If not *A*, then not *B*."

inverse function (p. 330) A function that reverses the action of another function.

isometric drawing (p. 476) A method for representing a three-dimensional object in two dimensions.

isometry (p. 58) The quality of a transformation that preserves a figure's length. Translations, rotations, and reflections are isometric.

isosceles trapezoid (p. 438) A trapezoid with legs of equal length and two pairs of congruent base angles.

isosceles triangle (p. 195) A triangle with two sides of the same length.

kite (p. 441) A quadrilateral with two pairs of congruent sides and with opposite sides that are not congruent.

lateral face (p. 484) In a solid, any face other than the base or bases.

law of cosines (p. 334) A set of relations in trigonometry that helps to solve oblique triangles. The law states that for any $\triangle ABC$:
$a^2 = b^2 + c^2 - 2bc \cos A$
$b^2 = a^2 + c^2 - 2ac \cos B$
$c^2 = a^2 + b^2 - 2ab \cos C$

law of sines (p. 338) In a triangle, the ratios of the sine of any angle and the side opposite it are equal: $\dfrac{\sin A}{a} = \dfrac{\sin B}{b} = \dfrac{\sin C}{c}$

leg (p. 33) Either of the two sides of a right triangle that are not the hypotenuse.

line (p. 37) A one-dimensional figure that can be defined by the two points it passes through. A line continues forever in both directions and has no thickness.

linear pair (p. 134) Two adjacent angles that sum to 180°. The rays of linear pairs form a line. Also called *linear angles*.

line of symmetry (p. 70) A line that divides a figure into congruent halves that are reflection images of each other across the line.

line segment (p. 37) A part of a line with two endpoints.

major arc (p. 363) The enclosed arc of a central angle greater than 180°. The part of a circle not enclosed by a minor arc.

major axis (ellipse) (p. 552) The line segment connecting the vertices of an ellipse.

median (triangle) (p. 254) A line segment from a triangle's vertex to the midpoint of the opposite side.

midpoint (p. 46) The midpoint of a line segment is equidistant from its endpoints.

midsegment (p. 233) A segment that connects the midpoints of two sides of a polygon.

minor arc (p. 363) The enclosed arc of a central angle less than 180°.

minor axis (ellipse) (p. 552) A line segment that passes through the center of an ellipse and is perpendicular to the major axis. The endpoints of the minor axis are called the *co-vertices*.

monomial (p. 19) A real number, a variable, or a product of real numbers and variables.

multiplication rule (p. 599) In probability, a rule that states that the product of two independent events occurring equals the product of their individual probabilities. With two independent events A and B, $P(A \text{ and } B) = P(A) \cdot P(B)$.

mutually exclusive (p. 607) Two events that cannot occur at the same time.

negation (p. 126) The opposite of a statement. The negation of "A" is "not A."

net (p. 483) A two-dimensional (flat) figure that can be folded up to become the surface of a solid. Think of a flat piece of cardboard that can be folded up to become a box.

oblique solid (p. 508) A solid with a base (or bases) that are not at a right angle to the lateral surfaces.

oblique triangle (p. 334) A triangle that has no right angle.

observation (p. 575) In probability, the noting of the result of an event.

obtuse angle (p. 39) An angle greater than 90°, but less than 180°.

obtuse triangle (p. 195) A triangle with an angle greater than 90°.

opposite leg (p. 317) In trigonometry, the leg opposite the angle in question.

orthocenter (p. 258) The point where the three altitudes of a triangle meet. The orthocenter can be inside, on, or outside the triangle.

outcome (p. 575) In probability, a possible result of an observation, such as "heads" or "tails" for a coin toss.

parabola (p. 26) A conic section most simply described by an equation of the form $y = ax^2$. It can also be described as the set of points equidistant from its focus and directrix.

paragraph proof (p. 59) A proof written and justified in paragraph format instead of in two columns.

parallel (lines) (p. 149) Lines on the same plane that never intersect. Parallel lines have the same slope.

parallel (planes) (p. 149) Planes that never intersect.

parallelogram (p. 407) A quadrilateral in which each pair of opposite sides are parallel and equal in length.

perfect square (p. 23) The square of an integer or polynomial.

perimeter (p. 30) The distance around a two-dimensional shape.

permutation (p. 588) An ordered arrangement of the objects of a set. For example, XYZ, YZX, and ZYX are three permutations of the set made up of the last three letters of the alphabet.

perpendicular bisector (p. 169) A perpendicular line that divides a line segment in half.

perspective (p. 479) An artistic representation of three dimensions on a surface, involving the use of one or more vanishing points.

plane (p. 37) A two-dimensional figure that continues forever in both directions. A plane can be defined by listing any three points on it which are not in a line.

point (p. 37) A point occupies no volume or space—a zero-dimensional thing. It is a location and is represented with a dot.

point of concurrency (p. 248) The point where three or more segments, rays, or lines intersect.

polygon (p. 52) A closed figure formed by three or more line segments connected end to end. When all of the sides of a polygon have the same length and all of the interior angles have the same measure, the figure is a regular polygon.

polyhedron (p. 473) A solid whose surfaces are polygons. Prisms, boxes, and pyramids are polyhedrons, while spheres or cones are not since they have curved surfaces. "Polyhedra" is the plural form.

postulate (p. 37) A statement that is accepted to be true without proof.

prism (p. 484) A solid with two identical faces called *bases* that lie in parallel planes. A triangular prism has two identical triangular bases; a rectangular prism has two identical rectangular bases, and so forth.

probability (p. 575) The study of how likely it is that an event will occur. The probability of an event is expressed by a number between 0 and 1, inclusive.

proof (p. 130) A series of statements arranged logically, each supported by a reason, such as a mathematical property or a postulate, that demonstrates the truth of an assertion.

proportion (p. 7) An equation that states two ratios are equal.

pyramid (p. 473) A solid that has a base and three or more triangular faces that meet at a point above the base called the *apex*.

Pythagorean theorem (p. 33) In a right triangle, the square of the length of the hypotenuse is equal to the sum of the squares of the lengths of the legs: $a^2 + b^2 = c^2$.

Pythagorean triple (p. 302) A set of three integers that satisfies the Pythagorean theorem.

quadratic equation (p. 528) An equation that can be written with a quadratic polynomial on one side and zero on the other side.

quadrilateral (p. 407) A polygon with four sides.

radians (p. 392) A unit of measure for angles. One radian is equal to $\dfrac{180}{\pi}$ degrees.

radius (circle) (p. 31) The distance from the center to a point on a circle.

radius (polygon) (p. 457) The distance from the center of a regular polygon to a vertex.

ratio (p. 7) A quotient that compares two quantities.

ray (p. 37) A portion of a line that starts at a point and extends forever in some direction.

reason (p. 130) A reason supports or negates a statement; it explains why the statement is true or false.

rectangle (p. 407) A parallelogram with four right angles.

rectangular prism (p. 484) A prism with identical rectangular bases.

rectilinear figure (p. 407) A rectilinear figure is a polygon for which all its edges meet at right angles. Squares and rectangles are examples of rectilinear figures.

reflection (p. 50) A figure created when a figure is "flipped" across a reflection axis to create a mirror image.

regular polygon (p. 407) A polygon in which all sides are congruent and all interior angles are congruent.

regular pyramid (p. 486) A pyramid in which the base is a regular polygon.

rhombus (p. 407) A parallelogram with four congruent sides.

right angle (p. 39) A 90° angle.

right solid (p. 508) A solid in which the base is at a right angle to the lateral surface.

right triangle (p. 33) A triangle with one right angle.

rigid motion (p. 51) Description of a transformation that produces a congruent figure, with sides of the same lengths and angles of the same measures.

rotation (p. 62) A transformation that turns a figure about a fixed point called the *center of rotation*.

rotational symmetry (p. 77) A figure has rotational symmetry if it can be rotated about a central point through an angle of less than 360° to perfectly overlap itself.

sample space (p. 576) In theoretical probability, the set of all possible outcomes.

scale factor (p. 89) The ratio of the lengths of corresponding sides in similar figures.

scalene triangle (p. 195) A triangle with no congruent sides and no congruent angles.

secant (p. 355) A line that intersects a circle at two points.

sector of a circle (p. 389) Part of the interior of a circle bounded by two radii and an arc of the circle.

semicircle (p. 364) One-half of a circle; a figure bounded by a diameter and a 180° circular arc.

side-angle-side (SAS) postulate (p. 213) In trigonometry, the law of cosines can be used to calculate the third side of an oblique triangle, given the other two sides and the angle between them.

side-angle-side (SAS) similarity theorem (p. 291) If the lengths of two corresponding sides of two triangles are proportional and the angles the sides form are congruent, then the triangles are similar.

side-side-side (SSS) postulate (p. 209) In trigonometry, the law of cosines can be used to find the measures of the angles of a triangle when the three sides are known.

side-side-side (SSS) similarity theorem (p. 287) If the corresponding sides of two triangles are proportional, then the triangles are similar.

similar figures (p. 89) Figures that have congruent angles, but may be different sizes.

similarity transformation (p. 109) The composition of a rigid motion and dilation. A similarity transformation creates a similar figure.

sine (p. 317) In a right triangle, the sine of an angle is the ratio of the length of the leg opposite the angle to the length of the hypotenuse.

skew lines (p. 149) Two lines that are not in the same plane and that never intersect.

slope (p. 11) The measure of the steepness of a line. Slope is a number calculated by dividing the rise—vertical change between any two points—by the run, or horizontal change between the same two points, with respect to a coordinate system.

solid (p. 473) A three-dimensional shape. A solid occupies space; it has volume.

solving by elimination (p. 17) Solving a system of equations by eliminating one of the variables, usually by adding the equations, or equivalent equations, together. In the case of two unknown variables, the result is a single equation with one variable that you then solve, making it possible to substitute that expression for the variable in any one of the original equations.

solving by substitution (p. 16) Solving a system of equations by solving one equation for one of the variables, and then, for two unknown variables, substituting that expression for the variable in the other equation.

sphere (p. 473) A ball—a solid with all of the points on its surface the same distance from its center. That distance is the radius, r.

square (p. 407) A parallelogram with four right angles and four congruent sides; also, a rhombus with four right angles or a rectangle with four congruent sides.

standard form of the equation for a circle (p. 538) $(x - h)^2 + (y - k)^2 = r^2$

standard form of the equation for a circle centered at the origin (p. 528) $x^2 + y^2 = r^2$

standard form of the equation for an ellipse centered at the origin (p. 551)

$$\frac{x^2}{a^2} + \frac{y^2}{b^2} = 1$$

standard form of the equation for a hyperbola centered at the origin (p. 559)

$$\frac{x^2}{a^2} - \frac{y^2}{b^2} = 1 \text{ or } \frac{y^2}{b^2} - \frac{x^2}{a^2} = 1$$

standard form of the equation for a parabola (p. 544) Vertical parabola (opening up or down): $y - k = \frac{1}{4p}(x - h)^2$; horizontal parabola (opening left or right):

$$x - h = \frac{1}{4p}(y - k)^2$$

standard form of the equation for a parabola centered at the origin (p. 533) Vertical parabola (opening up or down): $y = \frac{1}{4p}x^2$; horizontal parabola (opening left or right):

$$x = \frac{1}{4p}y^2$$

straight angle (p. 39) An angle of 180°.

subtraction rule (p. 608) In probability: $P(\text{not } A) = 1 - P(A)$.

supplementary angles (p. 134) Two angles that sum to 180°. If supplementary angles are adjacent, their rays form a line.

symmetrical (p. 70) A descriptive term for a figure that maps onto itself after undergoing a transformation. For example, a square is symmetrical when rotated about its center by multiples of 90°.

system of equations (p. 16) Two or more equations with the same set of variables that you seek to solve together.

tangent (circle) (p. 355) A line that intersects a circle at only one point and that is contained in the same plane as the circle it intersects.

tangent (trigonometry) (p. 317) In a right triangle, the tangent of an angle is the ratio of the length of its opposite leg to the length of its adjacent leg.

theorem (p. 81) A conditional statement that can be proven true using postulates and other theorems.

theoretical probability (p. 576) Probability determined using reasoning and analysis.

total surface area (p. 483) The total area of the outside of a solid.

transformation (p. 50) A change in the location, orientation, size, or other geometrical property of a figure.

translation (p. 56) A type of transformation in which a figure is moved to a new location, creating a new figure that is congruent with the original. In a translation, each point in a figure moves the same distance in the same direction. Also called a *glide*.

transversal (p. 150) A line that intersects two other lines.

trapezoid (p. 437) A quadrilateral with at least one pair of parallel sides.

tree diagram (p. 586) In probability, a way to count the outcomes resulting from several choices, where each choice is represented by a "branch" of the "tree."

triangle (p. 195) A polygon formed by three line segments.

triangular prism (p. 474) A prism with bases that are triangles.

trigonometric ratio (p. 317) A ratio of the lengths of two sides of a right triangle. Examples are sine, cosine, and tangent.

trigonometry (p. 317) The study of the relationships of the sides and angles of triangles.

vertex (p. 473) In a two-dimensional figure, a point where two sides meet. In a three-dimensional figure, a point where three or more edges meet.

vertex angle (p. 198) The angle opposite the base of an isosceles triangle.

vertical angles (p. 134) A pair of angles, opposite from one another, formed by two intersecting lines.

vertices of an ellipse (p. 552) The two points farthest from each other on an ellipse. The vertices are the endpoints of the major axis.

vertices of a hyperbola (p. 558) The pair of points, one on each branch of a hyperbola, that are closest to each other.

volume (p. 495) The amount of space a solid occupies.

Digital Activities
and Real-World Model Problems

This Geometry text includes Digital Activities, which are indicated by the open computer icon. For access to these activities, please visit **www.amscomath.com**.

Activities

This text also includes Real-World Model Problems, indicated by the globe icon. These problems are examples of situations that students might find in the real world.

Real-World Model Problems

Index

E

Edge, 473, 474

Elevation, angle of, 322

Elimination, solving by, 17–18

Ellipse, 550
  deriving equation of, 554–556
  equations of, 551, 558
  foci of, 550
  geometric definition of, 550
  graphing of, 552
  standard form at origin, 551–552
  vertices, axes, and center of, 552–553

Endpoint, 37

Equality, properties of, 5, 136–137

Equation. *See also* Theorem(s)
  addition rule in probability, 606
  angle of rotation, 62
  arc length, 388
  area of circle, 31
  area of kite and rhombus using diagonals, 452
  area of parallelogram and rhombus, 445
  area of rectangle, 31
  area of regular polygon, 457
  area of sector of circle: degree measure of
      central angle, 389
  area of sector of circle: radian measure of
      central angle, 395
  area of square, 31
  area of trapezoid, 450
  area of triangle, 31
  area of triangle using trigonometry, 338
  circle centered at origin, 528
  circles centered off origin, 538
  circles: complete the square, 540–541
  circumference of circle, 31
  combinations, 592
  conditional probability, 613
  cosine, 317
  diameter of circle, 31
  distance between point and line (not
      horizontal or vertical), 179
  ellipse centered at origin, 551
  Euclid's formula for Pythagorean triples, 303
  expected value, 583
  experimental probability, 575
  hypotenuse of special right triangles, 312
  law of cosines, 334
  law of sines, 338
  length of line segment, 46
  measure of interior angle in regular polygon,
      432
  midpoint, 46
  number of diagonals in polygon, 435
    parabola, 544
    perimeter of rectangle, 30
    perimeter of square, 30
    perimeter of triangle, 30
    permutations of n objects taken r at a time, 590
    pi, 353
    radian measure of angle, 392
    radius of circle, 31
    sine, 317
    sine, cosine, and tangent in 30-60-90 triangles,
        324
    sine, cosine, and tangent in 45-45-90 triangles,
        325
    slopes for perpendicular lines, 177
    subtraction rule in probability, 608
    sum of interior angles, 432
    surface area of cone, 488
    surface area of cube and box, 483
    surface area of cylinder, 485
    surface area of prism, 484
    surface area of pyramid, 487
    surface area of sphere, 489
    tangent, 317
    theoretical probability, 576
    translation, 56
    volume of cube and box, 495
    volume of oblique solid, 508
    volume of prism and cylinder, 497
    volume of pyramid and cone, 498
    volume of sphere, 500

Equation(s)
  graphing linear, 13–14
  for a line, 14
  solving a system of, 16–18
  solving literal, 6–7
  solving one-variable, 5–6

Equilateral triangle, 195
  construction of, 200–203
  theorems for, 200

Euclid's formula for Pythagorean triples, 303

Euler-Descartes polyhedral formula, 474–475

Event(s), 575
  compound, 602–603
  dependent, 613
  independent, 599
  mutually exclusive, 607–608

Expected value, 583–584, 585

Experimental probability, 575–576

Exterior angle
  of polygon, 184, 434

Exterior angle theorem, 184

GEOMETRY
January 2016

Part I

Answer all 24 questions in this part. Each correct answer will receive 2 credits. Utilize the information provided for each question to determine your answer. Note that diagrams are not necessarily drawn to scale. For each statement or question, choose the word or expression that, of those given, best completes the statement or answers the question. [48]

Use this space for computations.

1 William is drawing pictures of cross sections of the right circular cone below.

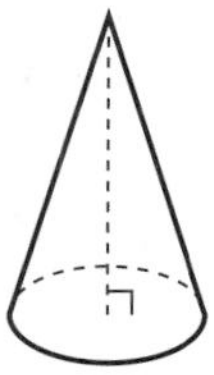

Which drawing can *not* be a cross section of a cone?

(1)

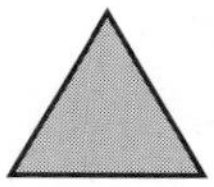

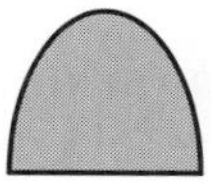

(3)

(2)

(4)

2 An equation of a line perpendicular to the line represented by the equation $y = -\frac{1}{2}x - 5$ and passing through $(6,-4)$ is

(1) $y = -\frac{1}{2}x + 4$ (3) $y = 2x + 14$

(2) $y = -\frac{1}{2}x - 1$ (4) $y = 2x - 16$

Use this space for computations.

3 In parallelogram $QRST$ shown below, diagonal $\overline{TR}$ is drawn, U and V are points on $\overline{TS}$ and $\overline{QR}$, respectively, and $\overline{UV}$ intersects $\overline{TR}$ at W.

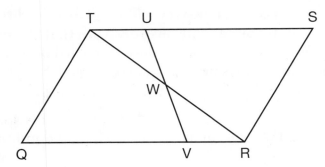

If $m\angle S = 60°$, $m\angle SRT = 83°$, and $m\angle TWU = 35°$, what is $m\angle WVQ$?

(1) 37° (3) 72°

(2) 60° (4) 83°

4 A fish tank in the shape of a rectangular prism has dimensions of 14 inches, 16 inches, and 10 inches. The tank contains 1680 cubic inches of water. What percent of the fish tank is empty?

(1) 10 (3) 50

(2) 25 (4) 75

5 Which transformation would result in the perimeter of a triangle being different from the perimeter of its image?

(1) $(x,y) \rightarrow (y,x)$ (3) $(x,y) \rightarrow (4x,4y)$

(2) $(x,y) \rightarrow (x,-y)$ (4) $(x,y) \rightarrow (x + 2,y - 5)$

6 In the diagram below, $\overleftrightarrow{FE}$ bisects $\overline{AC}$ at B, and $\overleftrightarrow{GE}$ bisects $\overline{BD}$ at C.

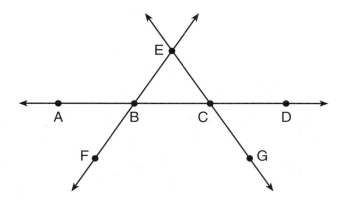

Which statement is always true?

(1) $\overline{AB} \cong \overline{DC}$

(2) $\overline{FB} \cong \overline{EB}$

(3) $\overleftrightarrow{BD}$ bisects $\overline{GE}$ at C.

(4) $\overleftrightarrow{AC}$ bisects $\overline{FE}$ at B.

7 As shown in the diagram below, a regular pyramid has a square base whose side measures 6 inches.

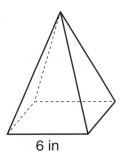

6 in

If the altitude of the pyramid measures 12 inches, its volume, in cubic inches, is

(1) 72

(2) 144

(3) 288

(4) 432

8 Triangle *ABC* and triangle *DEF* are graphed on the set of axes below.

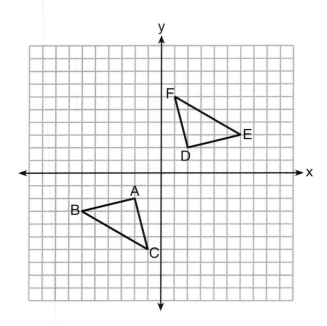

Which sequence of transformations maps triangle *ABC* onto triangle *DEF*?

(1) a reflection over the *x*-axis followed by a reflection over the *y*-axis

(2) a 180° rotation about the origin followed by a reflection over the line $y = x$

(3) a 90° clockwise rotation about the origin followed by a reflection over the *y*-axis

(4) a translation 8 units to the right and 1 unit up followed by a 90° counterclockwise rotation about the origin

9 In $\triangle ABC$, the complement of $\angle B$ is $\angle A$. Which statement is always true?

(1) $\tan \angle A = \tan \angle B$ (3) $\cos \angle A = \tan \angle B$

(2) $\sin \angle A = \sin \angle B$ (4) $\sin \angle A = \cos \angle B$

10 A line that passes through the points whose coordinates are $(1,1)$ and $(5,7)$ is dilated by a scale factor of 3 and centered at the origin. The image of the line

(1) is perpendicular to the original line

(2) is parallel to the original line

(3) passes through the origin

(4) is the original line

11 Quadrilateral $ABCD$ is graphed on the set of axes below.

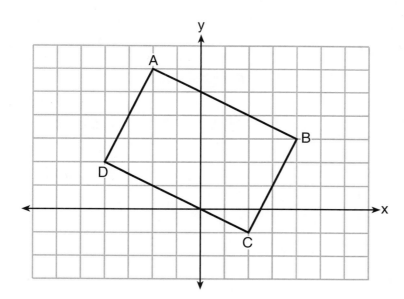

When $ABCD$ is rotated $90°$ in a counterclockwise direction about the origin, its image is quadrilateral $A'B'C'D'$. Is distance preserved under this rotation, and which coordinates are correct for the given vertex?

(1) no and $C'(1,2)$ (3) yes and $A'(6,2)$

(2) no and $D'(2,4)$ (4) yes and $B'(-3,4)$

Use this space for computations.

12 In the diagram below of circle O, the area of the shaded sector LOM is 2π cm^2.

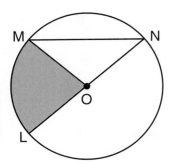

If the length of $\overline{NL}$ is 6 cm, what is m$\angle N$?

(1) 10°
(2) 20°
(3) 40°
(4) 80°

13 In the diagram below, $\triangle ABC \sim \triangle DEF$.

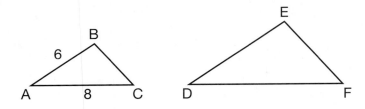

If $AB = 6$ and $AC = 8$, which statement will justify similarity by SAS?

(1) $DE = 9$, $DF = 12$, and $\angle A \cong \angle D$
(2) $DE = 8$, $DF = 10$, and $\angle A \cong \angle D$
(3) $DE = 36$, $DF = 64$, and $\angle C \cong \angle F$
(4) $DE = 15$, $DF = 20$, and $\angle C \cong \angle F$

14 The diameter of a basketball is approximately 9.5 inches and the diameter of a tennis ball is approximately 2.5 inches. The volume of the basketball is about how many times greater than the volume of the tennis ball?

(1) 3591
(2) 65
(3) 55
(4) 4

15 The endpoints of one side of a regular pentagon are $(-1,4)$ and $(2,3)$. What is the perimeter of the pentagon?

(1) $\sqrt{10}$

(3) $5\sqrt{2}$

(2) $5\sqrt{10}$

(4) $25\sqrt{2}$

16 In the diagram of right triangle ABC shown below, $AB = 14$ and $AC = 9$.

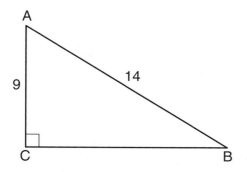

What is the measure of $\angle A$, to the *nearest degree*?

(1) 33

(3) 50

(2) 40

(4) 57

17 What are the coordinates of the center and length of the radius of the circle whose equation is $x^2 + 6x + y^2 - 4y = 23$?

(1) $(3,-2)$ and 36

(3) $(-3,2)$ and 36

(2) $(3,-2)$ and 6

(4) $(-3,2)$ and 6

18 The coordinates of the vertices of $\triangle RST$ are $R(-2,-3)$, $S(8,2)$, and $T(4,5)$. Which type of triangle is $\triangle RST$?

(1) right

(3) obtuse

(2) acute

(4) equiangular

Use this space for computations.

19 Molly wishes to make a lawn ornament in the form of a solid sphere. The clay being used to make the sphere weighs .075 pound per cubic inch. If the sphere's radius is 4 inches, what is the weight of the sphere, to the *nearest pound*?

(1) 34
(2) 20
(3) 15
(4) 4

20 The ratio of similarity of $\triangle BOY$ to $\triangle GRL$ is 1:2. If $BO = x + 3$ and $GR = 3x - 1$, then the length of $\overline{GR}$ is

(1) 5
(2) 7
(3) 10
(4) 20

21 In the diagram below, $\overline{DC}$, $\overline{AC}$, $\overline{DOB}$, $\overline{CB}$, and $\overline{AB}$ are chords of circle O, $\overleftrightarrow{FDE}$ is tangent at point D, and radius $\overline{AO}$ is drawn. Sam decides to apply this theorem to the diagram: "An angle inscribed in a semi-circle is a right angle."

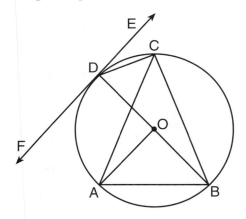

Which angle is Sam referring to?

(1) $\angle AOB$
(2) $\angle BAC$
(3) $\angle DCB$
(4) $\angle FDB$

22 In the diagram below, $\overline{CD}$ is the altitude drawn to the hypotenuse $\overline{AB}$ of right triangle ABC.

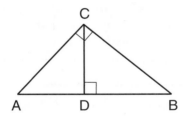

Which lengths would *not* produce an altitude that measures $6\sqrt{2}$?

(1) $AD = 2$ and $DB = 36$ (3) $AD = 6$ and $DB = 12$

(2) $AD = 3$ and $AB = 24$ (4) $AD = 8$ and $AB = 17$

23 A designer needs to create perfectly circular necklaces. The necklaces each need to have a radius of 10 cm. What is the largest number of necklaces that can be made from 1000 cm of wire?

(1) 15   (3) 31

(2) 16   (4) 32

24 In $\triangle SCU$ shown below, points T and O are on $\overline{SU}$ and $\overline{CU}$, respectively. Segment OT is drawn so that $\angle C \cong \angle OTU$.

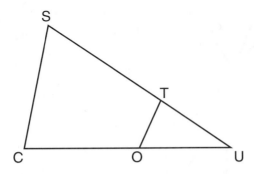

If $TU = 4$, $OU = 5$, and $OC = 7$, what is the length of $\overline{ST}$?

(1) 5.6   (3) 11

(2) 8.75   (4) 15

Part II

Answer all 7 questions in this part. Each correct answer will receive 2 credits. Clearly indicate the necessary steps, including appropriate formula substitutions, diagrams, graphs, charts, etc. Utilize the information provided for each question to determine your answer. Note that diagrams are not necessarily drawn to scale. For all questions in this part, a correct numerical answer with no work shown will receive only 1 credit. All answers should be written in pen, except for graphs and drawings, which should be done in pencil.   [14]

25 Triangle ABC is graphed on the set of axes below. Graph and label $\triangle A'B'C'$, the image of $\triangle ABC$ after a reflection over the line $x = 1$.

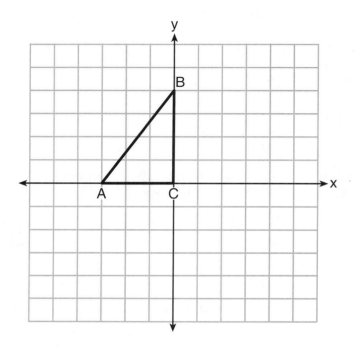

26 In the diagram below of circle O with diameter $\overline{BC}$ and radius $\overline{OA}$, chord $\overline{DC}$ is parallel to chord $\overline{BA}$.

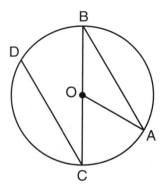

If m$\angle BCD = 30°$, determine and state m$\angle AOB$.

27 Directed line segment *PT* has endpoints whose coordinates are $P(-2,1)$ and $T(4,7)$. Determine the coordinates of point *J* that divides the segment in the ratio 2 to 1.

[The use of the set of axes below is optional.]

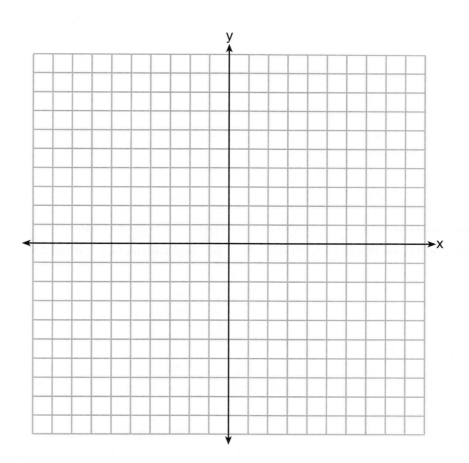

28 As graphed on the set of axes below, △A'B'C' is the image of △ABC after a sequence of transformations.

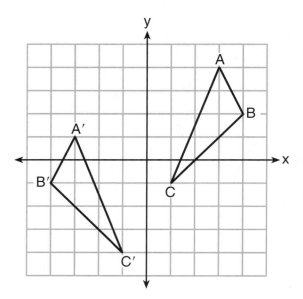

Is △A'B'C' congruent to △ABC? Use the properties of rigid motion to explain your answer.

---

29 A carpenter leans an extension ladder against a house to reach the bottom of a window 30 feet above the ground. As shown in the diagram below, the ladder makes a 70° angle with the ground. To the *nearest foot*, determine and state the length of the ladder.

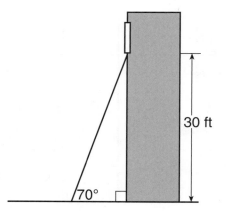

30 During an experiment, the same type of bacteria is grown in two petri dishes. Petri dish *A* has a diameter of 51 mm and has approximately 40,000 bacteria after 1 hour. Petri dish *B* has a diameter of 75 mm and has approximately 72,000 bacteria after 1 hour.

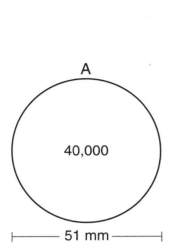

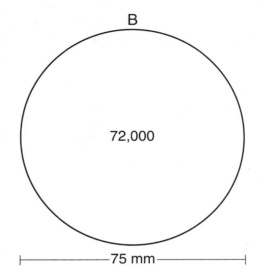

Determine and state which petri dish has the greater population density of bacteria at the end of the first hour.

31 Line ℓ is mapped onto line *m* by a dilation centered at the origin with a scale factor of 2. The equation of line ℓ is $3x - y = 4$. Determine and state an equation for line *m*.

Part III

Answer all 3 questions in this part. Each correct answer will receive 4 credits. Clearly indicate the necessary steps, including appropriate formula substitutions, diagrams, graphs, charts, etc. Utilize the information provided for each question to determine your answer. Note that diagrams are not necessarily drawn to scale. For all questions in this part, a correct numerical answer with no work shown will receive only 1 credit. All answers should be written in pen, except for graphs and drawings, which should be done in pencil. [12]

32 The aspect ratio (the ratio of screen width to height) of a rectangular flat-screen television is 16:9. The length of the diagonal of the screen is the television's screen size. Determine and state, to the *nearest inch*, the screen size (diagonal) of this flat-screen television with a screen height of 20.6 inches.

33 Given the theorem, "The sum of the measures of the interior angles of a triangle is 180°," complete the proof for this theorem.

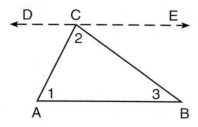

Given: △ABC

Prove: m∠1 + m∠2 + m∠3 = 180°

Fill in the missing reasons below.

Statements	Reasons
(1) △ABC	(1) Given
(2) Through point C, draw $\overleftrightarrow{DCE}$ parallel to $\overline{AB}$.	(2) _____ _____ _____
(3) m∠1 = m∠ACD, m∠3 = m∠BCE	(3) _____ _____ _____
(4) m∠ACD + m∠2 + m∠BCE = 180°	(4) _____ _____ _____
(5) m∠1 + m∠2 + m∠3 = 180°	(5) _____ _____ _____

34 Triangle *XYZ* is shown below. Using a compass and straightedge, on the line below, construct and label △*ABC*, such that △*ABC* ≅ △*XYZ*. [Leave all construction marks.]

Based on your construction, state the theorem that justifies why △*ABC* is congruent to △*XYZ*.

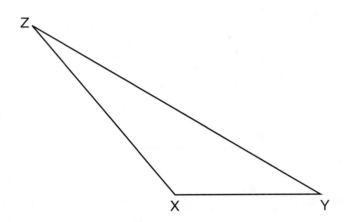

Part IV

Answer the 2 questions in this part. Each correct answer will receive 6 credits. Clearly indicate the necessary steps, including appropriate formula substitutions, diagrams, graphs, charts, etc. Utilize the information provided for each question to determine your answer. Note that diagrams are not necessarily drawn to scale. For all questions in this part, a correct numerical answer with no work shown will receive only 1 credit. All answers should be written in pen, except for graphs and drawings, which should be done in pencil. [12]

35 Given: Parallelogram *ANDR* with $\overline{AW}$ and $\overline{DE}$ bisecting $\overline{NWD}$ and $\overline{REA}$ at points *W* and *E*, respectively

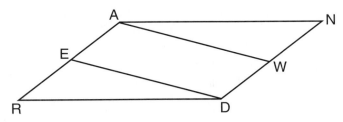

Prove that $\triangle ANW \cong \triangle DRE$.

Prove that quadrilateral *AWDE* is a parallelogram.

36 Cathy wants to determine the height of the flagpole shown in the diagram below. She uses a survey instrument to measure the angle of elevation to the top of the flagpole, and determines it to be 34.9°. She walks 8 meters closer and determines the new measure of the angle of elevation to be 52.8°. At each measurement, the survey instrument is 1.7 meters above the ground.

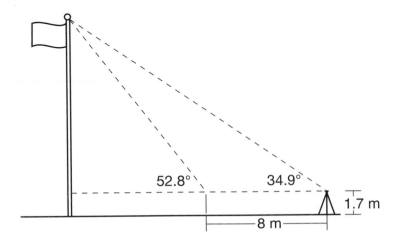

Determine and state, to the *nearest tenth of a meter*, the height of the flagpole.

High School Math Reference Sheet

1 inch = 2.54 centimeters   1 kilometer = 0.62 mile   1 cup = 8 fluid ounces

1 meter = 39.37 inches   1 pound = 16 ounces   1 pint = 2 cups

1 mile = 5280 feet   1 pound = 0.454 kilogram 1 quart = 2 pints

1 mile = 1760 yards   1 kilogram = 2.2 pounds   1 gallon = 4 quarts

1 mile = 1.609 kilometers   1 ton = 2000 pounds   1 gallon = 3.785 liters

                                                                 1 liter = 0.264 gallon

                                                                 1 liter = 1000 cubic centimeters

Triangle	$A = \frac{1}{2}bh$
Parallelogram	$A = bh$
Circle	$A = \pi r^2$
Circle	$C = \pi d$ or $C = 2\pi r$
General Prisms	$V = Bh$
Cylinder	$V = \pi r^2 h$
Sphere	$V = \frac{4}{3}\pi r^3$
Cone	$V = \frac{1}{3}\pi r^2 h$
Pyramid	$V = \frac{1}{3}Bh$

Pythagorean Theorem	$a^2 + b^2 = c^2$
Quadratic Formula	$x = \dfrac{-b \pm \sqrt{b^2 - 4ac}}{2a}$
Arithmetic Sequence	$a_n = a_1 + (n - 1)d$
Geometric Sequence	$a_n = a_1 r^{n-1}$
Geometric Series	$S_n = \dfrac{a_1 - a_1 r^n}{1 - r}$ where $r \neq 1$
Radians	1 radian $= \dfrac{180}{\pi}$ degrees
Degrees	1 degree $= \dfrac{\pi}{180}$ radians
Exponential Growth/Decay	$A = A_0 e^{k(t - t_0)} + B_0$

GEOMETRY
June 2016

Part I

Answer all 24 questions in this part. Each correct answer will receive 2 credits. No partial credit will be allowed. Utilize the information provided for each question to determine your answer. Note that diagrams are not necessarily drawn to scale. For each statement or question, choose the word or expression that, of those given, best completes the statement or answers the question. Record your answers on your separate answer sheet. [48]

Use this space for computations.

1 A student has a rectangular postcard that he folds in half lengthwise. Next, he rotates it continuously about the folded edge. Which three-dimensional object below is generated by this rotation?

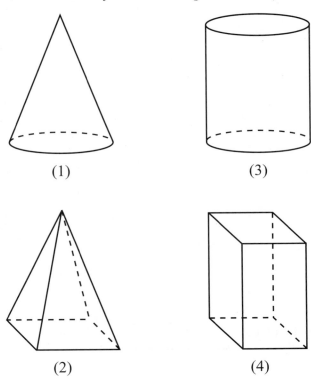

(1)

(3)

(2)

(4)

2 A three-inch line segment is dilated by a scale factor of 6 and centered at its midpoint. What is the length of its image?

(1) 9 inches   (3) 15 inches

(2) 2 inches   (4) 18 inches

3 Kevin's work for deriving the equation of a circle is shown below.

$$x^2 + 4x = -(y^2 - 20)$$

STEP 1 $x^2 + 4x = -y^2 + 20$

STEP 2 $x^2 + 4x + 4 = -y^2 + 20 - 4$

STEP 3 $(x + 2)^2 = -y^2 + 20 - 4$

STEP 4 $(x + 2)^2 + y^2 = 16$

In which step did he make an error in his work?

(1) Step 1   (3) Step 3

(2) Step 2   (4) Step 4

4 Which transformation of $\overline{OA}$ would result in an image parallel to $\overline{OA}$?

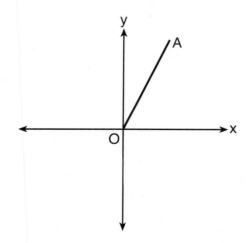

(1) a translation of two units down

(2) a reflection over the x-axis

(3) a reflection over the y-axis

(4) a clockwise rotation of 90° about the origin

5 Using the information given below, which set of triangles can *not* be proven similar?

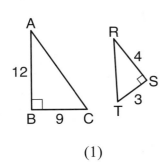

(1)

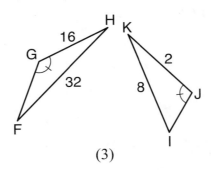

(3)

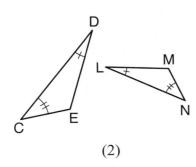

(2)

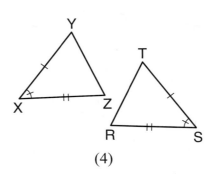

(4)

6 A company is creating an object from a wooden cube with an edge length of 8.5 cm. A right circular cone with a diameter of 8 cm and an altitude of 8 cm will be cut out of the cube. Which expression represents the volume of the remaining wood?

(1) $(8.5)^3 - \pi(8)^2(8)$

(3) $(8.5)^3 - \frac{1}{3}\pi(8)^2(8)$

(2) $(8.5)^3 - \pi(4)^2(8)$

(4) $(8.5)^3 - \frac{1}{3}\pi(4)^2(8)$

7 Two right triangles must be congruent if

(1) an acute angle in each triangle is congruent

(2) the lengths of the hypotenuses are equal

(3) the corresponding legs are congruent

(4) the areas are equal

Use this space for computations.

8 Which sequence of transformations will map $\triangle ABC$ onto $\triangle A'B'C'$?

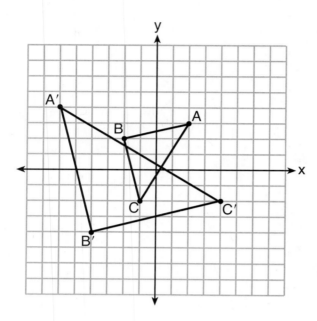

(1) reflection and translation
(2) rotation and reflection
(3) translation and dilation
(4) dilation and rotation

9 In parallelogram $ABCD$, diagonals $\overline{AC}$ and $\overline{BD}$ intersect at E. Which statement does *not* prove parallelogram $ABCD$ is a rhombus?

(1) $\overline{AC} \cong \overline{DB}$
(2) $\overline{AB} \cong \overline{BC}$
(3) $\overline{AC} \perp \overline{DB}$
(4) $\overline{AC}$ bisects $\angle DCB$.

Use this space for computations.

10 In the diagram below of circle O, $\overline{OB}$ and $\overline{OC}$ are radii, and chords $\overline{AB}$, $\overline{BC}$, and $\overline{AC}$ are drawn.

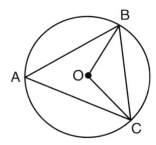

Which statement must always be true?

(1) $\angle BAC \cong \angle BOC$

(2) $m\angle BAC = \frac{1}{2} m\angle BOC$

(3) $\triangle BAC$ and $\triangle BOC$ are isosceles.

(4) The area of $\triangle BAC$ is twice the area of $\triangle BOC$.

11 A 20-foot support post leans against a wall, making a 70° angle with the ground. To the *nearest tenth of a foot*, how far up the wall will the support post reach?

(1) 6.8 (3) 18.7

(2) 6.9 (4) 18.8

12 Line segment NY has endpoints $N(-11,5)$ and $Y(5,-7)$. What is the equation of the perpendicular bisector of $\overline{NY}$?

(1) $y + 1 = \frac{4}{3}(x + 3)$ (3) $y - 6 = \frac{4}{3}(x - 8)$

(2) $y + 1 = -\frac{3}{4}(x + 3)$ (4) $y - 6 = -\frac{3}{4}(x - 8)$

13 In △RST shown below, altitude $\overline{SU}$ is drawn to $\overline{RT}$ at U.

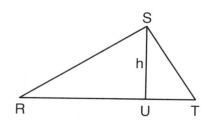

If $SU = h$, $UT = 12$, and $RT = 42$, which value of h will make △RST a right triangle with ∠RST as a right angle?

(1) $6\sqrt{3}$

(2) $6\sqrt{10}$

(3) $6\sqrt{14}$

(4) $6\sqrt{35}$

14 In the diagram below, △ABC has vertices $A(4,5)$, $B(2,1)$, and $C(7,3)$.

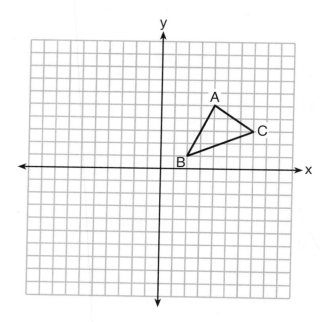

What is the slope of the altitude drawn from A to $\overline{BC}$?

(1) $\dfrac{2}{5}$

(2) $\dfrac{3}{2}$

(3) $-\dfrac{1}{2}$

(4) $-\dfrac{5}{2}$

15 In the diagram below, $\triangle ERM \sim \triangle JTM$.

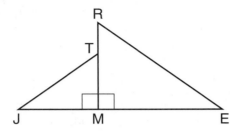

Which statement is always true?

(1) $\cos J = \dfrac{RM}{RE}$ (3) $\tan T = \dfrac{RM}{EM}$

(2) $\cos R = \dfrac{JM}{JT}$ (4) $\tan E = \dfrac{TM}{JM}$

16 On the set of axes below, rectangle $ABCD$ can be proven congruent to rectangle $KLMN$ using which transformation?

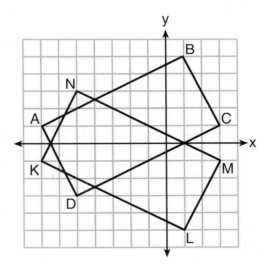

(1) rotation

(2) translation

(3) reflection over the x-axis

(4) reflection over the y-axis

17 In the diagram below, $\overline{DB}$ and $\overline{AF}$ intersect at point C, and $\overline{AD}$ and $\overline{FBE}$ are drawn.

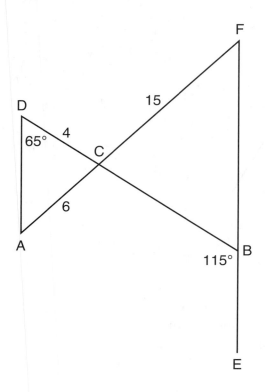

If $AC = 6$, $DC = 4$, $FC = 15$, m$\angle D = 65°$, and m$\angle CBE = 115°$, what is the length of $\overline{CB}$?

(1) 10   (3) 17

(2) 12   (4) 22.5

18 Seawater contains approximately 1.2 ounces of salt per liter on average. How many gallons of seawater, to the *nearest tenth of a gallon*, would contain 1 pound of salt?

(1) 3.3   (3) 4.7

(2) 3.5   (4) 13.3

Use this space for computations.

19 Line segment EA is the perpendicular bisector of $\overline{ZT}$, and $\overline{ZE}$ and $\overline{TE}$ are drawn.

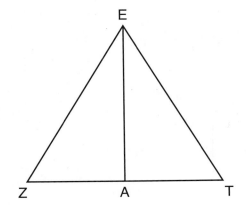

Which conclusion can *not* be proven?

(1) $\overline{EA}$ bisects angle ZET.

(2) Triangle EZT is equilateral.

(3) $\overline{EA}$ is a median of triangle EZT.

(4) Angle Z is congruent to angle T.

20 A hemispherical water tank has an inside diameter of 10 feet. If water has a density of 62.4 pounds per cubic foot, what is the weight of the water in a full tank, to the *nearest pound*?

(1) 16,336

(2) 32,673

(3) 130,690

(4) 261,381

21 In the diagram of $\triangle ABC$, points D and E are on $\overline{AB}$ and $\overline{CB}$, respectively, such that $\overline{AC} \parallel \overline{DE}$.

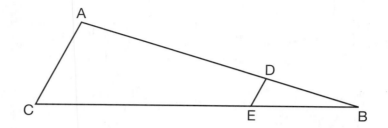

If $AD = 24$, $DB = 12$, and $DE = 4$, what is the length of $\overline{AC}$?

(1) 8　　　　　　　　(3) 16

(2) 12　　　　　　　(4) 72

22 Triangle RST is graphed on the set of axes below.

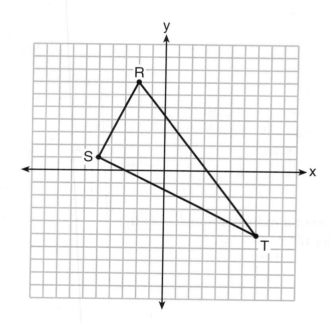

How many square units are in the area of $\triangle RST$?

(1) $9\sqrt{3} + 15$　　　　(3) 45

(2) $9\sqrt{5} + 15$　　　　(4) 90

23 The graph below shows $\overline{AB}$, which is a chord of circle O. The coordinates of the endpoints of $\overline{AB}$ are $A(3,3)$ and $B(3,-7)$. The distance from the midpoint of $\overline{AB}$ to the center of circle O is 2 units.

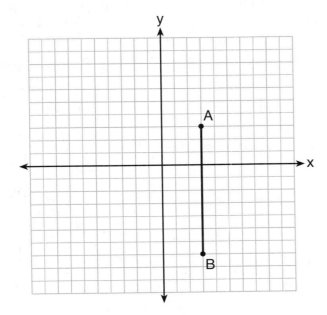

What could be a correct equation for circle O?

(1) $(x - 1)^2 + (y + 2)^2 = 29$

(2) $(x + 5)^2 + (y - 2)^2 = 29$

(3) $(x - 1)^2 + (y - 2)^2 = 25$

(4) $(x - 5)^2 + (y + 2)^2 = 25$

24 What is the area of a sector of a circle with a radius of 8 inches and formed by a central angle that measures 60°?

(1) $\dfrac{8\pi}{3}$ (3) $\dfrac{32\pi}{3}$

(2) $\dfrac{16\pi}{3}$ (4) $\dfrac{64\pi}{3}$

Part II

Answer all 7 questions in this part. Each correct answer will receive 2 credits. Clearly indicate the necessary steps, including appropriate formula substitutions, diagrams, graphs, charts, etc. Utilize the information provided for each question to determine your answer. Note that diagrams are not necessarily drawn to scale. For all questions in this part, a correct numerical answer with no work shown will receive only 1 credit. All answers should be written in pen, except for graphs and drawings, which should be done in pencil.   [14]

25 Describe a sequence of transformations that will map △ABC onto △DEF as shown below.

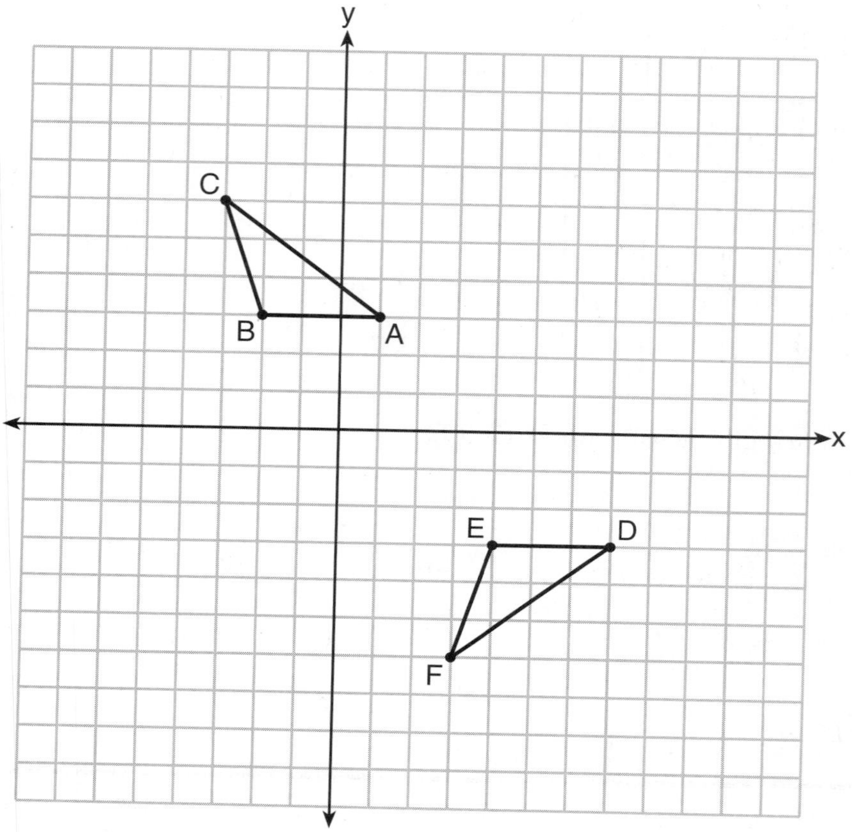

26 Point P is on segment AB such that $AP{:}PB$ is 4:5. If A has coordinates (4,2), and B has coordinates (22,2), determine and state the coordinates of P.

27 In $\triangle CED$ as shown below, points A and B are located on sides $\overline{CE}$ and $\overline{ED}$, respectively. Line segment AB is drawn such that $AE = 3.75$, $AC = 5$, $EB = 4.5$, and $BD = 6$.

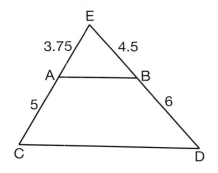

Explain why $\overline{AB}$ is parallel to $\overline{CD}$.

28 Find the value of R that will make the equation $\sin 73° = \cos R$ true when $0° < R < 90°$. Explain your answer.

29 In the diagram below, Circle 1 has radius 4, while Circle 2 has radius 6.5. Angle A intercepts an arc of length π, and angle B intercepts an arc of length $\dfrac{13\pi}{8}$.

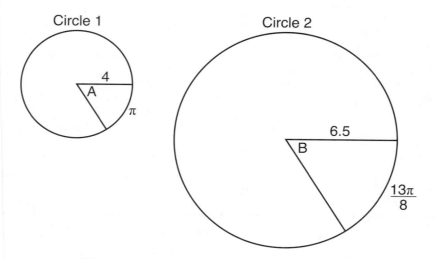

Circle 1

Circle 2

Dominic thinks that angles A and B have the same radian measure. State whether Dominic is correct or not. Explain why.

30 A ladder leans against a building. The top of the ladder touches the building 10 feet above the ground. The foot of the ladder is 4 feet from the building. Find, to the *nearest degree*, the angle that the ladder makes with the level ground.

31 In the diagram below, radius $\overline{OA}$ is drawn in circle O. Using a compass and a straightedge, construct a line tangent to circle O at point A. [Leave all construction marks.]

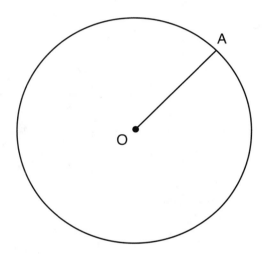

Part III

Answer all 3 questions in this part. Each correct answer will receive 4 credits. Clearly indicate the necessary steps, including appropriate formula substitutions, diagrams, graphs, charts, etc. Utilize the information provided for each question to determine your answer. Note that diagrams are not necessarily drawn to scale. For all questions in this part, a correct numerical answer with no work shown will receive only 1 credit. All answers should be written in pen, except for graphs and drawings, which should be done in pencil. [12]

32 A barrel of fuel oil is a right circular cylinder where the inside measurements of the barrel are a diameter of 22.5 inches and a height of 33.5 inches. There are 231 cubic inches in a liquid gallon. Determine and state, to the *nearest tenth*, the gallons of fuel that are in a barrel of fuel oil.

33 Given: Parallelogram $ABCD$, $\overline{EFG}$, and diagonal $\overline{DFB}$

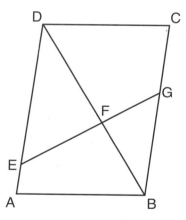

Prove: $\triangle DEF \sim \triangle BGF$